Statistical Inference

Statistical Inference

HELEN M. WALKER
Professor of Education
Teachers College, Columbia University

JOSEPH LEV
Senior Statistician
Department of Civil Service
State of New York

HENRY HOLT AND COMPANY
NEW YORK

Library of Congress Catalog Card Number: 52[illegible]13908

Printed in the United States of America

Preface

A person using statistical data finds himself beset by many uncertainties. Usually, in dealing with groups which have not been studied, he wishes to use conclusions based on the study of one group. How reliable are such conclusions? On what basis shall he choose among the various available measures of average, spread, and relationship? How large a sample shall he take and what design shall he follow in selecting his cases?

Answers to such questions are considered in this book from the unified point of view of the relation of sample to population. From this point of view, the statistical problems turn out to be matters of testing hypotheses, estimation, and experimental design. Persons working with statistical data often think that their interest is only in an analysis of the data at hand. In most cases, however, further reflection shows that the interest in the data at hand is due to its bearing on situations or groups other than those actually observed.

Because of this point of view, the concept of inference is introduced in the very first chapter by use of simple examples. By wholly intuitive reasoning the reader is led to make his own inferences without any complex mathematics, or even tables. The next two chapters deal with problems from a population of only two classes. In this simple context are developed most of the concepts of statistical inference which are used throughout the book.

The intuitive approach is used to introduce all concepts. Many simple numerical examples and graphic devices help to maintain the clarity of exposition. Per cents and proportions are considered first because they are the simplest summary measures with which one deals. Means, standard deviations, and a variety of measures of simple and multiple relationship are introduced later, together with their sampling theory.

Diverse experimental designs are considered. The simplest is the comparison of two proportions and of two means. More complex designs are described under the headings of analysis of variance and analysis of covariance. The use of the power function in experimental design, still a novelty in textbook literature, is described.

Elementary computations are introduced as needed in the text, for example, reading the normal curve in Chapter 2, computation of mean and standard deviation of a sample in Chapter 7, computation of regression and correlation in Chapter 10. Consequently, no previous course is needed by the person who has good facility in quantitative thinking and who handles symbolism with ease. However, the person who works with difficulty in such materials will profit by having had a slow-paced introductory course in which he works with descriptive statistics and masters computational skills (and students have remarkable ability to appraise their own competences and needs in these matters.)

The book does not presuppose any college training in mathematics and does not present mathematical derivations of formulas. At first glance it may look more mathematical than most texts intended for the non-mathematician because of its use of probability symbolism, multiple subscripts, and the expressed limits of summation. However, the reader is given careful explanation and practice exercises related to these usages. We are convinced that the effort of learning these symbols is more than repaid by increased clarity of understanding. While the text is planned for the non-mathematical reader, we believe that a mathematically competent student who intends to study the mathematical theory of statistics will profit by such an introductory course which consistently attempts to develop concepts in relation to real problems.

The diversity of techniques used by the research workers in any field is today so great that very careful selection must be made in order to cover the most essential in a two-semester course. However many students are able to take only a one-semester course and subsequently find themselves in need of methods other than those studied, for which they must usually consult sources using unfamiliar style and symbolism. If the first 9 chapters of this book are covered in a one-semester course, the student will have acquired understanding of the basic concepts and will be in possession of a text in which he can readily locate other techniques as he finds need for them. If more class time is available, the book provides material appropriate for a two-semester course.

The first 10 chapters are so tightly organized that little change in the order of presentation is advisable. Any of the later chapters can be omitted, or the order shifted, without great disadvantage. If a teacher wishes to include correlation (Chapter 10) in a one-semester course, the following sections might be omitted without affecting the clarity of the remaining material:

Many of the exercises are developmental in nature and should not be omitted. Answers are provided in order that students may appraise their own progress. Additional exercises and review questions will be provided by the publishers at nominal cost.

In a course in statistical inference for non-mathematical students a crucial problem is the treatment of probability. One familiar approach is to give careful instruction in the routine of reading tables without attempting to develop any real understanding of the meaning of the values obtained from such reading. Another is to give considerable instruction in combinatory probabilities and the binomial distribution for its own sake using problems of the type commonly found in college algebra texts, without making clear the relevance of such work to concrete problems. The first approach admittedly leaves the student rigid, unable to make even slight adaptations in the methods he has been taught, because he does not really understand them. The second often frightens the non-mathematician out of the course. We have tried to steer clear of both pitfalls by an intuitive development of probability concepts as an aid to the solution of statistical problems.

A decimal subscript attached to a statistic always relates to the percentile rank of that statistic, not its significance level. In this departure from tradition we have followed the example of Dixon and Massey. Experience with the new practice in six classes convinces us that it obviates the confusion produced under the usual practice by which t and z are given subscripts based on a two-sided region and χ^2 and F subscripts based on a one-sided region.

Data for illustrative purposes have been taken from the published work of many persons and to each of these, named at the places where their data are introduced, we express our thanks.

A modern text presents statistical theory and methods originated by a large number of persons and discussed by various successive writers each of whom adds some new facet to the development, so that a proper acknowledgment of the sources of the authors' ideas would require an extensive historical analysis not appropriate for a text of this type. An unfortunate concomitant of this situation is the tendency of some readers to ascribe credit to a textbook writer for everything he presents. In this as in other texts, only a few formulas were originated by the authors and these few are not identified. References placed at the ends of chapters are selected not so much to acknowledge original sources as to acquaint the reader with additional material he is likely to find helpful. The authors gladly recognize their indebtedness to all the great writers and teachers of statistical theory, from whose work they have profited beyond all possibility of acknowledgment.

Certain tables and charts have by permission been reproduced in part or in entirety from the publications of Z. W. Birnbaum, C. J. Clopper, H. A. David, F. N. David, R. A. Fisher, J. C. Flanagan, T. L. Kelley, F. J. Massey, M. Merrington, F. Mosteller, E. S. Pearson, N. Smirnov, G. W. Snedecor, C. M. Thompson, and F. Wilcoxon. The usefulness of any modern text depends in large measure upon the generosity of the authors and publishers of such tables and charts. Still other tables such as those of square roots, logarithms, and the normal curve have become almost common property and specific acknowledgment of the computers is well nigh impossible.

For assistance in checking computations and in making the answer key we are glad to acknowledge the help of Ying Chan, Philip Jackson, and Herman Ravitch. For expert typing of difficult material in three preliminary mimeographed editions and preparing the final copy for the printer, we owe much to Gertrude Ramsdell. The criticisms and suggestions of the students who struggled through three mimeographed versions are responsible for some of the helpful features of the text, but these students are too numerous to name individually. We are particularly indebted to Lincoln Moses, who wrote the final chapter, and who, as the result of his experience in using the third mimeographed version in one of his classes, pointed out several places which needed clarification.

New York City
Albany, N.Y.
May 15, 1953

H. M. W.
J. L.

Table of Contents

1 Inferences Based on Simple Experiments

It is the purpose of this chapter to introduce the reader to some of the simpler aspects of statistical inference in an intuitive way. Before describing the basis for and the logic of such inference some remarks on the nature of statistical inquiry may be appropriate.

The Nature of Statistical Inquiries. Problems calling for statistical treatment always involve empirical, or observed, evidence but not all problems involving empirical evidence are statistical. Factual information about a single individual is not statistical information. When was Shakespeare born? Is John taller than Sam? What does this load of coal weigh? Did the prisoner go to his home before or after he had been with the murdered man? These are factual but not statistical questions.

A statistical question always relates to a group of individuals rather than to a single individual and asks what is true of the group.

Statistical inquiries are of two types. One type of inquiry calls only for a description of the group of individuals actually observed. Summary measures, or statistics, such as per cents, averages or measures of variability are computed from the observations made on members of the group. The statistics are then used for description of this particular group, but they are not used as foundation for a general theory applicable to similar individuals that have not been examined.

A second type of statistical inquiry is more characteristic of scientific investigation. It involves a search for principles which have some degree of generality. If an investigation deals with matters of any general interest, the findings are usually applied to a much larger domain than the cases actually observed. We may call that larger domain the *universe* or the *population* and may call the group of cases observed the *sample*. Now the group characters of the sample, that is the *statistics* obtained from the sample, are to be used to obtain information concerning the unknown group characters of the population. Such generalization from sample to universe is *statistical inference*, as contrasted with descriptive statistics which apply only to the group from which they are derived.

General conclusions inferred from limited sets of observations are necessarily uncertain. When we reach a conclusion by inference from sample data we do so at the risk of being in error. This risk can be expressed as a probability and can be given a numerical value. It is the purpose of this book to describe methods which lead to valid inferences and to calculate the risk of error involved in those inferences. This book is concerned with principles and methods used in statistical inquiries from which general principles can be derived.

Experiments in Judging Intelligence from Photographs. A good many people are convinced that they are able to judge the intelligence of a person by simply looking at his photograph. This ability seems to be of a kind which lends itself to study by experimental methods.

A simple experiment might be to present to the subject two photographs of persons whose intelligence has been well determined. In order to reduce the effect of extraneous cues, these should be photographs of two persons of same age and sex, similarly dressed and similarly posed. The subject is then asked to arrange the photographs in order of intelligence. We may ask how conclusive the outcome of this experiment will be. Clearly there are only two possible outcomes. Either he arranges them correctly, or he arranges them incorrectly. Suppose he arranges them incorrectly. Then surely he has failed to demonstrate ability to judge intelligence from photographs. Suppose, however, he arranges the photographs correctly. Are we then to accept the conclusion that he can judge intelligence correctly from photographs?

A difficulty in accepting this conclusion is the important part which chance could play. If the subject did not look at the photographs at all but only at their backs, or if the photographs were marked A and B and he chose one letter as indicating the more intelligent person without looking at the photographs at all, we might say that he had made a chance arrangement. Under these circumstances the two possible outcomes (both photographs right or both wrong) are equally likely. The probability of each result by chance is therefore said to be $\frac{1}{2}$. Since the probability of reaching a correct result by chance is so great, when a correct result has been reached one can have little confidence that it was due to some cause other than chance.

The experiment just described is evidently not sufficiently extensive to reveal satisfactory evidence of ability even when it exists. The probability of obtaining a correct result by chance alone can be reduced by using more photographs. If three photographs, A, B, and C, are used there are six possible orders in which they can be arranged, namely, ABC, ACB, BAC, BCA, CAB and CBA. Only one of these orders is correct. Let us assume that order to be ABC. Under the hypothesis that chance alone operates in the arrangement, each order has the same probability and that probability is $\frac{1}{6} = .167$. Consequently, if the person whose ability is being questioned arranges these photographs correctly, we would have some confidence that the outcome is not due to chance. However, the probability of arriving at a true answer on a chance basis is still greater than that which statisticians accept as desirable.

Before proceeding with a discussion of a more extensive experiment it is worth while examining the six arrangements a little further. Here a correct placement will be indicated by a capital letter, an incorrect placement by a lower case letter.

One arrangement is entirely correct: ABC

Three arrangements have one correct placement: Acb, baC, and cBa.

Two arrangements have no correct placement: cab and bca.

Therefore the probability of three correct placements by chance is $\frac{1}{6}$; of two correct is 0; of one correct is $\frac{3}{6}$; of none correct is $\frac{2}{6}$.

The elementary outcomes have now been grouped in accordance with the number of correct placements, and to each number of correct placements has been attributed a probability. The placements and their probability may be exhibited as follows:

Number of correct placements	*Probability*
3	$\frac{1}{6} = .167$
2	0
1	$\frac{3}{6} = .500$
0	$\frac{2}{6} = .333$
TOTAL	1.000

This is an example of a probability distribution of which more will be said in the next chapter.

Consider now an experiment with four photographs. There are 24 possible arrangements of which only one is completely accurate. Under the hypothesis that chance only operates, the probability of a completely correct arrangement is $\frac{1}{24}$ or .042. Consequently one would be inclined to give considerable credence to the idea that a subject who can arrange four photographs in the same order of intelligence as that of the persons photographed does have ability to judge intelligence from photographs.

In Table 1.1 are shown the 24 possible arrangements of four pictures grouped in accordance with the number of photographs in correct position. Capital letters show photographs in correct position, small letters shows photographs in incorrect position. The probability which corresponds to each group is shown in the column at the right.

TABLE 1.1 Classification of all Possible Arrangements of Four Photographs, A, B, C and D

Number correctly placed	Possible arrangements				Number of arrangements	Probability
4	*ABCD*				1	$\frac{1}{24}$ = .042
3					0	0
2	*ABdc*	*dBCa*	*AcbD*		6	$\frac{6}{24}$ = .250
	AdCb	*cBaD*	*baCD*			
1	*Acdb*	*bdCa*	*cBda*	*cabD*	8	$\frac{8}{24}$ = .333
	Adbc	*daCb*	*dBac*	*bcaD*		
0	*badc*	*cadb*	*dabc*		9	$\frac{9}{24}$ = .375
	bdac	*cdab*	*dcab*			
	bcda	*cdba*	*dcba*			
				TOTAL	24	1.000

With five photographs the number of possible arrangements would be 120, only one of which is entirely correct. Under the hypothesis of pure chance all these 120 arrangements are equally likely and so the probability of achieving a correct arrangement by chance is $\frac{1}{120}$ = .008.

We might go on considering the use of larger and larger numbers of photographs. However, one purpose of this chapter is to present simple situations in which the reader can without too much difficulty enumerate the possible outcomes of an experiment. As the number of photographs increases such enumeration becomes exceedingly tedious. For 6 there are 720 possible arrangements. Therefore we shall carry this particular type of experiment no further.

Statistical Hypotheses and Their Verification. The procedures and modes of reasoning just described will be used so widely in the book that it is desirable to formulate them in general terms.

For convenience the general formulation of the procedure and its application to the preceding problem will be displayed in parallel columns as a series of steps.

General formulation	*Application to previous experiment*
1. An empirical population is defined	1. A population of photographs of persons with varying intelligence is defined.
2. A hypothesis about the population is formulated.	2. The hypothesis is formulated that any effort by the experimenter to arrange photographs in relation to intelligence will provide a result which is no better than a chance arrangement.
3. The consequences of the hypothesis are formulated. For this purpose a character of the sample called a *statistic* is formulated and the probability distribution of the statistic over all possible samples is determined. This distribution is called a *sampling distribution.*	3. In view of the hypothesis the probability distribution in Table 1.1 is obtained. This is the distribution of the statistic, "number of photographs in correct position."
4. A random sample of elements from the population is drawn and observations are made on those elements.	4. A random sample of four photographs is drawn, and the photographs are arranged by the experimenter in what appears to him to be the correct order of intelligence of the persons photographed.
5. The value of the statistic is ob-observed in the sample.	5. The number of objects in correct position is counted. This number is the observed value of the statistic.

6. The hypothesis is tested by comparing the value of the statistic in the observed sample with the probability distribution for all possible samples. If the observed statistic has little likelihood of occurring the hypothesis is rejected. Otherwise the hypothesis is accepted.

6. If the experiment results in all four photographs correctly arranged, then Table 1.1 shows that such a result has probability of only .008 under the hypothesis. Since this usually is considered a low probability the hypothesis is rejected.

Now let us consider a different design which might have been employed. Suppose pairs of photographs are obtained such that each pair shows two persons of the same sex and same age, similarly dressed and similarly posed, but one of the two persons has an intelligence quotient under 85 and the other an intelligence quotient over 120. Some pairs are male, some female; some are children, some adolescents, some adults. Suppose that many such pairs of photographs are available, and from this supply an experimenter selects five pairs by some random process, and fastens each pair on a large cardboard. To decide which picture shall be placed at the right, he tosses a coin. The test is then administered by a different person who does not know which picture is which, lest unconsciously he might give the subject a cue. Under each picture is an identifying number. Looking at each pair of pictures in turn, the subject tries to decide which picture belongs to a person with high intelligence and he records the number of that picture. For each pair on which he makes a correct judgment his paper is scored +, for each pair on which he is in error it is scored −.

The number of possible records is $2^5 = 32$. These are listed in Table 1.2. If each of the 32 records is equally probable, each has probability $\frac{1}{32} = .032$. Thus the probability of a perfectly correct result by chance is .03. Suppose the .05 level of probability has been agreed upon before the experiment was undertaken. A record of 5 correct choices has probability less than .05 and therefore gives sufficient evidence for rejecting the hypothesis that the choices were made by chance. A record of fewer than five correct choices is insufficient to reject the chance hypothesis.

TABLE 1.2 Probability Distribution of the Number Right out of Five Choices when Each Choice Is as Likely to be Right as to be Wrong

(+ indicates a right choice, − a wrong one)

Number of right choices	Record	Frequency	Probability if all records are equally probable
5	+ + + + +	1	$\frac{1}{32}$ = .0312
	+ + + + −		
	+ + + − +		
4	+ + − + +	5	$\frac{5}{32}$ = .1563
	+ − + + +		
	− + + + +		
	+ + + − −		
	+ + − − +		
	+ + − + −		
	+ − + + −		
	+ − + − +		
3	+ − − + +	10	$\frac{10}{32}$ = .3125
	− + + + −		
	− + + − +		
	− + − + +		
	− − + + +		
	+ + − − −		
	+ − + − −		
	+ − − + −		
	+ − − − +		
2	− + + − −	10	$\frac{10}{32}$ = .3125
	− + − + −		
	− + − − +		
	− − + + −		
	− − + − +		
	− − − + +		
	+ − − − −		
	− + − − −		
1	− − + − −	5	$\frac{5}{32}$ = .1563
	− − − + −		
	− − − − +		
0	− − − − −	1	$\frac{1}{32}$ = .0312
TOTAL		32	1.0000

2 Probability Distributions

A more formal treatment of probability and its relation to statistical inference will be presented in this chapter.

Observations. In any statistical study it is essential to observe some character of the objects under consideration and to make a record of that observation. Suppose, for example, that the character is age and that the objects are persons. The record of "observation" may take the form of a numerical measure such as "age in years at last birthday"; it may be merely the assigning of an individual to the appropriate one of a series of age categories; or it may be merely the record + or − in answer to such a question as "Is he of voting age?" The individuals in a group may be ranked in order of age and the numbers 1, 2, 3 . . . N assigned to them, and these ranks will also be called observations. Thus the term *observation* is a quite general term which includes such more specific terms as measure, score, category, rank, presence or absence of a trait. An observation is a record of information about an individual regardless of the form of that record. Sometimes for the sake of brevity an individual observation may be called "an individual."

Variables. When an observation is made on a characteristic of an individual, it is expected that one of several possible values of the characteristic will be observed. The values may be categorical, as when observations are made on sex; or may be scaled, as observations on age; or ordered, as A is greater than B and B is greater than C. A characteristic which may take several values is called a *variable.*

Two kinds of variables are considered in statistics, discrete and continuous. If a variable can take only a finite set of values it is called *discrete.* Variables like sex, marital status, or number of children in a family are discrete variables.

Variables like height and weight are considered *continuous* because they may take any value in a continuous interval of measurement. Because of the limitations of measuring instruments, the actual set of possible measures is finite, even in measurements on a continuous variable. Thus, in measurements on intelligence only a finite number of test scores can materialize. Nevertheless, it is convenient to deal with such variables as measures of a continuous underlying trait.

Sometimes it is convenient to deal with a continuous variable as if it were discrete. Thus one may divide ages of persons into groups, as, for example, ages below 40, ages 40 to 59, and ages 60 or above.

The first four chapters of this book deal mainly with discrete variables. Beginning with Chapter 5 considerable attention will be given to continuous variables.

Populations Defined on a Discrete Variable. The set of observations made in a statistical investigation may be considered as a sample from a larger, perhaps infinitely large, group of elements commonly called the *population* or the *universe,* and sometimes called the *supply.* When observations are made on a discrete variable, the values of the variable may be thought of as classes into which the totality of elements is distributed. From this point of view of the population an observation is merely a drawing of an element from one of the classes which make up the population.

The population is characterized by these classes and by the proportion of all elements in each class. We shall use the symbols C_i for the ith class, and P_i for the proportion of elements of the population contained in this class.

There are two kinds of populations. In one kind the elements making up the population actually exist. Such a population is encountered in making a survey of a community. If the variable studied is, say, family size, a single family is an element of the population, and all these elements may be considered as distributed in classes according to their numerical value. If the community is large the study of family size may be conducted by use of a sample.

Another kind of population is usually involved in experiments. Here the totality of elements is only conceptual and not existent. For such a population it is preferable to think of P_i as the *chance,* or *probability,* that an observation is in class C_i. Thus, in throwing a coin the population consists of the readings on all possible throws, but since "all possible throws" can never be made, the totality of all such readings is only conceptual. Suppose that the class C_1 is head and the class C_2 is tail. If the coin is unbiased and the throw is fair, then $P_1 = \frac{1}{2}$ is the chance of obtaining a head, and $P_2 = \frac{1}{2}$ is the chance of obtaining a tail. The experiments described in Chapter 1 were based on populations which are conceptual. For these reasons the conclusions drawn from an experiment are conclusions about a hypothetical population defined by the classes and by related proportions, rather than about an existing population.

Random Observations. Statistical logic has as its goal the generalizing from a sample to a population. The degree of confidence which can be placed in such a generalization can be estimated only if the observations may be considered as drawn at *random* from the population. Consequently, much thought must be given to methods of achieving randomness when a statistical investigation is planned.

When a statistical study deals with observations on a finite population, say the population of a city, an element is considered to be drawn at random if, and only if, some device is used by means of which any one element of the population is as likely to be drawn as any other element. This situation never obtains by conscious choice. It is completely impossible for a person to pick a book at "at random" from a bookcase or even to pluck a blade of grass "at random" if he looks at it. Some device designed to produce a random selection is essential. If the population is finite, each individual in it may be given a number, those numbers may be written on little tags, the tags placed in a large container and thoroughly stirred, and a tag drawn out by a blindfolded person, or shaken out by some mechanical device. That would be correct but laborious. An easier and equally correct procedure is to make use of a table of random numbers such as is described in Chapter 6.

The criterion that every individual in the population must have the same chance to be included in the sample is necessary but is not sufficient to define a random sample. Suppose, for example, that one has 5000 cards of members of a union arranged alphabetically, and that a sample of 50 is needed. Suppose the method for sampling is to select an individual card at random and then take every 10th card in succession after it until 50 cards have been drawn. Any individual has the same chance to be chosen as any other but this is not a random sample. It is also necessary that every *set of 50* must have the same chance to be chosen as any other set of 50 and there are many sets of 50 cards which could not possibly be obtained by this procedure. A better way would be to go on drawing individuals at random until 50 have been chosen. Strictly speaking, each card should be returned to the file after it has been drawn so that it could possibly be drawn more than once, but that is seldom done and failure to replace the individual after drawing has negligible effect on the outcome unless the population is small.

In an experimental study it is not possible to enumerate all elements and to sample them randomly in the manner just described. In such a study it is necessary to plan the experiment so as to provide a fair representation of the population. To take a simple example, consider an experiment to test the hypothesis that a given coin is unbiased, that in a fair toss it is as likely to fall head up as to fall tail up. An experiment requires that a number of fair tosses be made. To insure fairness several persons may be asked to make tosses. The several samples of tosses may then be compared, or combined.

If the problem is extended to a test of whether all 25-cent coins are unbiased, evidence from one coin would not be sufficient. Samples from a number of sources would be selected and each coin subjected to tosses by one or more individuals.

The experiments described in Chapter 1 must also be approached from this point of view. The photographs must be selected so as to provide a fair representation of the material which the subject may normally be expected to compare. Also the time chosen for the experiment must be fair to the subject. It is obviously impossible to choose these elements randomly from all possible elements. However, random devices can help in assuring fairness.

In the experiment in which photographs are to be arranged in the order of intelligence of the persons photographed, the photographs may be chosen randomly from a larger stock of available photographs. In this way the bias of the experimenter is eliminated. If possible the time, or repetitions of time, of the experiment may be randomized.

In the experiment in which pairs of photographs are compared, it is desirable not only to choose them at random from a larger set of pairs, but also to randomize the order in which the pairs are presented. In addition each pair should be shuffled so that the photograph representing the higher intelligence is as often on the right as it is on the left. The composition of the pairs may itself be determined by a random process.

In each experiment the element of randomization must be considered to insure a fair representation of the population which is studied. In an experiment comparing two teaching methods both methods may be tried by several teachers in each of several communities. Ideally the communities should be chosen at random. In addition, within each community, half the available teachers should be assigned at random to teach by one of the methods and half by the other. If such precautions are followed, the probability laws discussed in this book are applicable to the experiment.

Probability. Suppose that in a population each observation falls in one and only one of the classes $C_1, C_2 \ldots C_k$; and suppose the proportion of observations in these classes to be $P_1, P_2 \ldots P_k$. If an observation is drawn at random from the entire population, P_1 is the probability that it will come from class C_1; the probability that it will come from C_2 is P_2; and, in general, the probability that it will come from C_i is P_i. In Table 1.1 on page 4 there are five classes (or categories) defined in terms of the number of photographs correctly placed. These classes may be designated C_0, C_1, C_2, C_3, and C_4, and the corresponding proportions are $\frac{9}{24}$, $\frac{8}{24}$, $\frac{6}{24}$, $\frac{0}{24}$ and $\frac{1}{24}$. These proportions are properly called probabilities. Similarly Table 1.2 has six classes and the corresponding proportions are called probabilities.

In the situations considered in Chapter 1 the student could compute the probability that a random observation would fall in a particular class, because he could enumerate all possible forms that an observation could take. Later on we shall deal with problems for which the appropriate probability must be read from a table prepared by a mathematician. Before that stage is reached, it is important for the student to develop clear concepts about the meaning of probability in these simpler situations.

Probability Distribution. A distribution showing a set of defined classes $C_1, C_2 \ldots C_k$ and the probability that a random observation X will fall in each of those classes is called a *probability distribution*. Thus the tables in Chapter 1 display probability distributions.

Sometimes this random observation is a group character computed from a sample, such as a mean, or a standard deviation, or a per cent, or a coefficient of correlation, etc. A group character obtained from an observed sample is called a *statistic*. A probability distribution showing the probability that a statistic from a random sample will fall in each of a set of defined classes is called a *sampling distribution.* In later chapters we shall speak of the sampling distribution of the mean, the sampling distribution of a per cent, and the like.

Symbolism. A shorthand manner of writing probability statements is convenient because it reduces the amount of writing to be done and enables the eye to take in at a glance an idea which would be grasped more slowly if expressed entirely in words. The sentence "P_i is the probability that a random observation X will fall in the class C_i" would be written symbolically as

$$P(X \text{ is in } C_i) = P_i$$
$$\text{or} \quad Pr(X \text{ is in } C_i) = P_i$$

Sometimes curled braces { } are used instead of round parentheses. The expression inside the parentheses may be varied to suit the occasion. Thus for the data of Table 1.1 one might write

$$P\{4 \text{ correct placements}\} = .042$$
$$P\{3 \text{ correct placements}\} = .250, \text{ etc.}$$

and for the data of Table 1.2 on page 7 one might write

$$Pr(\text{all choices correct}) = .0312$$
$$Pr(3 \text{ choices correct}) = .3125, \text{ etc.}$$

The probability that a head will appear on a single toss of a coin might be written merely P(head) or $P(H)$. P_i is, also for brevity, called *the probability of the class* C_i.

Symbolic Statements of Probability

Words	*Symbol*
The probability that an observation X will fall in Class C	$P(X \text{ is in } C)$
The probability that an observation X will fall either in Class C_1 or in Class C_2	$P(X \text{ is in } C_1 \text{ or } C_2)$
The probability that if a first observation has been found to be in Class C_i, a second will be found to be in Class C_j	$P(X_2 \text{ is in } C_j \mid X_1 \text{ is in } C_i)$

Sometimes it is desirable to include in the probability symbolism a conditional clause, such as "the probability of four correct choices when the number of choices to be made is 5," or "the probability of placing exactly 2 photographs in correct position if the number of photographs to be arranged is 4," or "the probability that a second observation falls in class j when a first observation has already fallen in class i." For this purpose a vertical line is used to mean "when" or "if" and the conditional clause is written after the line. The three sentences just quoted might be written as follows:

$$P(4 \text{ choices correct} \mid N = 5)$$
$$P(2 \text{ correct} \mid N = 4)$$
$$P(X_2 \text{ is in } C_j \mid X_1 \text{ is in } C_i)$$

Mutually Exclusive Classes. In a system of classification, if it is impossible for the same observation to be placed in each of two classes simultaneously, those classes are said to be *incompatible* or *mutually exclusive.* Thus, if children are classified by age, the class of 5-year olds and the class of 6-year olds are mutually exclusive. If children are classified by sex the class of boys and the class of girls are mutually exclusive. However, the class of boys and the class of 6-year olds are not mutually exclusive because an individual may belong in both classes simultaneously.

Exhaustive Classes. If in a system of classification every observation must be in at least one of the classes named, then those classes are *exhaustive.* Thus in Table 1.1 every possible selection must fall in one of the five classes named, no other classes are possible in this experiment, so these five classes are exhaustive as well as mutually exclusive.

In a group of children aged 4 to 10, the class of 5-year olds and the class of 6-year olds are mutually exclusive but not exhaustive; the class of age 4 to 7 and the class of age 6 to 10 are exhaustive but not mutually exclusive; the class of boys and the class of girls are both exhaustive and mutually exclusive.

If classes are both exhaustive and mutually exclusive the sum of their probabilities is 1, as in Tables 1.1 and 1.2.

Independence of Observations. Independence of observations is an important idea which will occur again and again throughout this book. *Two observations are considered to be independent when information about one of them provides no clue whatever as to the other.* Two observations are considered to be *dependent* if it is possible to make a better guess about one of them when you know what the other one is.

An illustration will clarify this concept. Suppose a housing survey of a community is to be made by means of a sample in order to determine the extent of overcrowding, and suppose a list of all dwelling units in the community is available. Suppose further that by some random procedure a dwelling is selected, the interviewer visits it, and finds that it is a one-family house of 10 rooms occupied by 3 people. Now let a second dwelling unit be selected at random. Does the nature of the first observation affect in any way the probability that the second observation will be a substandard dwelling? A superior housing unit? If selection is made at random, the probability of obtaining a particular type of home is the same at every selection regardless of what was obtained on an earlier observation. In such a situation observations are *independent*.

Now by contrast, let us assume that in order to save time and travel, an interviewer who has been asked to visit 5 homes takes all of them in the same block. If one of these homes is the 10-room house with 3 occupants mentioned in the preceding paragraph, the probability that any of the others will be a cold-water flat of 3 rooms occupied by 5 persons is very much smaller than the probability that a dwelling drawn at random from the entire list would be such a cold-water flat. These 5 observations made on homes in one block are *not independent*.

Observations which are independent with respect to one population may be dependent with respect to another. If the population being studied is the families living in Van Buren County, Iowa, a random sample of families from that county provides a set of independent observations. However, if the population being studied is the families in rural Iowa, then a random sample of the families in Van Buren County provides a set of dependent observations.

Laws for the Combination of Probabilities

Addition Law: If two or more classes are mutually exclusive, the probability that an observation will be in one or the other is the sum of the probabilities of the separate classes.

Multiplication Law: If X_1 and X_2 are independent observations, the joint probability that X_1 will be in C_i and X_2 will be in C_j is the product of their separate probabilities.

Several observations on one individual may be considered independent if that individual alone is being studied. For example, one might be interested in variations of his blood pressure and might make observations at varying times. In this case, generalization would be to the blood pressure of this particular person. If a population of persons is being studied, several measurements of the blood pressure of the same person on different occasions would be dependent.

The Probability of Two or More Occurrences. The importance of the ideas of dependence and independence among observations is due to the probability relations in the possible outcomes of the observations.

Consider again the survey of a community with the purpose of determining overcrowding in homes. Suppose that a standard of comfort in the home has been adopted and that by this standard one third of the families in the community live in overcrowded conditions. Suppose also, that the community is fairly large. Then, if two families are observed independently, the probability that *both* live in overcrowded conditions is $\frac{1}{3} \times \frac{1}{3} = \frac{1}{9}$. In a sample of independent observations, the probability that all or even a considerable proportion of families selected independently for observation live in overcrowded conditions is very small. The probability is high that in such a sample the proportion of families living in overcrowded homes will not differ greatly from $\frac{1}{3}$.

If, however, one observation is made by choosing a family at random and then a neighbor of this family is questioned to provide a second observation, the probability that the second family will live in an overcrowded home is determined by the home conditions of the first family. If the first family lives in an overcrowded home then the chance that their neighbor will also live in such a home is likely to be far in excess of $\frac{1}{3}$. The joint probability that both families live in overcrowded homes is then a number far greater than $\frac{1}{9}$. If an entire sample is chosen from the same neighborhood the proportion of overcrowded homes in the sample is likely to differ greatly from the corresponding proportion in the population.

Consider a very extreme case in which one family is chosen at random and then all the other families in the sample are taken from the immediate neighborhood of the first one. The survey might very well indicate that all families in the community lived in substandard houses, or that all lived in affluence. It could not yield information of much value.

It should be recognized that in some situations it is an excellent procedure to choose many neighborhoods (say m) at random and then to make observations on a predetermined number of individuals (say n) in each neighborhood. However, the results cannot be treated as a random sample of mn individuals, but must be treated by special methods. Moreover, the number of randomly selected neighborhoods must not be too small.

EXERCISE 2.1

1. Let X represent the result of throwing a die. All possible results may be grouped in six classes, each class defined by the number appearing on the exposed face of the die. Thus to say $X = 5$ is to state that the result falls in the class characterized by having the exposed number a 5. As these six classes are exhaustive and mutually exclusive, the sum of the probabilities associated with them is 1. If the die is perfectly balanced, all classes have the same probability and so the probability of any one class (that is the probability of the appearance of any particular face) is $\frac{1}{6}$. Translate the following statements into symbols. *Note:* Slight variations from the form given in the answer key may be acceptable.

a. The probability of obtaining a 5 is $\frac{1}{6}$. *Ans.* $P(X = 5) = \frac{1}{6}$

b. The probability of obtaining a 1 is the same as the probability of obtaining a 2 or a 3 . . . or a 6.

c. The probability of obtaining a 1 or a 2 is $\frac{1}{6} + \frac{1}{6} = \frac{1}{3}$

d. The probability of obtaining an odd number is $\frac{1}{6} + \frac{1}{6} + \frac{1}{6} = \frac{1}{2}$

e. The probability of obtaining a number smaller than 4 is $\frac{1}{2}$. Note these definitions:

$X > A$	X is greater than A
$X < A$	X is less than A
$X \geqq A$	X is greater than or equal to A, that is X is not less than A
$X \leqq A$	X is less than or equal to A, that is X is not greater than A

Ans.
$$\begin{aligned} P(X < 4) &= P(X = 1 \text{ or } 2 \text{ or } 3) \\ &= P(X = 1) + P(X = 2) + P(X = 3) \\ &= \tfrac{1}{6} + \tfrac{1}{6} + \tfrac{1}{6} = \tfrac{1}{2} \end{aligned}$$

f. The probability of not obtaining a 6 is 1 minus the probability of obtaining a 6, and this is $1 - \frac{1}{6} = \frac{5}{6}$.

2. Two perfectly balanced dice are thrown. Let X_1 represent the number exposed on the first and X_2 the number exposed on the second. Translate the following symbols into words.

a. $P(X_1 = 3 \text{ and } X_2 = 3) = P(X_1 = 3) \cdot P(X_2 = 3) = \frac{1}{6} \cdot \frac{1}{6} = \frac{1}{36}$

b. $P(X_1 + X_2 = 2) = P(X_1 = 1) \cdot P(X_2 = 1) = \frac{1}{6} \cdot \frac{1}{6} = \frac{1}{36}$

c. $P(X_1 + X_2 = 3) = P(X_1 = 1 \text{ and } X_2 = 2) + P(X_1 = 2 \text{ and } X_2 = 1)$
$$= \tfrac{1}{6} \cdot \tfrac{1}{6} + \tfrac{1}{6} \cdot \tfrac{1}{6} = \tfrac{2}{36} = \tfrac{1}{18}$$

d. $P(X_2 = 5 \mid X_1 = 6) = \frac{1}{6}$

e. $P(X_2 = 6 \mid X_1 = 6) = \frac{1}{6}$

f. $P(X_1 \text{ and } X_2 \text{ are both odd}) = P(X_1 \text{ odd}) \cdot P(X_2 \text{ odd})$
$= P(X_1 = 1 \text{ or } 3 \text{ or } 5) \cdot P(X_2 = 1 \text{ or } 3 \text{ or } 5) = (\frac{1}{6} + \frac{1}{6} + \frac{1}{6})(\frac{1}{6} + \frac{1}{6} + \frac{1}{6})$
$= \frac{1}{2} \cdot \frac{1}{2} = \frac{1}{4}$

g. $P(X_1 \text{ and } X_2 \text{ both} < 6) = P(X_1 < 6) \cdot P(X_2 < 6)$
$= (1 - \frac{1}{6})(1 - \frac{1}{6}) = \frac{5}{6} \cdot \frac{5}{6} = \frac{25}{36}$

h. $P(X_1 + X_2 = 11) = P(X_1 = 6 \text{ and } X_2 = 5) + P(X_1 = 5 \text{ and } X_2 = 6)$
$= P(X_1 = 6) \cdot P(X_2 = 5) + P(X_1 = 5) \cdot P(X_2 = 6)$
$= \frac{1}{6} \cdot \frac{1}{6} + \frac{1}{6} \cdot \frac{1}{6} = \frac{1}{18}$

Factorial. It is convenient to have a term and a symbol to represent the product of consecutive integers beginning with 1. Thus $1 \cdot 2 \cdot 3 \cdot 4 \cdot 5 \cdot 6 \cdot 7 = 5040$ is called *factorial* 7 or 7 *factorial.* It is denoted by the symbol 7! In general if N is a positive integer,

(2.1) $$N! = N(N-1)(N-2) \cdot \cdot \cdot 4 \cdot 3 \cdot 2 \cdot 1$$

It is convenient to define factorial zero as equal to 1. This definition simplifies notation and is consistent with other notation of factorials.

The symbol $\binom{N}{r}$ is used to represent a relation which occurs often in work with probability, especially in developing the binomial distribution, below. It is defined as

(2.2) $$\binom{N}{r} = \frac{N!}{r!(N-r)!}$$

This relation is of interest because it gives the number of ways in which r objects can be selected from a group of N objects.

EXERCISE 2.2

1. Verify the following relations:

a. $4! = 4 \cdot 3 \cdot 2 \cdot 1 = 24$

b. $5! = 5 \cdot 4 \cdot 3 \cdot 2 \cdot 1 = 120$

c. $\frac{5!}{4!} = \frac{5 \cdot 4 \cdot 3 \cdot 2 \cdot 1}{4 \cdot 3 \cdot 2 \cdot 1} = 5$

d. $\frac{9!}{7!} = 72$

e. $\frac{8!}{10!} = \frac{1}{90}$

f. $\frac{12!}{10!2!} = 66$

g. $8! = 8(7!)$

h. $20! = 20(19)(18!)$

i. $\frac{20!}{18!} = 380$

j. $9! = 9(8)(7)(6!)$

k. $\frac{9!}{6!} = 9(8)(7)$

l. $\frac{10!}{6!4!} = 210$

2. Find the values of the following expressions:

a. $\frac{6!}{3!}$ c. $\frac{19!}{20!}$ e. $0!3!$ g. $\frac{5!7!}{6!4!}$

b. $\frac{15!}{13!}$ d. $\frac{10!}{9!1!}$ f. $\frac{16 \cdot 15 \cdot (14!)}{15!}$ h. $\frac{10!6!4!}{3!12!}$

3. Verify the following:

a. $\binom{8}{3} = 56$ d. $\binom{8}{8} = 1$ g. $\binom{29}{29} = 1$

b. $\binom{9}{4} = 126$ e. $\binom{12}{3} = 220$ h. $\binom{12}{9} = 220$

c. $\binom{20}{1} = 20$ f. $\binom{25}{3} = 2300$ i. $\binom{16}{5} = 4368$

A Population of Two Classes. Perhaps the simplest population which can be considered is one which consists of only two classes. Such a population was described in Chapter 1 in the experiment to judge the ability to select the more intelligent of two persons by comparing their photographs. The population considered there consists of two classes: 1. *the class of correct selections,* and 2. *the class of incorrect selections.* A population or sample divided into two classes is often termed a *dichotomy.*

The hypothesis formulated in Chapter 1 that a correct selection was as likely to occur as an incorrect may be formulated in the language of this present chapter by saying that the proportion of elements in each class is one half.

A different hypothesis as to the number of correct solutions would provide a different description of the population. Consider, for example, the hypothesis that a correct selection is four times as likely to occur as an incorrect selection. The class of correct selections would then contain $\frac{4}{5}$ of the elements, whereas the class of incorrect selections would contain $\frac{1}{5}$ of the elements. The two populations described by these two hypotheses are displayed graphically in Figures 2–1 and 2–2. The proportion of correct selections may be any number between zero and one depending on the circumstances. The proportion of incorrect selections is one minus the proportion of correct selections.

Populations consisting of two classes occur very often, for example: male and female, married and unmarried, passed and failed. Any population of two classes is fully determined by the proportion of elements in either one of the classes. For convenience in writing formulas the symbol P will be introduced to signify the proportion of elements in one of the classes of a two-class population. The proportion in the other class is $1 - P$. For simplicity in writing it is customary to use the symbol Q for $1 - P$.

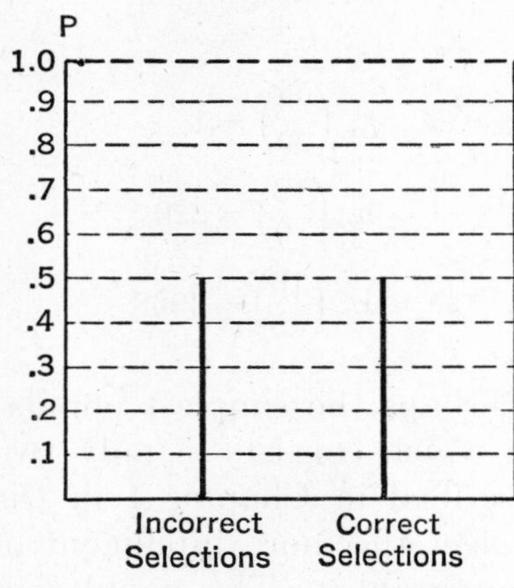

FIG. 2–1. Population distribution under the hypothesis that correct and incorrect selections are equally likely.

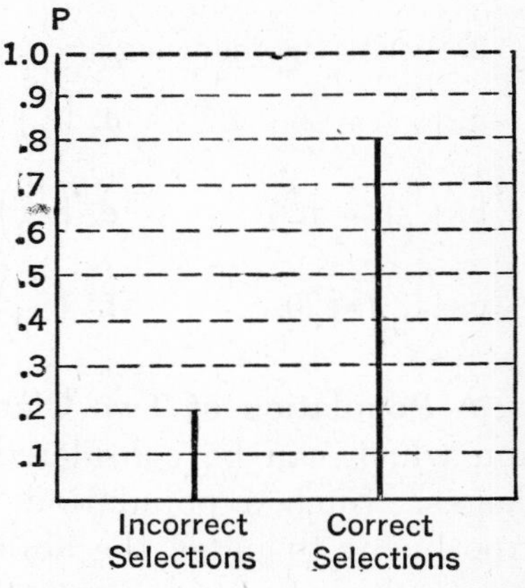

FIG. 2–2. Population distribution under the hypothesis that correct selections are four times as likely as incorrect.

While P may vary from population to population it is a fixed number for any one population. The proportion in a sample should be distinguished from that in the population. Thus if a population of persons contains 50% men, a sample, even though random, might contain 40%, or 70%, or even 100%, men. If the sample is random, and not very small, the probability of extreme deviation from 50% men is small.

To distinguish between the proportion in the population, which we have called P and the proportion in a sample, we shall use a lower case p to denote the latter.

Parameter and Statistic. A quantity like P which distinguishes one population from another similar population is called a *parameter*. The reader should note that P stands for proportion and *not* for parameter. Other parameters such as the mean and standard deviation will be introduced later. Many populations involve more than one parameter. The sample proportion p is called a statistic. It varies from sample to sample of any given population. Thus for random samples out of a population with parameter P, the sample statistic p fluctuates around P.

The Binomial Distribution. The binomial distribution is the sampling distribution of p for random samples out of a two-class population. This statement means that the terms of the binomial distribution provide the probability for each possible value that p may take in a random sample of N elements.

To make the discussion concrete, let us return to the experiment for selecting the more intelligent of two persons by a comparison of their photographs. Suppose that in the population the probability of a correct solution is P and hence the probability of an incorrect solution is Q. Suppose a random sample of two pairs of photographs is taken. Since the two pairs are independent observations, the multiplication law for combining probabilities applies. The four possible outcomes and the probability associated with each are:

Outcome	*First selection*	*Second selection*	*Probability*
1	Correct	Correct	$P \times P = P^2$
2	Correct	Incorrect	$P \times Q = PQ$
3	Incorrect	Correct	$Q \times P = PQ$
4	Incorrect	Incorrect	$Q \times Q = Q^2$

These four outcomes might be described in terms of the *numbers of correct selections,* which are respectively 2, 1, 1, and 0. They might also be described in terms of the *proportions of selections made correctly,* which are respectively $\frac{2}{2} = 1.00$, $\frac{1}{2} = .50$, $\frac{1}{2} = .50$, and $\frac{0}{2} = 0$. In either case the two middle outcomes may be grouped together, as they yield the same number of correct selections. The sampling distribution for samples of 2 cases is then:

Np *Number of correct selections*	p *Proportion of correct selections*	*Probability*
2	1.00	P^2
1	.50	$2PQ$
0	.00	Q^2

The sum of the probabilities is $Q^2 + 2PQ + P^2$ which is

$$(Q + P)^2 = (1)^2 = 1.$$

For samples of any number of pairs the sampling distribution may be developed in similar fashion, but the task is a very tedious one unless N is small. The student may find it instructive to work out the distribution for samples of 3. The following presentation shows probabilities for samples of 5 pairs. Generalization from 5 to other values of N can be facilitated by writing the numerical coefficients in the $\binom{N}{r}$ notation, and that has been done in the right-hand column.

Np *Number of correct selections in samples of 5*	p *Proportion of correct selections in samples of 5*	*Probability*
5	1.00	$P^5 = \binom{5}{5} P^5$
4	.80	$5QP^4 = \binom{5}{4} QP^4$
3	.60	$10Q^2P^3 = \binom{5}{3} Q^2P^3$
2	.40	$10Q^3P^2 = \binom{5}{2} Q^3P^2$
1	.20	$5Q^4P = \binom{5}{1} Q^4P$
0	.00	$Q^5 = \binom{5}{0} Q^5$

The sum of the six probabilities is $(Q + P)^5 = (1)^5 = 1$. Here we have shown the binomial sampling distribution for samples of 5. To generalize, call the elements in one of the two population classes "successes" and let P be the probability of a success. Then for a random sample of N cases the probability of exactly r successes is

$$\binom{N}{r} P^r Q^{N-r} \tag{2.3}$$

This generalization leads to the sampling distribution of p for samples of N cases from a two-class population, which is given in Table 2.1.

The probabilities in the informal table previously given for samples of 5, and the probabilities in Table 2.1 for samples of any size apply either to the *proportion* of successes or to the *number* of successes.

The fact that the sum of probabilities in the right column is $(Q + P)^N$ is of interest since it illustrates the fact that the binomial distribution is a special case of the *binomial expansion* which is treated in textbooks on algebra. Because $Q + P$ is always

TABLE 2.1 The Binomial Distribution

Sampling distribution for p from samples of N cases from a two-class population

Np Number of successes	p	Probability
N	$\frac{N}{N}$	$\binom{N}{N} P^N$
$N-1$	$\frac{N-1}{N}$	$\binom{N}{N-1} P^{N-1}Q$
$N-2$	$\frac{N-2}{N}$	$\binom{N}{N-2} P^{N-2}Q^2$
...	...	...
r	$\frac{r}{N}$	$\binom{N}{r} P^rQ^{N-r}$
...	...	...
2	$\frac{2}{N}$	$\binom{N}{2} P^2Q^{N-2}$
1	$\frac{1}{N}$	$\binom{N}{1} PQ^{N-1}$
0	$\frac{0}{N}$	$\binom{N}{0} Q^N$
TOTAL		$(Q+P)^N = 1$

equal to 1, $(Q + P)^N = 1$ no matter what value N has. Inasmuch as the classes defined by the number of successes are mutually exclusive and exhaustive, the sum of their probabilities must be 1.00.

The Graphic Representation of the Binomial Distribution. Figures 2–1 and 2–2 on page 20 showed two populations in which $P = .5$ and $P = .8$ respectively. Suppose a sample of 5 cases is drawn from each of these populations. The number of successes which can be obtained in that sample can only be one of the integers, 0, 1, 2, 3, 4, or 5 and so the proportion of successes can only be $\frac{0}{5}$, $\frac{1}{5}$, $\frac{2}{5}$, $\frac{3}{5}$, $\frac{4}{5}$, or $\frac{5}{5}$, as shown in Figure 2–3. These values

FIG. 2–3. Possible values of p in samples of 5 cases.

are represented as discrete points on a linear scale. The variable exists only at these points. The probability associated with each value of p for samples of 5 from a population in which $P = .5$

is given numerically in column 3 of Table 2.2 and shown by a vertical line in Figure 2–4. These probabilities are the respective terms of $(.5 + .5)^5$. The corresponding probabilities when $P = .8$, obtained from the terms of $(.2 + .8)^5$, are given numerically in column 5 of Table 2.2 and shown graphically in Figure 2–5.

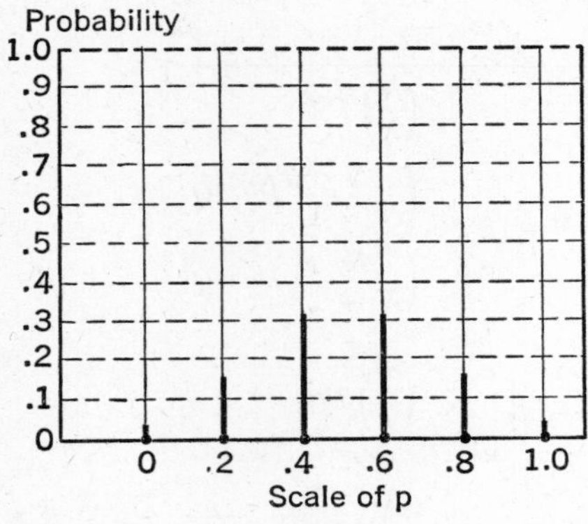

FIG. 2–4. Distribution of p in samples of 5 from a two-class population in which $P = .5$, p being represented as a discrete variable.

FIG. 2–5. Distribution of p in samples of 5 from a two-class population in which $P = .8$, p being represented as a discrete variable.

Even in elementary work in statistics it often is found convenient to treat a discrete variable as though it were continuous. Thus the mean number of children in a group of families might be reported as $\overline{X} = 1.53$, or the 90th percentile reported as 3.87.

TABLE 2.2 Probability Associated with each Possible Value of *p* in Samples of 5 when *P* = .5 and when *P* = .8, and Corresponding Cumulative Probability

Value of Np	Value of p	$P = .5$ Probability	$P = .5$ Cumulative probability	$P = .8$ Probability	$P = .8$ Cumulative probability
1	2	3	4	5	6
5	1.0	.03125	1.00000	.32768	1.00000
4	.8	.15625	.96875	.40960	.67232
3	.6	.31250	.81250	.20480	.26272
2	.4	.31250	.50000	.05120	.05792
1	.2	.15625	.18750	.00640	.00672
0	.0	.03125	.03125	.00032	.00032
		1.00000		1.00000	

These numbers are obviously artifacts but they are meaningful artifacts. No family has 1.53 children but the statistic gives useful information about the families under consideration. The distribution of the number of children per family might be represented graphically as a histogram where the numbers 0, 1, 2, . . . indicating number of children per family are represented not as discrete points on a line but as midpoints of intervals. In such a figure the number of families with 2 children would be represented by the area of a rectangle with base extending from 1.5 to 2.5 on the horizontal axis and with height proportional to the number of families having 2 children. The number 0 on the horizontal scale would be represented by an interval extending from $-.5$ to $+.5$ even though no families could have a negative number of children. All intervals being of the same width the areas of the rectangles which form the histogram are proportional to their heights and to the frequencies represented.

The binomial probability distribution may also be represented by a histogram which, although an artifact, brings out certain general concepts better than the discrete distribution. Figures 2–6 and 2–7 are such histograms superimposed on the graphs of the discrete distributions of Figures 2–4 and 2–5. In these figures probability is represented by area. The ordinate is then called the *probability density*.

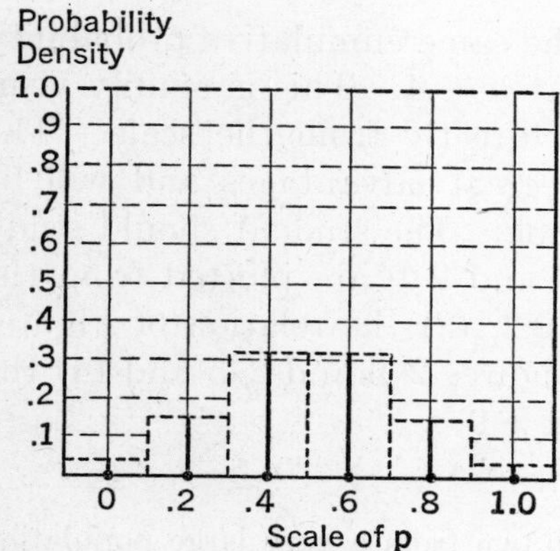

FIG. 2–6. Distribution of p in samples of 5 from a two-class population in which $P = .5$, p being represented as a continuous variable.

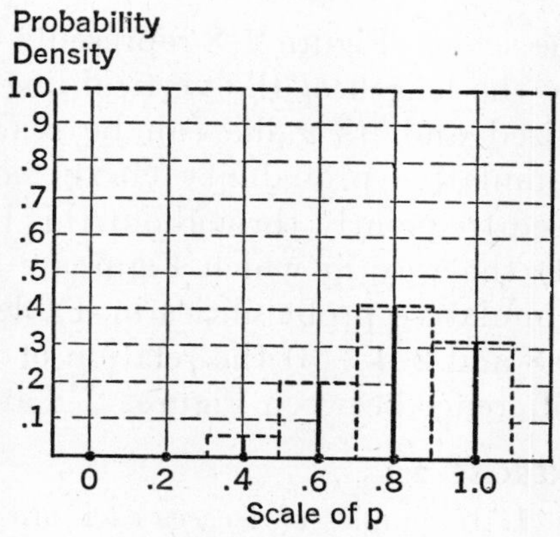

FIG. 2–7. Distribution of p in samples of 5 from a two-class population in which $P = .8$, p being represented as a continuous variable.

Suppose we wish to represent the probability that $p = .4$ or less when $P = .5$. By the Addition Law stated on page 15 this is

$$P(p = 0) + P(p = .2) + P(p = .4) = .03125 + .15625 + .31250 = .50$$

as indicated by the cumulative probability in column 4 of Table 2.2. This probability is the sum of the three vertical lines at $p = 0$, $p = .2$, and $p = .4$ in Figure 2–4 but that sum is not particularly easy to visualize. The same probability is represented by the area to the left of $p = .45$ in Figure 2–6. This area is easily visualized but its numerical value cannot be directly read from

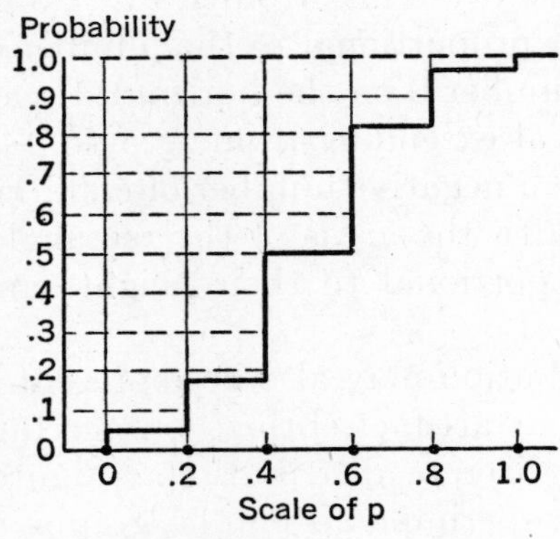

FIG. 2–8. Cumulative probability distribution of p in samples of 5 from a two-class population in which $P = .5$.

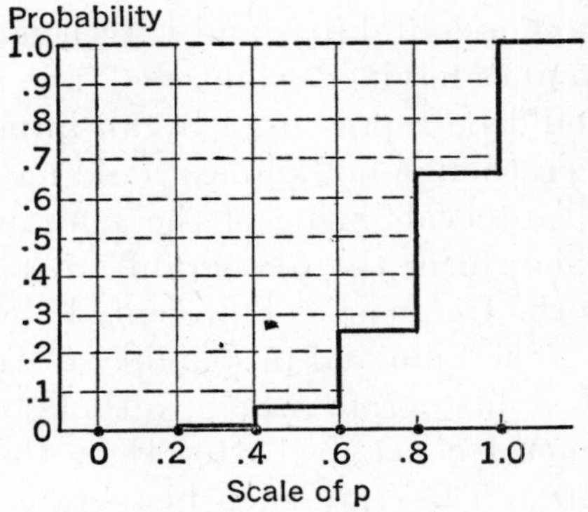

FIG. 2–9. Cumulative probability distribution of p in samples of 5 from a two-class population in which $P = .8$.

the scale. Figure 2–8 represents the same cumulative probability by the length of the vertical line at $p = .4$. This is readily visualized and its value can be read directly from the scale. The cumulative probability curve has great advantages and will be used frequently throughout this book. The student should study (1) the way in which Figures 2–8 and 2–9 are plotted from the cumulative probabilities in Table 2.2, (2) the relation of Figures 2–8 and 2–4; (3) the relation of Figures 2–9 and 2–5 and (4) the difference between Figures 2–8 and 2–9.

EXERCISE 2.3

1. If samples of 4 cases each are drawn from a very large population in which 30% of the individuals have a certain trait, what is the sampling distribution of the number having that trait? Make a graph of the population distribution. Make a graph of the sampling distribution.

2a. If samples of 3 cases each are drawn from a very large population in which $P = .50$, what is the sampling distribution of p? Make a graph of the population distribution; of the sampling distribution.

b. Do the same for samples of 6 cases.

c. Do the same for samples of 10 cases.

3. In drawing samples from a symmetric population in which $P = Q = .50$, what appears to be the effect of increasing the size of the samples? Base your answer on the results obtained in question 2.

4a. If samples of 3 cases each are obtained from a very large population in which $P = .60$, what is the sampling distribution of p? Make a graph of the population distribution; of the sampling distribution.

b. Do the same for samples of 6 cases.

c. Do the same for samples of 10 cases.

5. Answer the questions in item 4 for the case in which $P = .2$.

Mean of the Probability Distribution for a Discrete Variable. The familiar procedure of computing a mean will now be applied to a probability distribution in order to develop certain important new concepts. In Table 2.3, X is the discrete variable "proportion of successes in a sample of 5 cases." Instead of the frequencies you are accustomed to using in such computations, we here use the probabilities from column 3 of Table 2.2. The mean thus computed is found to be .5 which was the value of the population proportion. This mean is called the *expected value of p* or *the expectation of p* and is denoted by the symbol $E(p)$, read "E of p" or "expectation of p."

TABLE 2.3 Computation of the Mean and Variance of p in Samples of 5 from a Population in which $P = .5$

X = Value of p	Probability [Analogous to f]	(Probability)X [Analogous to fX]	(Probability)X^2 [Analogous to fX^2]
1.0	.03125	.03125	.03125
.8	.15625	.12500	.10000
.6	.31250	.18750	.11250
.4	.31250	.12500	.05000
.2	.15625	.03125	.00625
.0	.03125	.00000	.00000
Sum	1.00000	.50000	.30000

$$\text{Mean} = \frac{\Sigma(\text{Probability})X}{\Sigma\text{Probabilities}} = \frac{.5}{1.0} = .5$$

$$\text{Variance} = \frac{\Sigma(\text{Probability})X^2}{\Sigma\text{Probability}} - (\text{mean})^2 = \frac{.3}{1.0} - \left(\frac{.5}{1.0}\right)^2 = .05$$

$$\text{Standard deviation} = \sqrt{.05} = .224$$

As we shall wish to use the idea of expected value in reference to other statistics as well as p, let us now state it in more general terms. Let X denote the variable for which a probability distribution is given, and let $P_1, P_2 \ldots P_k$ be the probabilities of the values $X_1, X_2 \dots X_k$. Then the mean of the probability distribution of X is $E(X)$ and is computed as

$$\frac{\Sigma P_i X_i}{\Sigma P_i} = \Sigma P_i X_i$$

since $\Sigma P_i = 1$. ΣP_i is an abbreviation for "the sum of the P_i." A fuller description of this symbol is given in Chapter 5.

$$E(X) = \Sigma P_i X_i \tag{2.4}$$

The parenthesis around X must not be interpreted as indicating a product. The term *expected value* originated in games of chance. If in such a game there are k different possible outcomes with probabilities $P_1, P_2 \dots P_k$, and if the amount received by a player for each of these outcomes is $X_1, X_2 \dots X_k$ (where some of the X's may be negative if forfeits are involved) then in a long series of games $E(X)$ as given by Formula (2.4) is the player's expected return per game. The small Greek letter μ (pronounced mu) corresponding to the English letter m will be used as an abbreviation for the mean of a probability distribution.

$$\mu_X = E(X) \tag{2.5}$$

For the probability distribution of p,

$$\mu_p = E(p) = P \tag{2.6}$$

Variance and Standard Deviation of the Probability Distribution for a Discrete Variable. In Table 2.3 the variance and standard deviation of p have been computed in the manner presumably familiar to you with probabilities taking the place of frequencies.*

The computation might also have been carried out by subtracting P from each value of p in turn, squaring, multiplying by the probability and summing, thus:

$p - P$	$(p - P)^2$	$(p - P)^2$ (Probability)
$1.0 - .5 = .5$	.25	.0078125
$.8 - .5 = .3$	.09	.0140625
$.6 - .5 = .1$	.01	.0031250
$.4 - .5 = -.1$	.01	.0031250
$.2 - .5 = -.3$	.09	.0140625
$0 - .5 = -.5$	.25	.0078125
		.0500000

* Persons for whom this is a first course may find it helpful to study the computation of mean, variance, and standard deviation in an elementary text, or to turn to page 115 of this text.

This is exactly the same result as obtained in Table 2.3. The variance of p will be called the expected value of $(p - \mu_p)^2$ denoted by the symbol σ^2_p (σ is the small Greek letter corresponding to s and is pronounced sigma).

(2.7) $$\sigma^2_p = E(p - \mu_p)^2 = E(p - P)^2$$

In general if X is defined as before to be any variable for which the probability distribution is given,

(2.8) $$E(X - \mu)^2 = \Sigma P_i(X_i - \mu)^2 = \Sigma P_i X^2_i - \mu^2$$

(2.9) $$\sigma^2_X = E(X - \mu)^2$$

The standard deviation σ_X is the square root of the variance σ^2_X.

EXERCISE 2.4

For each of the following probability distributions compute $\mu = E(X)$ and $\sigma^2 = E(X - \mu)^2$.

1. The distribution in Table 1.1 on page 4 ($\mu = 1, \sigma^2 = 1$).

2. The distribution of p in samples of 5 from a population in which $P = .8$, using the probabilities given in column 5 of Table 2.2.

($\mu = .8, \sigma^2 = .032.$)

3. The distribution of the number of successes ($X = Np$) in samples of 5 from a population for which $P = .5$. Use the probabilities from Table 2.2. ($\mu = 2.5, \sigma^2 = 1.25.$)

4. The distribution of the number of successes ($X = Np$) in samples of 5 from a population for which $P = .8$. ($\mu = 4, \sigma^2 = .8.$)

5. The distribution in Table 3.1 on page 45. ($\mu = .5, \sigma^2 = .025.$)

Mean and Standard Deviation of a Sample. The notation and formulas used in the preceding two sections are applicable to the calculation of means and standard deviations of theoretical distributions. Other notation and formulas will be used in the calculation of these characteristics in samples. A discussion of these is deferred to Chapter 5.

Mean and Standard Deviation of the Binomial Distribution. In the preceding sections we dealt in general with the mean, variance, and standard deviation of any probability distribution. However when the probability distribution has the binomial form the computation can be greatly simplified. Let X represent the *number* of individuals having a given trait in a sample of N individuals from a population in which P is the *proportion* having that trait. Then the mean is

(2.10) $$\mu_X = E(X) = NP,$$

the variance is

$$\sigma^2_X = E(X - \mu)^2 = NPQ \tag{2.11}$$

and the standard deviation is

$$\sigma_X = \sqrt{E(X - \mu)^2} = \sqrt{NPQ} \tag{2.12}$$

The reader may gain understanding of these formulas by applying them in problems 3 and 4 of Exercise 2.5 where they should give results identical with those obtained by the longer method of computation.

Let p represent the *proportion* of individuals having a given trait in a sample of N individuals from a population in which P is the proportion having that trait. The mean of the sampling distribution of p has already been given in Formula (2.6) as

$$\mu_p = E(p) = P$$

The variance is

$$\sigma^2_p = E(p - P)^2 = \frac{PQ}{N} \tag{2.13}$$

and the standard deviation is

$$\sigma_p = \sqrt{E(p - P)^2} = \sqrt{\frac{PQ}{N}} \tag{2.14}$$

The reader may gain understanding of these formulas by applying them in problems 2 and 5 of Exercise 2.4.

EXERCISE 2.5

1. Suppose a class which is studying sampling distributions decides that each member will spin each of 10 pennies once and record the number of heads which appear. Assume the pennies to be relatively free from bias so that the probability of a head appearing on one particular spin of one penny is $P = .5$.

a. What is the expected number of heads on each spin of 10 pennies?

b. Will this expected number be affected by the number of repetitions of the experiment? Will it be related to the number of persons in the class?

c. Will this expected number be changed if each person spins 20 instead of 10 pennies at one time?

d. Suppose 500 students carry out the experiment and each records as an observation the-number-of-heads-on-one-throw-of-10-pennies. Imagine the frequency distribution of these observations. An observation may have any value from 0 to 10. Can you state approximately the value of the variance of these observations? Why would this result be only an approximation? Would the approximation be better or worse if 10,000 students report observations than if 500 do so (assuming of course that the 10,000 observations are made with equal care)?

e. If each student throws 20 pennies instead of 10 would that change the variance discussed in question 1d?

2. Suppose 500 persons agree to take part in the experiment described in the preceding question (or a smaller number of persons make repeated throws until there are 500 records).

a. What are the expected frequencies for the distribution of heads on the 500 throws? Let X = number of heads appearing on one throw. Then $P(X_i)$ is the probability obtained by taking the appropriate term in the expansion of $(.5 + .5)^{10}$. The expected frequency for a given X_i is $500P(X_i)$ and is the appropriate term in the expansion of $500(.5 + .5)^{10}$. Complete the entries in columns F, FX, and FX^2.

X	$P(X)$	F	FX	FX^2
10	.00098	.49	4.9	49
9	.00977	4.88	43.9	395.1
8	.04395	21.98	175.8	
7	.11719			
6	.20508			
5	.24609			
4	.20508			
3	.11719			
2	.04395			
1	.00977			
0	.00098			
	1.00003	500.03	———	———

b. Compute the mean and the variance for the distribution in question 2a. Compare these answers with the values for μ_x and σ_x obtained by use of Formulas (2.10) and (2.12).

c. Would the outcome of question 2a have been different if there had been 100 repetitions instead of 500?

d. If the experiment were carried out as described could you be confident that the distribution of the number of heads in 500 replications would exactly conform to the frequency distribution of question 2a? Why?

Approximation to the Binomial Distribution. The computations made and the graphs drawn in Exercise 2.3 suggest the following generalizations:

a. If $P = .5$, the graph of the binomial distribution is symmetrical regardless of the size of N.

b. If P is not .5 the graph of the binomial distribution is asymmetrical, or skewed, when N is small but becomes more nearly symmetrical as N increases.

c. As N increases, the steps in the graph of the binomial distribution become smaller and the graph takes on more the appearance of a smooth curve.

We may even go further and say that if P is not too near 0 or 1 and if N is large, the smooth curve called the "normal curve" provides a very good approximation to the binomial. The sum of any number of terms of the binomial can then be obtained approximately from the corresponding area under the normal curve. The larger the value of N the better the approximation is. In fact, the first treatise ever written about the normal curve appeared under the title *Approximatio ad Summam Terminorum Binomii* $\overline{a+b}|^n$ *in Seriem Expansi.* Being translated this is "An Approximation to the Sum of the Terms of the Binomial $(a + b)^n$ Expanded in Series." In this seven-page pamphlet written in Latin and dated 1733, Abraham De Moivre wrote "although the solution of problems of chance often require that several terms of the binomial $(a + b)^n$ be added together, nevertheless in very high powers the thing appears so laborious, and of so great difficulty that few people have undertaken the task." Then he proceeds to obtain the formula for the ordinate of the probability curve and for the proportion of area lying between ordinates at selected points.

The Normal Distribution. The normal probability distribution in the adjacent sketch is a probability distribution on a *continuous* variable. The scale for values of this variable is located on the base line. For a continuous probability distribution one does not speak of a probability corresponding to a particular value of the variable, but rather of the probability that a value of the variable is less than a given number or more than a given number, or that it occurs between two given numbers. The probability is then an area under the curve. The probability that a value of the variable is less than A is the area under the curve, above the base line, and to the left of the ordinate at A. The probability that a value of the variable is between A and B is the area under the curve, above the base line, and between the ordinates at A and B. Since the normal distribution is a probability distribution the total area under the curve is one.

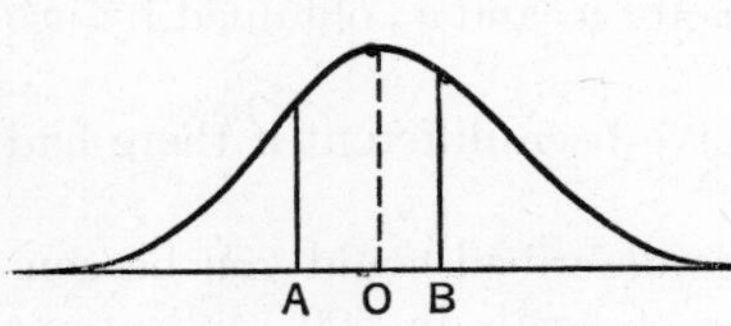

For the normal distribution the point O, shown in the sketch, is at the same time the mean, median, and mode. It is most often referred to as the mean. For convenience in reading tables related to the normal curve, the mean of the distribution is taken as the origin from which values of the variable are measured. Scale values are most conveniently expressed in standard deviation units. When the origin of a normal probability distribution is placed at the mean (μ) and values are scaled in terms of the standard deviation (σ), the distribution is called *unit normal.* The unit normal distribution has mean zero and variance 1. In this book the letter z will be used to denote a value of a variable so distributed.

If X is any normally distributed variable with mean μ and standard deviation σ, then

$$z = \frac{X - \mu}{\sigma} \tag{2.15}$$

It is convenient to attach a subscript to the letter z to indicate what proportion of the area under the normal curve lies to the left of an ordinate drawn at z. In the adjacent sketch 30% of the area lies to the left of an ordinate at $z_{.30}$ and 90% to the left of an ordinate at $z_{.90}$; therefore $z_{.30}$ is the 30th percentile of the curve and $z_{.90}$ is the 90th percentile.

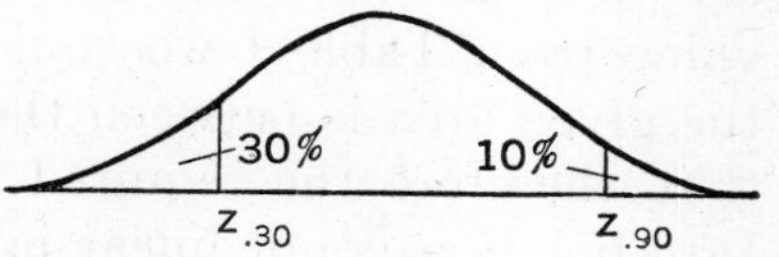

Reading a Table of Normal Probability. Tables I, II and III in the Appendix may be used for obtaining the probabilities of the normal distribution.

In Table I are shown area values corresponding to given abscissa values ranging from -4 to $+4$. Points to the left of the origin have negative abscissas and these are listed in the first column under the heading z_α. Then α denotes the area to the left of an ordinate at z_α. Points to the right of the origin have positive abscissas and these are listed in the second column under the heading $z_{1-\alpha}$. The area to the left of an ordinate at $z_{1-\alpha}$ is $1 - \alpha$ and the area to the right is α. Thus $z_\alpha = -z_{1-\alpha}$. The area outside the ordinates at z_α and $z_{1-\alpha}$ is 2α, the area between these two ordinates is $1 - 2\alpha$. Thus the table indicates that the area to the left of an ordinate at $z = -.9$ is .200. This means that the 20th percentile of the normal curve is $-.9$. This table is convenient to use when a value of z is known and the corresponding probability value is required.

Verify the following statements by identifying the appropriate entry in Table I.

$$P(z < -2.5) = .006 \qquad P(z < -2.1) = .018$$
$$P(z < 2.5) = .994 \qquad P(z < 2.1) = .982$$
$$P(z < -.4) = .345 \qquad P(z < -2.6) = .005$$
$$P(z < .4) = .655 \qquad P(z < 2.6) = .995$$

The percentile rank of $z = -2.5$ is .6
The percentile rank of $z = .4$ is 65.5

$z = 2.1$ is the 98th percentile.
$z = -2.1$ is the 2d percentile.

In Table II the roles of the two columns in Table I are reversed, making Table II particularly convenient to use when a probability value is known and the corresponding value of z is required. Thus, if we want to know the 30th percentile of the unit normal curve we want a value of z such that 30% of the area lies to the left of the ordinate at that point, and this is read directly from the table as $z_{.30} = -.524$. If we had tried to obtain this same value from Table I we could only have noted that .30 which is the given area is between the tabulated values .308 and .274 and that therefore the required value of z is between $-.5$ and $-.6$. Interpolation is not linear in these tables and could not be relied upon for more than one additional digit. It is much less laborious and more accurate to use Table II than to try to interpolate in Table I and vice versa. Verify the following statements by identifying the appropriate entry in Table II, then look at Table I to see how nearly you could have estimated the same value from it.

For the unit normal curve

the 10th percentile is -1.282
the 44th percentile is $-.151$
the 50th percentile is 0
the 95th percentile is 1.645

Table III is set up in a fashion similar to that of Table I but with these modifications. The z column has been headed x/σ and entries are at intervals of .01 instead of .1. It is to be understood that x/σ has here the same meaning as z_α in Table I. Areas are expressed as areas between the ordinate at z and the ordinate at the mean instead of areas to the left of the ordinate at z.

Thus for $z = -1.20$ Table I would give the area as .115 and Table III would give it as $.5 - .3849 = .1151$. For $z = -.65$, interpolation in Table I would give the area as $\frac{1}{2}(.274 + .242) = .258$ while Table III would give $.5 - .2422 = .2578$. To estimate the same value from Table II we could note that the tabulator entry nearest to $-.65$ is $-.6745$ and the corresponding area is .25.

The reader should be warned that practice in texts is not uniform as to what areas of the normal curve are tabulated, and so a full understanding of the relations involved is necessary if one is to make correct use of whatever tables are at hand. In most tables the maximum ordinate is given as .3989 as in Table III, but in some tables the maximum ordinate is given as 1.00 and all other ordinates are expressed as proportions of the maximum. Such a table is a table of the normal curve but not of the unit normal.

It is important that the reader understand certain relationships, which will be briefly stated here. Exercise 2.6 provides practice in recognizing these.

The subscript of z denotes an area while z denotes a distance on the baseline measured from the mean, or it denotes a point on the baseline at distance z from the mean.

> If the subscript is less than .50, z is negative.
> If the subscript is exactly .50, z is zero.
> If the subscript is greater than .50, z is positive.

In subsequent chapters the small Greek letter α (alpha) will often be used to designate a small area in one of the tails of a probability curve, as in the adjacent sketch. Then

$$z_\alpha = -z_{1-\alpha}$$
$$-z_\alpha = z_{1-\alpha}$$
$$z_\alpha + z_{1-\alpha} = 0$$

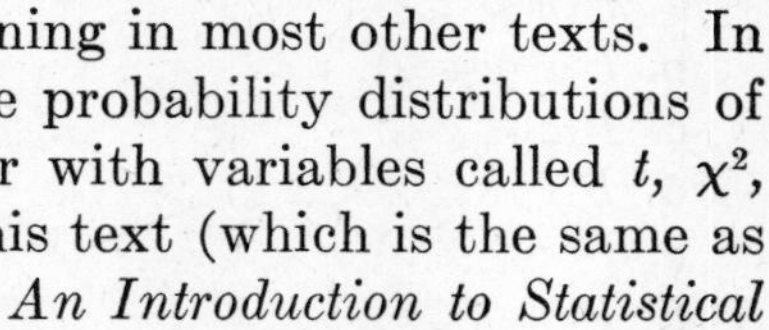

The reader must be warned that the numerical subscript is used with a somewhat different meaning in most other texts. In later chapters we shall deal with the probability distributions of several other variables, in particular with variables called t, χ^2, and F. In the symbolism used in this text (which is the same as that used by Dixon and Massey in *An Introduction to Statistical Analysis*, McGraw-Hill, 1951), $t_{.05}$, $\chi^2_{.05}$ and $F_{.05}$ each means the fifth percentile of the corresponding probability distribution. In the symbolism commonly used in other texts, t_{05} is the 97.5 percentile, χ^2_{05} and F_{05} are the 95th percentiles, while the 5th percentiles of those distributions are denoted as $-t_{10}$, χ^2_{95} and F_{95}. Obviously the notation introduced by Dixon and Massey and followed in this text is much more consistent and less confusing.

EXERCISE 2.6

1. By reference to Tables I, II, or III verify each of the following statements and indicate the number of the table which can be most conveniently used.

a. $P(z > 2.05) = .5 - .4798 = .0202$ (III)
b. $P(z < -.2) = .421$ (I)
c. $P(0 < z < 1.32) = .4066$ (III)
d. $P(-.64 < z < 0) = .2389$ (III)
e. $P(z < .5) = .692$ (I)
f. $P(z < .52) = .5 + .1985 = .6985$ (III)
g. $P(z > .57) = .5 - .2157 = .2843$ (III)
h. $P(-.3 < z < .3) = 1 - 2(.382) = .236$ (I)
$= 2(.1179) = .2358$ (III)
i. $P(z < -.3 \text{ or } z > .3) = 2(.382) = .764$ (I)
$= 1 - 2(.1179) = .7642$ (III)
j. $P(z < -2.5 \text{ or } z > 2.5) = 2(.006) = .012$ (I)
$= 1 - 2(.4938) = .0124$ (III)
k. $z_{.05} = -1.645$ (II)
l. $z_{.98} = -z_{.02} = 2.054$ (II)
m. $z_{.001} = -3.09$ (II)
n. $z_{.998} = -z_{.002} = 2.878$ (II)

2. Verify the following statements and translate them into words:

a. $z_{.30} = -z_{.70}$
b. $z_{.12} = -z_{.88}$
c. $z_{.90} = -z_{.10}$
d. $z_{.95} = -z_{.05}$
e. $z_{.20} + z_{.80} = 0$
f. $z_{.41} + z_{.59} = 0$
g. $z_{.08} + z_{.92} = 0$
h. $z_{.25} = -z_{.75}$
i. $z_{.995} = -z_{.005}$
j. $z_{.03} + z_{.97} = 0$

3. Without reference to any table, state the value of the following:

a. $P(z < z_{.12})$
b. $P(z > z_{.86})$
c. $P(z < z_{.99})$
d. $P(z_{.40} < z < z_{.45})$
e. $P(z_{.01} < z)$
f. $P(z_{.01} < z_{.99})$
g. $P(z > z_{.95})$
h. $P(z_{.10} < z < z_{.32})$
i. $P(z > z_{.97})$
j. $P(z > z_{.15})$
k. $P(z < z_{.05} \text{ or } z > z_{.95})$
l. $P(z < z_{.60})$
m. $P(z > z_{.995})$
n. $P(z < z_{.001} \text{ or } z > z_{.999})$
o. $P(z < z_{.03} \text{ or } z > z_{.97})$

4. If A represents some particular number find the value of A for which each of the following statements is satisfied.

a. $P(z > A) = .15$
b. $P(z < A) = .04$
c. $P(-A < z < A) = .30$
d. $P(z > A) + P(z < -A) = .50$
e. $P(z > A) = .05$
f. $P(-A < z < A) = .95$
g. $P(z > A) + P(z < -A) = .01$
h. $P(z > A) = .995$
i. $P(z < A) = .975$
j. $P(-A < z < A) = .50$

Computing Binomial Probabilities by Use of Normal Probability Tables. Since the normal distribution approximates closely the binomial, the table of areas under the normal curve may be used to compute probabilities of the binomial distribution.

Consider the following problem. In 100 fair throws of an unbiased coin what is the probability that heads will be exposed more than 60 times?

This is a sample of 100 from a population of two classes for which $P = Q = .5$. The exact probability distribution is given by the terms of the binomial for which $N = 100$ and $P = .5$. To calculate exactly the probability called for would require adding the terms

$$\binom{100}{100}\left(\frac{1}{2}\right)^{100} + \binom{100}{99}\left(\frac{1}{2}\right)^{100} + \cdots + \binom{100}{62}\left(\frac{1}{2}\right)^{100} + \binom{100}{61}\left(\frac{1}{2}\right)^{100}$$

To avoid this formidable task, the normal curve may be used to obtain an approximation — and a very good approximation. This approximation is accomplished by means of the statistic

$$z = \frac{p - P}{\sqrt{\dfrac{PQ}{N}}} \tag{2.16}$$

Notice that this statistic is zero at the mean of the distribution when $p = P$; it has unit standard deviation because of its denominator, and its distribution is approximately normal. Consequently it can be treated like the z of the unit normal distribution.

Returning now to the problem stated at the beginning of this section, we have $P = .5$, $p = .6$, and $N = 100$, hence

$$z = \frac{.6 - .5}{\sqrt{\dfrac{(.5)(.5)}{100}}} = 2$$

Table I shows that $P(z > 2) = .023$. Hence the chance that more than 60 throws will show heads is .023.

Consider also the following example: A mental test of 80 multiple-choice items each having 5 alternatives is presented to a subject who knows nothing whatever about the topic and guesses the answers to all of the questions. What is the chance that he will answer more than 24 of the questions correctly?

Here $P = \frac{1}{5} = .2$, $p = \frac{24}{80} = .3$, and $N = 80$, so

$$z = \frac{.3 - .2}{\sqrt{\frac{(.2)(.8)}{80}}} = 2.24$$

The chance that the subject will answer more than 24 questions correctly by guessing is $P(z > 2.24) = .0125$ by Table III.

The Closeness of Approximation of the Normal Curve to the Binomial. In order to see how well the normal curve fits a binomial

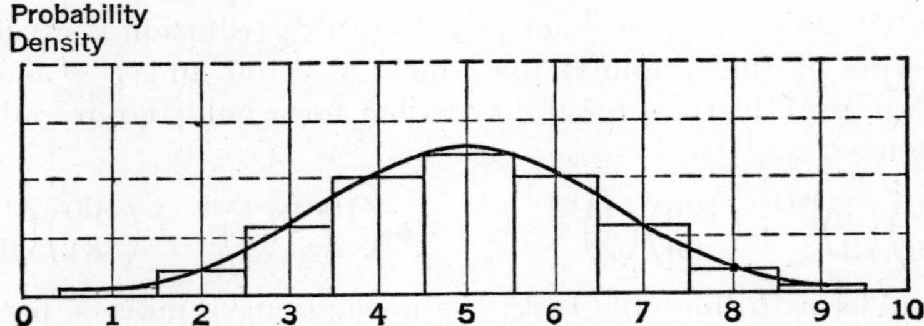

FIG. 2–10. Binomial probability distribution with $P = .5$ and $N = 10$ and normal distribution with mean $= PN = 5$ and standard deviation $= \sqrt{NPQ} = 1.58$.

distribution we may consider a small sample in which actual probabilities can be computed and compared. Consider the probability distribution of X in a sample of 10 cases where X runs from 0 to 10 with probabilities given by the binomial distribution for which $P = .5$ and $N = 10$. X is a discrete variable with probabilities as given in the adjacent list. For the sake of comparison of binomial and normal distributions, X is represented in Figure 2–10 as a continuous variable. Thus instead of the point $X = 6$ we have the interval $5.5 < X < 6.5$, and instead of $X = 0$ we have the interval $-.5 < X < .5$.

X	$P(X)$
10	.001
9	.010
8	.044
7	.117
6	.205
5	.246
4	.205
3	.117
2	.044
1	.010
0	.001

In such comparisons it is more effective to use *cumulative* distributions. The cumulative binomial probability that X will be no greater than a given value is shown in the second column of Table 2.4. Thus

$$P(X = 0 \text{ or } 1 \text{ or } 2 \text{ or } 3) = P(X < 3.5)$$
$$= .001 + .010 + .044 + .117 = .172$$

To obtain the corresponding probabilities on the assumption that X is normally distributed we must first find the mean and standard deviation of the binomial distribution. By Formula (2.10), $\mu = 5$ and by Formula (2.12) $\sigma = \sqrt{2.5} = 1.58$. We must next find the z value corresponding to each division point (such as .5, 1.5, 2.5, etc.) between intervals. For example, if

$$X = 1.5,\ z = \frac{1.5 - 5}{1.58} = -\ 2.21.$$

These z values are entered in column 3 of Table 2.4. The normal probability, that is, the area to the left of the ordinate at z, is shown in the final column of this table.

The two cumulative probability distributions tabulated in Table 2.4 are shown graphically in Figure 2–11. The values of X listed in Table 2.4 are the midpoints of intervals in the graph. At these points the smooth curve and the step curve are very

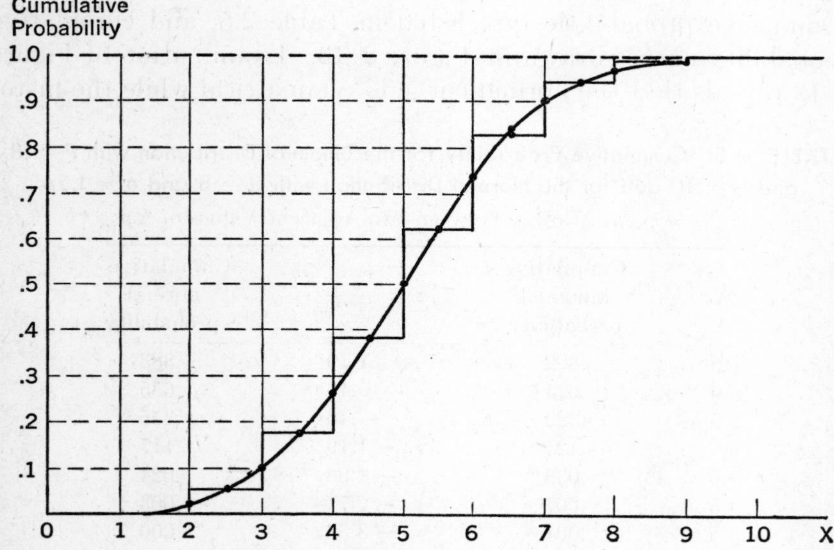

FIG. 2–11. Cumulative binomial probability distribution with $P = .5$ and $N = 10$ and cumulative normal distribution with mean $= PN = 5$, and standard deviation $= \sqrt{NPQ} = 1.58$.

close together, indicating that the smooth curve provides a good approximation to the step curve.

TABLE 2.4 Cumulative Probability for the Binomial Distribution with $P = .5$ and $N = 10$ and for the Normal Distribution with $\mu = 5$ and $\sigma = 1.58$

X_0 = point Midway between two Adjacent Values of Np

X_0	Cumulative binomial probability	$z = \frac{X_0 - 5}{1.58}$	Cumulative normal probability
9.5	.999	2.85	.998
8.5	.989	2.21	.986
7.5	.945	1.58	.943
6.5	.828	.95	.829
5.5	.623	.32	.625
4.5	.377	− .32	.375
3.5	.172	− .95	.171
2.5	.055	− 1.58	.057
1.5	.011	− 2.21	.014
.5	.001	− 2.85	.002

By way of contrast, the same treatment has been applied to the binomial with $P = .8$ and $N = 10$. The probability histogram and superimposed normal curve are shown in Figure 2–12, the cumulative probabilities are listed in Table 2.5, and cumulative probability curves drawn in Figure 2–13. Examination of Figure 2–12 reveals that the normal curve is symmetrical while the histo-

TABLE 2.5 Cumulative Probability for the Binomial Distribution with $P = .8$ and $N = 10$ and for the Normal Distribution with $\mu = 8$ and $\sigma = 1.26$

X_0 = point Midway between two Adjacent Values of Np

X_0	Cumulative binomial probability	$z = \frac{X_0 - 8}{1.265}$	Cumulative normal probability
9.5	.892	1.19	.883
8.5	.624	.40	.655
7.5	.322	− .40	.345
6.5	.121	− 1.19	.117
5.5	.033	− 1.98	.024
4.5	.007	− 2.77	.003
3.5	.001	− 3.56	.000
2.5	.000	− 4.35	.000
1.5	.000	− 5.14	.000
.5	.000	− 5.93	.000

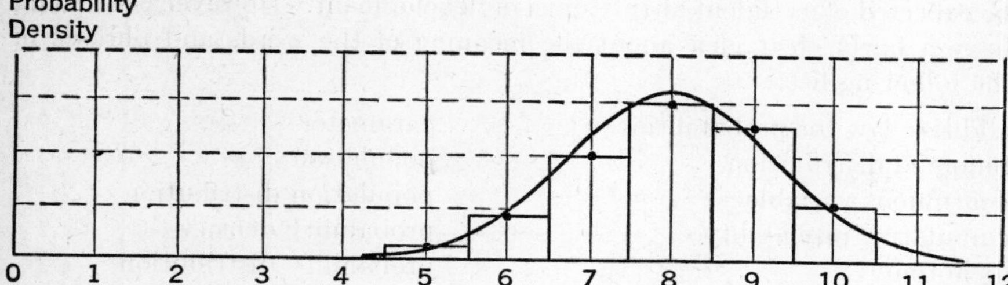

FIG. 2–12. Binomial probability distribution with $P = .8$ and $N = 10$ and normal distribution with mean $= PN = 8$ and standard deviation $= \sqrt{NPQ} = 1.26$.

gram is not. Examination of Figure 2–13 reveals that at the midpoints of intervals the smooth curve and the step curve do not coincide as well as they did in Figure 2–11. Even here, however, the discrepancy is less than many people would have expected.

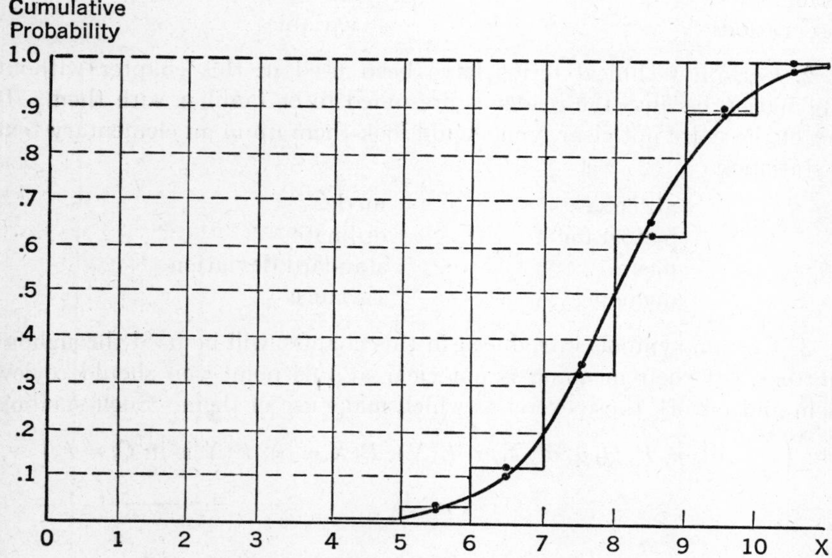

FIG. 2–13. Cumulative binomial probability distribution with $P = .8$ and $N = 10$ and cumulative normal distribution with mean $= PN = 8$, and standard deviation $= \sqrt{NPQ} = 1.26$.

REVIEW EXERCISE

1. This chapter has introduced a number of technical terms which are new to most readers. To phrase a completely satisfactory formal definition of some of these terms would require more erudition than is to be expected of a student at this stage of development. However you should have a fairly clear idea about the meaning of the words and phrases in the following list:

additive law for probabilities
binomial distribution
continuous variable
cumulative probability
dichotomy
dichotomous population
discrete variable
exhaustive classes
expectation
expected value
factorial
independent observations
multiplication law for probabilities
mutually exclusive classes
normal curve
observations
parameter
population
population distribution
probability density
probability distribution
probability of a class
random observation
random sample
random selection
random variable
sampling distribution
statistic
step curve
unit normal curve
universe
variable

2. Certain technical terms have been used in this chapter without explanation because the reader is presumed to be familiar with them. If any of these are not clear, you should look them up in an elementary text in statistics:

abscissa
histogram
mean
median
mode
ordinate
standard deviation
variance

3. Certain symbols introduced in this chapter will be used throughout the text. If their meaning is not clear at this point you should review them and rework those exercises which make use of them. Such symbols are: $\binom{N}{r}$, $6!$, p, P, Q, μ, σ^2, Σ, z, $E(X)$, $P(X = 5)$, $P(X \text{ is in } C_i = P_i)$

3 Inferences Concerning Proportions

The general logic of statistical inference was outlined somewhat sketchily in Chapter 1, and was there applied to some very simple problems in which the statistic computed was either the *number* of observations having a certain characteristic, or the *proportion* of observations having that characteristic. The simplest aspects of probability were developed in Chapter 2 as well as the technique of computing binomial probabilities and reading probabilities from a normal probability table. The concepts and methods of Chapter 2 will now be applied to a greater variety of problems of statistical inference related to proportions or per cents. (If 16 out of 25 individuals possess a given trait the *proportion* having the trait is $16/25 = .64$ and the *per cent* having it is

$$100(16/25) = 64.)$$

In many statistical studies the crucial issue relates to the size of a per cent or the comparison of two or more per cents. A new drug is discovered which appears to have curative properties for a hitherto baffling disease. What per cent of cases treated by the new drug recover? In what per cent of cases does the drug produce harmful results? Is the per cent of cases helped by this drug greater than the per cent helped by a remedy already in use? In a manufacturing process the company is concerned with the per cent of defective articles produced and must continually measure samples in order to keep that per cent within bounds. If the per cent becomes greater than some predetermined value it may be presumed that something has gone wrong with the machinery or that some other aspect of the manufacturing process should be investigated. A distributor of garden seed must make continual tests of the seed he sells. If he tested all of it he would have nothing left to sell, so he examines samples. Among the things he wants to know is the per cent of seeds of a given type which can be expected to germinate, and whether a larger per cent will germinate under one or another type of cultivation. The variety of practical situations in which samples are used to answer questions about population per cents is endless. Any reader can quickly think of many such in his own field of study.

The *content* which may be explored in problems of the kind discussed in this chapter is practically inexhaustible. The *types* of such problems are relatively few. Therefore, it seems economical of the student's effort to organize the presentation in terms of types of problems with one illustration for each type, and to expect that the reader can apply the method to similar situations in the content of his own field.

Test of Hypothesis $P = .5$ by Use of the Binomial Distribution. In order to make the discussion concrete let us return to the problem of selecting the more intelligent of two persons by comparing their photographs. This problem was introduced at the end of Chapter 1 by considering an experiment based on five pairs of photographs. The analysis will be more interesting if the experiment is now extended to include more pairs of photographs, say 10.

It was pointed out in Chapter 2 that the population studied by means of this experiment is a dichotomous or two-class population. The parameter P of the population is the probability of correctly selecting the more intelligent member of any random pair.

A variety of hypotheses might be formulated about this unknown P. Let us consider first the hypothesis that the experimenter has no ability to distinguish levels of intelligence by comparing photographs, so that a correct comparison is as likely as an incorrect comparison. In terms of the parameter the hypothesis is $P = .5$.

The consequences of this hypothesis are stated in terms of the sampling distribution of the statistic p which is, for an observed sample, the proportion of comparisons in which the correct selection is made. This distribution of p appears in Table 3.1. It is a special case of the binomial distribution shown in Table 2.1 when $N = 10$ and $P = .5$. The reader will note that the sampling distribution of p was constructed without knowledge of the proportion observed in any actual sample. The distribution supplies a statement of the probability, if the hypothesis is true, of obtaining in a sample of the given size one of the eleven possible values of p.

The hypothesis $P = .5$ can now be tested by actually performing the experiment with ten pairs of photographs and comparing the observed proportion of correct selections with the sampling distribution of p in Table 3.1.

Under the hypothesis that correct selections will be made in approximately half the comparisons ($P = .5$) it is reasonable to anticipate that in a sample of 10 cases an observed proportion p will be not far from .5. If it is very far from .5, say 0 or 1.0, most people intuitively feel that the observation contradicts the hypothesis, throws doubts upon it, renders it implausible. But intuitively, different people might hold different opinions as to what "very far from .5" means. The function of the sampling distribution is to provide an aid to intuition and to regularize intuitive decisions. "Very far from P" will take on different meanings as sample size changes and as P changes and so cannot provide a dependable rule for dealing with hypotheses. However, it can be agreed that an observed sample and a hypothesis are to be considered in conflict whenever, under the hypothesis, the probability of obtaining a sample as extreme as the one observed is not greater than some specified small number, say $1/20 = .05$ or $1/100 = .01$. In subsequent chapters various sampling distributions will be considered. Regardless of the nature of the sampling distribution, or the statistic to which it relates, one may always agree to consider that the extreme observations having this specified small probability warrant rejecting the hypothesis tested.

TABLE 3.1 The Sampling Distribution of an Observed Proportion p in Samples of 10 Cases from a Population in which $P = .5$

p	Probability for any value of P	Probability for $P = .5$
1.0	P^{10}	1/1024 = .001
.9	$10P^9Q$	10/1024 = .010
.8	$45P^8Q^2$	45/1024 = .044
.7	$120P^7Q^3$	120/1024 = .117
.6	$210P^6Q^4$	210/1024 = .205
.5	$252P^5Q^5$	252/1024 = .246
.4	$210P^4Q^6$	210/1024 = .205
.3	$120P^3Q^7$	120/1024 = .117
.2	$45P^2Q^8$	45/1024 = .044
.1	$10PQ^9$	10/1024 = .010
0	Q^{10}	1/1024 = .001
		1.000

According to Table 3.1 we see that under the hypothesis $P = .5$ the probability that $p = 0$ or 1.0 is

$$P(p = 0 \text{ or } 1.0 \mid N = 10 \text{ and } P = .5) = \frac{1}{1024} + \frac{1}{1024} = .002$$

Also the probability that p will be as extreme as .1 or .9 is the probability that p will be either 0, .1, .9 or 1.0 and this is

$$P(p = 0, .1, .9, \text{ or } 1.0 \mid N = 10 \text{ and } P = .5)$$
$$= \tfrac{1}{1024} + \tfrac{10}{1024} + \tfrac{10}{1024} + \tfrac{1}{1024} = \tfrac{22}{1024} = .022$$

This probability is so small that practically all research workers would agree that if one of these values of p is observed in a sample the hypothesis $P = .5$ should be rejected. Values of p which, when observed in a sample, lead to rejection of a hypothesis will be called *rejection values.* If the hypothesis $P = .5$ is rejected whenever one of these values of p appears in a sample, then in the long run a *true* hypothesis will be rejected in 22 out of 1000 samples. Most people consider that $\frac{22}{1000} = .022$ is a small risk to take. These four values of p are said to constitute a *critical region,* or a *region of rejection,* or *region of significance.* The remaining possible values of p, that is, $p = .2, .3, .4, .5, .6, .7$, and .8 are then said to constitute a *region of acceptance.* The probability of .022 is called the *level of significance* or the *size of the region of rejection.* The probability $1.00 - .022 = .978$ is then the *size of the region of acceptance.*

Some readers may be inclined to include the points .2 and .8 in the region of rejection. The probability of a sample as extreme as these under the hypothesis $P = .5$ is

$$P(p = 0, .1, .2, .8, .9, \text{ or } 1.0) = \tfrac{112}{1024} = .11$$

Most research workers are reluctant to adopt a rule which would cause them to reject a true hypothesis in 11 out of 100 samples and so they would prefer to classify .2 and .8 as acceptance values.

If a sampling distribution is continuous, as for example the normal probability curve, the level of significance can be chosen arbitrarily, and for this purpose some small conveniently rounded number such as $\frac{1}{20}$ or $\frac{1}{100}$ is commonly chosen. If a sampling distribution is discrete such an arbitrarily chosen level of significance may not conform to any probability which can possibly be obtained by cumulating probabilities at the extremes of the distribution. Thus we have just seen that in the present problem, the level of significance can be set at .022 or at .11 and not at any intermediate value. If the research worker wants to work at the .05 level, about the best he can do in such cases is to say he will make the size of the region of rejection *not larger than .05* and the size of the region of acceptance *not smaller than .95.*

In Figure 3–1, the region of rejection consists of the points marked with heavy dots. The region of acceptance consists of the points marked with circles. The size of each region is represented by the sum of the ordinates drawn at points in that region. Suppose that among comparisons of 10 pairs of photographs, correct selections have been made in 9 pairs. The observed value $p = .9$ falls in the critical region, the region of rejection. Therefore the hypothesis $P = .5$ must be relinquished.

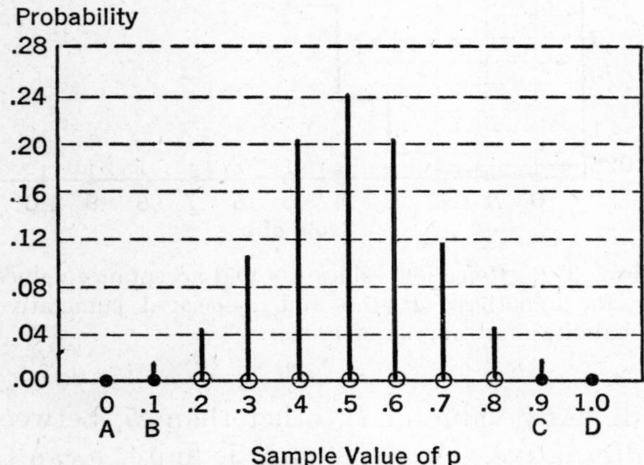

FIG. 3–1. Rejection values • • and acceptance values ○ ○ for hypothesis $P = .5$ and associated probabilities for samples of 10 cases.

The critical region can be located directly in the cumulative probability graph of Figure 3–2. Suppose you have decided to use a critical region of size α and to locate half of it in each tail. For illustration, let us assume you have decided on $\alpha = .05$. On the vertical axis mark the point corresponding to $\frac{1}{2}(.05) = .025$, and draw a horizontal line through it. This horizontal line meets the step graph of Figure 3–2 at $p = .2$. All values of p to the left of this intersection, not including $p = .2$, form the left critical region with probability not greater than .025. On the vertical axis mark the point corresponding to $1 - \frac{1}{2}(.05) = .975$ and draw a horizontal line through it. This horizontal line meets the step graph in the point $p = .8$. All values of p to the right of this intersection, not including $p = .8$, form the right critical region with probability not greater than .025. As in Figure 3–1, heavy dots have been used to represent rejection values.

Tests of Several Hypotheses on *P*. Inasmuch as the hypothesis $P = .5$ has proved unacceptable, alternative hypotheses

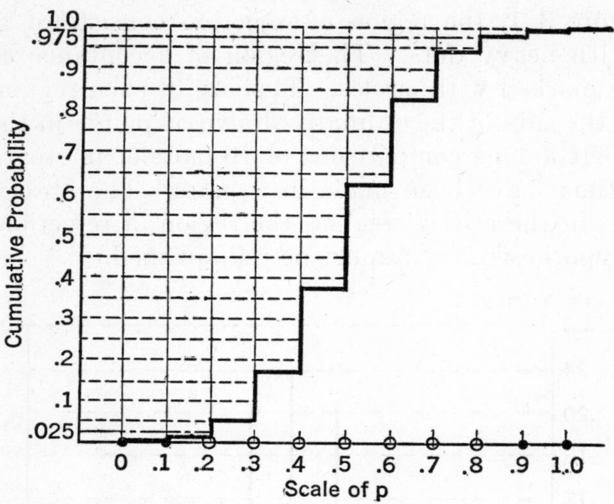

FIG. 3–2. Rejection values • • and acceptance values ∘ ∘ for hypothesis $P = .5$ and associated cumulative probabilities for samples of 10 cases.

may be tried. Any value of P, other than .5, between 0 and 1 may be an alternative. As the sample is finite, p can take values at the points $0/N, 1/N, 2/N, \cdots (N-1)/N, N/N$ and at no other points. Therefore the scale for p consists of discrete points. While P is a constant for any one population, we are here considering all possible dichotomous populations, and so the scale for P is a continuum extending from 0 to 1. For certain selected hypothetical values of P the probability distribution of p has been computed and is shown in Table 3.2. Each horizontal row of the table is a sampling distribution for which the sum would be 1.00 except for rounding errors. The vertical columns are *not* probability distributions.

We shall now seek rejection values for each of these distributions and shall represent them graphically in Figure 3–3 in such a way as to be able to study them all at one time in one unified picture.

Suppose it has been agreed that the region of rejection shall have probability .025 or less at each end of the distribution. Now let us see how this would work out for a particular row of Table 3.2, say the row for which $P = .70$. The sum of the probabilities for $p = 0$, $p = .1$, $p = .2$ and $p = .3$ is approximately .010 which is considerably less than the specified .025. However if the proba-

TABLE 3.2 Sampling Distribution of an Observed Proportion *p* in Samples of 10 Cases for Selected Values of *P*

(Decimal points omitted to save space)

	Probability of a given value of p											
P	0	.1	.2	.3	.4	.5	.6	.7	.8	.9	1.0	Sum
.95							001	010	075	315	599	1000
.90						002	011	057	194	387	349	1000
.85					001	008	040	130	276	347	197	999
.80				001	006	026	088	201	302	268	107	999
.75				003	016	058	146	250	282	188	056	999
.70			001	009	037	103	200	267	233	121	028	999
.65		001	004	021	069	154	238	252	176	072	013	1000
.60		002	011	042	111	201	251	215	121	040	006	999
.55		004	023	075	160	234	238	166	076	021	003	1000
.50	001	010	044	117	205	246	205	117	044	010	001	1000
.45	003	021	076	166	238	234	160	075	023	004		1000
.40	006	040	121	215	251	201	111	042	011	002		999
.35	013	072	176	252	238	154	069	021	004	001		1000
.30	028	121	233	267	200	103	037	009	001			999
.25	056	188	282	250	146	058	016	003				999
.20	107	268	302	201	088	026	006	001				999
.15	197	347	276	130	040	008	001					999
.10	349	387	194	057	011	002						1000
.05	599	315	075	010	001							1000

bility for $p = .4$ is included the sum becomes .047 which is considerably larger than the specified .025. On Figure 3–3 heavy dots mark rejection values. These are so chosen that the probability for the region of rejection in each tail is .025 or less.

In Figure 3–3 regions of rejection have been drawn in similar fashion for each of the selected values of P. The probabilities associated with these regions are not uniform, as can be seen by computing a few of them from the figures in Table 3.2. As a kind of compromise among these various regions, the pair of curved lines has been drawn on Figure 3–3. Whenever there is a region of probability approximately .025 the lines pass near the end point of that region.

These curved lines can be used to obtain a region of rejection for some value of P not listed in Table 3.2, say $P = .47$. The point .47 is located on the vertical axis and a horizontal line drawn across the chart, cutting the curves at points for which p_1 is approximately .13 and p_2 approximately .85. All values

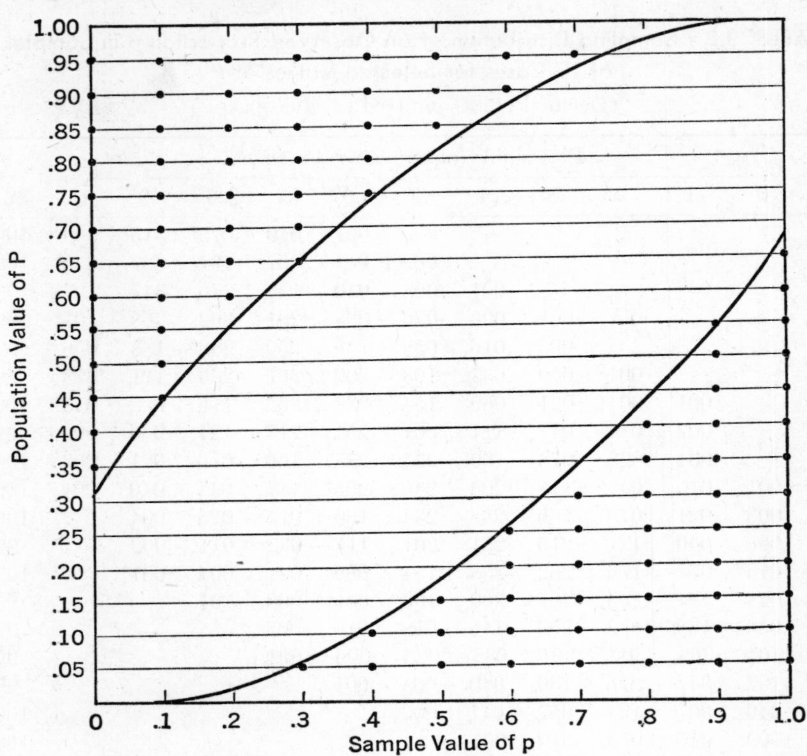

FIG. 3–3. Regions of rejection • • and acceptance for testing hypotheses concerning P on evidence from a sample of 10 cases at .05 level of significance.

for which $.13 < p < .85$ are acceptance values and all points for which $p > .85$ or $p < .13$ are rejection values for the hypothesis $P = .47$ at significance level .05. Actually for the discrete distribution this means that the values 0, .1, .9, and 1.0 are rejection values with probability somewhat smaller than .05. In this manner the range of rejection values can be obtained for any value of P.

A sample with proportion p drawn from a population with proportion P would be represented on Figure 3–3 by a point with coordinates (p, P). Such a point is called a *sample point*. Locate the following sample points and note that all of them are between the pair of curved lines and near the upper line:

$$(p = .4,\ P = .7),\ (p = .6,\ P = .8),\ (p = .8,\ P = .9).$$

Locate the following sample points, all of which are below the lower curved line:

$$(p = .6,\ P = .2),\ (p = .8,\ P = .3),\ (p = .4,\ P = .05).$$

Locate the following sample points all of which are above the upper curved line:

$$(p = .3, P = .9), (p = .5, P = .85), (p = .6, P = .95).$$

The area between the curved lines in Figure 3–3 is a region of acceptance and the area outside them a region of rejection, or critical region. Whenever the two coordinates of a sample point (p, P) are such that the point falls in the region of rejection, the observed value p is considered to furnish evidence justifying the rejection of the hypothesis concerning P. Thus the figure furnishes us a short cut to the testing of hypotheses about proportions. In the problem concerning the judgment of intelligence from photographs, suppose the experimenter is correct in 9 out of 10 pairs, so $p = .9$. The sample point for which $p = .9$ and $P = .5$ lies in the region of rejection. So does every sample point for which $p = .9$ and $P < .5$. Sample points for which $p = .9$ and $.55 < P < .98$ (approximately) are in the region of acceptance.

EXERCISE 3.1

1. Test each hypothesis (a) to (f) by locating a point on Figure 3–3.

If $N = 10$ and $p = .4$,	(a) $P = .45$	(c) $P = .2$	(e) $P = .57$
	(b) $P = .9$	(d) $P = .65$	(f) $P = .73$
If $N = 10$ and $p = .5$,	(a) $P = .53$	(c) $P = .16$	(e) $P = .61$
	(b) $P = .20$	(d) $P = .73$	(f) $P = .94$
If $N = 10$ and $p = .2$,	(a) $P = .75$	(c) $P = .04$	(e) $P = .57$
	(b) $P = .61$	(d) $P = .01$	(f) $P = .49$

2. From the answers to the three parts of question 1, formulate a general statement as to the range of hypotheses acceptable at the .05 level when $N = 10$ and (a) $p = .4$; (b) $p = .5$; (c) $p = .2$.

Estimation of *P*. To this point we have been concerned with tests of hypotheses about the value of the population proportion, P. A problem which is perhaps of greater interest is to find from the information in the sample an *estimate* of the value of P. We shall discuss two methods of estimating P, (1) by a single value and (2) by an interval.

Estimation by a Single Value. On page 28, it was found that $E(p) = P$. This means that if an unlimited number of samples were drawn and p calculated for each of them, even if the number of cases in each sample were very small, the average of all the computed values of p would be P. Thus, even though one must

expect to be wrong in nearly every instance, he may expect to be right on the average, in the long run.

If a statistic has a population parameter as its expected value, the statistic is called an *unbiased estimate* of that parameter. In later chapters we shall meet statistics which do not possess this highly desirable quality.

The sample proportion is also called a *consistent estimate* of the population proportion because for large samples the value of p is likely to be close to P. In Chapter 2, the standard deviation of p was given by Formula (2.14) as $\sigma_p = \sqrt{\frac{PQ}{N}}$. To see what this means in relation to the value of N, consider samples of 25, 100, and 1000 cases from a population in which P is actually .5.

$$\text{If } N = 25,\ \sigma_p = .1$$
$$\text{If } N = 100,\ \sigma_p = .05$$
$$\text{If } N = 1000,\ \sigma_p = .0158$$

consequently

$$P(.30 < p < .70 \mid N = 25) = .95$$
$$P(.40 < p < .60 \mid N = 100) = .95$$
$$P(.47 < p < .53 \mid N = 1000) = .95$$

To put this more concretely, suppose a poll is conducted to determine what proportion of residents of a community are in favor of a particular issue. If half of them are actually in favor of the issue ($P = .5$), there is probability .05 that in a sample of 25 cases the observed proportion p will be in error by .20 or more, that in a sample of 100 cases it will be in error by .10 or more, and that in a sample of 1000 cases it will be in error by .03 or more.

Interval Estimate. A statistic with the desirable qualities of unbiasedness and consistency provides an estimate of the parameter which may be assumed to be numerically close to that parameter. An estimate of a parameter which is often more satisfactory is one that uses *two* statistics, unequal in value, which jointly provide an *interval estimate* of the parameter.

The parameter is stated as lying between these statistics in much the same way that one might say "I feel confident John's age is between 25 and 30." There are two important differences between this somewhat casual estimate of John's age as lying in the interval 25–30 and the statistical intervals about to be discussed: (1) In the statistical estimate the degree of confidence will be decided upon before the interval is obtained and will be described in numerical terms, whereas in the popular expression the word "confident" means different things to different people. (2) In the statistical estimate, the numbers which define the interval are computed from the data by a rule which guarantees the degree of confidence to be placed in the interval estimate, whereas in the popular expression the numbers are more or less impressionistic.

If one makes the interval wider, he can have greater confidence that his statement is correct. Thus the estimate that "John's age is between 5 and 95" might be made with practically complete confidence but the interval would be so wide as to be of little practical value; the estimate that "John's age is between 26 years, 6 months, and 26 years, 7 months," could be made far with less confidence if John's age is actually unknown.

An interval estimate is a statement about a parameter such as "P is between .3 and .5." The statement is either true or false and we do not know which, but the methods by which the statement is obtained furnish a measure of the confidence with which the assertion may be made. That measure of confidence, called a *confidence coefficient,* is usually a value between .90 and 1.00. After this confidence coefficient has been chosen, two statistics are computed from the sample, both from the same sample. For convenience we shall call these two numbers A and B, with A less than B. Then the interval estimate of P is the statement

$$A < P < B.$$

The numbers A and B are called the *confidence limits* and the interval from A to B is called a *confidence interval.*

Interval Estimate for *P* when *N* = 10. The abstract discussion of the preceding paragraph will now be illustrated by a computation making use of Figure 3–3, which applies to samples of 10 cases. The first step in obtaining the numbers A and B is to select a confidence coefficient. If we are to make use of Figure 3–3 which has been constructed with $\alpha = .05$, we must in this illustration use a confidence coefficient of $1 - .05 = .95$. The relation between the confidence coefficient and α will be explained below. We shall now assume that in a sample of 10 cases, 3 individuals have been found to possess a particular characteristic, so $p = .3$. The proportion P of the population is unknown.

On the baseline of Figure 3–3, locate the observed sample value, $p = .3$ and place a ruler or the edge of a card so as to indicate the vertical line through this point. Note where this line cuts the two curves. On the vertical scale read the values of these intersections, calling the smaller value A and the larger B. For $p = .3$ we find $A = .05$ and $B = .65$. The interval estimate

$$.05 < P < .65$$

can therefore be made with confidence coefficient .95. To distinguish a confidence statement from a probability statement, this text will use the notation

$$\text{Conf}(.05 < P < .65) = .95$$

or

$$C(.05 < P < .65) = .95$$

This may be expressed in words thus: "We have confidence .95 that the unknown proportion lies between .05 and .65" or "We assert that P is not smaller than .05 and not larger than .65 and we have arrived at these numbers by a procedure which if applied repeatedly would yield interval estimates of which 5% would not contain the true value and of which the remaining 95% would contain it."

To understand why an interval estimate computed by the method just described is correct in 95% of samples, note that the curves in Figure 3–3 were drawn so that for any given value of P the probability is .95 that the sample point (P, p) is between the curves. Since this holds for any value of P it holds for the unknown P of the population being sampled. This means that for 95% of samples from the same population the values of p will determine a sample point which is on the horizontal line through P and which lies between the two curves. For all these values of p the confidence limits will contain P between them. Hence the statement that P is contained between the calculated limits can be made with .95 confidence.

Figure 3–3 was constructed with level of significance $\alpha = .05$. It is apparent now that the confidence coefficient is $1 - \alpha$, and the confidence interval for P may be stated in general as

$$C(A < P < B) = 1 - \alpha \tag{3.1}$$

Location of Confidence Limits for Samples of Varying Size by the Use of Charts. The intervals which can be read from Figure 3–3 are only approximately correct because of the discontinuity of the actual sampling distribution for $N = 10$. When

N becomes larger, the binomial probability distribution appears smoother because the steps are smaller and more numerous so that there is less and less discrepancy between it and a fitted smooth distribution. For small samples such as $N = 10$ it is not possible to mark off exactly 2.5% of the area at each end of each distribution and so the volume outside the curved lines cannot be assumed to be precisely 5% of the total volume. These difficulties tend to disappear when samples of larger size are used.

If the rejection points of Figure 3–3 are not marked but only the curves drawn, it is possible to draw on one chart the confidence belts for samples of several different sizes. Such charts for confidence coefficients of .99 and .95 have been published by C. J. Clopper and E. S. Pearson.[1]* Additional charts for confidence coefficients of .90 and .80 are published on pages 332 and 333 of *Techniques of Statistical Analysis*.[3] The Clopper-Pearson chart for confidence coefficient .95 is reproduced here as Chart VI in the Appendix. The small numbers written on the curved lines indicate the size of sample for which the confidence belt applies. $N = 10, 15, 20, 30, 50, 100, 200$, and 1000. Study of this chart reveals that for a given confidence coefficient the belt becomes narrower as sample size increases. As the size of the sample approaches that of the population, the belt narrows to a mere line. For any given sample size, the confidence belt would be wider if the confidence coefficient were larger. For any finite value of N, the confidence belt would narrow to a line as the confidence coefficient approaches zero.

Confidence Intervals for Other Parameters. The preceding discussion of confidence intervals applies also to parameters other than P. A confidence statement about a population mean made with confidence coefficient .90, for instance, might read

$$C(46.3 < \mu < 52.7) = .90$$

and one about a population variance made with confidence .99 might read

$$C(18.3 < \sigma^2 < 21.5) = .99$$

Rules for obtaining the interval estimates for the mean, the variance, and the correlation coefficient will be developed in later chapters.

Probability and Confidence. Some discussion of the two terms *probability* and *confidence* is needed to clarify the difference be-

* References referred to by number will be found at the end of the Chapter.

tween them. An analogy between sampling and games of cards will help to clarify the distinction.

We may conceive of the deck of cards as a population, and of a hand dealt after shuffling the deck as a random sample. There are two ways of reasoning about the deck of cards and the dealt hand:

(1) From a known or hypothesized characteristic of the deck we can calculate the probability that the hand will have some characteristic. We can, for example, calculate the *probability* that in a game of bridge a hand will contain 10 or more spades. This form of reasoning is analogous to computing the probability of a characteristic of a random sample from a known, or hypothesized, characteristic of the population.

(2) From the known composition of a hand we wish to draw some conclusion about the unknown composition of the deck. A player who sees his opponent draw a hand consisting of 13 spades may lose confidence in the notion that the deck is the standard bridge deck. He may go further and say he has confidence that the deck has any one of certain types of composition and that it does not have certain other types.

The concept of probability is used in reasoning from a known population to a random sample. The concept of confidence is used in reasoning from an observed sample to its unknown population.

EXERCISE 3.2

1. From Chart VI read the confidence interval for the population proportion if in a sample of 30 cases 9 cases have shown a particular characteristic, $p = \frac{9}{30} = .3$. Place a card or edge of a ruler on the chart to mark the vertical line through the point .3 on the horizontal axis. Note the points where this line cuts the two curves marked 30. The scale values of the ordinates of these points appear to be approximately .15 and .50. Thus the interval sought is $.15 < P < .50$.

2. From Chart VI verify the following interval estimates:

a. If $N = 20$ and $p = .4$, $.19 < P < .64$
b. If $N = 30$ and $p = .4$, $.22 < P < .60$
c. If $N = 100$ and $p = .4$, $.30 < P < .50$
d. If $N = 1000$ and $p = .4$, $.37 < P < .43$

3. What interval would you read from Chart VI if $N = 50$ and $p = .43$? The scale point .43 is not marked on the horizontal axis but can be estimated by eye with fair accuracy. Then $.29 < P < .58$.

4. What interval would you read if $N = 40$ and $p = .75$? For $N = 30$, the interval is $.55 < P < .89$. For $N = 50$ it is $.60 < P < .87$. A rough estimate for $N = 40$ would place the interval limits between these two but a little closer to the limits for $N = 50$. A fairly good guess would be $.58 < P < .88$.

5. Read estimates for P from Chart VI when

a. $N = 20$ and $p = .65$
b. $N = 100$ and $p = .65$
c. $N = 250$ and $p = .65$
d. $N = 30$ and $p = .25$
e. $N = 50$ and $p = .25$
f. $N = 1000$ and $p = .25$

6. Comparing the answers obtained in question 5, what appears to be the effect on a confidence interval of changing the size of the sample while keeping the confidence coefficient constant?

7. In a sample of 100 ball bearings chosen at random from those coming from a factory during one morning, 10 have too large a diameter and are considered defective. What interval estimate can be read from Chart VI for the proportion with too large diameter in the entire morning's output of the factory?

8. In a random sample of 96 parents of grade school children in City A it is found that 75 are in favor of using tax money to establish a nursery school in connection with the public schools. Formulate an interval estimate with $\alpha = .05$ for the proportion of all parents holding the same opinion.

Aids Available for Computing Binomial Probabilities. Computation of the terms of the binomial distribution is so laborious for large values of N that anyone who needs to make tests about proportions will wish to make use of published aids and also of methods of approximation. In the Appendix of this book are tables which can be used to reduce arithmetic labor.

Table IVB gives the cumulative probability, or the sum, of the first $m + 1$ terms in either tail of the symmetrical binomial distribution for which $P = .5$, for values of N running from 5 to 25. The entries in the right-hand column of Table 3.1 on page 45 were taken from the entries in the row $N = 10$ of Table IVB.

Thus for $m = 1$, $\quad .011 = .001 + .010$
$\qquad m = 2$, $\quad .055 = .001 + .010 + .044$
$\qquad m = 3$, $\quad .172 = .001 + .010 + .044 + .117$

For $P = .75$, the cumulative probability for the first $m + 1$ terms in the *left* tail is given in Table IVA, and for the last $m + 1$ terms in the *right* tail in Table IVC.

For $P = .25$, the cumulative probability for the first $m + 1$ terms in the *left* tail is given in Table IVC, and for the last $m + 1$ terms in the *right* tail in Table IVA.

Suppose now that we wish to test the hypothesis $P = .75$ by means of a sample of 24 cases, using approximately the .05 level of significance. Suppose further that we wish to discard the hypothesis if p is either too much larger or too much smaller than .75. What is the region of significance? If we had the entire distribution of $(.25 + .75)^{24}$, we could find the left critical region by adding terms at the first end of the distribution,

$$(.25)^{24} + \binom{24}{1}(.25)^{23}(.75) + \binom{24}{2}(.25)^{22}(.75)^2 + \cdots$$

until the sum of those terms was approximately .025. The same result can be achieved painlessly by looking in row $N = 24$ of Table IVA for the entry nearest .025. This is .021 in column $m = 13$, and it indicates that

$$P(X = 0, 1, 2 \cdots 12 \text{ or } 13 \mid N = 24 \text{ and } P = .75) = .021$$

Then the left critical region consists of the values $X = 0, 1 \cdots 13$ or of $p = \frac{0}{24}, \frac{1}{24}, \cdots \frac{13}{24}$. To find the right critical region, we could add terms at the right end of the distribution

$$(.75)^{24} + \binom{24}{23}(.25)(.75)^{23} + \binom{24}{22}(.25)^2(.75)^{22} + \cdots$$

until their sum was approximately .025. This result can be achieved painlessly by looking in row $N = 24$ of Table IVC for the entry nearest .025. This is .040 in the column $m = 2$. It may be read to mean either that

$$P(X = 0, 1 \text{ or } 2 \mid N = 24 \text{ and } P = .25) = .040$$

or that $P(X = 24, 23, \text{ or } 22 \mid N = 24 \text{ and } P = .75) = .040$

The latter interpretation provides us with the right critical region needed. It is $X = 24$, 23 and 22 or $p = \frac{24}{24}, \frac{23}{24}$, and $\frac{22}{24}$. These two regions combined have probability $.021 + .040 = .061$. Because of the discrete nature of the distribution this is as near to the .05 level as we can come.

Under the same circumstances if we wish to use a one-tailed test, rejecting the hypothesis only for values of X much smaller than those expected under the hypothesis, we should look in Table IVA for the entry nearest .05. This is .055 in the column $m = 14$. It indicates that the critical region consists of $X = 0$, 1, 2, . . . 14. If we wish to use a one-tailed test rejecting the hypothesis only for values of X much larger than those expected under the hypothesis, we should look in Table IVC for the entry nearest .05. It is .040 and indicates that the critical region with probability .04 consists of $X = 24$, 23 and 22.

If some value of P other than .25, .50 or .75 is needed, Table V may be used. It provides the binomial coefficients $\binom{N}{m}$ from which the terms of the binomial distribution can be obtained by multiplication. The $(m + 1)$st term of the distribution for given N and P is obtained by multiplying the number in row N and column m of this table by $Q^{N-m}P^m$. Up to $N = 10$ all the coefficients are shown. For $N > 10$ the page is too narrow to accommodate the entire set, but as the set is always symmetrical the remaining coefficients can easily be obtained from those presented. The coefficient for term $N - m$ is the same as for term m. Table V is useful only for N not larger than 20.

Very extensive tables of the binomial probability distribution have been published by the National Bureau of Standards.[5] These give values of the individual terms of $(Q + P)^N$ for values of P from .01 to .50 by intervals of .01 and for values of N from 2 to 49 by intervals of 1. They also give values of the sum of the terms for the same values of P and N.

EXERCISE 3.3

1. Suppose that from the rolls of a large university the cards of 22 students are selected at random and these students are asked to agree or disagree with a statement of opinion on some public issue of the day, but are not permitted to say they are undecided or uninformed. Let p be the proportion answering "Yes" and q the proportion answering "No." If the hypothesis that $P = .5$ proves tenable, it will be concluded that the students in this university have no consistent opinion on this issue. What number of "Yes" answers would constitute a critical region for the rejection of this hypothesis? Answer for the .02 level of significance, and for the .05 level.

Solution. The population which is the entire student body of the university, is not infinite but is large. The hypothesis will be refuted if either too many or too few students answer "Yes." At the .02 level of significance, the critical region will consist of the most extreme terms at the lower end of the binomial with $P = .5$ and $N = 22$ such that the sum of the probabilities of those terms is .01 and the most extreme terms at the upper end of the distribution such that the sum of the probabilities of those terms is .01. On line $N = 22$ of Table IVB we see that .008 is the sum of 6 terms at one end of the distribution. Therefore if X is the number of "Yes" answers, at the .016 level of significance (which is the nearest possible value to .02 when the critical region is in both tails), the critical region consists of values of $X \leqq 5$ and $X \geqq 17$. At the .05 level of significance the critical region is $X \leqq 6$ and $X \geqq 16$.

2. Answer the question of problem 1 under the following circumstances:

a. $N = 14$ and level of significance is .06

b. $N = 18$ and level of significance is .03

c. $N = 25$ and level of significance is .05

One-sided and Two-sided Tests of Hypotheses. In Chapter 1, in testing the hypothesis that a subject's intelligence could not be inferred from his photograph, it was tacitly assumed that ranking photographs in completely wrong order (DCBA when ABCD is correct) or misjudging every pair of photographs (thus making the record $- - - - - -$) would not throw suspicion on the hypothesis. Therefore the critical region was located entirely in one tail of the probability distribution. Such tests are called *one-tailed tests*, or *one-sided tests*, or tests of a *one-sided hypothesis*. In Figure 3–1 on page 47 and the test related to it, the critical region was located in both tails of the distribution, half of the region being in each tail. Such tests are called *two-tailed tests* or *two-sided tests*, or tests of a *two-sided hypothesis*. Up to this point the choice between a one-sided and a two-sided test has been made more or less intuitively from the general logic of the question to be answered by the test. We shall now develop certain concepts which will assist in clarifying the reasons for the location of the critical region.

The letter H is customarily used as an abbreviation for hypothesis. Thus $H : P = .5$ means "the hypothesis that in the population the proportion of cases having the given characteristic is .5" while $H : P \geqq .5$ means "the hypothesis that in the population the proportion of cases having a given characteristic is .5 or greater."

Two Kinds of Error. Rejecting a hypothesis when it is true is called an *error of the first kind*. The level of significance is the probability of making an error of this kind. As the level of significance is commonly called α (the small Greek letter alpha corresponding to the English a), an error of the first kind is also called an *alpha error*. The probability of an error of this kind can be made arbitrarily small by making alpha small, but unfortunately a reduction in the probability of rejecting a hypothesis when it is true is accompanied by an increase in the probability of accepting it when some alternative to the hypothesis is true. This latter error is called an *error of the second kind* or a *beta error*.

The Greek letter β (*beta*) is used to represent the probability of accepting a hypothesis when some alternative is true. Most statisticians do not look with favor upon choosing an extremely small level of significance because that would expose them to a large risk of error of the second kind. This relation will be clarified in the following paragraphs.

Suppose that P is actually .6 but we do not know that fact and we test the hypothesis $P = .5$ using a sample of 10 cases. Suppose also that, knowing the probability distribution of p under the hypothesis tested, we decide upon $p = 0, .1, .9$ or 1.0 as the region of rejection. Thus

$$\alpha = .001 + .010 + .010 + .001 = .022 \text{ or } .02.$$

What is the probability that the hypothesis $P = .5$ will be rejected when P is really .6? Accepted when $P = .6$?

Table 3.2 on page 49 provides a very easy means of answering this question. As we are assuming that P is actually .6, the true probability distribution of p is given in the row for which $P = .6$. Then

$$P(p = 0, .1, .9 \text{ or } 1.0 \mid P = .6) = 0 + 0 + .040 + .006 = .046$$

and $$P(.2 \leqq p \leqq .8 \mid P = .6) = 1 - .046 = .954$$

The risk of a false acceptance of $H : P = .5$ when $P = .6$ is therefore $\beta = .954$. With a larger discrepancy between the true value of P and the value under the hypothesis, the risk of acceptance of a false hypothesis would be less. For example

$$P(p = 0, .1, .9 \text{ or } 1.0 \mid P = .1) = .349 + .387 + 0 + 0 = .74$$

and $$P(.2 \leqq p \leqq .8 \mid P = .1) = 1 - .74 = .26$$

Hence the risk of false acceptance is only .26 when $P = .1$. The probabilities here treated as zero are not absolutely zero but are merely numbers so small that only zeros occur in the first three decimal places. Rounding errors cause some of the totals at the right of Table 3.2 to be slightly different from 1.000.

Similar computations have been made for each of the values of P shown in Table 3.2 and these have been recorded in columns 2 and 3 of Table 3.3. For all these the level of significance was taken as $\alpha = .02$ and the region of significance as $p = 0, .1, .9$ or 1.

If the region of significance is increased to include $p = .2$ and $p = .8$, the significance level becomes $\alpha = .11$. The probability of rejecting $H : P = .5$ for this situation has been computed for each of the same values of P and recorded in column 4 of Table 3.3; the probability of accepting $H : P = .5$ is recorded in column 5.

TABLE 3.3 The Probability of Accepting the Hypothesis $P = .5$ on Evidence from a Sample of 10 cases when P has a Specified Value, if $\alpha = .02$ and if $\alpha = .11$

	$\alpha = .02$		$\alpha = .11$	
True Value of P	Probability of rejecting $H : P = .5$	Probability of accepting $H : P = .5$	Probability of rejecting $H : P = .5$	Probability of accepting $H : P = .5$
.95	.91	.09	.99	.01
.90	.74	.26	.93	.07
.85	.54	.46	.82	.18
.80	.38	.62	.68	.32
.75	.24	.76	.53	.47
.70	.15	.85	.38	.62
.65	.09	.91	.27	.73
.60	.05	.95	.18	.82
.55	.03	.97	.13	.87
.50	.02	.98	.11	.89
.45	.03	.97	.13	.87
.40	.05	.95	.18	.82
.35	.09	.91	.27	.73
.30	.15	.85	.38	.62
.25	.24	.76	.53	.47
.20	.38	.62	.68	.32
.15	.54	.46	.82	.18
.10	.74	.26	.93	.07
.05	.91	.09	.99	.01

Rejection values are $p = 0, .1, .9$ and 1.0 when $\alpha = .02$
Rejection values are $p = 0, .1, .2, .8, .9$ and 1.0 when $\alpha = .11$

The test of a statistical hypothesis involves *a statistic* and *a critical region.* The probability that the statistic will fall in the critical region is the probability that the hypothesis will be rejected. *This probability of rejecting a hypothesis is called the power of the test.* The power is a variable which depends upon what alternative to the hypothesis is actually true. If we knew that a certain alternative were true we should not need to test the hypothesis. So we cannot establish the power of the test for the one correct alternative but must consider the power in general for various alternatives. If two tests are equally satisfactory as to the level of significance and so involve the same risk of rejecting a hypothesis when it is true, but one test is more powerful than the other because it is more likely to cause rejection of a false hypothesis, then the more powerful test is to be preferred. An illustration of this situation will be given presently.

Certain important relations can be brought out more clearly by means of a graph. In Figure 3–4 values of P which are alternatives to the hypothesis are laid off on the horizontal scale.

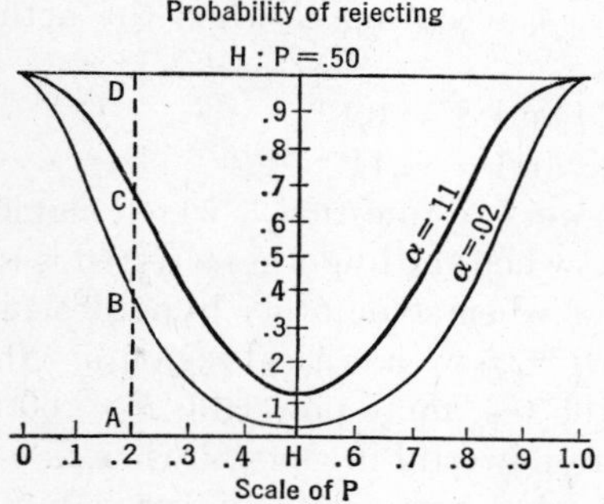

FIG. 3–4. Power function of the test of hypothesis $P = .5$ for $N = 10$ at two levels of significance, $\alpha = .02$ and $\alpha = .11$.

The value under the hypothesis is marked H. The vertical axis passing through H is scaled to show probabilities from 0 to 1. At each of the indicated values of P an ordinate is erected with length proportional to the power of the test for that alternative. For the curve marked $\alpha = .02$ these ordinates represent the probabilities in column 2 of Table 3.3; for the curve marked $\alpha = .11$ the ordinates represent the probabilities in column 4. The curved line which connects the tops of one set of these ordinates is the graph of the *power function* of the test concerned. This graph crosses the vertical axis at a point whose ordinate is the level of significance.

EXERCISE 3.4

1. Verify the probabilities stated in Table 3.3 by computation from the data of Table 3.2.

2. Make similar computations with $\alpha = .002$ and critical region $p = 0$ or 1. Plot the corresponding power function on the chart of Figure 3–4. Note that it lies entirely below the other graphs. Does this mean the test with $\alpha = .002$ is more powerful or less powerful than the test with $\alpha = .02$?

3. Answer each of the following questions by naming a line segment in Figure 3–4. Place the letter J where the lower curve and K where the upper curve cut the vertical axis. Place M at top of that axis.

a. $\alpha = .02$ **b.** $\alpha = .11$

c. the probability of rejecting H at significance level $\alpha = .02$ if P is .2
d. the probability of rejecting H at significance level $\alpha = .11$ if P is .2
e. the probability of accepting H when it is true if $\alpha = .02$
f. the probability of accepting H when it is true if $\alpha = .11$
g. the probability of accepting H when the actual value is $P = .2$ if $\alpha = .02$
h. the probability of accepting H when the actual value is $P = .2$ if $\alpha = .11$
i. β when $P = .20$ and $\alpha = .02$
j. β when $P = .20$ and $\alpha = .11$

4. From your answers to question 3 which significance level provides the more desirable test when the hypothesis tested is true? Which provides the more desirable test when some other hypothesis is true?

5. In testing $H : P = .5$ with critical region $p = 0, .1, .9$, and 1, against which alternative is the test more powerful, $P = .60$ or $P = .80$?

6. Is the test more powerful in general when $\alpha = .02$ or when $\alpha = .11$?

7. In Figure 3–4 what represents the probability of error when the hypothesis is true? When it is not true?

8. Suppose a one-sided test with critical region $p = .7, .8, .9$, and 1 is made of $H : P = .50$. What is the value of α? Compute the power of this test for each alternative value of P shown in Table 3.2. Make a graph of the power function of this test.

9. Suppose a one-sided test with critical region $p = 0, .1, .2$, and .3 is made of $H : P = .50$. What is the value of α? Compute the power of this test for each alternative value of P shown in Table 3.2. Make a graph of the power function of this test.

Choice of Critical Region. Figure 3–5 displays the power function for each of three different tests of the hypothesis $P = .50$. These tests differ as to the location of the critical region. For test A the region is located wholly in the upper tail; for test C it is wholly in the lower tail; for test B half of the region is in the upper tail and half in the lower. The power function for test B has already been drawn in Figure 3–4 and is reproduced here for the sake of comparison with those for the one-sided tests. The situations in which one of these three tests is more powerful than the others could be explained better if it were possible to make all three regions identical in size, that is to give all three tests the same level of significance. However, the discrete nature of the binomial distribution makes it impossible to choose a level of significance arbitrarily and so it is impossible to find a one-sided region and a two-sided region having exactly the same probability. Later when we work with continuous probability distributions it will be possible to draw a figure similar to Figure 3–5 but with all three curves crossing the vertical axis at the same point. The meaning of these graphs will be clarified by the answers to the questions in Exercise 3.4 and you may wish to study that exercise before you read the following paragraph.

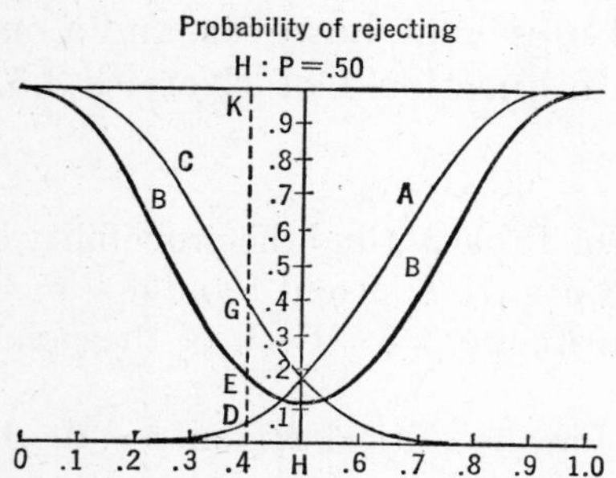

FIG. 3–5. Power function of the test of hypothesis $P = .5$ for $N = 10$.

A. With $\alpha = .17$ and critical region $p = .7, .8, .9$, and 1.0.
B. With $\alpha = .11$ and critical region $p = 0, .1, .9$, and 1.0.
C. With $\alpha = .17$ and critical region $p = 0, .1, .2$, and .3.

Certain generalizations can now be made. (1) When a hypothesis is true, the probability of falsely rejecting it depends only on the level of significance and is not at all affected by the location of the critical region. The probability of an α error is fixed and is the same no matter whether a one-sided test is employed or a two-sided test. (2) After the probability of type I error has been controlled by the arbitrary selection of the significance level, the critical region can be so located as to secure maximum power against a particular alternative or set of alternatives. If the logic of the problem makes it important to reject H when $P > P_H$ and unimportant to reject when $P < P_H$, then the critical region should consist of values at the extreme of the right-hand tail. On the other hand if there is no logical need to reject H when the true value is larger than the hypothesized value but every reason to reject it when the true value is smaller, then the lower tail will be critical. If deviations from hypothesized value in one direction are logically just as damaging to the hypothesis as deviations in the other direction, then a two-sided test should be used with half of the critical region in each tail. (3) Other things being equal, an increase in α is accompanied by a decrease in β and vice versa.

The form in which the hypothesis is stated may be used to indicate the location of the critical region, thus:

$H: P \geqq .8$, implies a one-sided test with left tail critical
$H: P \leqq .8$, implies a one-sided test with right tail critical
$H: P = .8$, implies a two-sided test

This practice is not universal, however, and a one-sided hypothesis may be written as in question 1 of Exercise 3.5.

EXERCISE 3.5

1. From the data of Table 3.2 find the probability of rejecting $H : P = .5$ if the critical region is $p = .7, .8, .9$ and 1 and if $P = .35, .40, .60, .70$. Plot these probabilities on Figure 3–5. Each of the points should fall on the curve marked A.

2. Do the same for the critical region $p = 0, .1, .2$, and .3. These points should fall on the curve marked C.

3. What is the probability of rejecting a true hypothesis if test A is used? Test B? Test C?

4. When the hypothesis is true, does the critical region for B provide a more or less satisfactory test than the critical regions for A and for C? Make your decision in the light of your answer to question 3.

5. When the true probability is $P = .40$, estimate from the graph

a. the probability of rejecting $H : P = .50$ when critical region is $p = .7, .8, .9$, and 1

b. the probability of rejecting $H : P = .50$ when critical region is $p = 0, .1, .9$, and 1

c. the probability of rejecting $H : P = .50$ when critical region is $p = 0, .1, .2$, and .3.

d. the probability of an error of the second kind when Test A is used

e. the probability of an error of the second kind when Test B is used

f. the probability of an error of the second kind when Test C is used

6. If $P > P_H$, which of the three tests has the greatest power? Which has the least power?

7. If $P < P_H$, which has the greatest power? Which the least?

8. A research worker has tested the hypothesis $P \geqq .75$ using a sample of 20 cases. He decides to make α as near .05 as possible.

a. What is the critical region? *Ans.* From the way in which the hypothesis is stated, we see that the critical region should be located in the left tail of the binomial for which $P = .75$ and $N = 20$. Reference to the row $N = 20$ of Table IV shows $\alpha = .041$ as the value nearest to $\alpha = .05$. This value corresponds to $m = 11$, or $p = \frac{m}{N} = \frac{11}{20} = .55$. Hence the critical region is $p \leqq .55$.

b. If he obtains a value of $p = .40$ what decision should he make concerning the hypothesis? *Ans.* Reject it.

c. In making this decision, what risk does he take of making an error of the first kind? *Ans.* Risk is less than $\alpha = .041$.

d. In making this decision, what risk does he take of making an error of the second kind? *Ans.* None whatever, he has accepted no hypothesis at all so cannot possibly have accepted a false one.

9. Answer the same four questions if the sample value had been $p = .70$.

a. Same answer.

b. Accept hypothesis.

c. No risk whatever of rejecting true hypothesis.

d. There is a risk of error of second type but that risk depends on the alternative P_A and cannot be assessed from the data presented.

10. Below are several statements of hypotheses, with critical region and level of significance for each. By reference to Table IV, verify the correspondence of significance level and critical region. In the column headed Decision, record *A* or *R* to indicate whether the hypothesis should be accepted or rejected. In the next column indicate the risk of error of the first type. In the final column, record *O* if there is no risk of error of the second type and record *X* if there is such risk. The magnitude of such risk cannot be computed from the given data.

Situation	N	H	*Critical region*	α	*Observed* p	*Decision*	*Risk of error First type*	*Risk of error Second type*
1	25	$P \geqq .75$	$p \leqq .6$	.071	.5	——	——	——
2	20	$P = .5$	$\begin{cases} p \leqq .3 \\ p \geqq .7 \end{cases}$	.114	.4	——	——	——
3	24	$P \geqq .25$	$p \leqq .125$	.115	.10	——	——	——
4	24	$P = .5$	$\begin{cases} p \geqq .75 \\ p \leqq .25 \end{cases}$	.022	.63	——	——	——
5	22	$P \geqq .75$	$p \leqq .50$	.010	.67	——	——	——

Large Sample Tests Concerning Proportions. The approximation of the normal distribution to the binomial discussed in Chapter 2 can be used as a basis for large sample tests of hypotheses on proportions. Use of the normal distribution for this purpose means that areas under the unit normal curve replace sums of terms in the tails of the distribution. For this purpose the statistic

$$z = \frac{p - P}{\sqrt{\frac{PQ}{N}}} \tag{3.1}$$

introduced in Chapter 2 is treated as a normal deviate.

To test a hypothesis about P on the basis of a sample value p, making use of the normal distribution, we first choose a level of significance α, say $\alpha = .05$ or $\alpha = .01$. Then we decide from the logic of the problem where the critical region should be located. The hypothesis is rejected whenever

for a one-tailed test with right-tail critical, $z > z_{1-\alpha}$
for a one-tailed test with left-tail critical, $z < z_{\alpha}$
for a two-tailed test, $z < z_{\frac{1}{2}\alpha}$ or $z > z_{1-\frac{1}{2}\alpha}$

As an application consider the following problem:

The proportion of all births which are male is known to be approximately .51, a number which is generally held to be unrelated to any easily identified factor such as geographic location, race or economic status of parents. It has, however, sometimes been asserted that the ratio of male births tends to be higher in the years following a war or other great disaster. Suppose that in the 12-month period immediately following the close of World War II the birth records of a certain city showed 217 male births and only 184 female, the proportion of male births being thus $\frac{217}{401} = .54$ instead of .51. Is this excess of male births over expectation to be interpreted as evidence that some factor has been at work to increase the ratio?

As phrased the question calls for a one-sided test of $H : P = .51$, since we wish to reject that hypothesis only if the proportion of male births is too high and not if it is too low. Suppose the level of significance is chosen to be $\alpha = .05$. Then $z_{.95} = 1.645$ and the region of rejection is $z > 1.645$. But the observed value of z is

$$z = \frac{.54 - .51}{\sqrt{\frac{(.51)(.49)}{401}}} = 1.20$$

As $z = 1.20$ does not fall in the critical region, the hypothesis $P = .51$ is accepted. The deviation from hypothetical value is no greater than may be expected to arise by chance as the result of random sampling.

Confidence Limits for Proportions Computed from Large Samples. From Chart VI confidence limits can be obtained for selected values of N when the confidence coefficient is .95. However, a chart cannot well accommodate lines for all sizes of N, and a separate chart is required for every size of confidence coefficient. Moreover, sometimes greater accuracy is required than can be obtained by graphic methods. It is desirable to have a method for obtaining confidence limits by formula. As before it must be assumed that N is not small and P is not near 0 or 1, so the normal approximation to the binomial may be used.

To obtain the confidence limits we first select the confidence coefficient arbitrarily. The confidence limits are then derived from the large sample distribution of the sample proportion p. We know that for samples from a two-class population with given P the probability is $1 - \alpha$ that

$$z_{\frac{1}{2}\alpha} < \frac{p - P}{\sqrt{\frac{PQ}{N}}} < z_{1-\frac{1}{2}\alpha} \tag{3.2}$$

This inequality can be restated in the following form:

$$\frac{2p + \frac{z^2_{\frac{1}{2}\alpha}}{N} - \sqrt{\frac{z^2_{\frac{1}{2}\alpha}}{N}\left(4pq + \frac{z^2_{\frac{1}{2}\alpha}}{N}\right)}}{2\left(1 + \frac{z^2_{\frac{1}{2}\alpha}}{N}\right)} < P < \frac{2p + \frac{z^2_{\frac{1}{2}\alpha}}{N} + \sqrt{\frac{z^2_{\frac{1}{2}\alpha}}{N}\left(4pq + \frac{z^2_{\frac{1}{2}\alpha}}{N}\right)}}{2\left(1 + \frac{z^2_{\frac{1}{2}\alpha}}{N}\right)} \tag{3.3}$$

The second inequality is obtained from the first by algebraic manipulation which does not change the probability. These extremes are, therefore, confidence limits with confidence coefficient $1 - \alpha$ when p is the proportion observed in a sample.

A good approximation to the inequality in Formula (3.3) is given by the inequality

$$p + z_{\frac{1}{2}\alpha}\sqrt{\frac{pq}{N}} < P < p + z_{1-\frac{1}{2}\alpha}\sqrt{\frac{pq}{N}} \tag{3.4}$$

Number of Cases Needed to Obtain a Confidence Interval of a Given Width. Suppose a polling organization has been asked to estimate the number of voters in a given state who are in favor of a particular proposition. The specifications are that the estimate shall be made in the form of an interval

$$C(A < P < B) = .99$$

in which the width of the interval $B - A = W$ is not greater than .05. By taking enough cases in their sample the agency can keep the interval to any predetermined value. Therefore an important part of their planning is the decision as to how many cases to use. Let us suppose that some preliminary information is available from which they estimate that P will be somewhere near .75. They now have agreed that

$$1 - \alpha = .99$$
$$p' = .75$$
$$W = .05$$

As only a fairly rough estimate of N is required, they may begin work with Formula (3.4) from which

$$A = p' + z_{\frac{1}{2}\alpha}\sqrt{\frac{p'q'}{N}} \quad \text{and} \quad B = p' + z_{1-\frac{1}{2}\alpha}\sqrt{\frac{p'q'}{N}}$$

so that

$$W = B - A = z_{1-\frac{1}{2}\alpha}\sqrt{\frac{p'q'}{N}} - z_{\frac{1}{2}\alpha}\sqrt{\frac{p'q'}{N}}$$

$$= 2z_{1-\frac{1}{2}\alpha}\sqrt{\frac{p'q'}{N}} = -\,2z_{\frac{1}{2}\alpha}\sqrt{\frac{p'q'}{N}}$$

(3.5) Therefore $$N = \frac{4z^2_{\frac{1}{2}\alpha}\,p'q'}{W^2}$$

Substituting the given values yields

$$N = \frac{4(2.576)^2(.75)(.25)}{(.05)^2} = 1991$$

On the basis of this preliminary analysis, the agency might decide to take a sample of 1991, or it might decide to ask the authorities to allow it to work with a lower confidence coefficient which would not require so large a sample.

Suppose a sample of 1991 cases is taken and the observed value of p found to be .70. As the sample is so large, Formula (3.4) may be used to compute the confidence interval. The obtained interval is then

$$.6735 < P < .7265$$

and $W = .7265 - .6735 = .053$ is very close to the width of interval which has been agreed upon as acceptable. The practical difficulty in this problem would be to obtain a *random* sample. If the sample is taken by some non-random method, say by the quota method often used by polling agencies, there is no assurance that p will have the probability distribution which is assumed in the formula employed.

Sampling from a Finite Population. Some readers may have questioned whether the methods we have been using are appropriate if the population is finite. To illustrate with an extreme case, consider a population of 100 individuals of whom 60 possess a given characteristic, and 40 do not, so that $P = .60$. Now suppose samples of 99 individuals are drawn. It is intuitively clear that a sample of 99 individuals must be quite similar to the entire population of 100. Since such a sample must contain all of the population except one individual, there are 60 different samples which can be obtained by eliminating one individual which possesses the trait and 40 samples obtained by eliminating one which does not possess that trait.

Composition of sample	*Number of different samples*	*Value of* p
60 cases with trait, 39 without it	40	$\frac{60}{99} = .6060$
59 cases with trait, 40 without it	60	$\frac{59}{99} = .5959$
	100	

$$E(p) = \frac{40(.6060) + 60(.5959)}{40 + 60} = .60$$

$$\sigma^2_p = \frac{40(.6060 - .60)^2 + 60(.5959 - .60)^2}{40 + 60} = .000024486$$

This manner of computing σ^2_p might be very laborious, but the result can be obtained by formula. If M represents the number of cases in the population and N the number in the sample, then

$$\sigma^2_p = \frac{PQ}{N} \cdot \frac{M - N}{M - 1} \tag{3.6}$$

In the situation for which we have already computed σ^2_p directly, $P = .60$, $M = 100$, $N = 99$, and therefore

$$\sigma^2_p = \frac{(.60)(.40)}{99} \cdot \frac{100 - 99}{100 - 1}$$

$$= \frac{.24}{9801} = .000024487,$$

which differs from the previously obtained value only in the final digit because of a rounding error.

The formula $\frac{PQ}{N}$ is a special case of $\frac{PQ}{N} \cdot \frac{M - N}{M - 1}$ when M is so large that the fraction $\frac{M - N}{M - 1}$ may be treated as unity.

Sometimes samples are drawn *with replacement,* each individual being returned to the supply before the next one is drawn. In such a case the sampling is in effect as from an infinite universe and the multiplier $\frac{M-N}{M-1}$ should not be used. If N is large and M is considerably larger than N, the statistic

$$z = \frac{p - P}{\sqrt{\frac{PQ}{N} \cdot \frac{M-N}{M-1}}} \tag{3.7}$$

has a sampling distribution which is approximately normal. This statistic can be used to test hypotheses about P as was done in the case of sampling from an infinitely large population using the statistic in formula (2.16) on page 37.

The corresponding confidence interval for P with coefficient $1 - \alpha$ is (approximately)

$$p + z_{\frac{1}{2}\alpha}\sqrt{\frac{pq}{N} \cdot \frac{M-N}{M-1}} < P < p + z_{1-\frac{1}{2}\alpha}\sqrt{\frac{pq}{N} \cdot \frac{M-N}{M-1}} \tag{3.8}$$

If it is proposed to plan an experiment so that the confidence interval is to be of size W with confidence coefficient $1 - \alpha$ then the number of cases needed is

$$N = \frac{4Mz^2_{\frac{1}{2}\alpha}p'q'}{4z^2_{\frac{1}{2}\alpha}p'q' + (M-1)W^2} \tag{3.9}$$

For M very large these formulas differ very little from the earlier formulas where the population was taken to be infinite.

Sample Size in Tests of Hypotheses. The important statistical problem of deciding upon the number of cases to be included in a sample has already been considered in relation to studies in which the objective is determination of a confidence interval for a proportion. A similar decision must, of course, be made when the objective is a test of a hypothesis. In this type of investigation, sample size is determined by the necessity for minimizing the error of the second kind.

The error of the first kind is controlled by selecting the level of significance α, which determines the risk of rejecting the hypothesis when it is true. The probability, β, of accepting the hypothesis when some alternative is true is then controlled by the decision as to the size of the sample.

Figure 3–6 shows the power curves for a test of $H : P = .5$ at significance level $\alpha = .11$ made on samples of three different sizes ($N = 10$, $N = 20$, $N = 48$). In the discrete binomial distribution only certain values of α can be realized. The three values of N used here were chosen because in each of the three binomial distributions with $P = .5$ and $N = 10$, $N = 20$, and $N = 48$, it was possible to find a two-tailed critical region with approximately the same value of α, namely $\alpha = .11$.

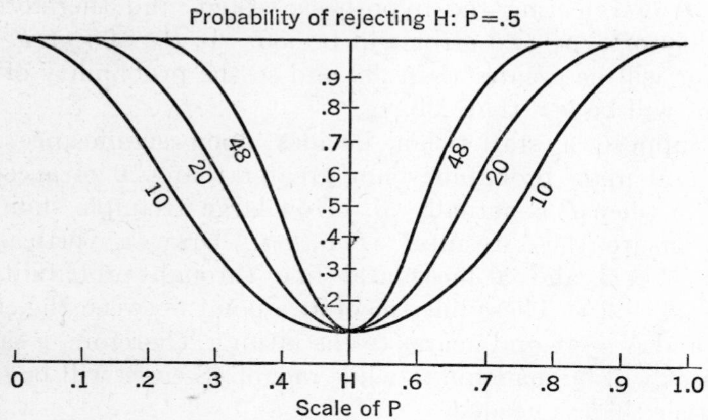

FIG. 3–6. Power function for test of hypothesis $P = .5$ with $\alpha = .11$ for samples of size $N = 10$, 20, and 48.

If the hypothesis tested is true, all three samples entail approximately the same probability of false rejection, that is $\alpha = .11$. However if some alternative is true, such as $P = .6$, the larger sample provides much greater probability of rejecting the false hypothesis $P = .5$.

It will be helpful to answer several questions by examination of Figure 3–6.

(a) What is the probability of rejecting $H : P = .5$ when P is actually .6 if $N = 10$? If $N = 20$? If $N = 48$? (*Answer:* .18, .26, .42)

(b) What is the probability of rejecting $H : P = .5$ when $P = .2$ if $N = 10$? If $N = 20$? If $N = 48$? (*Answer:* .68, .91, .999)

(c) Suppose a statistician decides to accept the risk of rejecting the hypothesis $P = .5$ in 11% of samples if it is true and a risk of accepting the hypothesis in 30% of samples if some alternative is true, that is $\alpha = .11$ and $\beta = .30$. If he uses a sample of 48 cases, how much will P have to differ from .5 in order that he may detect the discrepancy with the probability agreed upon? *Solution:* Figure 3–6 is drawn with $\alpha = .11$, hence referring to that diagram insures the chosen probability of type one error. If $\beta = .30$ the probability of rejecting must be $1 - .30 = .70$. Draw a horizontal line through the point marked .7 on the vertical scale. This line intersects the curve for $N = 48$ at two points for which $P = .35$ and $P = .65$. Then for $.35 < P < .65$ the test will have power less than .70 and therefore will have probability greater than .30 of failing to reject $H : P = .50$. If P is .65 or .35 the test will have power .70 of rejecting the hypothesis tested, and therefore the probability of type two error will be .30. If $P > .65$ or $P < .35$ the power will be greater than .30 and so the probability of type two error will be less than .30.

(d) Suppose a statistician decides upon significance level $\alpha = .11$ and upon probability not greater than .20 of accepting $H : P = .5$ when P is actually .3. How large a sample should he take to insure these results? *Solution:* Draw a vertical line through $P = .3$ and a horizontal line through probability .8. ($\beta = 1 - .8 = .2$.) These lines meet at a point between the curves $N = 20$ and $N = 48$ and nearer to the latter. Therefore, a sample of 20 cases will be inadequate while one of 48 cases will be somewhat larger than is needed.

To solve problems of this sort by reference to a chart would require a separate chart for each different value of α which might be chosen, a separate chart for each value of the hypothesis tested, and on that chart a curve for each of many different values of N. As such charts are not available, and as such problems are very real, it will be advantageous to develop another method of approach.

Suppose that a State Superintendent of Instruction is concerned with the number of children in his state who hold superstitious beliefs and with devising some means of reducing that number. He devises a measurement instrument, and trying it out in the ninth grade classes in a large number of schools, he finds that about 70% of the pupils return answers which would indicate they are "very superstitious." A committee of teachers then develops teaching materials which they believe will reduce the prevalence of superstitious beliefs, but the teaching methods are somewhat time-consuming. Before they are put into general use it seems desirable to gain assurance that they really effect a reduction in the proportion of superstitious pupils.

Therefore it is planned that a new sample of ninth grade pupils shall be taught by the new materials and then given the same test on which previously 70% of the former sample were rated "very superstitious." The research worker conducting the study asks a statistician how large the new sample should be. To find a basis for answering that question certain requirements are decided on: (1) *The hypothesis* to be tested is to be that the new method is no better than the old one. This is formulated as $P \geqq .70$. As this hypothesis is to be rejected only if p is smaller than .70, the critical region is in the left tail. (2) To limit the *risk of adopting the new method if it is not superior* to the old, they decide to adopt as significance level $\alpha = .05$. (3) To limit the *risk of not recognizing the superiority of the new method if such superiority exists,* they decide that if P is really as small as .60 or smaller, they are willing to take only a 10% risk of not discovering that superiority. That is $\beta = .10$ so the power of the test against the alternative $P = .60$ will be .90.

Having agreed upon these requirements they can solve the question as to what size of N will be required. It must be assumed that the sample is large enough to treat p as normally distributed with mean P and standard error $\sqrt{\dfrac{PQ}{N}}$. There are two distributions to be considered, one distribution under the hypothesis $P_H = .70$ and another under the alternative $P_A = .60$. These two distributions are shown in Figure 3–7.

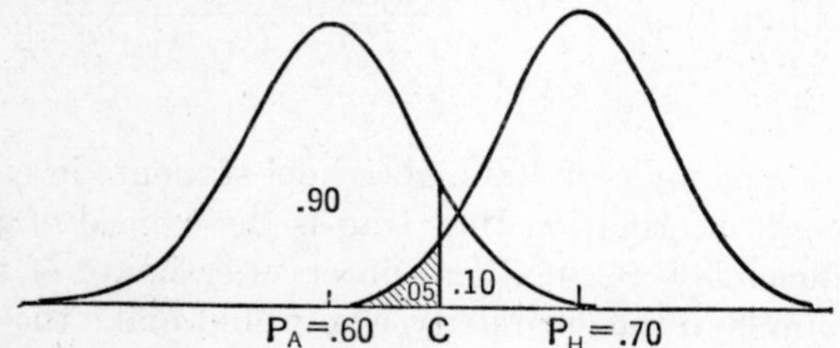

FIG. 3–7. The distribution of p under the hypothesis $P_H = .7$ and under the alternative $P_A = .6$.

Critical region under H is baseline to left of C
$\alpha = .05$ is represented by shaded area to left of C under curve specified by $H: P = .70$
$\beta = .10$ = area to right of C under curve specified by alternative $P = .6$
Power of test = .90 = area to left of C under curve specified by alternative $P = .6$

Since $\alpha = .05$, we have from the curve at the right

$$z_{.05} = \frac{C - .7}{\sqrt{\dfrac{(.7)(.3)}{N}}}$$

and since $\beta = .10$, we have from the curve at the left

$$z_{.90} = \frac{C - .6}{\sqrt{\frac{(.6)(.4)}{N}}}$$

When the numerical values of $z_{.05} = -1.645$ and $z_{.90} = 1.282$ are substituted in these expressions, each one is solved for C and the results are equated, we get the equation

$$.7 - 1.645\sqrt{\frac{.21}{N}} = .6 + 1.282\sqrt{\frac{.24}{N}}$$

Solving this equation for N gives

$$N = \left(\frac{1.645\sqrt{.21} + 1.282\sqrt{.24}}{.7 - .6}\right)^2 = 191$$

as the estimated sample size necessary to meet the conditions agreed upon.

To make the procedure general, let

P_H = the proportion under the hypothesis to be tested
P_A = the proportion under the alternative
α = significance level = probability of rejecting H when it is true
β = probability of accepting H when the alternative is true

$$\text{(3.10)} \qquad \text{Then } N = \left\{\frac{z_{1-\alpha}\sqrt{P_H Q_H} + z_{1-\beta}\sqrt{P_A Q_A}}{P_H - P_A}\right\}^2$$

EXERCISE 3.6

1. In a random sample of 400 high school students in city A, 168 said in a test of general information that Iraq is the capital of Iran. Using a confidence coefficient of .99, make an interval estimate of the proportion of high school pupils in the entire city who would make the same mistake.

2. A superintendent of schools has stated that at least 60% of high school seniors expect to attend college. In a random sample of 200 cases, only 96 say they are planning for college. Does this refute the superintendent's statement? (Use a one-sided test with $\alpha = .02$.)

3. How large a sample will be needed to test the hypothesis that $P \leqq .30$ at significance level .02 if it is agreed that the test shall have power .80 when $P = .35$?

4. Answer the same question if it is agreed that the test shall have power .90 when $P = .50$.

5. How large a sample will be needed to test the hypothesis $P \leqq .50$ at significance level .01 if it is agreed that the test shall have power .90 when $P = .52$?

Test of Hypothesis That Two Population Proportions Are Equal When Each Is Estimated from a Large Number of Observations and When the Estimated Common Proportion Is Not Near 0 or 1. In a public opinion poll taken in Peekskill, N.Y. in 1946, Hedlund [4] compared two methods of selecting a sample of persons to be interviewed on certain matters concerning the Peekskill public schools. The Control Sample consisted of 97 adults selected at random by interviewing one person at every 38th address listed in the street guide of the latest Peekskill directory. The Experimental Sample consisted of 365 persons selected by high school students from among their adult acquaintances. The method of selecting individuals for the experimental sample is obviously more economical. However, if the proportion of persons reported to hold a given opinion differs significantly from one sample to the other, the selection of the experimental sample must be presumed to involve bias.

One of the questions asked by Hedlund was, "Would you be in favor of spending public money to add an evening school for adults to the services now offered by the Peekskill Public Schools?" The responses were obtained from populations of persons which may be the same or different in respect to their opinions on this issue. One may formulate the hypothesis that adult acquaintances of high school students have the same attitudes toward an evening school as the population of adults as a whole.

There are two populations. One consists of the responses which might have been obtained by questioning all adults in Peekskill, and the other consists of responses which might have been obtained from all acquaintances of high school students in this city. Both are finite populations but large enough for sampling distribution theory based on an infinite population to apply. The mathematical description of the populations can be formulated as in the adjacent display.

Class	All adults	All acquaintances
Answering "Yes"	P_1	P_2
Answering "No" or "No opinion"	Q_1	Q_2

The question to be asked about the two populations might be phrased: Is the proportion of "Yes" responses the same in both? Mathematically the hypothesis can be formulated as $P_1 = P_2 = P$ or as $P_1 - P_2 = 0$. A hypothesis which states that the difference between two parameters is zero is called the *null* hypothesis.

Level of significance and location of critical region must be decided before data are examined. Let us assume that α is to be .05. The logic of the problem appears to call for a two-sided test, because we want to detect a difference in either direction.

Let N_1 be the number of cases in the sample for which the observed proportion is p_1 and let N_2 and p_2 be the corresponding values in the other sample. Then in the combined samples the proportion of "Yes" answers is

$$(3.11) \qquad p = \frac{N_1 p_1 + N_2 p_2}{N_1 + N_2}$$

and the proportion not answering "Yes" is $q = 1 - p$. Let $N = N_1 + N_2$. The required statistic is

$$(3.12) \qquad z = \frac{p_1 - p_2}{\sqrt{\frac{p(1-p)(N_1+N_2)}{N_1 N_2}}} = \frac{p_1 - p_2}{\sqrt{\frac{pqN}{N_1 N_2}}}$$

As before, z denotes a variable with unit normal distribution.

Formula (3.12) requires an unnecessary amount of arithmetic and risk of unnecessarily large rounding errors.

Let n_1 be the number of individuals answering "Yes" in the first sample and n_2 be the number of individuals answering "Yes" in the second

$$n = n_1 + n_2$$
$$N = N_1 + N_2$$

Then using the integers listed above instead of the decimals p_1 and p_2, Formula (3.12) can be reduced to

$$(3.13) \qquad z = \frac{N_2 n_1 - N_1 n_2}{\sqrt{\frac{N_1 N_2 n(N-n)}{N}}}$$

These two formulas will now be applied to the data from Hedlund's study. Both the numbers and the proportions in the two classes are shown.

Class	Number			Proportion		
	Adults	Acquaint-ances	Both	Adults	Acquaint-ances	Both
Those answering "Yes"	62	241	303	.6392	.6598	.6558
Those not answering "Yes"	35	124	159	.3608	.3402	.3442
Entire group	97	365	462	1.0000	1.0000	1.0000

By Formula (3.12)

$$z = \frac{.6392 - .6598}{\sqrt{\frac{(.6558)(.3442)(462)}{(97)(365)}}} = \frac{-.0206}{.0534} = -.386$$

By Formula (3.13) $$z = \frac{(124)(62) - (35)(241)}{\sqrt{\frac{(97)(365)(303)(159)}{462}}} = -.388$$

As the numerator and denominator of the first computation are carried to 3 significant digits only, an error must be expected in the third digit of the result.

For large samples the statistic given in Formulas (3.12) and (3.13) has a distribution which is approximately normal. If neither N_1 nor N_2 nor n nor $N - n$ is small the normal approximation will be satisfactory. A correction to be used in small samples will be found in Chapter 4 on page 106, where a statistic closely related to this one is discussed.

Since it was agreed that α should be .05 we read $z_{.975}$ from the normal probability table as 1.96 and $z_{.025}$ as -1.96. The region of acceptance is therefore $-1.96 < z < 1.96$. The observed value $z = -.389$ falls well within this region. The observed difference in percentages is not large enough to throw any serious suspicion on the hypothesis $P_1 - P_2 = 0$. Inasmuch as one method of taking a sample is much easier than the other, and inasmuch as no evidence has been found to indicate that the methods produce a difference in proportions, the investigator is justified in using the easier method of drawing the sample.

REVIEW EXERCISE

1. The following terms have been introduced in this chapter. Be sure that the meaning of them is clear to you.

acceptance value
alternative to a hypothesis
confidence belt
confidence coefficient
confidence interval
confidence limits
consistent estimate
critical region
error of the first type
error of the second type
finite population
interval estimate
level of significance
null hypothesis
one-sided hypothesis
power function
power of a test
region of acceptance
region of rejection
region of significance
rejection value
sample point

size of a region
standard error
test
two-sided hypothesis
unbiased estimate

2. Translate into words each of the following symbolic expressions:

a. $H: P = .3$

b. $E(p) = P$

c. $\sigma_p^2 = \dfrac{PQ}{N}$

d. $P(p = .7 \mid P = .6 \text{ and } N = 40) = ?$

e. $C(.43 < P < .49) = .98$

3. For each of several situations there is given the hypothesis to be tested, the observed value of the statistic, the region of acceptance. Draw a circle around the letter *A* or *R* to indicate whether the decision should be to accept or reject the hypothesis. Draw a circle around the number I or II to indicate which type of error you are certain has *not* been made.

H	*p*	*Region of acceptance*	*Decision*	*Type of error which has not been made*
$P = .75$	.82	$.725 < p < .775$	*A R*	I II
$P = .40$	.31	$p < .50$	*A R*	I II
$P = .50$	.59	$.44 < p < .56$	*A R*	I II
$P > .80$	.78	$p > .74$	*A R*	I II
$P = .42$	.41	$.40 < p < .44$	*A R*	I II

REFERENCES

1. Clopper, C. J. and Pearson, E. S., "The Use of Confidence or Fiducial Limits Illustrated in the Case of the Binomial," *Biometrika*, 26 (1934), 404–413.
2. David, F. N., *Probability Theory for Statistical Methods*, 1949, Cambridge University Press. Chapter 1, Fundamental Ideas. Chapter 2, Preliminary Definitions and Theorems. Chapter 3, The Binomial Theorem in Probability. Chapter 4, Evaluation of Binomial Probabilities.
3. Eisenhart, C., Hastay, M. W. and Wallis, W. A., *Selected Techniques of Statistical Analysis*, New York, 1947, McGraw-Hill Book Company, Inc., 331–335.
4. Hedlund, Paul A., *Measuring Public Opinion on School Issues*, unpublished Ed. D. thesis, 1947, on file in the Library of Teachers College, Columbia University.
5. National Bureau of Standards, Applied Mathematics Series 6, *Tables of Binomial Probability Distribution*, Washington, D.C., 1949, U.S. Government Printing Office.
6. Neyman, Jerzy, *First Course in Probability and Statistics*, New York, 1950, Henry Holt and Company. Chapter 2, Probability.
7. Walker, H. M., *Mathematics Essential for Elementary Statistics*, New York, 1951, Henry Holt and Company, 2d ed. Chapter 19, The Binomial Expansion
8. Wilks, S. S., *Elementary Statistical Analysis*, Princeton, 1949, Princeton University Press. Chapter 10, Confidence Limits for Population Parameters. Chapter 11, Statistical Significance Tests.

4 Chi-square

The simplest type of population — and a very important type — is the dichotomy discussed in the preceding chapters. Many of the most fundamental concepts of statistical inference have already been developed in relation to this simple two-class population and its parameter P, and will now be applied to problems from other types of population. In this chapter we shall study populations composed of several discrete classes. In later chapters we shall deal with populations on one or more continuous variables. A greater variety of questions can be asked — and answered — about such populations. Samples from them will furnish new statistics and some of those statistics will have sampling distributions other than the binomial and the normal distribution, so that new probability tables must be employed. However we shall still be concerned with such basic ideas as the sampling distribution of a statistic, its expectation and its standard error, critical region, significance level, two types of error, and tests of hypotheses.

Populations Consisting of Several Discrete Classes. Such populations are very common. Again we shall introduce the topic with a problem in which there are so few alternatives that the probabilities can be obtained by direct enumeration. The illustration we shall use is a study by an advertising agency to determine which of three color tones is most desirable for a certain display. In order to ascertain the reaction of the public, the display is prepared in each of the three colors and is shown to a sample of persons. Each person is asked to state which of the three displays he prefers.

The statistician in charge of the study would probably select a large sample of persons. A procedure for testing hypotheses with large samples will be described later. However, in order to provide a background for that procedure a calculation will first be carried through on the assumption that only three judges are used in the study.

The possible responses of the 3 judges may be classified in terms of the amount of agreement thus:

1. All three judges may vote for the same display. For convenience we shall call this type of response 3, 0, 0. Since the display for which they vote may be either I, II, or III, there are 3 ways in which they can make this type of response.

2. Two judges may agree on one display and the third judge vote for a different one. For convenience we shall call this type of response 2, 1, 0. It can be made in 18 different ways, which are tedious but not difficult to enumerate. A few of these 18 ways are listed here, the letters A, B, and C representing judges, and the numerals I, II, and III the displays for which they vote

Response	*I*	*II*	*III*
1	*A*	—	*BC*
2	*B*	*AC*	—
3	*AC*	—	*B*

3. Each judge may select a different display. We shall call this type of response 1, 1, 1. It can be made in 3! = 6 different ways.

The three types of response and their probabilities under the hypothesis that a randomly selected judge is as likely to vote for one display as for another, are therefore:

Type of response	*Number of ways in which response can be made*	*Probability under the hypothesis*
1, 1, 1	6	.222
2, 1, 0	18	.667
3, 0, 0	3	.111
		1.000

Assume now that the three judges are chosen randomly and cast their votes independently and that all 3 vote for display II. Can the advertising agency be fairly sure that the public in general will prefer II? Could the agreement be a matter of chance? Let us test the hypothesis that in the population preferences are equally distributed so that a randomly selected judge is as likely to vote for one display as for another and consequently any of the 27 possible responses is as likely as any other. Then the probability that all three judges will select the same display is $3/27 = .111$. Since the highest agreement possible among 3 judges has so large a probability of occurring by chance in the absence of any real preference on the part of the general population, it must be concluded that 3 judges are not enough to reach any dependable conclusion. Let us therefore consider the same problem with 6 judges.

Sampling Distribution of Response Types. We found there were $3^3 = 27$ possible ways in which the votes of 3 judges could be assigned to 3 displays, and that these 27 ways could be classified under the three types 3, 0, 0; 2, 1, 1; and 1, 1, 1. With 6 judges there will be $3^6 = 729$ possible ways in which their votes can be allocated to the three displays.

Assume that the six judges are chosen randomly, and that of the six, four choose display I, one chooses display II and one display III. On the basis of these frequencies the statistician wishes to test the hypothesis that in the population, from which the judges are a sample, the preferences are equally distributed.

The 729 possible responses can be classified into the 7 types shown in the first column of Table 4.1. The number of different

TABLE 4.1 The Number of Possible Responses of Six Judges Each of Whom Chooses any one of Three Displays Classified by Type of Response under the Hypothesis that One Display is as Likely to be Chosen as Another.

Type	Number of responses in type	Probability of type	Cumulative probability
2, 2, 2	90	.1235	.1235
3, 2, 1	360	.4938	.6173
3, 3, 0	60	.0823	.6996
4, 1, 1	90	.1235	.8231
4, 2, 0	90	.1235	.9466
5, 1, 0	36	.0494	.9960
6, 0, 0	3	.0041	1.0001
TOTAL	729	1.0001	

responses giving rise to each type is shown in the second column of that table. The student is not expected to verify these numbers but may be interested in knowing how they were obtained. Consider the type, 3, 2, 1. Three out of 6 judges vote for one of the displays and these 3 judges can be selected in $\binom{6}{3} = 20$ ways. Two out of the remaining judges vote for another display and they can be chosen in $\binom{3}{2} = 3$ ways. The remaining judge will then vote for the remaining display. The number of ways of grouping votes of the 6 judges is therefore $20 \times 3 \times 1 = 60$. However the votes of 3, 2, 1 can be assigned in 6 different ways to the 3 displays, and therefore the total number of possible responses which produce this type is $6 \times 60 = 360$. The other frequencies are arrived at in similar fashion, though it is not particularly important for the student to compute them.

Under the hypothesis that out of all judges who could be consulted the same proportion would vote for each display, so that a randomly selected judge is as likely to vote for one display as for another, the expected type of the votes of 6 judges is 2, 2, 2. In Table 4.1 the 7 types have been arranged according to the degree of their conformity to this hypothetical type. The first type shows complete conformity, the last one, 6, 0, 0, shows the greatest possible discrepancy. In the next section will be presented a statistic by which that discrepancy can be measured. Clearly one would be quite ready to reject the hypothesis if a sample yields the type 6, 0, 0, since the risk of error in falsely rejecting a true hypothesis would then be only .004. If the observed type were 5, 1, 0, the probability that this type or one showing even less agreement with the hypothetical frequencies should occur when the hypothesis is true is $.049 + .004 = .053$, and most investigators would reject the hypothesis on the evidence of such data.

In the problem as stated, the judges' votes were 4, 1, 1. There are 3 types of response which disagree with the hypothesis more than this one and the sum of the probabilities for these three is .177. The probability, under the hypothesis, of the observed pattern or something still more unlikely is $.124 + .177 = .301$. Clearly on the evidence from this response the advertising agency cannot assume display I to be more pleasing in general than displays II and III.

The calculation just described is quite laborious for six cases. In a more realistic situation, where many more than six cases would be studied, the calculation would become utterly forbidding. It is customary in such problems to compute a statistic which measures the discrepancy between observed and hypothetical frequencies and to study the sampling distribution of that statistic. The statistic is known as χ^2, or *chi-square*.

Chi-square as a Measure of Discrepancy between Observed and Expected Frequencies. For convenience in writing formulas we shall adopt the following symbolism:

f_i is the number, or frequency, observed in the ith class,

F_i is the number, or frequency, expected in the ith class in accordance with the proportions indicated by the hypothesis.

The expected frequencies are computed on the assumption that the cases in the sample are apportioned according to the hypothesis so that the total expected frequency is the same as the total observed. The three displays define three classes over which the judges' votes are distributed. The frequencies expected under the hypothesis are then $F_1 = 2$, $F_2 = 2$, and $F_3 = 2$, while the corresponding observed frequencies are $f_1 = 4$, $f_2 = 1$, and $f_3 = 1$.

The sum of all the differences $f_i - F_i$ will always be 0 since $\Sigma f_i = \Sigma F_i$. (The reader unfamiliar with the symbol Σ should refer to page 111.) Therefore $\Sigma(f_i - F_i)$ cannot be used as a measure of discrepancy. If these differences are squared before summing, the negative signs will conveniently disappear. The size of $(f_i - F_i)^2$ needs to be taken in relation to the expected value F_i, inasmuch as a difference of, say 5 when F_i was, say 10 would be much more important than a difference of 5 when F_i was, say 100. (The formula was of course arrived at mathematically and not by such intuitive argument as is advanced here.) Then the statistic

$$\chi^2 = \frac{(f_1 - F_1)^2}{F_1} + \frac{(f_2 - F_2)^2}{F_2} + \frac{(f_3 - F_3)^2}{F_3}$$

or in general

(4.1) $$\chi^2 = \sum_{i=1}^{k} \frac{(f_i - F_i)^2}{F_i}$$

measures discrepancy between observed and expected frequencies. The computation is then as follows:

Class	f_i	F_i	$f_i - F_i$	$(f_i - F_i)^2$	$(f_i - F_i)^2/F_i$
I	4	2	2	4	2.0
II	1	2	−1	1	.5
III	1	2	−1	1	.5
Sum	6	6	0		$3.0 = \chi^2$

The Greek letter χ^2 (or chi-square) was first used to describe this statistic by Karl Pearson in 1900.[8] Its use is practically universal. In fact it is one of the very few statistical symbols used by almost every writer. There is no parameter corresponding to this statistic.

Chi-square is a discrete variable. It is never negative, since each term in the numerator is a square and each denominator is a positive number. If the observed frequencies should agree completely with the hypothetical, χ^2 would be zero. χ^2 increases in size as the observed frequencies depart more and more from the hypothetical.

The reader should compute χ^2 for each of the response types in Table 4.1 in the manner shown above for type 4, 1, 1 and compare his results with the values shown in Table 4.2.

Exact Probabilities of Chi-square Obtained by Enumeration. In order to decide what to do with the hypothesis we are testing it is necessary to set up a critical region. In order to set up a critical region for χ^2 it is necessary to know its sampling distribution. We already have, in Table 4.1, the probability distribution of response type under the hypothesis that all possible responses are equally likely. However, response type is not a statistic which has any general usefulness, whereas χ^2 can be used in a very wide variety of situations to measure the discrepancy between observed and expected frequencies. We shall therefore convert the probability distribution for response type of Table 4.1 into the exact sampling distribution for χ^2, merely by computing the value of χ^2 corresponding to each response type. The two response types 4, 1, 1 and 3, 3, 0 are then found to yield the same value of chi-square and so have been combined in Table 4.2. The probabilities in Table 4.2 are those already given in Table 4.1. The cumulative probability in the final column is the probability of obtaining by chance a value of chi-square which does not exceed the value listed in the χ^2 column.

TABLE 4.2 Values of χ^2 Measuring Discrepancy between a Response Type and the Type 2, 2, 2, with Corresponding Probabilities and Cumulative Probabilities. (Probabilities as in Table 4.1.)

Type		χ^2	Probability	Cumulative probability
A	2, 2, 2	0	.124	.124
B	3, 2, 1	1	.494	.617
C	4, 1, 1 3, 3, 0	3 3	.206	.823
D	4, 2, 0	4	.124	.947
E	5, 1, 0	7	.049	.996
F	6, 0, 0	12	.004	1.000

Chi-square Curves and Table. To obviate the detailed and laborious computation required to determine the distribution of χ^2 as indicated in Tables 4.1 and 4.2, a set of smooth curves is

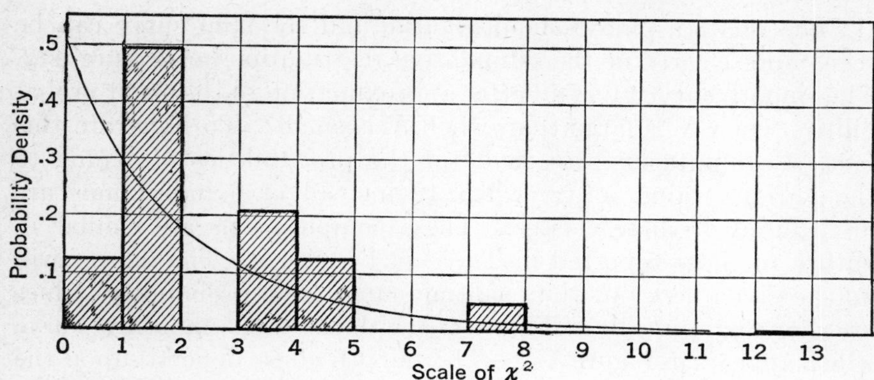

FIG. 4–1. Exact and smooth χ^2 distribution for samples of six cases grouped in three classes.

available, and probabilities calculated from areas under these curves may be used as approximations to the exact χ^2 distributions calculated by enumeration. The approximation is very accurate for large samples. Good results from the use of these curves may be obtained when the expected frequency in each class is at least five. Figure 4–1 shows the relationship between χ^2 distribution as calculated by enumeration and the smooth curve. The exact probabilities in this figure are obtained from Table 4.1, and the smooth curve from the mathematical formula for the curve.

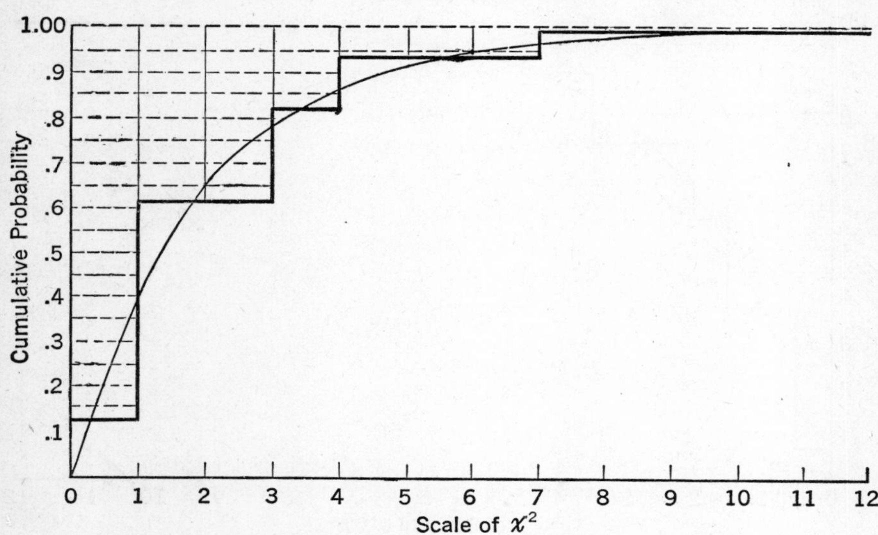

FIG. 4–2. Exact and smooth cumulative χ^2 distribution for samples of six cases grouped in three classes.

The relation of the smooth curve and the step curve can be seen more clearly in the cumulative distributions of Figure 4–2. The smooth curve gives a better approximation to the exact probabilities when N is large than when N is small. To illustrate this fact, a computation was made of the probabilities attaching to the various values of χ^2 when 12 instead of 6 individuals are distributed in three classes. These computations are similar in nature to those reported in Tables 4.1 and 4.2. The figures will not be given here but the resulting cumulative probability values are shown graphically in Figure 4–3 with the same smooth χ^2 curve which appears in Figure 4–2. The smooth curve depends upon the number of classes and not on the number of individuals in those classes. In Figure 4–2 the steps are larger and so the probabilities read from the smooth curve and the step curve show greater disagreement than in Figure 4–3. The smooth curve provides probabilities which approximate fairly well the exact probabilities of the step curve in Figure 4–3 for probability values of .90 or more, and it is in the range of cumulative probabilities from .90 to 1.00 that the accuracy of approximation becomes important. As N increases, the exact probabilities come in general closer and closer to the approximate values read from the smooth χ^2 curve.

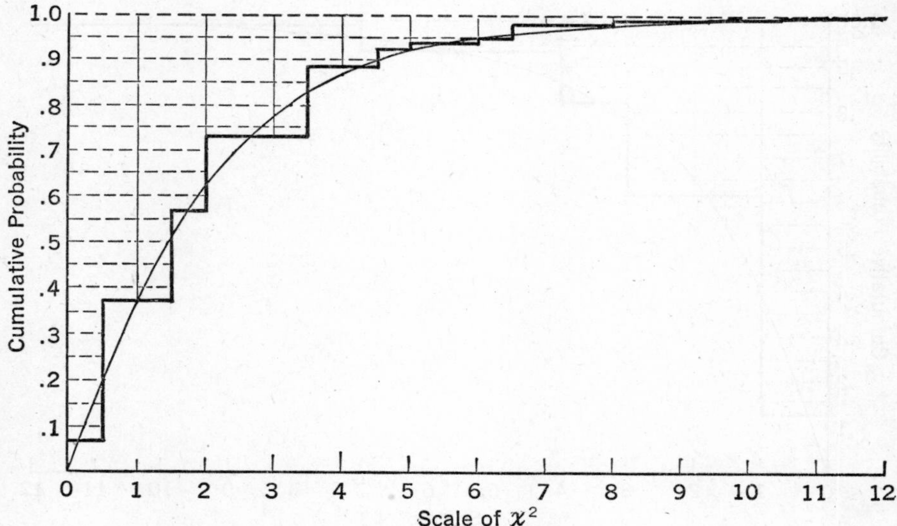

Fig. 4–3. Exact and smooth cumulative χ^2 distributions for samples of twelve cases grouped in three classes.

The burden of studying hypotheses in populations consisting of several classes can now be shifted to probabilities calculated, by use of the calculus, from the smooth χ^2 curves. These probabilities are tabulated in Table VIII in the Appendix.

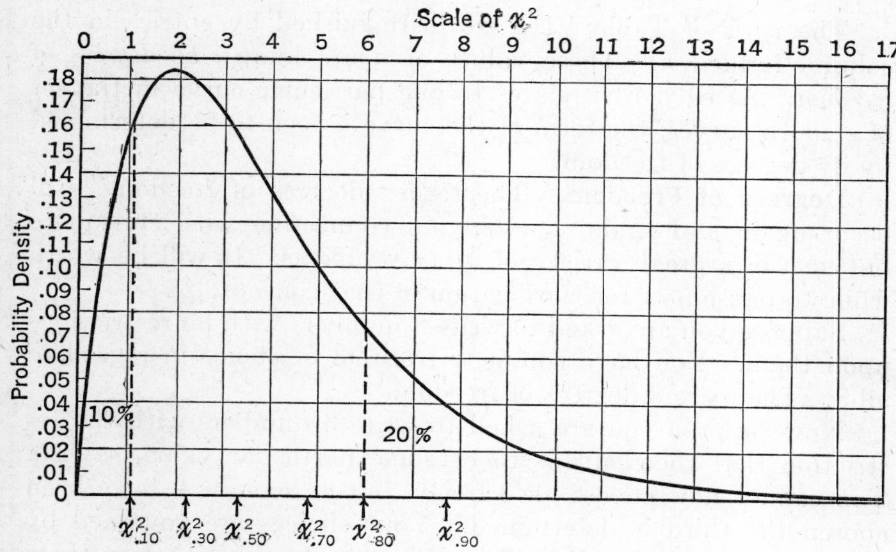

FIG. 4–4. Smooth χ^2 curve for 4 degrees of freedom, with selected percentiles indicated on the baseline.

We have already seen that what is called "the binomial distribution" is actually not one distribution but a whole family of distributions, the members of that family differing from each other as P and N change. The chi-square curve is also not a single curve but a family of curves. In Table VIII each horizontal row relates to one particular curve in this family of smooth curves. Subscripts of χ^2 at the top of the table indicate per cents of area under the curve. The relation of these per cents of area to the tabular entries is illustrated in Figure 4–4 which shows the curve for the horizontal row $n = 4$. Select one of the columns in Table VIII, say the one headed $\chi^2_{.10}$, and read the tabular entry in the given row and column. It is 1.1. The relation between $\chi^2_{.10}$, and 1.1 may be expressed in any one of the following ways, all of which have the same meaning, but with slightly different emphasis:

10% of the area under this curve lies to the left of an ordinate at $\chi^2 = 1.1$

$P(\chi^2 < 1.1) = .10$
$P(\chi^2 > 1.1) = .90$
The 10th percentile of this distribution is $\chi^2 = 1.1$
$\chi^2_{.10} = 1.1$

The rows of Table VIII are distinguished by entries in the column headed n. These values of n are known as *degrees of freedom.* As each row relates to one particular curve in the set of smooth curves, the form of the curve is seen to be determined by its degrees of freedom.

Degrees of Freedom. The term "degrees of freedom" will occur again and again, not only in connection with chi-square but also in a great variety of other problems. It will be worth while to pause now for clarification of that concept.

Suppose you are asked to write 3 numbers with no restrictions upon them. You have complete freedom of choice in regard to all 3. There are 3 degrees of freedom.

Now suppose you are asked to write 3 numbers with the restriction that their sum is to be some particular value, say 20. You cannot now choose all 3 freely, but as soon as 2 have been chosen the third is determined. Your choices are governed by the necessary relation $X_1 + X_2 + X_3 = 20$. In this situation there are only 2 degrees of freedom. The number of variables is 3, but the number of restrictions upon them is 1, and the number of "free" variables, or independent choices, is $3 - 1 = 2$.

Now suppose you are asked to write 5 numbers such that their sum is 30 and also such that the sum of the first two is 18. There are 5 variables but you do not have freedom of choice with respect to all 5. You cannot write 5 numbers arbitrarily and have them conform to the 2 restrictions that $X_1 + X_2 = 18$ and

$$X_1 + X_2 + X_3 + X_4 + X_5 = 20.$$

As soon as you select X_1, then $X_2 = 18 - X_1$ and is completely determined. Since $X_3 + X_4 + X_5 = 30 - 18 = 12$, only two of the numbers, X_3, X_4, and X_5, can be freely chosen. As one of the numbers X_1 and X_2 can be freely chosen there are 3 free choices. The number of degrees of freedom is $n = 5 - 2 = 3$.

In every statistical problem in which degrees of freedom are involved it is necessary to determine the number of "free variables" by first noting the total number of variables and reducing that number by the number of independent restrictions upon them. In the preceding paragraph, for instance, one might think there are 3 restrictions, namely

$$X_1 + X_2 = 18; \quad X_3 + X_4 + X_5 = 12; \quad \text{and } X_1 + X_2 + X_3 + X_4 + X_5 = 30.$$

However only two of these are independent, since any one of them can be deduced from the other two. (For further discussion of degrees of freedom, see references 11 and 12.)

Returning now to the problem of the advertising agency we note that the responses of six persons are distributed in three classes. Let X_1, X_2, and X_3 be the numbers in those classes. There are thus 3 variables. These are restricted by the relation $X_1 + X_2 + X_3 = 6$. Only two of the variables can be chosen freely; two are free and the third is bound. (Do not be troubled by the fact that you are not free to choose a negative number, or a fraction, or a number larger than 6 in this problem. Even though choice of a variable can be made only from the digits 0, 1, 2, 3, 4, 5 or 6 the variable is still considered free.) If instead of 6 judges there had been 1000 we should have had $X_1 + X_2 + X_3 = 1000$ and the number of degrees of freedom would still be $n = 3 - 1 = 2$. Thus for all problems testing a hypothesis about the proportion of cases falling in each of 3 classes, when no restriction is laid down except that giving the total number of cases (here 6), the chi-square table may be entered with 2 degrees of freedom. In general, if there are k classes in such a problem there would be $k - 1$ degrees of freedom, regardless of how many cases are distributed in the k classes. Other types of problem with a variety of numbers of restrictions and of degrees of freedom will be considered in succeeding sections.

Reading the Chi-square Table. In Figure 4–5 are shown five of the smooth χ^2 curves for which probabilities are listed in Table VIII namely, the curves for which $n = 1, 2, 4, 8$, and 10. It may be helpful to consider the table and this figure together. Select one of the curves, say the one for which $n = 3$. Now find those entries in row $n = 3$ of Table VIII which may be interpreted symbolically to mean the following:

$$P(\chi^2 < .35 \mid n = 3) = .05$$
$$P(\chi^2 < 6.3 \mid n = 3) = .90$$

Locate .35 and 6.3 on the baseline of Figure 4–5 and draw an ordinate at each point. Look at the curve $n = 3$ to see that the proportion of area under the curve to the left of these ordinates appears to be approximately .05 and .90 respectively.

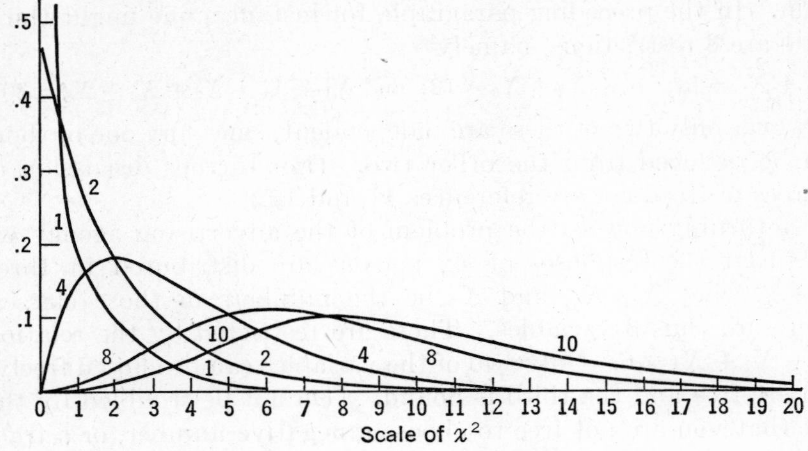

FIG. 4–5. χ^2 curves for 1, 2, 4, 8, and 10 degrees of freedom.

It is very convenient to remember that $E(\chi^2) = n$. This is almost the only guidepost which most people carry in their minds with respect to the χ^2 distribution. It means that if one obtains an observed value of χ^2 smaller than the number of degrees of freedom involved in a problem, one usually feels satisfied to decide at once, without consulting the probability table, that the discrepancy between hypothetical and observed frequencies is negligible.

EXERCISE 4.1

1. Verify the following statements by reference to Table VIII and translate them into words:

a. $P(\chi^2 < 9.9 \mid n = 21) = .02$
b. $P(\chi^2 < 43.6 \mid n = 27) = .975$
c. $P(\chi^2 < 2.7 \mid n = 1) = .90$
d. $P(\chi^2 > 30.6 \mid n = 15) = .01$
e. $P(\chi^2 > 15 \mid n = 6) = .02$
f. $P(\chi^2 > 8 \mid n = 16) = .95$
g. $P(\chi^2 > 40.1 \mid n = 27) = .05$
h. $P(14.6 < \chi^2 < 37.7 \mid n = 25) = .90$
i. $P(7.4 < \chi^2 < 41.3 \mid n = 20) = .99$
j. $P(8.5 < \chi^2 < 22.3 \mid n = 15) = .80$
k. $.01 < P(\chi^2 < 14 \mid n = 28) < .02$
l. $.05 < P(\chi^2 > 28 \mid n = 19) < .10$
m. $.005 < P(\chi^2 > 42 \mid n = 22) < .01$
n. $.01 < P(\chi^2 > 42 \mid n = 24) < .02$
o. $.025 < P(\chi^2 > 20 \mid n = 11) < .05$
p. $P(\chi^2 < 3.2 \mid n = 13) < .005$
q. $P(\chi^2 > 32 \mid n = 10) < .001$

2. Suppose you have decided that whenever the observed χ^2 is equal to or greater than $\chi^2_{.95}$ you will reject whatever hypothesis you are testing and whenever it is less than $\chi^2_{.95}$ you will accept that hypothesis. For each of the situations described below, read the appropriate value of $\chi^2_{.95}$ from the table and circle *A* or *R* to indicate whether the hypothesis under consideration should be accepted or rejected, as illustrated in **a**.

	n	χ^2	$\chi^2_{.95}$				n	χ^2	$\chi^2_{.95}$		
a.	2	3.7	6.0	(A)	R	**f.**	25	44.5	____	A	R
b.	7	4.6	____	A	R	**g.**	30	40.1	____	A	R
c.	7	18.2	____	A	R	**h.**	16	27.1	____	A	R
d.	7	19.3	____	A	R	**i.**	11	22.4	____	A	R
e.	15	14.6	____	A	R	**j.**	4	12.6	____	A	R

3. Carry out the instructions for the preceding questions but using the .01 significance level (that is, refer to $\chi^2_{.99}$) instead of the .05. Compare the decisions as to disposition of the hypothesis reached in the two situations.

Comparison of Observed and Theoretical Frequencies by Means of χ^2. The problem of testing a hypothesis regarding the proportion in the classes of a population has been discussed at length for a small sample. Now that the χ^2 table is available, problems involving a larger number of cases can be considered.

Suppose that in the study of preferences for advertising displays 60 cases have been used instead of 6. The hypothesis to be tested is still that the proportions in the population are equal. Then the 60 cases are expected to be distributed equally in their preference. Hence $F_1 = F_2 = F_3 = 20$. Suppose that the observed frequencies are 30, 18, 12; so that $f_1 = 30$, $f_2 = 18$, $f_3 = 12$. Substituting these values into Formula (4.1) we compute the value of chi-square as

$$\chi^2 = \frac{(30-20)^2}{20} + \frac{(18-20)^2}{20} + \frac{(12-20)^2}{20} = 8.4$$

The χ^2 table shows that this value leads to rejection of the hypothesis at both the .05 and .02 levels, but to its acceptance at the .01 level.

Problems leading to a comparison of observed with theoretical frequencies arise when one wishes to determine whether an observed sample has been drawn from a population having some theoretical form such as the normal. This problem will be taken up in Chapter 5.

EXERCISE 4.2

1. Several situations will be described briefly. No computations are to be made, but in each the task is to decide upon a number denoted n which is the number of degrees of freedom and upon another number denoted N which is the number of observations.

(a) In a college class of 10 students, each student is asked to appraise a text as either excellent (E), good (G), mediocre (M), or poor (P), and their appraisals are to be used to test the hypothesis that college students in general would show judgments evenly divided in the 4 categories. For text A the appraisals were E, 0; G, 5; M, 4; P, 1. Then $n =$ ——, $N =$ ——.

(b) Let the situation be the same as in question (a) except that there are 50 students whose appraisals of text A are E, 3; G, 31; M, 12; P, 4. Then $n =$ ——, $N =$ ——.

2. If the exact and the smooth χ^2 distributions were fitted to the data of questions (a) and (b) in the preceding example, do you think the fit of the smooth curve would be better in one situation than in the other? If so, in which?

3. In a toss of 4 pennies the distribution of number of heads falling upward has the following probabilities, obtainable from the binomial distribution:

Number of heads	0	1	2	3	4
Probability	$\frac{1}{16}$	$\frac{1}{4}$	$\frac{3}{8}$	$\frac{1}{4}$	$\frac{1}{16}$

Using these probabilities, what are the expected frequencies in the five classes, if the throw of four pennies is repeated 64 times?

What is χ^2 if the observed frequencies in 64 throws are

Number of heads	0	1	2	3	4
Observed frequency	2	12	23	20	7

Does the value of χ^2 warrant a judgment that one or more of the pennies are biased?

4. Answer question 3 if the pennies were tossed 128 times and observed frequencies of heads were 4, 24, 46, 40, and 14. The problem here is to note what happens to χ^2 when every f_i and every F_i is doubled.

5. Answer question 3 if the pennies were tossed $64r$ times and the observed frequencies of heads were $2r$, $12r$, $23r$, $20r$, and $7r$. Make a generalization as to effect on χ^2 of multiplying observed and theoretical frequencies by r, keeping proportions unchanged.

Computing Chi-square from Data in Form of Per Cents. When data are given in per cents rather than frequencies it is convenient to compute χ^2 by the formula

$$\chi^2 = N\Sigma \frac{(p_i - P_i)^2}{P_i} \tag{4.2}$$

where p_i is the observed proportion in the ith class and P_i is the expected proportion. If *only* per cents are given and the total sample size N is unknown χ^2 cannot be computed. To use per cents as though they were frequencies would be to proceed as though N were 100. If N is less than 100 this would give too large a value of χ^2 and might lead to false rejection of a true hypothesis more often than is indicated by the level of significance. If N is greater than 100, χ^2 would be underestimated and the hypothesis accepted more often than should be the case.

Tests of Independence in Contingency Tables. The foregoing discussion has dealt with tests of hypotheses that the population proportions in several classes are in agreement with certain hypothetical proportions. We shall now consider situations in which individuals are classified according to two discrete variables, and the problem deals with the relationship between those variables.

As an example of such a situation consider data taken from Rope's study of *Opinion Conflict and School Support.*[9] Each of 1464 adult residents of Pittsburgh, Pa., was interviewed on a variety of issues related to tax support. One of the questions asked was, "Do you think tax money should, or should not, be spent on nursery schools for children less than four and a half years old?" Responses were classified as (1) favorable, (2) no opinion, and (3) unfavorable. The problem was to determine whether there is a relationship between type of response and age of respondent. Each individual was then classified both according to type of response and according to age. The resulting distribution appears in Table 4.3.

TABLE 4.3 Frequency of Observed Response to the Question of Spending Tax Money for Nursery Schools, Classified According to Nature of Response and Age of Respondent.*

	Group aged 20–34	Group aged 34–54	Group over 54	Total
Favorable response	153	182	65	400
No opinion	35	50	25	110
Unfavorable response	377	417	160	954
TOTAL	565	649	250	1464

* Taken from Rope, *Opinion Conflict and School Support.*

A two-way distribution like that in Table 4.3 in which the categories are discrete is called a *contingency table.* To study the problem of relationship between the variables, the hypothesis of *independence* is formulated. This hypothesis is then tested by an application of the χ^2 method.

The methods of dealing with the hypothesis of independence will be developed in its most general form for a contingency table with more than two classes in each of the variables. While these methods are applicable to all two-variable contingency tables simplifications of the computational techniques are available for contingency tables in which (1) one of the variables has two classes and the other more than two classes, and (2) each of the variables has two classes

a. *More than two classes for each variable.* This situation is illustrated by the data in Table 4.3. If the hypothesis of independence is true, then, in the population, the proportions in any one response row are equal to those in every other response row, and the proportions in any one age column are equal to the proportions in every other age column. Therefore, the best estimates of the population proportions in any row are the proportions indicated by column totals and the best estimates of the proportions in any column are the proportions indicated by the row totals. Either row totals or column totals can be used to obtain expected values for a χ^2 test.

If we use row totals then for any of the age groups the population proportions are as follows:

Favorable: 400/1464
No opinion: 110/1464
Unfavorable: 954/1464

The expected frequencies for any age group can be computed by apportioning all the individuals in the age group according to these proportions. Thus for the 20–34 age group the expected frequencies are

$$\begin{array}{ll} \text{Favorable:} & (400/1464)(565) = 154.4 \\ \text{No opinions:} & (110/1464)(565) = 42.4 \\ \text{Unfavorable:} & (954/1464)(565) = \underline{368.2} \\ & 565.0 \end{array}$$

By use of the same proportions the individuals in the remaining age groups may be apportioned similarly according to response pattern. The expected values resulting from these computations are displayed in Table 4.4.

TABLE 4.4 Expected Frequency of Response to the Question of Spending Tax Money for Nursery Schools, on the Hypothesis that Age and Response are Independent. (Data from Table 4.3.)

	Group aged 20–34	Group aged 35–54	Group over 54	Total
Favorable response	154.4	177.3	68.3	400
No opinion	42.4	48.8	18.8	110
Unfavorable response	368.2	422.9	162.9	954
TOTAL	565.0	649.0	250.0	1464

To write formulas for χ^2 the following notation for the observed and expected values will be adopted:

Observed Frequencies			*Expected Frequencies*		
f_{11}	f_{12}	f_{13}	F_{11}	F_{12}	F_{13}
f_{21}	f_{22}	f_{23}	F_{21}	F_{22}	F_{23}
f_{31}	f_{32}	f_{33}	F_{31}	F_{32}	F_{33}

The formula for χ^2 can now be written as

$$\chi^2 = \Sigma\Sigma \frac{(f_{ij} - F_{ij})^2}{F_{ij}}$$

From the values in Tables 4.4 and 4.3, χ^2 can be calculated by Formula (4.1). However, a simpler computational routine is provided by Formula (4.3).

(4.3) $$\chi^2 = \Sigma\Sigma \frac{f_{ij}^2}{F_{ij}} - N$$

If data are in the form of proportions this formula becomes

(4.4) $$\chi^2 = N\left(\Sigma\Sigma \frac{p_{ij}^2}{P_{ij}} - 1\right)$$

Direct substitution in Formula (4.3) is carried out as follows:

$$\chi^2 = \frac{(153)^2}{154.4} + \frac{(35)^2}{42.2} + \cdots + \frac{(25)^2}{18.8} + \frac{(160)^2}{162.9} - 1464 = 4.1$$

The computed value of $\chi^2 = 4.1$ measures the discrepancy between the set of observed frequencies and the set of theoretical frequencies. But is that discrepancy extreme? Is the distribution of observed frequencies unusual in view of the hypothesis? The number of possible patterns in which the 1464 cases could be distributed in 9 classes is enormous. To compute the exact distribution and obtain from it the probability of a frequency distribution at least as exceptional as the one observed, as was done for a small sample in the first of this chapter, would be a very large task. The smooth χ^2 curve with appropriate number of degrees of freedom will provide a close approximation to the exact probability.

The number of degrees of freedom is the number of classes less the number of restrictions. When there are r rows and c columns the number of classes is rc. There is one restriction for each of the r rows, namely

$$f_{i1} + f_{i2} + \cdots + f_{ic} = F_{i1} + F_{i2} + \cdots + F_{ic}.$$

This equation means that for any one row, there is a free choice of frequency for all cells but one (that is for $c - 1$ cells) and the frequency of that cell must be whatever is needed to make the sum of the f_i for the row equal to the sum of the F_i for that row. Similarly there is one restriction for each of the c columns, and in that column there is free choice of frequency for all cells but one (that is for $r - 1$ cells). However there are not $r + c$ different restrictions but only $r + c - 1$, for any one of them can be obtained from the others.

The number of classes minus the number of restrictions is therefore $rc - (r + c - 1) = rc - r - c + 1 = (r - 1)(c - 1)$. Also the number of degrees of freedom is the number of classes for which there is a free choice of frequency. In any one row there is such free choice for $c - 1$ classes. If $c - 1$ frequencies are filled arbitrarily in $r - 1$ of the rows, the frequencies for all classes in the remaining row will be foreordained. Therefore the number of classes for which there is free choice of frequency is

$$n = (r - 1)(c - 1) \tag{4.5}$$

which is the number of degrees of freedom in problems of this type.

For this problem $n = 4$ and $\chi^2 = 4.1$. In the χ^2 table the entry which is next larger than the observed value is $\chi_{.75}^2 = 5.4$. If all possible samples of the given size were drawn from a population with the given theoretical frequencies, over 25% of those samples would have frequency distributions for which χ^2 was greater than the observed χ^2. This sample is indeed not exceptional under the hypothesis. It is appropriate to assume that the three age groups are homogeneous with respect to opinion on the use of tax money for nursery school. It would *not* be appropriate to seek for a possible explanation as to why the per cent of favorable response was larger (28.1%) for the group aged 35–54 than for the older group (26.0%) inasmuch as it has been shown that chance provides a reasonable explanation for the observed differences.

b. *Two classes for one variable, more than two for the other.* This type of problem may also be illustrated with data from Rope's *Opinion Conflict and School Support.* In his sample of 1464 persons, 707 were men and 757 women. To the question "Some say that in future years the only way the schools can keep up the services they are giving today is to increase taxes. If this is true, should school services be cut or taxes increased?" they expressed opinions distributed as in Table 4.5. Are these data consistent with the hypothesis that the per cent holding opinions in each of the three categories is unrelated to the sex of respondents?

TABLE 4.5 Frequency of Observed Response to the Question of Increasing Taxes to Support Current School Services, Classified by Type of Response and Sex of Respondent.*

	Men	Women	Total
Approve increasing taxes	296	236	532
Have no opinion	183	295	478
Do not approve increasing taxes	228	226	454
TOTAL	707	757	1464

* Data taken from Rope, *Opinion Conflict and School Support.*

In this type of problem χ^2 can be computed exactly as it was computed in the preceding section, but there is available an equivalent routine which involves less numerical work. Let a_i and b_i be frequencies in the two groups in the ith class and $n_i = a_i + b_i$.

$$\text{Let} \qquad \sum_{i=1}^{k} a_i = A, \quad \sum_{i=1}^{k} b_i = B, \quad \sum_{i=1}^{k} n_i = N$$

Then $A + B = N$. There are $2k$ classes. The number of degrees of freedom is $n = k - 1$. The usual formula for χ^2 can be shown to reduce to a special formula, valid only for the case described in the heading of this paragraph or described alternately as the study of the independence of two traits when one of them is a dichotomous trait.

$$\chi^2 = \frac{\sum_{i=1}^{k} \frac{a_i^2}{n_i} - \frac{A^2}{N}}{\frac{A}{N} \cdot \frac{B}{N}} = \frac{\sum_{i=1}^{k} \frac{b_i^2}{n_i} - \frac{B^2}{N}}{\frac{A}{N} \cdot \frac{B}{N}} \tag{4.6}$$

The numerical computations for the data of Table 4.5 are shown in Table 4.6. The student should verify them by carrying through the same procedure using the b_i frequencies instead of the a_i. He may also wish to use Formula (4.3) to convince himself that the method of Formula (4.6) is algebraically equivalent to the general method.

With an observed χ^2 of 31.3 when $\chi^2_{.999}$ is only 13.8, it is clear that men and women cannot be presumed to hold similar opinions concerning the issue under discussion.

Table 4.6 Computation of χ^2 from the Data of Table 4.5.

a_i	n_i	$\frac{a_i}{n_i}$	$a_i \frac{a_i}{n_i}$	
				$\frac{A}{N} = \frac{707}{1464} = .48292$
296	532	.55639	164.69	$\frac{B}{N} = \frac{757}{1464} = .51708$
183	478	.38284	70.06	$\frac{A}{N} \cdot \frac{B}{N} = .24971$
228	454	.50220	114.50	
Sum A = 707	N = 1464		$349.25 = \Sigma \frac{a^2_i}{n_i}$	$\frac{A^2}{N} = 341.43$
			341.43	
			7.82	

$$\chi^2 = \frac{7.82}{.2497} = 31.3$$

$$n = (3 - 1)(2 - 1) = 2$$

c. *Two classes for each variable.* From the data described in the preceding paragraph there might be made a test of the hypothesis that the per cent of persons undecided is the same among men as among women. The observed per cents holding "no opinion" are 25.88% for men and 38.97% for women. The frequency distribution presented as a *double dichotomy* is shown in Table 4.7. The two computing routines previously described are each applicable here and the student may gain practice by applying them. However the method about to be described will produce the same outcome with less computation.

TABLE 4.7 Frequency of Observed Response to the Question of Increasing Taxes to Support Current School Services, Classified by Indecision and Sex of Respondent.*

	Men	Women	Total
Holding definite opinion	524	462	986
Holding no opinion	183	295	478
TOTAL	707	757	1464

* Data taken from Rope, *Opinion Conflict and School Support.*

The four frequencies will be denoted a, b, c, and d, with marginal frequencies $a + b$, $c + d$, $a + c$, and $b + d$, $N = a + b + c + d$.

a	b	$a + b$
c	d	$c + d$
$a + c$	$b + d$	N

The number of degrees of freedom is $n = 1$.

The general formula for χ^2 reduces in this case to the special formula

$$\chi^2 = \frac{(ad - bc)^2 N}{(a + b)(c + d)(a + c)(b + d)} \tag{4.7}$$

Here $ad - bc = (524)(295) - (462)(183) = 70034$ and

$$\chi^2 = \frac{(70034)^2(1464)}{(986)(478)(707)(757)} = 28.5$$

whereas for 1 degree of freedom $\chi^2_{.999}$ is only 10.8.

The hypothesis of equal per cents of undecided persons in the two populations is untenable in face of such data.

Relation of χ^2 to the Statistic of Formula (3.12). The reader will recall that in Chapter 3, page 77, a problem very similar to the one of the preceding paragraph was solved by obtaining the difference between observed per cents in two independent samples, dividing that difference by its estimated standard deviation and referring the result to a table of the normal probability curve. It may now be stated that the two methods lead to the same result.

For a large sample if χ^2 has 1 degree of freedom, $\sqrt{\chi^2}$ has a distribution which is the right-hand half of a normal distribution. The general proof of the preceding statement involves calculus and so will not be presented here. However the algebraic equivalence of

$$\chi^2 = \frac{(ad - bc)^2 N}{(a + b)(a + c)(c + d)(b + d)} \quad \text{and} \quad z^2 = \frac{(p_1 - p_2)^2}{\dfrac{p(1 - p)(N_1 + N_2)}{N_1 N_2}}$$

is very easily established by sheer algebraic manipulation, using either the substitution

$$N_1 = a + c \qquad N_2 = b + d \qquad N = N_1 + N_2$$

$$p_1 = \frac{a}{N_1} \qquad p_2 = \frac{b}{N_2} \qquad p = \frac{a + b}{N}$$

or the substitution

$$N_1 = a + b \qquad N_2 = c + d \qquad N = N_1 + N_2$$

$$p_1 = \frac{a}{N_1} \qquad p_2 = \frac{c}{N_2} \qquad p = \frac{a + c}{N}$$

The equivalence of the two methods for the data of Table 4.7 may be seen by computation as follows:

Let $\quad p = \frac{986}{1464} = .6735 \quad \text{and} \quad q = 1 - p = \frac{478}{1464} = .3265$

$$\frac{p(1 - p)(N_1 + N_2)}{N_1 N_2} = \frac{(.3265)(.6735)(1464)}{(707)(757)} = .0006015$$

$$p_1 = \tfrac{524}{707} = .7412$$

$$p_2 = \tfrac{462}{757} = .6103$$

$$z^2 = \frac{(.2588 - .3897)^2}{.0006015} = \frac{.0171348}{.0006015} = 28.49$$

which agrees with the value previously given for χ^2.

Inasmuch as the normal distribution is tabulated for finer intervals of the argument than the chi-square distribution, it is a satisfactory procedure to compute χ^2 by Formula (4.7), to obtain z by taking the square root of χ^2, and to refer the result to a table of normal probability. If the logic of the problem seems to relate to the difference of two per cents, the outcome may be discussed as a test of the hypothesis $P_1 = P_2$. If the logic seems to relate to the independence of two variables the outcome may be discussed in those terms.

Comparison of Two Proportions Based on the Same Individuals. An interesting type of problem arises when the same individuals are measured on two different occasions and a comparison of the per cents registering a given characteristic on the two occasions is required.[4] Suppose, for example, that in an elementary school a test of racial prejudice is administered to 200 pupils of whom 78 return highly prejudiced answers. A movie designed to reduce prejudice is shown them a week or so later, and after another day the same test is readministered, this time with only 52 pupils showing highly prejudiced answers. None of the methods previously described in this chapter can be used, for in all of them the per cents to be compared were based on *different* individuals.

Let $\quad b + d$ = number of children showing prejudice on first test
$\qquad c + d$ = number of children showing prejudice on second test

Then $\quad b$ = number showing prejudice on first but not on second
and $\quad c$ = number showing prejudice on second but not on first

We are interested in the hypothesis that in the population the proportion showing prejudice only on the first test is equal to the proportion showing it only on the second. This hypothesis is tested by computing

$$\chi^2 = \frac{(b - c)^2}{b + c} \text{ with 1 degree of freedom} \tag{4.8}$$

It is therefore necessary to have not only the two figures $b + d = 78$ and $c + d = 52$ but also to have at least one of the four cell entries. Suppose we know that 30 pupils showed prejudice on both tests, so $d = 30$.

Then

$$b = 78 - 30 = 48$$
$$c = 52 - 30 = 22$$
$$\chi^2 = \frac{(48 - 22)^2}{48 + 22} = \frac{676}{70} = 9.66$$
$$z = \sqrt{\chi^2} = \sqrt{9.66} = 3.1$$

The reduction from $p_1 = \frac{78}{200} = .39$ to $p_2 = \frac{52}{200} = .26$ is highly significant and cannot be attributed to chance.

The Two-by-two Contingency Table in Very Small Samples. That a smooth curve does not provide a very close approximation to exact probabilities when samples are quite small has been noted in Chapter 3 and in the early part of this chapter. In Chapter 3 the normal curve was seen to provide a good approximation to the binomial for large values of N but not for small. In this chapter the smooth chi-square curve was seen to provide a good approximation to the exact χ^2 probabilities for large N and not for small. This situation raises the question as to how to deal with problems similar to those discussed in the preceding section when the samples are quite small. The question of what is meant by "quite small" will be disregarded for the moment but discussed later on.

In his study of *Adolescent Fantasy*,[10] Symonds asked adolescents to write a story about each of a set of pictures he presented to them. Each story was then read and categorized as using or not using a particular theme such as violence, sex, bad companions, illness, etc. One of the questions in which he was interested was the possible discovery of a sex difference with respect to the use of a particular theme. Each child was classified as using the theme if it occurred in at least two of his stories and as not using it if it occurred in one or none of his stories.

Symonds used the same number of boys and girls. In order that the student may see the method in a more general form without the special condition introduced by keeping the size of the two samples equal, the original data will be changed slightly. Suppose that 16 boys and 18 girls have been included in such an experiment, and that of the boys 7 have used the theme of violence while of the girls only 1 has used it. The corresponding observed proportions are $p_b = \frac{7}{16} = .4375$ and $p_g = \frac{1}{18} = .0556$. Is the difference between these proportions compatible with the hypothesis that in the population the proportions are equal, $P_b = P_g = P$?

It is convenient to present the observed results in the form of a contingency table, as follows:

	Boys	Girls	Total
Using the theme of violence	7	1	8
Not using the theme of violence	9	17	26
TOTAL	16	18	34

We shall now consider the hypothesis that sex is unrelated to the tendency to use a theme of violence and shall assume that all samples have the same marginal totals:

	Boys	Girls	
Using theme	a	b	8
Not using theme	c	d	26
	16	18	34

Under this restriction there are 9 sets of possible values which can be taken by the cell frequencies a, b, c and d, and these are listed as arrangements A to I in Table 4.8. The probability of any one arrangement is given by formula

$$\frac{(a+b)!(c+d)!(a+c)!(b+d)!}{N!a!b!c!d!} \tag{4.9}$$

The probability for each of the 9 possible arrangements has been worked out in Table 4.8.

The probability distribution of Table 4.8 might be represented graphically in the manner of Figures 3–1 and 3–2. Now suppose .05 has been selected as the level of significance and the critical

TABLE 4.8 All Possible Arrangements of Cell Frequencies in a Two-by-Two Table with Fixed Marginal Frequencies, and the Probability Associated with Each Arrangement.

Arrangement				*Probability*
A	$\begin{array}{r\|r} 8 & 0 \\ \hline 8 & 18 \end{array}$	$\frac{26!\,18!\,16!\,8!}{34!\,18!\;\;8!\,8!\,0!}$	$= \frac{715}{1008678} =$	.00071
B	$\begin{array}{r\|r} 7 & 1 \\ \hline 9 & 17 \end{array}$	$\frac{26!\,18!\,16!\,8!}{34!\,17!\;\;9!\,7!\,1!}$	$= \frac{11440}{1008678} =$	.01134
C	$\begin{array}{r\|r} 6 & 2 \\ \hline 10 & 16 \end{array}$	$\frac{26!\,18!\,16!\,8!}{34!\,16!\,10!\,6!\,2!}$	$= \frac{68068}{1008678} =$	.06748
D	$\begin{array}{r\|r} 5 & 3 \\ \hline 11 & 15 \end{array}$	$\frac{26!\,18!\,16!\,8!}{34!\,15!\,11!\,5!\,3!}$	$= \frac{198016}{1008678} =$	.19631
E	$\begin{array}{r\|r} 4 & 4 \\ \hline 12 & 14 \end{array}$	$\frac{26!\,18!\,16!\,8!}{34!\,14!\,12!\,4!\,4!}$	$= \frac{309400}{1008678} =$	.30674
F	$\begin{array}{r\|r} 3 & 5 \\ \hline 13 & 13 \end{array}$	$\frac{26!\,18!\,16!\,8!}{34!\,13!\,13!\,5!\,3!}$	$= \frac{266560}{1008678} =$	.26437
G	$\begin{array}{r\|r} 2 & 6 \\ \hline 14 & 12 \end{array}$	$\frac{26!\,18!\,16!\,8!}{34!\,14!\,12!\,6!\,2!}$	$= \frac{123760}{1008678} =$	.12270
H	$\begin{array}{r\|r} 1 & 7 \\ \hline 15 & 11 \end{array}$	$\frac{26!\,18!\,16!\,8!}{34!\,15!\,11!\,7!\,1!}$	$= \frac{28288}{1008678} =$	.02804
I	$\begin{array}{r\|r} 0 & 8 \\ \hline 16 & 10 \end{array}$	$\frac{26!\,18!\,16!\,8!}{34!\,16!\,10!\,8!\,0!}$	$= \frac{2431}{1008678} =$	.00241
	TOTAL		$= \frac{1008678}{1008678} =$	1.00000

region is to be so chosen that it will subtend .025 of the area in each tail. Then it is clear that arrangements *A* and *B* with probabilities .00071 + .01134 = .01205 fall in the critical region at one end of the distribution and that arrangement *I* falls into the critical region at the other. Any one of these three arrangements would be held incompatible with the hypothesis; none of the other six would be considered as throwing suspicion on that hypothesis. Since the observed data have shown arrangement *B*, the data present evidence of a sex difference with boys tending to use the theme of violence oftener than girls.

Because of the arithmetic involved the method just described can be recommended only for very small samples. Certain aids are available. A table of the logarithms of factorials is to be found in *Statistical Tables* [6] by Fisher and Yates.

In small samples the usual computation of χ^2 gives too large a value, leading to rejection of the hypothesis more often than would the direct computation of probability by factorials. This error can be offset by a procedure commonly known as *Yates' correction* [2, 3, 13]. The procedure is to change the frequency in each cell by .5, keeping the marginal totals unchanged, and *reducing* the size of χ^2. Thus observed frequencies $\frac{5 \mid 10}{7 \mid 2}$ with $\chi^2 = 4.4$ would be changed to $\frac{5.5 \mid 9.5}{6.5 \mid 2.5}$ with $\chi^2 = 2.8$. The same effect can be produced more easily without rewriting the frequencies by subtracting $\frac{1}{2}N$ from the absolute value of $ad - bc$. Thus in the illustration $N = 24$ and $ad - bc = 10 - 70 = -60$, and $|ad - bc| - \frac{1}{2}N = 60 - 12 = 48$. The vertical bars around a number indicates its numerical value without regard to sign.

If χ_y^2 represents a value of χ^2 adjusted by Yates' correction, then

$$\chi_y^2 = \frac{(|ad - bc| - N/2)^2 N}{(a + b)(a + c)(b + d)(c + d)} \qquad (4.10)$$

Verify that applying Formula (4.10) to the frequencies on the left gives the same result as applying the usual χ^2 formula to the adjusted frequencies on the right.

a. $\frac{10 \mid 4}{2 \mid 4}$ $\qquad$ $\frac{9.5 \mid 4.5}{2.5 \mid 3.5}$

b. $\frac{5 \mid 4}{15 \mid 2}$ $\qquad$ $\frac{5.5 \mid 3.5}{14.5 \mid 2.5}$

c. $\frac{20 \mid 6}{5 \mid 15}$ $\qquad$ $\frac{19.5 \mid 6.5}{5.5 \mid 14.5}$

When the expected frequency in every cell is large, application of Yates' correction will have a negligible effect on χ^2. The following working rule is suggested: (1) If the significance level obtained from χ^2 is larger than the predetermined significance level, the hypothesis may be retained. (2) If the significance level obtained from χ^2 is smaller than the predetermined significance level, the "corrected" χ_y^2 should be computed. If the probability obtained from it is also smaller than the significance level, the hypothesis may be rejected. (3) If decisions based on χ^2 and on "corrected" χ_y^2 are in disagreement, the exact probability should be calculated by the method described on page 103.

Use of the Chi-square Approximation when Expectations Are Small. Use of the table of areas under the chi-square curve as an approximation to the discrete chi-square distribution is justified mathematically when the number of cases in the sample is large.

The research worker, who needs some exact definition of the word "large" in this situation, can find no simple answer to his question [2, 3, 7, 13]. The discussion in this section is directed toward finding practical rules that are reasonable and clear.

The word "large" relates to the number of cases *expected* (not the number observed) in a cell. Theory requires that all expectations shall be "large." It is commonly stated that the chi-square curve provides an adequate approximation when the least expectation in any cell is five. This requirement seems excessively high.

Figure 4–3, which is based on samples of only 12 cases in three cells, the expected value per cell under the hypothesis tested being only 4, shows fairly close approximation of the values computed by the chi-square curve to the exact chi-square probabilities. Similar results were obtained by Neyman and Pearson [7] on the basis of ten cases in three cells. Cochran [4] discusses the situation when the expected number of cases is small for one of the cells and large for all the remaining cells and the number of degrees of freedom is two or more. In this situation the χ^2 table will provide a good fit even if the expectation in the one cell is as small as one.

The following practical rules of thumb are suggested for testing significance by use of the tables of areas under the chi-square curve.

1. If there is only 1 degree of freedom, follow the suggestion previously given for the use of Yates' correction.

2. If there are 2 or more degrees of freedom and the expectation in each cell is more than 5, the chi-square table assures a good approximation to the exact probabilities.

3. If there are 2 or more degrees of freedom and roughly approximate probabilities are acceptable for the test of significance, an expectation of only 2 in a cell is sufficient.

4. If there are more than 2 degrees of freedom and the expectation in all the cells but one is 5 or more, then an expectation of only one in the remaining cell is sufficient to provide a fair approximation to the exact probabilities.

5. If the logic of the problem permits, combine some of the classes to increase the expectations in the cells when several cells have very small expectations.

Summary. Three new ideas are presented in this chapter, (1) the idea of χ^2 as a measure of discrepancy between a set of observed frequencies and the corresponding frequencies expected under some hypothesis, (2) the idea of a contingency table, and (3) the idea of degrees of freedom. Several methods of computing the statistic χ^2 are presented and it is important to understand the circumstances under which each may be used. The principal skill developed is the ability to use a table of the χ^2 distribution.

REFERENCES

1. Bliss, C. I., "A Chart of the Chi-square Distribution," *Journal of the American Statistical Association*, 39 (June, 1944), 246–248.
2. Cochran, W. G., "The Chi-square Distribution for the Binomial and Poisson Series with Small Expectations," *Annals of Eugenics*, 7 (1936), 207–217.
3. Cochran, W. G., "The Chi-square Correction for Continuity," *Iowa State College Journal of Science*, 16 (1942), 421–436.
4. Cochran, W. G., "The Comparison of Percentages in Matched Samples," *Biometrika*, 37 (December, 1950), 256–266.
5. Eisenhart, C., Hastay, M. W., and Wallis, W. A., *Selected Techniques of Statistical Analysis*, New York, 1947, McGraw-Hill Book Co.
6. Fisher, R. A. and Yates, F., *Statistical Tables for Biological, Agricultural and Medical Research*, New York, 1948, Hafner Publishing Company, 3d ed.
7. Neyman, J. and Pearson, E. S., "Further Notes on the χ^2 Distribution," *Biometrika*, 22 (1931), 298–305.
8. Pearson, K., "On a Criterion that a Given System of Deviations from the Probable in the Case of a Correlated System of Variables is such that it Cannot be Reasonably Supposed to Have Arisen from Random Sampling," *Philosophical Magazine*, 5th series, 50 (1900), 339–357.
9. Rope, Frederick T., *Opinion Conflict and School Support*, New York, 1941, Teachers College, Columbia University, Bureau of Publications.
10. Symonds, P. M., *Adolescent Fantasy; an Investigation of the Picture-story Method of Personality Study*, New York, 1949, Columbia University Press.
11. Walker, H. M., "Degrees of Freedom," *Journal of Educational Psychology*, 31 (1940), 253–269.
12. Walker, H. M., *Mathematics Essential for Elementary Statistics*, New York, 1951, Henry Holt and Company, Chapter 22, Degrees of Freedom. Equations with Several Variables.
13. Yates, F., "Contingency Tables Involving Small Numbers and the χ^2 Test," *Supplement to the Journal of the Royal Statistical Society*, 1 (1934), 217–235.

5 Populations and Samples on a Continuous Variable

The methods considered in the first four chapters are suitable for obtaining inferences from data classified in discrete classes. In dealing with data arising from measurement of a continuous variable these methods are insufficient, although the logic used is in its general outlines the same as that already described. This chapter will present some general concepts regarding distributions on a continuous variable. It will present symbolism, formulas for obtaining the mean and standard deviation of a sample, and methods for testing the hypothesis that a population distribution is normal. A student who has had an introductory course should be able to read pages 111 to 117 very rapidly; others will need practice with symbolism and computation.

Mathematical Model of the Population. The first populations considered in this book were dichotomies. For these the mathematical model consisted of a definition of the two discrete classes and a statement that the proportion of cases in one class was P and in the other Q. Later P and Q were called the probabilities of these classes and the population distribution thus specified was recognized as a probability distribution. Subsequently we considered populations having more than two discrete classes, the mathematical model for such being a definition of the classes and a statement of the probability of each class. For populations on a continuous variable, probabilities are defined by areas under a curve. There are many forms of probability curves of which the most widely known is the normal curve. Practice in computing probabilities as segments of area between two ordinates of the normal curve has already been given in Chapter 2.

The Mean and Variance of a Population. A population may be considered to have a variety of characteristics, among which are the mean and the standard deviation. If X represents the variable, these have already been defined as

$$\mu = E(X) \quad \text{and} \quad \sigma = \sqrt{E(X - \mu)^2}$$

If the probability distribution of the population is known exactly, μ and σ can be calculated by means of the integral calculus, the procedure being analogous to that used in Formulas (2.4) and (2.8) on pages 28 and 29 for discrete distributions. If the probability distribution is not known exactly but some information about its nature is available, the mean and variance or standard deviation can be *estimated* from a sample. Thus for probability distributions known to have the binomial form, the estimation of the mean was discussed in Chapter 3. Methods of estimating characteristics of continuous populations will be discussed in later sections.

Normal Populations. The normal distribution was described in Chapter 2 as an approximation to the binomial distribution, and was used in Chapter 3 to compute probabilities of samples. An important use of the normal distribution is to provide a mathematical description for populations. A population so described is called a *normal population.* Most of the methods discussed in the following chapters, with the exception of those in Chapter 18, are based on the assumption that observations are drawn from a normal population. Some aspects of the normal distribution not previously considered will now be described.*

The normal probability curve is a smooth distribution with unlimited range in each direction and with probability density given by the equation

$$y = \frac{1}{\sigma\sqrt{2\pi}} e^{-\frac{(X-\mu)^2}{2\sigma^2}} \tag{5.1}$$

y is the ordinate of the curve, called the *probability density.*

X is the variable for which (5.1) furnishes the probability distribution, and is distributed along the horizontal axis in all the graphs of the normal curve presented in this text.

π is the familiar number with approximate value 3.1416.

e is a number with approximate value 2.718.

$\mu = E(X)$ is the expected value of X. Being the mean of the normal distribution, it determines the location of the distribution along the scale of X. It may be positive, negative or zero. The mean, median and mode of the normal curve are identical in value.

* Readers who are not mathematicians and who desire further discussion of the equation of the normal curve than is given here may consult pages 245–248 of Walker, *Mathematics Essential for Elementary Statistics.*

$\sigma^2 = E(X - \mu)^2$ and may have any positive value. The standard deviation σ of X is the unit of measure for the horizontal axis. The area under the curve of Formula (5.1) is unity.

The ordinate y depends not only on the particular value of X which defines the point where the ordinate is erected but also depends on the values of μ and σ. When μ and σ are given particular values, an ordinate y can be calculated for each X and a curve represented by these ordinates can be drawn. For another pair of values of μ and σ another curve is obtained. Thus Formula (5.1) represents a *family of curves*. Variables like μ and σ, specific values of which determine a particular member of a family of curves, are called *parameters*.

The symbols e and π represent numbers which always have the same value. The symbols μ and σ represent numbers which are constant for any one curve but vary from one curve to another. The symbols y and X represent variables which fluctuate even for one particular curve.

In Figure 5–1 are three normal curves corresponding to three pairs of values of μ and σ, drawn on the same scale of values of X.

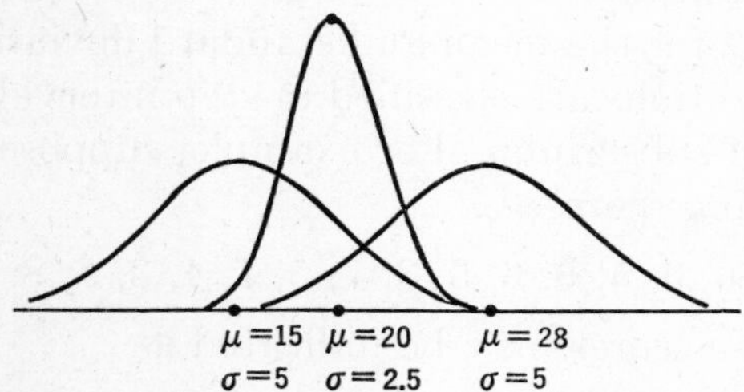

FIG. 5–1. Three normal curves with same area but different values of μ and σ.

Strictly speaking a sample cannot have a normal distribution. As soon as actual values are observed, those values have some finite range instead of the unlimited range of the normal curve; the values if plotted take the form of a histogram instead of a smooth curve; and sampling irregularities distort the form of the curve slightly. Therefore the normal curve is best considered as a probability distribution describing either a population distribution or the sampling distribution of a statistic but not describing an observed distribution of a sample.

Use of Summation Sign. One of the most widely used symbols in statistical literature is the large Greek letter sigma, Σ, corresponding to a capital S. It is called the *summation sign*. Before giving the formulas for the mean and the standard deviation of a sample, the use of the summation sign may well be reviewed.

If X_1 represents the score of the first individual, X_i the score of the ith, and N the entire number of individuals in a sample,

$$X_1 + X_2 + \cdots + X_i + \cdots + X_N = \sum_{i=1}^{N} X_i$$

$\sum_{i=1}^{N} X_i$ may be read "the sum of the scores of individuals 1 to N," or "the sum of values X_i where i ranges from 1 to N" or "summation X extending from X_1 to X_N."

The purpose of the variable subscript and the limits of summation is *clarity*. They may be omitted if they are not needed to prevent confusion. In elementary work summation is almost always over the N individuals in a sample and therefore because the limits of summation are assumed to be from 1 to N they are usually not written. In later sections of this book beginning with Chapter 9 observations may be classified on several traits simultaneously and formulas may be ambiguous unless the limits of summation are indicated.

The formulas for the mean and standard deviation of a sample when the observations are classified in step intervals may be clarified by means of subscripts. For example, suppose 20 individuals have the following scores:

2, 4, 9, 6, 3, 5, 6, 6, 3, 3, 7, 5, 7, 4, 3, 8, 8, 6, 5, 4

The sum of these scores may be indicated as

$$\sum_{i=1}^{20} X_i = 104$$

or as

$$\sum_{j=1}^{8} f_j X_j = 1(9) + 2(8) + 2(7) + 4(6) + 3(5) + 3(4) + 4(3) + 1(2) = 104$$

When the mean of these 20 scores is computed in the customary manner for grouped data, each class index X_j is multiplied by the frequency in the class f_j and the results are summed, $\Sigma f_j X_j$. But here the variable subscript j does not run from 1 to N but takes only as many values as there are class intervals, which in this example is 8. Therefore we write either

$$\sum_{i=1}^{20} X_i = 104 \quad \text{or} \quad \sum_{j=1}^{8} f_j X_j = 104$$

Note carefully the effect of parentheses in the following:

$$\sum_{i=}^{5}(X_i + a) = (X_3 + a) + (X_4 + a) + (X_5 + a)$$
$$= X_3 + X_4 + X_5 + 3a$$
$$\sum_{i=3}^{5} X_i + a = X_3 + X_4 + X_5 + a$$
$$\sum_{i=3}^{5}(X_i + Y_i) = (X_3 + Y_3) + (X_4 + Y_4) + (X_5 + Y_5)$$
$$= (X_3 + X_4 + X_5) + (Y_3 + Y_4 + Y_5) = \sum_{i=3}^{5} X_i + \sum_{i=3}^{5} Y_i$$

EXERCISE 5.1

1. Study the summations represented by the following symbols and their equivalents:

$$\sum_{i=3}^{6} X_i = X_3 + X_4 + X_5 + X_6$$
$$\sum_{i=10}^{12} ax_i = ax_{10} + ax_{11} + ax_{12} = a(x_{10} + x_{11} + x_{12})$$
$$\sum_{i=6}^{10}(X_i - 5) = (X_6 - 5) + (X_7 - 5) + (X_8 - 5) + (X_9 - 5) + (X_{10} - 5)$$
$$= X_6 + X_7 + X_8 + X_9 + X_{10} - 25$$
$$\sum_{i=6}^{8} 3y_i^2 = 3y_6^2 + 3y_7^2 + 3y_8^2 = 3(y_6^2 + y_7^2 + y_8^2)$$
$$\sum_{i=5}^{8} 2(Z_i - b) = 2(Z_5 - b) + 2(Z_6 - b) + 2(Z_7 - b) + 2(Z_8 - b)$$
$$= 2(Z_5 + Z_6 + Z_7 + Z_8) - 8b$$
$$\sum_{i=7}^{9} x_i y_i = x_7 y_7 + x_8 y_8 + x_9 y_9$$
$$\sum_{j=1}^{4} f_j X_j = f_1 X_1 + f_2 X_2 + f_3 X_3 + f_4 X_4$$

2. Write an equivalent expression for each of the following, making use of the summation sign:

a. $X_6 + X_7 + X_8 + X_9$
b. $4x_5 + 4x_6 + 4x_7 + 4x_8$
c. $3x_6y_6 + 3x_7y_7 + 3x_8y_8$
d. $(Y_5 - A) + (Y_6 - A) + (Y_7 - A) + (Y_8 - A)$
e. $f_1X_1 + f_2X_2 + f_3X_3 + f_4X_4 + f_5X_5 + f_6X_6$

3. Assume the following individual scores:

Individual	1	2	3	4	5	6	7	8	9	10	11	12
Score = X	5	3	6	6	5	4	5	4	7	3	8	4

Find the numerical value of the following expressions:

a. $\sum_{i=1}^{12} X_i$ e. $\sum_{i=1}^{4} (X_i - 2)$ i. $\frac{\left(\sum_{i=1}^{5} X_i\right)^2}{5}$

b. $\overline{X} = \frac{1}{12} \sum_{i=1}^{12} X_i$ f. $\sum_{i=1}^{4} (X_i - 2)^2$ j. $\sum_{i=1}^{12} X_i^2 - \frac{\left(\sum_{i=1}^{12} X_i\right)^2}{12}$

c. $\sum_{i=1}^{12} (X_i - \overline{X})$ g. $\left(\sum_{i=5}^{9} X_i\right)^2$

d. $\sum_{i=1}^{12} (X_i - \overline{X})^2$ h. $\frac{1}{12}\left(\sum_{i=1}^{12} X_i\right)$

4. Assume that each of $N = 10$ individuals has been measured on variable X and also on variable Y with results as follows:

Individual	1	2	3	4	5	6	7	8	9	10
Score on X	7	9	4	3	6	10	7	8	2	4
Score on Y	2	1	0	1	3	4	5	0	3	1

Find the numerical value of the following expressions:

a. $\overline{Y} = \frac{1}{N} \sum_{i=1}^{N} Y_i$ d. $\sum_{i=1}^{N} X_i Y_i$ g. $\sum_{i=1}^{N} X_i^2 - \frac{(\Sigma X_i)^2}{N}$

b. $\overline{X} = \frac{1}{N} \sum_{i=1}^{N} X_i$ e. $\sum_{i=1}^{N} (X_i - \overline{X})(Y_i - \overline{Y})$ h. $\sum_{i=1}^{N} Y_i^2 - \frac{(\Sigma Y_i)^2}{N}$

c. $\sum_{i=1}^{N} X_i^2$ f. $\sum_{i=1}^{N} (X_i - \overline{X})^2$ i. $\sum_{i=1}^{N} (Y_i - \overline{Y})^2$

Definition of Mean, Variance, and Standard Deviation for a Sample. In any sample there is likely to be duplication of scores. Even when no two observations are precisely equal, it is usually convenient to group observations into intervals at least some of which have frequencies larger than 1. Both of these situations will be referred to as situations in which data are *grouped*. When working at a computing machine it is often convenient to take scores one at a time as they come, without grouping them. Such situations will be referred to as computation *without grouping*.

Definitional formulas for the mean and variance will now be given for both grouped and ungrouped data. Computational formulas will be given in the following section. The standard deviation is defined as the square root of the variance and does not require a separate formula.

(5.2) Mean, without grouping $\overline{X} = \frac{\sum_{i=1}^{N} X_i}{N} = \frac{\Sigma X}{N}$

(5.3) Mean, with grouping $$\overline{X} = \frac{\sum_{j=1}^{k} f_j X_j}{\sum_{j=1}^{k} f_j} = \frac{\Sigma f X}{N}$$

In Formula (5.3) each of the k different values of X_j may be thought of as defining a class. Then f_j/N is the proportional frequency in that class and may be denoted p_j for the sample or P_j for the population. Then

(5.4) $$\overline{X} = \sum_{j=1}^{k} p_j X_j$$

(5.5) Let $$x_i = X_i - \overline{X} \quad \text{or} \quad x_j = X_j - \overline{X}$$

Then the variance without grouping is

(5.6) $$s^2 = \frac{\sum_{i=1}^{N} (X_i - \overline{X})^2}{N - 1} = \frac{\Sigma x^2}{N - 1}$$

and the variance with grouping is

(5.7) $$s^2 = \frac{\sum_{j=1}^{k} f_j (X_j - \overline{X})^2}{\sum_{j=1}^{k} f_j - 1} = \frac{\Sigma f x^2}{N - 1}$$

Some readers will be accustomed to using N rather than $N - 1$ in the denominator of variance and standard deviation. The reason for using $N - 1$ is that it leads to a more satisfactory estimate of the population variance as will be explained in later sections of this chapter. $N - 1$ is the number of degrees of freedom associated with the variance.

Formulas for the Computation of the Mean, Variance, and Standard Deviation for a Sample. In computation it would usually be an uneconomical procedure to subtract the mean from each individual score. Instead deviations are taken from some arbitrarily chosen value as origin and the computation is completed by a formula which is algebraically equivalent to the definition formula.

Taking the origin at zero is particularly convenient when computation is made by machine. Deviations from zero are called "gross scores" or "raw scores." The variance of ungrouped scores with origin at zero may be computed from Formula (5.8)

(5.8) $$s^2 = \frac{\sum_{i=1}^{N} X_i^2 - \left(\sum_{i=1}^{N} X_i\right)^2 / N}{N - 1} = \frac{\Sigma X^2 - (\Sigma X)^2/N}{N - 1}$$

or by the equivalent Formula (5.8a) which has the advantage that no rounding errors occur until the final division by $N(N - 1)$.

(5.8a) $$s^2 = \frac{N \sum_{i=1}^{N} X_i^2 - \left(\sum_{i=1}^{N} X_i\right)^2}{N(N - 1)} = \frac{N\Sigma X^2 - (\Sigma X)^2}{N(N - 1)}$$

For grouped scores with origin at zero the equivalent formulas are:

(5.9) $$s^2 = \frac{\sum_{j=1}^{k} f_j X_j^2 - \left(\sum_{j=1}^{k} f_j X_j\right)^2 / N}{N - 1} = \frac{\Sigma f X^2 - (\Sigma f X)^2/N}{N - 1}$$

(5.9a) $$s^2 = \frac{N \sum_{j=1}^{k} f_j X_j^2 - \left(\sum_{j=1}^{k} f_j X_j\right)^2}{N(N - 1)} = \frac{N\Sigma f X^2 - (\Sigma f X)^2}{N(N - 1)}$$

Taking deviations from an arbitrary origin near the middle of the distribution reduces the size of the numbers involved in the computations, and is therefore an advantage when the work is to be done with pencil and paper. Grouping scores into intervals and coding the intervals further reduces the size of the numbers involved. The width of the interval is often called i and will be so denoted here. It will require a little attention on the part of the student to distinguish the variable subscript i from the letter i which indicates the width of the step interval. As has been noted before, there are not enough letters in the alphabet to provide a unique letter for every use and it is often necessary to use the same letter in more than one meaning. If any confusion arises it will quickly subside.

(5.10) Let $$ix_j' = X_j - A$$

where i is the width of the interval and A is an arbitrary origin.

When deviations are taken from an arbitrary origin A the mean is computed by formula

(5.11) $$\overline{X} = A + i \frac{\left(\sum_{j=1}^{k} f_j x_j'\right)}{N} = A + i\left(\frac{\Sigma f x'}{N}\right)$$

and the variance by

$$(5.12)\quad s^2 = i^2 \frac{N\sum_{j=1}^{k} f_j(x_j')^2 - \left(\sum_{j=1}^{k} f_j x_j'\right)^2}{N(N-1)} = i^2 \frac{N\Sigma f(x')^2 - (\Sigma f x')^2}{N(N-1)}$$

In computing the standard deviation it is obviously simpler to multiply by i *after* taking the square root unless the variance also is needed.

The computation of the mean and variance from grouped data is shown in Table 5.1.

TABLE 5.1 Computation of Mean and Standard Deviation from Grouped Data.

Interval	X_j	f_j	x_j'	$f_j x_j'$	$f_j(x_j')^2$
1	2	3	4	5	6
78–82	80	3	4	12	48
73–77	75	6	3	18	54
68–72	70	7	2	14	28
63–67	65	12	1	12	12
58–62	60	15	0	0	0
53–57	55	13	− 1	− 13	13
48–52	50	9	− 2	− 18	36
43–47	45	7	− 3	− 21	63
38–42	40	4	− 4	− 16	64
33–37	35	2	− 5	− 10	50
28–32	30	1	− 6	− 6	36
TOTAL		79		56	404
				− 84	
				− 28	

$$\overline{X} = 60 + \frac{5(-28)}{79} = 60 - 1.77 = 58.23$$

$$s = 5\sqrt{\frac{79(404) - 28^2}{79(78)}} = 5\sqrt{\frac{31132}{6162}} = 5\sqrt{5.0523} = 11.25$$

$$s^2 = 25(5.0523) = 126.3$$

EXERCISE 5.2

1. Compute the mean and variance of the following scores, taking an arbitrary origin at $A = 40$. Scores: 42, 37, 49, 45, 42

Solution

X	$X - 40$	$(X - 40)^2$
42	2	4
37	− 3	9
49	9	81
45	5	25
42	2	4
SUM	15	123

$$\overline{X} = 40 + \tfrac{15}{5} = 43$$

$$s^2 = \frac{5(123) - (15)^2}{5(4)} = \frac{390}{20} = 19.5$$

2. Compute the mean and standard deviation of the following scores without grouping, taking an arbitrary origin at $A = 80$.
Scores: 74, 79, 87, 91, 76, 79, 85, 81, 80.

3. Compute the mean and variance for each of these sets of numbers

a. 15, 10, 19, 6, 5

b. 2, 4, −3, −7, 6, 7

c. 0, 3, 2, 0, 5, 7, 1

4. For the data of the worked example on page 117 compute the mean and standard deviation making use of a different arbitrary origin.

Sampling Distributions. The sampling distributions of the mean $\overline{X}$, of the variance s^2, of the standard deviation s, and of other statistics will be needed in this and later chapters for the purpose of making inferences about populations. Because a large number of new statistics will be used, certain concepts regarding sampling distributions already introduced in Chapter 3 will be described in the following sections.

The population from which a sample is drawn is often called the *parent population.* Theoretically if the parent population has been described mathematically by some hypothesis the exact sampling distribution of any statistic can be derived by mathematical methods. Actually the derivation of sampling distributions often presents considerable mathematical difficulty, so that the exact sampling distribution of a particular statistic may not be available for practical use even though the population distribution can be mathematically described.

When the exact sampling distribution is not known, or is too complex for practical use, an *approximate distribution* may be available. Examples of such approximation have already been met when the normal curve was used as an approximation for the binomial, and the smooth χ^2 curve was used to approximate the discontinuous exact χ^2 distribution. Such approximations will also be found useful for large samples from populations on a continuous variate.

The standard deviation of the sampling distribution of a statistic is commonly called the *standard error* of the statistic. Thus σ_p is the standard error of a proportion and $\sigma_{\overline{X}}$ the standard error of a mean. In Chapter 2 the mean and standard error of a proportion were given as

$$\mu_p = E(p) = P \text{ and } \sigma_p = \sqrt{E(p - P)^2} = \sqrt{\frac{PQ}{N}}$$

In Chapter 6 the mean and standard error of a mean will be given as

$$\mu_{\overline{X}} = E(\overline{X}) = \mu \quad \text{and} \quad \sigma_{\overline{X}} = \sqrt{E(\overline{X} - \mu)^2} = \frac{\sigma}{\sqrt{N}}$$

These cases illustrate the important generalization that *the mean and standard error of a statistic can be calculated directly from characteristics of the population and may be known even though the exact sampling distribution of the statistic is not known.* Early work in statistical theory placed great emphasis on the discovery of means and standard errors of statistics, and some textbooks still state formulas for standard errors without giving any information about the sampling distribution. Usually in such cases it is tacitly assumed that the sampling distribution is normal. Any text which gives the formula for σ_r or σ_{s^2} without any statement about the non-normality of the sampling distributions involved is living in the past. One distinctive aspect of modern statistical theory is its persistent search for the exact sampling distributions of statistics and satisfactory approximations to these distributions.

Unbiased Estimate of a Parameter. Suppose that it is desired to estimate some population parameter by means of a sample statistic. If the parameter is the expectation of the statistic, then the statistic is an *unbiased estimate* of the parameter. Thus p is an unbiased estimate of P and $\overline{X}$ an unbiased estimate of μ.

It is now possible to explain why $N - 1$ is used instead of N in the definition of the sample variance, s^2. It can be demonstrated mathematically that $\dfrac{\Sigma(X - \overline{X})^2}{N - 1}$ is an unbiased estimate of σ^2, or in symbols

(5.13) $$E\left(\frac{\Sigma(X - \overline{X})^2}{N - 1}\right) = \sigma^2$$

(5.14) while $$E\left(\frac{\Sigma(X - \overline{X})^2}{N}\right) = \frac{N - 1}{N}\sigma^2$$

Therefore Formula (5.14) gives a biased estimate of σ^2.

Test of Normality Applied to a Distribution of Sample Variances. The data for this computation were obtained by students in a class in statistics studying sampling. Each student made 16 throws of ten pennies thus obtaining samples for which $N = 16$, and computed the variance of each sample. The distribution of the variances from 256 such samples is shown graphically in Figure 5–2, with a superimposed normal curve having the same mean and standard deviation. The histogram appears a little more peaked than the normal curve. A test of normality employing χ^2 will now be applied to these data.

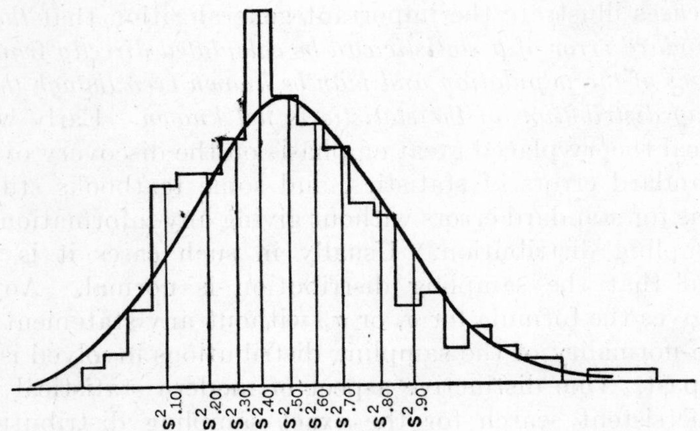

FIG. 5–2. Frequency distribution of 256 sample variances, with normal curve superimposed.

TABLE 5.2 Distribution of 256 Sample Variances

Variance	f	Variance	f	Variance	f
5.3–5.4	1	3.7–3.8	3	2.1–2.2	33
5.1–5.2	1	3.5–3.6	8	1.9–2.0	22
4.9–5.0	1	3.3–3.4	7	1.7–1.8	19
4.7–4.8	..	3.1–3.2	15	1.5–1.6	19
4.5–4.6	2	2.9–3.0	16	1.3–1.4	18
4.3–4.4	2	2.7–2.8	21	1.1–1.2	7
4.1–4.2	3	2.5–2.6	23	.9–1.0	3
3.9–4.0	5	2.3–2.4	25	.7– .8	2

1. The first step is to obtain the values of the 10th, 20th, 30th . . . 90th percentiles of a normal curve having

$$\mu = \overline{X} = 2.388 \quad \text{and} \quad \sigma = s = .816.$$

The values of $\dfrac{\overline{X} - \mu}{\sigma}$ corresponding to these points are read from a normal probability table and recorded in column 2 of Table 5.3. Each entry in that column is multiplied by $\sigma = .816$ to obtain the entries in column 3. To these are then added $\mu = 2.388$ to obtain the entries in column 4, which are the abscissa values of the percentiles $s^2_{.10}$, $s^2_{.20}$, etc., on the baseline in Figure 5–2.

TABLE 5.3 Computation of χ^2 Test for Normality of Distribution of 256 Sample Variances

Percentile point	$\frac{X-\mu}{\sigma}$	$X-\mu$	X	Frequency below X	Frequency in interval f_i	f_i^2
1	2	3	4	5	6	7
90	1.282	1.046	3.434	$223 + \frac{.184}{.200}(7) = 229.4$	26.6	707.56
80	.842	.687	3.075	$208 + \frac{.025}{.200}(15) = 209.9$	19.5	380.25
70	.524	.428	2.816	$171 + \frac{.165}{.200}(21) = 188.3$	21.6	466.56
60	.253	.206	2.594	$148 + \frac{.144}{.200}(23) = 164.6$	23.7	561.69
50	0	0	2.388	$123 + \frac{.038}{.200}(25) = 127.8$	36.8	1354.24
40	− .253	− .206	2.182	$90 + \frac{.132}{.200}(33) = 111.8$	16.0	256.00
30	− .524	− .428	1.960	$68 + \frac{.110}{.200}(22) = 80.1$	31.7	1004.89
20	− .842	− .687	1.701	$49 + \frac{.051}{.200}(19) = 53.8$	26.3	691.69
10	− 1.282	− 1.046	1.342	$12 + \frac{.092}{.200}(18) = 20.3$	33.5	1122.25
					20.3	412.09
					256.0	6957.22

$$\chi^2 = \frac{\Sigma f_i^2}{F_i} - N = \frac{6957.22}{25.6} - 256 = 15.8 \qquad n = 7$$

$$\chi^2_{.95} = 14.1 \qquad \chi^2_{.975} = 16.0$$

2. The second step is to compute the frequency in the histogram between each two of the successive points listed in Column 4. For this, the frequency is cumulated beginning at the lower end of the scale of scores, as in the computation of percentiles and of percentile ranks. The frequency *below* each point is then obtained as in column 5 of Table 5.3.

It may be helpful to explain in detail the computation of one of the entries in Column 5, say the first one. The frequency below the point $X = 3.434$ is desired. From Table 5.2 it is evident that the point $X = 3.434$ lies in the interval marked 3.3–3.4, that there are 7 cases in this interval and 223 cases below it. There-

fore below the point $X = 3.434$ there will be all of the 223 cases plus part of the 7 cases. What part of the 7 cases? The interval has as its *real limits* the values 3.25 and 3.45, so $X = 3.434$ stands nearly at the top of the interval. The proportion of the interval below this point is

$$\frac{3.434 - 3.25}{3.45 - 3.25} = \frac{.184}{.200}$$

and therefore the number of cases in the interval below $X = 3.434$ is $\frac{.184}{.200}(7) = 6.44$ and the entire number of cases below $X = 3.434$ is $223 + 6.4 = 229.4$.

The first entry in Column 6 is $256 - 229.4 = 26.6$ or the number of cases above $X = 3.434$. The second is $229.4 - 209.9 = 19.5$, or the number of cases between $X = 3.434$ and $X = 3.075$. All subsequent entries in this column are found in the same way. The last entry is $20.3 - 0$ or the number of cases below $X = 1.342$. The entries in Column 6 are treated as observed frequencies in the χ^2 formula.

3. Since each $F_i = N/10 = 25.6$, the remainder of the computation is very simple.

$$\chi^2 = \Sigma \frac{f_i^2}{F_i} - N = \frac{1}{25.6} \Sigma f_i^2 - 256 = \frac{6957.22}{25.6} - 256 = 15.8$$

There are 10 observations (10 values of f_i) and 3 restrictions upon them, namely

(1) $\Sigma f_i = \Sigma F_i$ — The number of cases in the fitted normal curve is assumed to be 256, which was the observed N.

(2) $\Sigma f_i X_i = \Sigma F_i X_i$ — This condition was imposed when the theoretical distribution was given the same mean as the observed distribution. The X's are arbitrary, the restriction being upon the frequencies.

(3) $\Sigma f_i(X_i - \overline{X})^2 = \Sigma F_i(X_i - \overline{X})^2$ — This condition was imposed when the theoretical distribution was given the same variance as the observed distribution.

The number of degrees of freedom is therefore $n = 10 - 3 = 7$. For 7 degrees of freedom, $\chi^2_{.95} = 14.1$ and $\chi^2_{.98} = 16.6$. This test justifies discarding the hypothesis of normality.

In this problem, μ and σ could have been obtained from the mathematical characteristics of the sampling distribution of s^2. However, in most similar situations where a χ^2 test is employed there are no *a priori* values for μ and σ and these must be estimated from $\overline{X}$ and s. The latter method has been used here to illustrate what is the usual procedure.

REVIEW EXERCISE

1. Some of the following terms have been used in earlier chapters, and all of them are important for understanding this chapter.

degrees of freedom	parent population
family of curves	sampling distribution of a statistic
limits of summation	standard error
normal population	statistic
normal probability curve	unbiased estimate
parameter	variable subscript

2. Review the meaning of these symbols, and decide which of them represent

(a) a number which always has the same value
(b) a number which has the same value for any given population but which may have different values for different populations
(c) a number which changes its value from sample to sample
(d) a symbol which indicates an operation to be performed

$\overline{X}$, μ, π, s, σ, χ^2, Σ, e, $\overline{X} - \mu$, σ_p, and $\mu_{\overline{X}}$.

6 Sampling Distributions

Purposes of the Chapter.* The principal goal of this chapter is to give the student a sense of familiarity with the different sampling distributions which are most often called for in research studies, to acquaint him with the general shape of these distributions and with the more common situations to which they apply. To this end empirical distributions will be obtained by drawing many small samples, computing statistics from these samples, and plotting the frequency distributions of the various statistics. On the empirical distribution of each statistic there will be superimposed a mathematical curve obtained from the formula for the sampling distribution of that statistic.

The chapter has been designed to accomplish certain secondary goals also. It provides experience in the use of a table of random numbers. It provides a review of the principal computations of elementary statistics, that review occurring incidentally in the course of obtaining the empirical data needed rather than occurring for its own sake. It provides an introduction to the material treated more fully in Chapters 7 to 9.

Here too the student may observe an instance of that amazing parallelism so often noted between certain aspects of the world of phenomena and the world of abstract mathematical theory. One performs certain physical operations, draws a large number of samples, measures the individuals in those samples, makes certain computations upon those measurements, draws a graph of the resulting statistics and lo, the form of the graph is similar to that of a curve determined by purely mathematical reasoning and having no implicit connection with the concrete data. Furthermore, the shape of the graph obtained through this extensive manipulation of concrete measures is independent of the nature of the trait measured. That shape is the same whether measurements are made of human beings, manufactured products or shell

* This chapter will be most helpful if you read it rapidly the first time without pressing too hard for complete understanding, and if you return to it often as you study the next three chapters. It would be wise to reread it completely after you have studied Chapter 9.

fish, whether the measures belong in the domain of physics, psychology, business, or public opinion. The shape of the graph depends only on certain characteristics of the population distribution, the size of the samples drawn, and the choice of the statistic computed.

The student who has completed the calculation of a statistic usually wishes to use that statistic as basis for assertions about an unknown value of a parameter in the population. Of necessity he must check the statistic against a table derived from the mathematically calculated sampling distribution of the statistic. The observed parallelism between the empirical and the mathematical distributions should convince the student that the mathematical tables are a reflection of experiential reality. Then if the mathematical distribution indicates that the research worker should accept a hypothesis because his sample may have originated from the hypothetical population by chance, repeated sampling, which usually he would be unable to carry out, would have given him the same information.

The student who goes carefully through the material of this chapter should never afterward fall prey to the popular fallacy that all sampling distributions are normal and he should know that the beneficent parallelism referred to in the preceding paragraph is not discovered automatically but must be striven for by learning which probability distribution belongs to any particular statistic.

The Data. In Table XXIV of the Appendix is a set of preregistration scores on the Cooperative Test Service English Test made by 447 college students. The distribution of scores has been tested for normality as described in Chapter 5 and the departure from normality has been found negligible.

Because of the close approximation of its distribution to the normal, the set of 447 scores will play the part of a normal population in the remainder of this chapter. Random samples drawn from this set of scores will be considered as random samples from a normal population and will illustrate sampling from a true normal population.

The mean, variance and standard deviation of the scores are

$$\mu = 121.6; \quad \sigma^2 = 1380.4; \quad \sigma = 37.15$$

In Table XXIV the entries in the first column are serial numbers identifying the subjects. Each serial number has 3 digits if zeros are inserted for missing digits in the tens or hundreds place, so that 9 is written 009 and 21 is written 021.

These scores in Table XXIV are now to be considered as defining a population from which random samples are to be drawn by means of a table of random numbers. If the same number should be drawn more than once, the individual represented by that serial number should be included as often as his number is drawn. This procedure is called *sampling with replacement* and has the effect of transforming the finite population of 447 cases into an infinite population with the same percentage distribution.

Use of Table of Random Sampling Numbers. Several lists of random numbers are available.* Appendix Table XXIII is a part of the Table of 105,000 Random Decimal Digits published by the Interstate Commerce Commission.

Suppose, for example, that it is desired to choose 6 cases at random out of a set of 50 cases. As 50 has 2 digits, we shall read 2-digit numbers from the table disregarding all those larger than 50. The first 6 numbers read will identify the 6 individuals selected. We should decide, preferably in a random manner, where to enter the table before we look at it, lest after we see the page we may be influenced by a possible desire to include or to exclude a particular individual.

If we should decide to begin with block 1 and line 1, using the first 2 digits, and to move downward across the table, the 6 individuals chosen would be those having code numbers 10, 22, 24, 42, 37, and 28. Note that 4 numbers have been passed over because they are larger than 50. If we should decide to begin in block 9 and row 50, using the first 2 digits and moving upward

* Tippet, L. H. C., *Random Sampling Numbers* with foreword by Karl Pearson, Cambridge University Press, 1927.

Fisher, R. A. and Yates, F., Table XXXIII in *Statistical Tables for Biological, Agricultural and Medical Research*, Oliver and Boyd, London, 1938.

Interstate Commerce Commission, Bureau of Transport, Economics and Statistics, *Table of 105,000 Random Decimal Digits*, Statement No. 4914, File No. 261–A–1, Washington, D.C., May 1949, 29 pp.

Kendall, M. G. and Smith, Babington B., *Tables of Random Sampling Numbers*, Tracts for Computers, No. 24, Cambridge University Press.

Snedecor, George W., *Statistical Methods*, Ames, Iowa, Iowa State College Press, 1946, pp. 10–13.

The general criteria that a set of such numbers must meet in order to be useful in sampling have been stated by Kendall and Smith in "Randomness and Random Sampling Numbers," *Journal of the Royal Statistical Society*, 101 (1938), pp. 147–166.

across the table, the individuals chosen would be those with code numbers 27, 2, 39, 32, 4, and 44.

It is permissible to begin at any point in the table, and to move in any direction which is convenient. The variety of ways of selecting digits from this table is enormous. Obviously a simple method by which numbers can be easily identified is preferable to a complicated method.

A Class Project in Drawing Samples, Computing Certain Statistics and Obtaining the Random Sampling Distributions of those Statistics. If this project is undertaken by any group of persons it is essential that (a) all samples be drawn at random, (b) all samples be of the same size, (c) any two samples be independent. Unless these conditions are observed, the statistics cannot be expected to conform to the pattern of the theoretically established sampling distribution. Condition (c) will require some planning if a table of random sampling numbers is employed, to provide that no two persons use the table in quite the same way. The steps listed below have been carried out and results recorded in Specimen Worksheets. The student will find it convenient to prepare similar forms in advance.

In the directions set down here the sample size has been kept small for several reasons. (1) As sample size increases, the distributions of many statistics become more like the normal curve. The difference in form of the various curves is more dramatically portrayed when N is small. (2) Drawing a number of small samples and combining them into one larger sample will help to make vivid the change which takes place in the sampling distribution of a statistic as N increases. (3) For a given expenditure of time the student will learn more by computing a variety of statistics for each of a few small samples than by computing fewer statistics for larger samples.

The steps in computing the required statistics are as follows:

1. From a table of random numbers draw 5 numbers of 447 or smaller and enter them in the first row of Worksheet I in the column for Sample I. Similarly draw and record 5 serial numbers for each of the other three samples.

2. Treating each number obtained in Step 1 as a serial number, read from Table XXIV the score of the subject that has that serial number and record it in row 2 of Worksheet I.

3. Carry out the computations indicated in rows 3 through 11 of Worksheet I and check in the manner indicated at the

SPECIMEN WORKSHEET I

Operation	Sample of 5				Composite Sample of 20
	1	2	3	4	
1. List of serial numbers selected	018, 074, 398, 328, 108	191, 296, 117, 420, 395	088, 015, 284, 071, 122	092, 414, 171, 102, 392	
2. Corresponding scores, X_{ij}	127, 165, 47, 103, 91	170, 157, 105, 51, 40	169, 137, 123, 104, 98	180, 78, 152, 142, 58	
3. Sum of scores $\sum_1^N X$	533	523	631	610	2297
4. Mean $\frac{1}{N}\sum_1^N X = \overline{X}$	106.6	104.6	126.2	122	114.85
5. Sum of squares of scores $\sum_1^N X^2$	64453	68775	82879	85116	301223
6. Correction term $\left(\sum_1^N X\right)^2/N$	56817.8	54705.8	79632.2	74420	263810.45
7. $\Sigma x^2 = \sum_1^N X^2 - \left(\sum_1^N X\right)^2/N$	7635.2	14069.2	3246.8	10696	37412.55
8. $s^2 = \sum_1^N x^2/(N-1)$	1908.8	3517.3	811.7	2674	1969.08
9. $d_j = \overline{X}_j - \overline{X} \cdots$	− 8.25	− 10.25	11.35	7.15	
10. ND_j^2	340.3125	525.3125	644.1125	255.6125	
11. $s = \sqrt{s^2}$	43.7	59.3	28.5	51.7	44.4

Checks: Row 3 $533 + 523 + 631 + 610 = 2297$
Row 4 $\frac{1}{4}(106.6 + 104.6 + 126.2 + 122) = 114.85$
Row 5 $64453 + 68775 + 82879 + 85116 = 301223$
Row 7 $7635.2 + 14069.2 + 3246.8 + 10696 = 35647.2$
Row 10 $340.3125 + 525.3125 + 644.1125 + 255.6125 = 1765.35$
Row 7, Entry in last column $= 37412.55$

bottom of the Worksheet. The mean ($\overline{X}$), the variance (s^2), and the standard deviation (s) have now been obtained for each small sample of 5 and for the composite sample of 20.

4. Enter the computed statistics on Worksheet II and complete the additional computations suggested there in rows 1 to 10.

SPECIMEN WORKSHEET II

Record of Statistics Computed from Samples

Statistic	Sample of 5				Sample of 20
	1	2	3	4	
1. $\overline{X}$	106.6	104.6	126.2	122	
2. $\overline{X}$					114.85
3. $\overline{X} - \mu = \overline{X} - 121.6$	− 15.0	− 17.0	4.6	.4	
4. $\overline{X} - \mu = \overline{X} - 121.6$					− 6.75
5. $(\overline{X} - \mu)\Big/\frac{\sigma}{\sqrt{N}} = (\overline{X} - 121.6)/16.61$	− .903	− 1.023	.277	.024	
6. $(\overline{X} - \mu)\Big/\frac{s}{\sqrt{N}} = (\overline{X} - 121.6)\sqrt{5}/s$	− .768	− .641	.362	.017	
7. $(\overline{X} - \mu)\Big/\frac{\sigma}{\sqrt{N}} = (\overline{X} - 121.6)/8.31$					− .812
8. $(\overline{X} - \mu)\Big/\frac{s}{\sqrt{N}} = (\overline{X} - 121.6)\sqrt{20}/s$					− .687
9. $\Sigma x^2/\sigma^2 = \Sigma x^2/1380.4$	5.53	10.19	2.35	7.75	
10. $\Sigma x^2/\sigma^2 = \Sigma x^2/1380.4$					27.10

5. On Worksheet III, enter the following statistics:

Line 1 The difference of two means taken from line 4. Thus $\overline{X}_1 - \overline{X}_2 = 106.6 - 104.6 = 2.0$

Line 2 The sum of 2 entries on line 7 of I

Line 3 Computation based on entry in preceding line

Line 4 Entry in line 1 divided by entry in line 3

Line 5 Ratio of two variances taken from line 8 of I. Thus 1908.8/3517.3 = .54

SPECIMEN WORKSHEET III

Record of Statistics for Comparison of Samples

Statistic	Samples compared		
	1, 2	2, 3	3, 4
1. $\overline{X}_i - \overline{X}_j$	2.0	− 21.6	4.2
2. $\Sigma x^2_i + \Sigma x^2_j$	21704.4	17316.0	13942.8
3. $s_{\overline{X}_i - \overline{X}_j} = \sqrt{\frac{\Sigma x_i^2 + \Sigma x_j^2}{20}}$	32.9	29.4	26.4
4. $(\overline{X}_i - \overline{X}_j)/s_{\overline{X}_i - \overline{X}_j}$	.06	− .73	.16
5. s_i^2/s_j^2	.54	4.33	.30

We shall now consider some general issues before examining the empirical distributions which have been produced by classes carrying out the sampling project which has been described above.

Samples from a Normal Population. A large part of this book is concerned with the theory of samples drawn from a normal population. The sampling distributions which will be used are, therefore, based on this assumption. However it should be recognized that empirical studies of samples from non-normal populations indicate that a considerable departure from normality does not invalidate the methods described.

We shall, in this chapter, describe four of the most useful smooth sampling distributions of statistics calculated for samples from a normal population. Before proceeding with the description of these distributions it is desirable to clarify the concepts of independence among statistics and of degrees of freedom.

Independence of Statistics. An unexpected property of statistics calculated for samples from a normal population is that certain pairs of statistics based on the same observations are independent of each other. This property does not hold for all statistics but it does hold for the mean and the variance and also for the mean and the standard deviation. It does not hold even for these statistics if the population is not normal.

When the mean and the standard deviation are both calculated for each of many samples, they vary independently of each other. This principle is proved mathematically in treatises on the mathematical theory of statistics. In this text the independence in the variation of the mean and the standard deviation is illustrated graphically in Figure 6–1 which shows the joint distribution of these two statistics from 144 samples of 5 cases each drawn by students carrying out the sampling project. Without this independence between $\overline{X}$ and s (or s^2) from the same sample several of the procedures about to be described would not be correct. It is indeed a beneficent principle which very few people would recognize intuitively. Statistics from two or more random samples are always independent regardless of the nature of the population which is being sampled.

Degrees of Freedom. The concept of degrees of freedom in connection with χ^2 was discussed in Chapter 4. It also arises in connection with observations made on a continuous scale and the correct choice of the number of degrees of freedom is often a very important part of the correct solution for a problem.

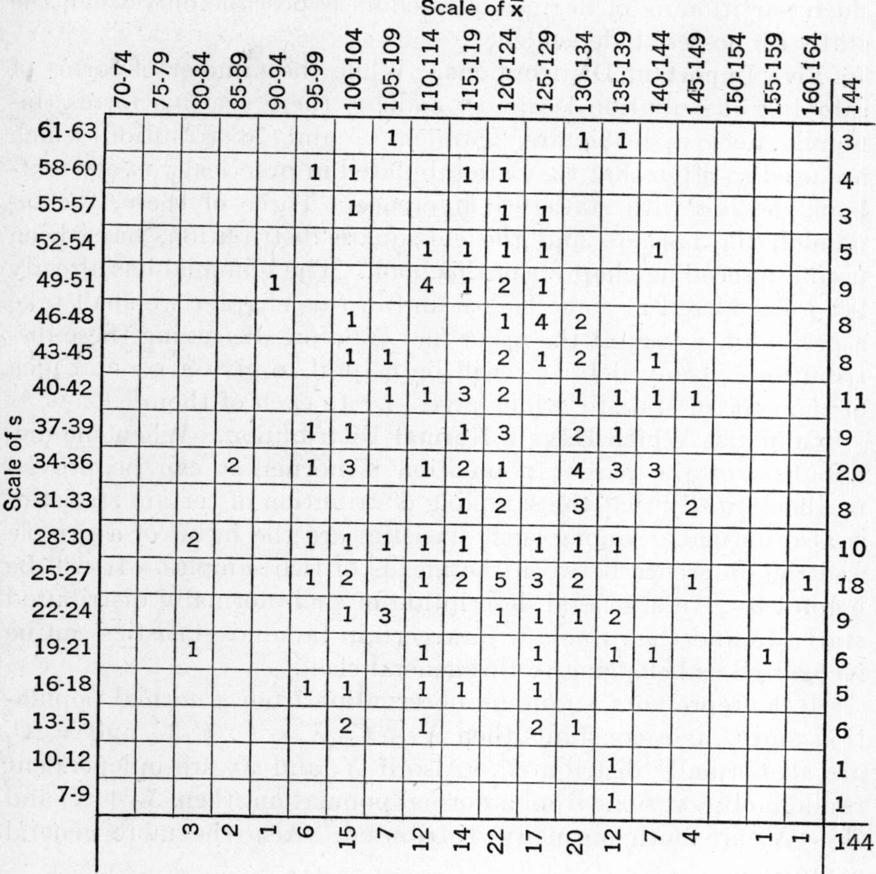

Scale of s \ Scale of $\bar{x}$	70-74	75-79	80-84	85-89	90-94	95-99	100-104	105-109	110-114	115-119	120-124	125-129	130-134	135-139	140-144	145-149	150-154	155-159	160-164	144
61-63								1					1	1						3
58-60						1	1			1	1									4
55-57							1				1	1								3
52-54									1	1	1	1			1					5
49-51					1				4	1	2	1								9
46-48							1				1	4	2							8
43-45							1	1			2	1	2		1					8
40-42								1	1	3	2		1	1	1	1				11
37-39						1	1			1	3		2	1						9
34-36				2		1	3		1	2	1		4	3	3					20
31-33										1	2		3			2				8
28-30			2			1	1	1	1	1		1	1	1						10
25-27						1	2		1	2	5	3	2			1			1	18
22-24							1	3			1	1	1	2						9
19-21			1						1			1		1	1			1		6
16-18						1	1		1	1		1								5
13-15							2		1			2	1							6
10-12														1						1
7-9														1						1
			3	2	1	6	15	7	12	14	22	17	20	12	7	4		1	1	144

FIG. 6–1. Joint frequency distribution of mean and standard deviation from 144 samples of 5 cases each.

$r = -.02$

If N independent observations are made, these observations have N degrees of freedom, since each observation is free to take any value in the possible range of values. If those N observations are from a normal population and if from them a mean and a standard deviation (or a variance) are both computed, then these N degrees of freedom are partitioned so that the distribution of the mean has 1 degree of freedom and the distribution of the standard deviation (or the variance) has $N - 1$ degrees of freedom. In succeeding chapters the N degrees of freedom of N independent observations will be partitioned in various ways among independent statistics computed from those observations.

Such partitioning of degrees of freedom is possible only when the statistics possess independence.

Five Important Distributions. While the number of forms of sampling distribution is almost endless, there are five forms (binomial, normal, chi-square, "Student's," and F distribution) which are used so often that they are tabulated in practically every textbook dealing with statistical inference. Three of these, the binomial, the normal, and the chi-square distribution, have been used in preceding chapters of this book. The binomial has already been considered at some length and in this chapter we shall take a preliminary look at the other four. Before discussing these distributions in any detail, it will be helpful to give a general idea of the type of statistic which gives rise to each of them.

Statistics Which Have a Normal Distribution. When the distribution of the parent population is normal it can be proved mathematically that the sampling distribution of certain statistics is also normal. Among such statistics are the mean of a sample and the difference between the means of two samples. It will be helpful to give a general description of such normally distributed statistics and then to show how certain familiar statistics can be recognized as belonging to this general class.

If X_i represents a random observation from a normal population and C_i is a constant, then $X_i + C_i$, $X_i - C_i$, C_iX_i, and X_i/C_i are all normally distributed. Also if X_i and X_j are independent random observations from a normal population, then $X_i + X_j$ and $X_i - X_j$ are both normally distributed. Also the more general expression

$$C_0 + C_1X_1 + C_2X_2 + \cdots + C_NX_N \tag{6.1}$$

represents a normally distributed variable if the C's are constants and the X's are independent random observations from a normal population. Since each term in (6.1) is of first degree in X that expression is called a *linear function of* X or a *linear function of the observations.*

The mean of a sample can be obtained from (6.1) by letting C_0 equal 0 and letting $C_1, C_2 \cdots C_N$ each equal $1/N$. Hence the mean of a random sample from a normal population is normally distributed.

An interesting and important fact is that even if the population is not normally distributed, the sampling distribution of the mean may often be well approximated by the normal distribution if samples are large (say $N > 30$). Under such circumstances, the distribution of the mean can be treated as normal with mean μ and standard error $\sigma/\sqrt{N}$.

If $\overline{X}$ is normally distributed, the statistic $\overline{X} - \mu$, obtained from $\overline{X}$ by subtracting a constant, is also normally distributed with mean 0 and standard error $\sigma/\sqrt{N}$. Then the statistic

$$\frac{\overline{X} - \mu}{\sigma/\sqrt{N}} = \frac{(\overline{X} - \mu)\sqrt{N}}{\sigma}$$

has the unit normal distribution. In Chapter 7 a normal distribution related to the difference between the means of two samples will be considered. In Chapter 10 a regression coefficient will be treated as a linear function of the observations and as therefore having a normal distribution.

Statistics Which Have a Chi-square Distribution. If X_i is normally distributed then certain statistics of the form

$$C_1(X_1 - \overline{X})^2 + C_2(X_2 - \overline{X})^2 + \cdots + C_N(X_N - \overline{X})^2 \tag{6.2}$$

have the chi-square distribution. Here the C's are constants and deviations from the mean are *squared.*

A very important statistic of this type is one in which all the C's have the same value, $1/\sigma^2$. This statistic

$$\frac{\Sigma(X_i - \overline{X})^2}{\sigma^2} = \frac{(N - 1)s^2}{\sigma^2}$$

will be discussed in Chapter 8. It has $N - 1$ degrees of freedom. When the subject of analysis of variance is discussed, the X's will often be replaced by the means of subsamples.

The statistic $\Sigma \dfrac{(f_i - F_i)^2}{F_i}$ treated in Chapter 4 is similar to (6.2) because for large samples $(f_i - F_i)$ has a distribution which is approximately normal with mean zero, like that of $(X - \overline{X})$, and C_i may be taken as $1/F_i$. Consequently the chi-square distribution was found to be a satisfactory approximation to the distribution of this statistic unless the number of observations is small.

Several classes of students in a statistics course have drawn random samples of 5 cases each from the data of Table XXIV as described at the beginning of this chapter. The statistic $\Sigma(X - \overline{X})^2/\sigma^2$ was computed from each of 125 of these samples and the results recorded in Table 6.1. Figure 6–2 shows the distribution of these empirical values with the theoretical χ^2 distribution for 4 degrees of freedom superimposed. Read a few values from Table VIII, and mark their position on the baseline of the graph, as for example $\chi^2_{.10} = 1.1$, $\chi^2_{.50} = 3.36$ and $\chi^2_{.90} = 7.8$. From each of the random samples you have yourself drawn compute the same statistic and mark its position on the baseline.

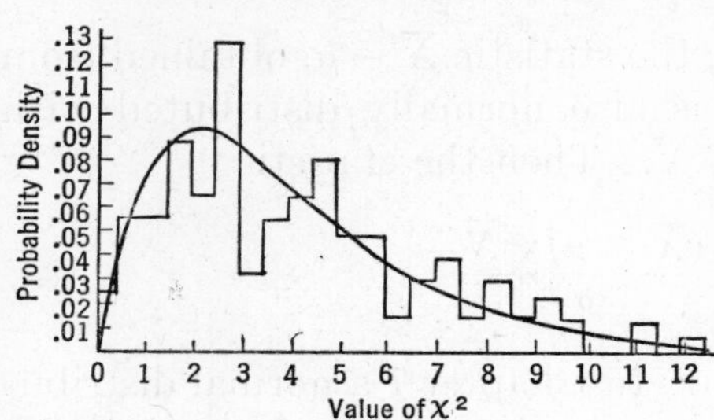

FIG. 6–2. Distribution of $\Sigma(X - \overline{X})^2/\sigma^2$ in 125 samples of 5 cases each, and theoretical χ^2 distribution with 4 degrees of freedom.

If the same statistic were computed for each of the component samples of 20 cases, its distribution would have 19 degrees of freedom instead of 4 and would be considerably less skewed than the one illustrated in Figure 6–2.

TABLE 6.1 Distribution of $\Sigma(X - \overline{X})^2/\sigma^2$ in 125 Samples of 5 Cases Each

$\frac{\Sigma(X - \overline{X})^2}{\sigma^2}$	f	cum. %	$\frac{\Sigma(X - \overline{X})^2}{\sigma^2}$	f	cum. %	$\frac{\Sigma(X - \overline{X})^2}{\sigma^2}$	f	cum. %
17.2 *	1	100%	11.7		95.2	5.7	6	74.4
16.7	1	99.2	11.2	2	95.2	5.2	6	69.6
16.2		98.4	10.7		93.6	4.7	10	64.8
15.7	1	98.4	10.2		93.6	4.2	8	56.8
15.2		97.6	9.7	2	93.6	3.7	7	50.4
14.7		97.6	9.2	3	92.0	3.2	4	44.8
14.2	1	97.6	8.7	2	89.6	2.7	16	41.6
13.7		96.8	8.2	4	88.0	2.2	8	28.8
13.2		96.8	7.7	2	84.8	1.7	11	22.4
12.7	1	96.8	7.2	5	83.2	1.2	7	13.6
12.2	1	96.0	6.7	4	79.2	.7	7	8.0
			6.2	2	76.0	.2	3	2.4

* Middle of the interval.

The cumulative χ^2 distribution with 4 degrees of freedom is drawn in Figure 6–3 and the points determined by the cumulative percents from the empirical distribution of Table 6.1 are drawn by heavy dots. The cumulative distributions show very strikingly the correspondence between the empirical distribution obtained from values computed by many different persons from random samples they had drawn and the χ^2 curve plotted from a mathematical formula.

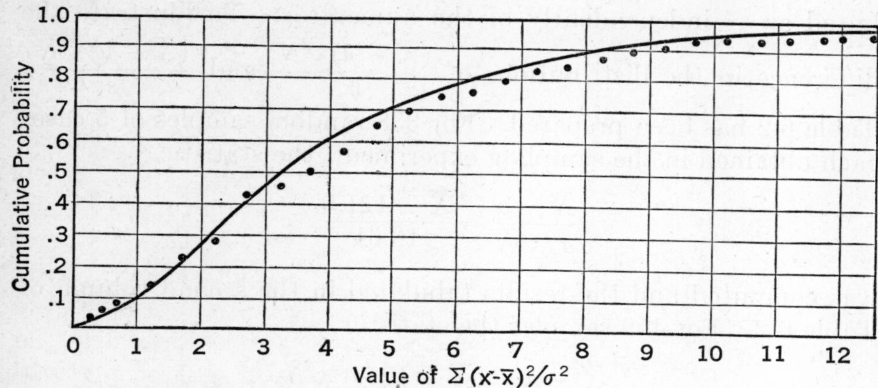

FIG. 6–3. Cumulative χ^2 distribution with 4 degrees of freedom and cumulative percents of distribution of 125 values of $\Sigma(X - \overline{X})^2/\sigma^2$ from samples of 5 cases.

Statistics Which Have "Student's" * Distribution. In making inferences about the mean of a population it is necessary to take into account the standard deviation of that population. In most practical situations neither μ nor σ is known and their estimates $\overline{X}$ and s must be used.

In Chapter 7 it will be seen that an important statistic in problems about the mean is

$$t = \frac{(\overline{X} - \mu)\sqrt{N}}{s} \tag{6.3}$$

which has "Student's" distribution when the observations are independent and normally distributed. This statistic can be written as $t = \dfrac{\overline{X} - \mu}{s_{\overline{X}}}$, where

$$s_{\overline{X}} = \frac{s}{\sqrt{N}} \tag{6.4}$$

is a sample estimate of the standard error $\sigma/\sqrt{N}$. In order that the t ratio shall have "Student's" distribution the numerator must be a normally distributed variable with mean zero and the denominator must be the square root of a variable which is distri-

* "Student" was a well-known British statistician named William Sealy Gosset (1876–1947) who was adviser to the Guiness brewery in Dublin. A ruling of that firm forbidding their employees to publish the results of research was relaxed to allow him to publish mathematical and statistical research under a pseudonym. His paper on "The Probable Error of a Mean," published in *Biometrika* in 1908, which first called attention to the fact that the normal curve does not properly describe the distribution of the ratio of mean to standard error in small samples, is now a classic.

buted as χ^2 independently of the numerator. To illustrate the difference in the distributions of $\frac{(\overline{X} - \mu)\sqrt{N}}{\sigma}$ and $\frac{(\overline{X} - \mu)\sqrt{N}}{s}$, Table 6.2 has been prepared. For 338 random samples of 5 cases each obtained in the sampling experiment, the statistic

$$\frac{\overline{X} - \mu}{\sigma/\sqrt{N}} = \frac{\overline{X} - 121.6}{16.61}$$

was computed and the results tabulated in the second column of Table 6.2. For 459 samples the statistic

$$\frac{\overline{X} - \mu}{s/\sqrt{N}} = \frac{(\overline{X} - 121.6)\sqrt{5}}{s}$$

was computed and the results tabulated in the third column. A glance at the table is enough to reveal that the latter distribution has a much wider spread and that extreme deviates are more frequent. The cumulative percents for the two distributions are shown in columns 4 and 5 of Table 6.2.

A cumulative normal curve has been drawn in Figure 6–4. (This is easily done from the figures in Table I or Table II in the Appendix.) The cumulative percents for the distribution of

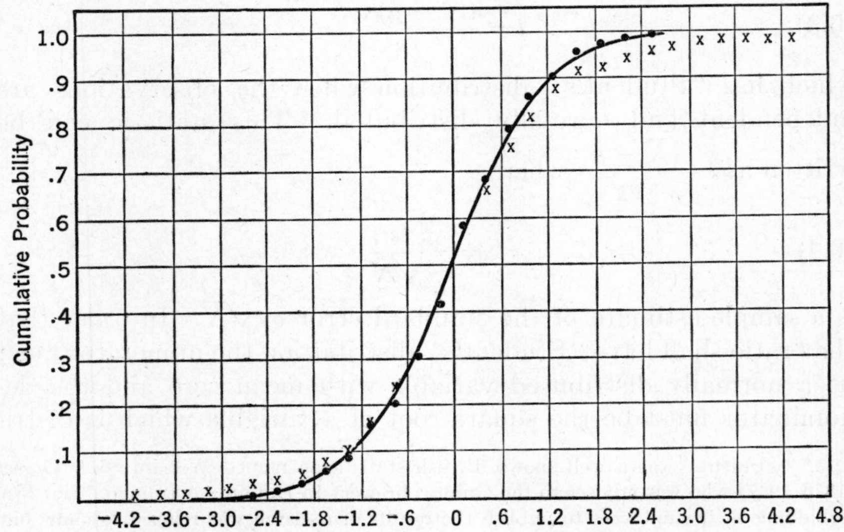

Fig. 6–4. Cumulative normal distribution with cumulative percents of distribution of $(\overline{X} - \mu)\sqrt{5}/\sigma$ shown by dots and cumulative percents of distribution of $(\overline{X} - \mu)\sqrt{5}/s$ by small crosses.

TABLE 6.2 Distribution of $\frac{(X-\mu)\sqrt{5}}{\sigma}$ and of $\frac{(X-\mu)\sqrt{5}}{s}$ from Samples of 5 Cases Each

Middle of Interval	Frequency in interval $\frac{(\overline{X}-\mu)\sqrt{5}}{\sigma}$	$\frac{(\overline{X}-\mu)\sqrt{5}}{s}$	Percent of frequency below upper limit of interval $\frac{(\overline{X}-\mu)\sqrt{5}}{\sigma}$	$\frac{(\overline{X}-\mu)\sqrt{5}}{s}$
4.5		1		100.0%
4.2				99.8
3.9				99.8
3.6		5		99.8
3.3		1		98.7
2.0		3		98.5
2.7		6		97.8
2.4	1	6	100.00%	96.5
2.1	6	10	99.7	95.2
1.8	7	7	97.6	93.0
1.5	15	14	95.9	91.5
1.2	17	30	91.4	88.4
.9	24	26	86.4	81.9
.6	36	40	79.3	76.3
.3	34	42	68.6	67.5
0	57	79	58.6	58.4
− .3	38	49	41.7	41.2
− .6	35	29	30.5	30.5
− .9	16	35	20.1	24.2
− 1.2	25	25	15.4	16.6
− 1.5	22	12	8.0	11.1
− 1.8	4	11	1.5	8.5
− 2.1		8	.3	6.1
− 2.4		5	.3	4.4
− 2.7	1	4	.3	3.3
− 3.0		3		2.4
− 3.3		4		1.7
− 3.6		1		.9
− 3.9		2		.6
− 4.2		1		.2
TOTAL	338	459		
MEAN	0.007	0.016		
VARIANCE	0.84	1.63		

$(\overline{X} - 121.6)/16.61$, listed in column 4 of Table 6.2, are represented by heavy dots which cluster closely around the cumulative normal curve. The cumulative percents for the distribution of

$$(\overline{X} - 121.6)\sqrt{5}/s,$$

taken from column 5, are represented by small crosses. These depart considerably from the normal curve at the ends of the distribution, and it is the ends of the distribution which are strategic in most problems.

In Chapter 7 there will be a discussion of the theoretic distribution to which these points do conform. It is "Student's"

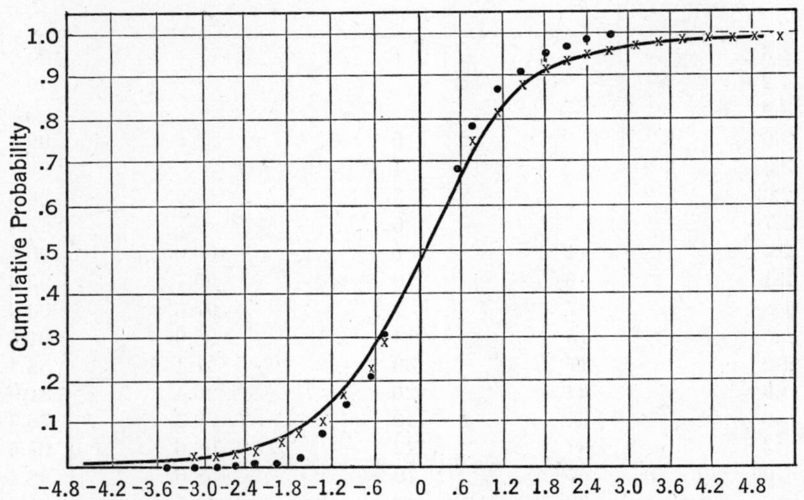

FIG. 6–5. Cumulative "Student's" distribution with 4 degrees of freedom, cumulative percents of distribution of $(\overline{X} - \mu)\sqrt{5}/\sigma$ shown by dots, and cumulative percents of distribution of $(\overline{X} - \mu)\sqrt{5}/s$ by small crosses.

distribution with $N - 1$ degrees of freedom, and for these samples $N - 1 = 4$. The cumulative curve for this distribution has been drawn in Figure 6–5, with empirical values shown by dots and crosses as before. Here the crosses representing points on the distribution for $(\overline{X} - 121.6)\sqrt{5}/s$ conform closely to the theoretical curve and the dots do not.

If the statistic $(\overline{X} - \mu)\sqrt{N}/\sigma$ were computed for each sample of 20 cases, obtained by combining 4 samples of 5 cases, its distribution would also approximate the unit normal distribution and its cumulative distribution would differ only by chance from that shown by dots in Figures 6–4 and 6–5.

However if the statistic $(\overline{X} - \mu)\sqrt{N}/s$ were computed for each sample of 20 cases, its distribution would be far more nearly normal than that obtained from the samples of 5 cases, and its cumulative distribution would differ considerably from that shown by the crosses in Figures 6–4 and 6–5.

The ratio of the difference between two means to the sample estimate of the standard error of that difference has under certain circumstances "Student's" distribution. Problems employing this ratio will be discussed in Chapter 7. The statistic $(\overline{X}_1 - \overline{X}_2)/s_{\overline{X}_1-\overline{X}_2}$ was computed on line 4 of Worksheet III. Under the circumstances in which these samples were obtained, this ratio should

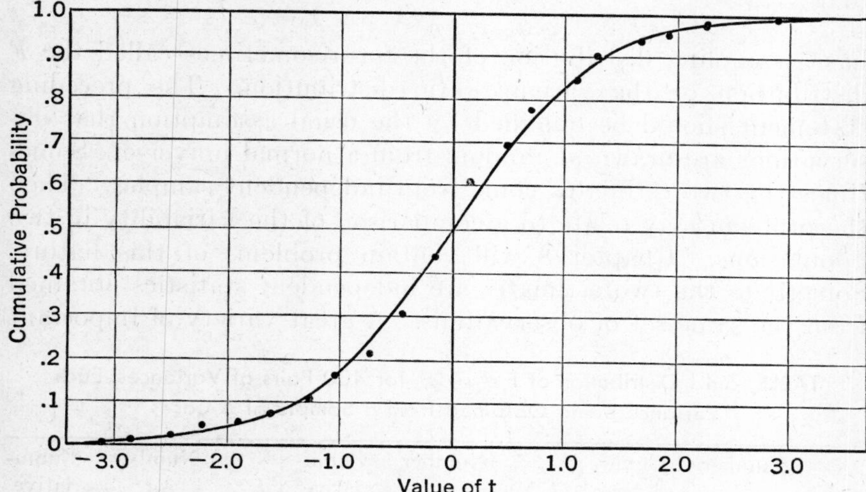

Fig. 6–6. Cumulative "Student's" distribution for 8 degrees of freedom and cumulative percents of distribution of $t = (\overline{X}_1 - \overline{X}_2)/s_{\overline{X}_1-\overline{X}_2}$ for 200 pairs of samples of 5 cases each.

have "Student's" distribution with 8 degrees of freedom. It has been computed for 200 pairs of samples and the results recorded in Table 6.3 and graphed in Figure 6–6.

TABLE 6.3 Distribution of $t = (\overline{X}_1 - \overline{X}_2)/s_{\overline{X}_1-\overline{X}_2}$ for 200 Pairs of Samples of 5 Cases Each

$\frac{\overline{X}_1 - \overline{X}_2}{s_{\bar{x}_1-\bar{x}_2}}$	f	$\frac{\overline{X}_1 - \overline{X}_2}{s_{\bar{x}_1-\bar{x}_2}}$	f	$\frac{\overline{X}_1 - \overline{X}_2}{s_{\bar{x}_1-\bar{x}_2}}$	f
4.1–4.3	1	1.4– 1.6	5	− 1.3–− 1.1	11
3.8–4.0		1.1– 1.3	12	− 1.6–− 1.4	6
3.5–3.7	1	.8– 1.0	14	− 1.9–− 1.7	4
3.2–3.4	1	.5– .7	16	− 2.2–− 2.0	3
2.9–3.1	1	.2– .4	16	− 2.5–− 2.3	5
2.6–2.8		− .1– .1	35	− 2.8–− 2.6	1
2.3–2.5	1	− .4–− .2	27	− 3.1–− 2.9	1
2.0–2.2	6	− .7–− .5	17	− 3.4–− 3.2	
1.7–1.9	4	− 1.0–− .8	11	− 3.7–− 3.5	1

$N = 200$ Mean $= 0$ Variance $= 1.37$

The ratios of other normally distributed statistics to the sample estimate of their standard errors will be considered in later chapters.

Statistics Which Have the F Distribution. Whenever there are two independent estimates of σ^2, the ratio of one estimate to the other

$$F = \frac{s^2_1}{s^2_2} \tag{6.5}$$

has a sampling distribution of the form sometimes called the F distribution or the variance-ratio distribution. The preceding statement should be qualified by the usual assumption that observations are drawn at random from a normal universe. Sometimes the two estimates come from independent samples. Then the problem may relate to a comparison of the variability in two populations. Chapter 8 will contain problems of this nature. Sometimes the two estimates are independent statistics obtained from the same set of observations. A great variety of important

TABLE 6.4 Distribution of $F = s^2_i/s^2_j$ for 400 Pairs of Variances, Each Variance being Obtained from a Sample of 5 Cases

F *	Number of samples	Cumulative %	F *	Number of samples	Cumulative %	F *	Number of samples	Cumulative %
18.0	1	100.00	12.0		97.75	6.0		93.25
17.7		99.75	11.7	1	97.75	5.7	5	93.25
17.4		99.75	11.4		97.50	5.4	1	92.00
17.1	1	99.75	11.1		97.50	5.1	2	91.75
16.8		99.50	10.8	1	97.50	4.8	4	91.25
16.5		99.50	10.5		97.25	4.5	3	90.25
16.2	1	99.50	10.2	1	97.25	4.2	6	89.50
15.9		99.25	9.9		97.00	3.9	11	88.00
15.6		99.25	9.6		97.00	3.6	9	85.25
15.3	1	99.25	9.3		97.00	3.3	7	83.00
15.0		99.00	9.0	2	97.00	3.0	11	81.25
14.7	2	99.00	8.7		96.50	2.7	12	78.50
14.4		98.50	8.4		96.50	2.4	22	75.50
14.1	1	98.50	8.1	1	96.50	2.1	17	70.00
13.8		98.25	7.8	2	96.25	1.8	22	65.75
13.5		98.25	7.5	1	95.75	1.5	27	60.25
13.2		98.25	7.2		95.50	1.2	35	53.50
12.9	1	98.25	6.9	2	95.50	.9	57	44.75
12.6		98.00	6.6	4	95.00	.6	76	30.50
12.3	1	98.00	6.3	3	94.00	.3	46	11.50

* Values of F are the upper limits of step intervals.

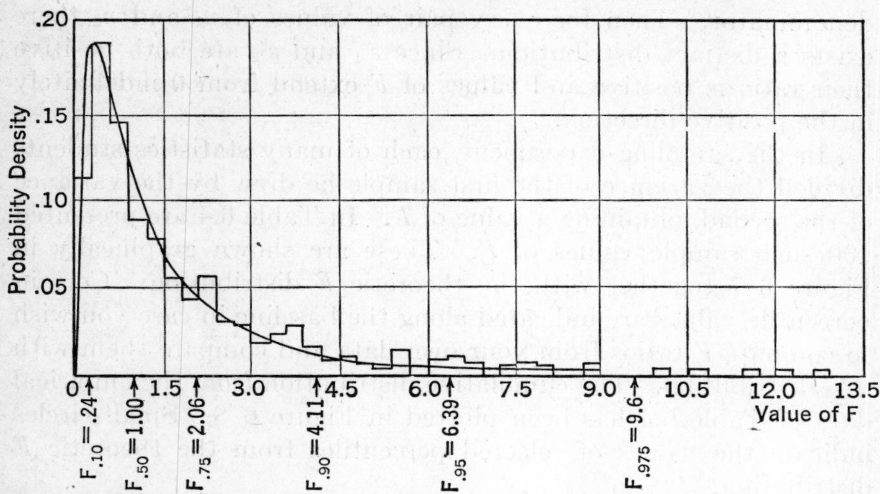

FIG. 6–7. Distribution of $F = s^2_i/s^2_j$ for 400 pairs of samples of 5 cases each, and theoretical F distribution for 8 degrees of freedom. (7 cases at upper end of distribution are not shown on graph.)

problems can give rise to such variances, one of the commonest being a test of the hypothesis that several populations have the same mean. This problem is discussed in Chapter 9.

Let n_1 represent the degrees of freedom associated with the numerator of F and n_2 the degrees of freedom associated with the

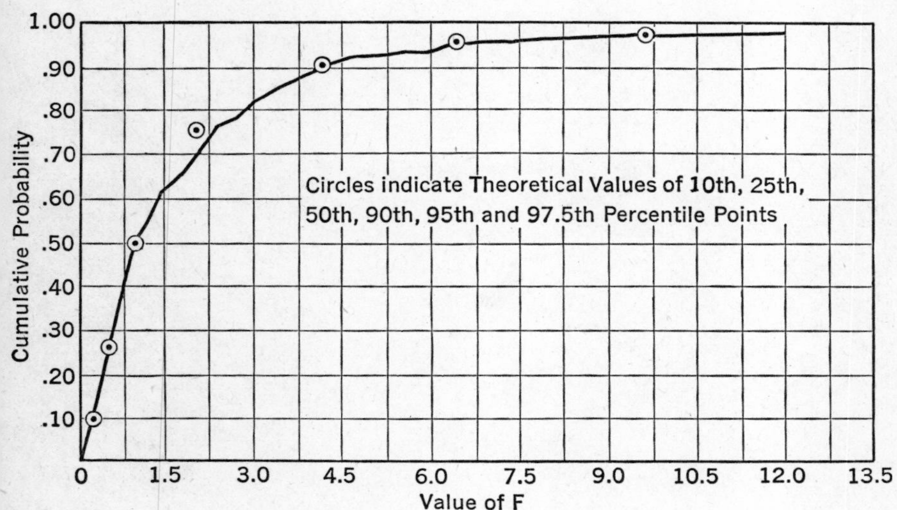

FIG. 6–8. Cumulative percentage distribution of 400 values of $F = s^2_i/s^2_j$, and certain selected percentiles of the theoretic F distribution.

denominator. Then for every pair of values of n_1 and n_2 there exists a distinct distribution. Since s^2_1 and s^2_2 are both positive their ratio is positive and values of F extend from 0 indefinitely in the positive direction.

In the sampling experiment, each of many statistics students divided the variance of the first sample he drew by the variance of the second, obtaining a value of F. In Table 6.4 are presented 400 such sample values of F. These are shown graphically in Figure 6–7 together with the theoretic F distribution. Certain percentile values are indicated along the baseline in case you wish to compute F ratios from your own data and compare them with this distribution. The cumulative distribution from the empirical data of Table 6.4 has been plotted in Figure 6–8. Small circles indicate the values of selected percentiles from the theoretic F distribution.

7 Inferences Concerning the Mean or the Difference Between Two Means

In this chapter, methods will be described for testing hypotheses regarding μ and for calculating estimates of μ. In addition, methods for comparing the means of two populations, μ_1 and μ_2, will be considered. For these purposes the normal distribution and "Student's" * distribution will be the required sampling distributions.

The Assumption of a Normal Population. In this chapter and in most of the following chapters the assumption will be made that measures in a sample are independently drawn from a normal population. This assumption is justified by the approximately normal shape assumed by many empirical distributions. Studies indicate that some departure from normality does not invalidate the methods to be described.

Where the assumption of normality or of independence is not made this fact will be indicated. Where it seems important to state explicitly the assumption of normality it will be stated.

The Central Limit Theorem. A theorem of far-reaching importance in statistics is called the Central Limit Theorem. It states that for a wide variety of populations statistics based on large random samples are distributed normally. This applies to nearly all populations which are likely to be considered in practice, and to most statistics considered in this book. This is especially true of statistics to be considered in this chapter. It is less true of the correlation coefficient to be considered in Chapter 10, and of the sample proportion p when P is near 1 or 0, because their distributions depart greatly from normality unless the sample is exceptionally large. Also if classes are few, distributions of χ^2 and F approach smooth χ^2-distribution, not normal, as sample size increases.

* See footnote on page 135.

$\overline{X}$ as an Estimate of μ. It was stated in Chapter 5 that $E(\overline{X}) = \mu$ and that, therefore, $\overline{X}$ is an *unbiased* estimate of μ. It is easy to see that $\overline{X}$ is also a *consistent estimate* of μ, for

$$\sigma_{\overline{X}} = \frac{\sigma}{\sqrt{N}} \tag{7.1}$$

and so $\sigma_{\overline{X}}$ decreases as N increases. For large samples $\overline{X}$ can be considered as normally distributed about μ with standard deviation $\sigma_{\overline{X}}$ even if the population has a non-normal distribution. Even for relatively small samples out of a non-normal population the mean has a distribution which is approximately normal. Since $\sigma_{\overline{X}}$ can be made arbitrarily small by making N sufficiently large, the probability that $\overline{X}$ deviates from μ by a given amount can also be made arbitrarily small. The argument for the consistency of $\overline{X}$ corresponds to the argument for the consistency of p given on page 52.

There are many other possible methods of estimating μ, such as using the median, or the mode, or the average of the 25th and 75th percentiles, or the average of the 7th and 93rd percentiles, or the midpoint of the range, etc. *In samples from a normal population every other estimate of μ has a standard error larger than $\sigma_{\overline{X}}$.* Since the mean is the estimate of μ which has the smallest standard error in samples from a normal population, it is called the *efficient estimate* of μ for such a population. When the population is not normal some other estimate such as the median may have a smaller standard error than the mean and so be more efficient. Thus $\overline{X}$ provides an estimate of μ which is unbiased, consistent, and efficient when the population is normal.

EXERCISE 7.1

1. For each of the given values of N and σ, find the value of $\sigma_{\overline{X}}$. Make a table of results and notice the way in which $\sigma_{\overline{X}}$ decreases as N increases, σ remaining constant. Notice also the way in which $\sigma_{\overline{X}}$ increases as σ increases, N remaining constant.

a. $\sigma = 5, N = 4$
b. $\sigma = 5, N = 25$
c. $\sigma = 5, N = 100$
d. $\sigma = 5, N = 10{,}000$
e. $\sigma = 2, N = 25$
f. $\sigma = 4, N = 25$
g. $\sigma = 10, N = 25$
h. $\sigma = 20, N = 25$

2. Suppose in a population $\mu = 48.5$ and $\sigma^2 = 15.4$. What is the probability that the mean of a sample of 20 cases will be larger than 50? Between 47 and 50? Answer the same questions if $N = 100$.

Tests About μ When σ Is Known. In practice this situation is not very common for usually if μ is unknown σ is also unknown.

However it is the simplest of the situations to be considered and a natural introduction to the others. The population of 447 cases used in Chapter 6 provides a good illustration. Here $\mu = 121.6$ and $\sigma = 37.15$. Suppose a student reports obtaining a sample of 5 cases in which $\overline{X} = 165.4$. This seems very large. If his computations are not available for examination shall it be assumed that he has made an error?

Since the population variance is known, $\sigma_{\overline{X}} = \sigma/\sqrt{N}$ and

$$z = \frac{\overline{X} - \mu}{\sigma/\sqrt{N}} = \frac{\sqrt{N}(\overline{X} - \mu)}{\sigma} \tag{7.2}$$

Applying Formula (7.2) to the reported data we have

$$z = \frac{\sqrt{5}(165.4 - 121.6)}{37.15} = 2.64$$

Tables of normal probability indicate that the area outside the two ordinates at $z = \pm 2.64$ is .008. The hypothesis that 165.4 is a purely random deviate from the expected value of 121.6 is scarcely tenable and it would be wise to examine the student's work to see whether he has misunderstood the procedure or made a mistake in computation. However it must be noted that if a thousand samples are drawn about 8 of them might be expected to have $|z| > 2.64$ and one should not be too confident that in any particular sample a large departure from the expected value is due to a mistake.

"Student's" Distribution. When σ is not known, $\sigma_{\overline{X}}$ must be estimated from sample data by the formula

$$s_{\overline{X}} = \frac{s}{\sqrt{N}} \tag{7.3}$$

If observations are drawn from a normal population, the ratio $\dfrac{\overline{X} - \mu}{s_{\overline{X}}}$ has what is called *"Student's" Distribution,* and is customarily denoted by the letter t to distinguish it from z which customarily denotes a variable with unit normal distribution.

$$t = \frac{\overline{X} - \mu}{s/\sqrt{N}} = \frac{\sqrt{N}(\overline{X} - \mu)}{s} \tag{7.4}$$

"Student's" distribution is sometimes called the *t*-distribution. Because this chapter presents the first situation in which "Student's" distribution is needed, it is necessary now to pause for a discussion of the form of that distribution and the tables available.

"Student's" distribution is symmetrical with maximum ordinate at $t = 0$. Its shape changes as the number of degrees of freedom changes. Therefore "the" curve is in reality a whole family of curves. As n increases, the curve approaches the normal form so that for n as large as 30 or 40 the normal probability table can be used satisfactorily in most problems. By calculus

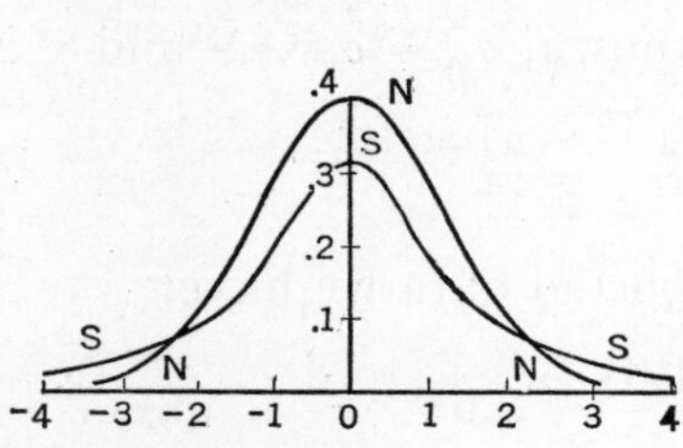

FIG. 7–1. The normal distribution (N) and "Student's" distribution with 1 degree of freedom (S).

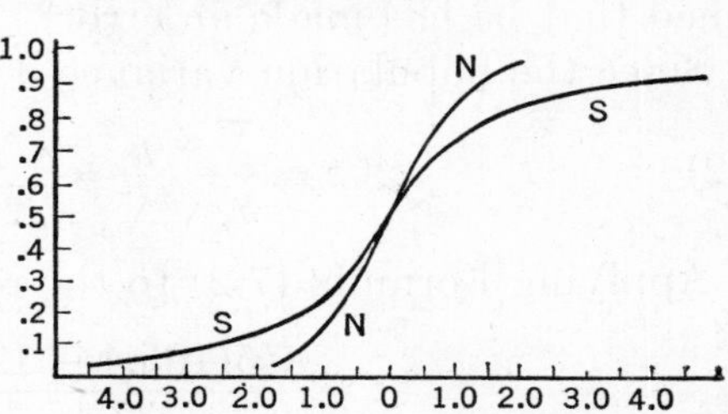

FIG. 7–2. Cumulative normal distribution (N) and cumulative curve of "Student's" distribution with 1 degree of freedom (S).

it can be shown that the formula for the normal curve is the limit approached by the formula for "Student's" distribution as n becomes very large. When n is very small the area in the tails of "Student's" distribution is considerably greater than the corresponding area in the tails of the normal distribution, as can be seen in Figures 7–1 and 7–2 where the normal distribution and "Student's" distribution with $n = 1$ are shown together. The same relation has already been seen in Figures 6–4 and 6–5.

In Table IX to be found in the Appendix, each row belongs to a different probability curve. These curves are distinguished by the number of degrees of freedom specified in the column at the left. The tabular entries are values of t. In the column headed $t_{.90}$ each entry is the 90th percentile of the probability distribution to which it belongs. A similar description applies to the other columns. Notice that when the subscript for t is less than .50 the value of t is negative. Thus $t_{.10} = -t_{.90}$, $t_{.005} = -t_{.995}$, etc. The entries in the last row of the table are percentile values for the normal curve.

EXERCISE 7.2

1. Study the following statements, translate them into words. Sketching a probability curve may help your understanding.

$P(t < t_{.95}) = .95$ $\qquad$ $P(t_{.04} < t < t_{.96}) = .92$

$P(t < t_{.01}) = .01$ $\qquad$ $P(t_{.08} < t < t_{.92}) = .84$

$P(t > t_{.99}) = .01$ $\qquad$ $P(t > t_{.99} \text{ or } t < t_{.01}) = .02$
$P(t > t_{.07}) = .93$ $\qquad$ $P(t > t_{.95} \text{ or } t < t_{.05}) = .10$

2. Examine Table IX to identify the entries which support the following statements:

$P(t < 1.4 \mid n = 8) = .90$ $\qquad$ $P(t > -1.34 \mid n = 15) = .90$
$P(t < -2.31 \mid n = 8) = .025$ $\qquad$ $P(-1.37 < t < 1.37 \mid n = 10) = .80$
$P(t < -1.35 \mid n = 13) = .10$ $\qquad$ $P(-2.18 < t < 2.18 \mid n = 12) = .95$
$P(t > 3.75 \mid n = 4) = .01$ $\qquad$ $P(-3.00 < t < 3.00 \mid n = 7) = .98$

3. Verify the following statements by reference to Table IX

a. For $n = 11$, $P(t > 2.2) = .025$
$P(t < 2.2) = .975$
$P(-2.2 < t < 2.2) = .95$

b. If ordinates are to be drawn to cut off the extreme 1% of the area in each tail of the curve
for $n = 5$, they should be drawn at -3.36 and $+3.36$
for $n = 10$, they should be drawn at -2.76 and $+2.76$
for $n = 25$, they should be drawn at -2.48 and $+2.48$
for the normal curve, they should be drawn at -2.326 and $+2.326$

c. As the eye follows down any selected column of the table, the entries grow smaller as n increases, and they appear to converge upon the entries in the last row of the table.

d. The entries in the row headed $n = \infty$ are identical with corresponding entries in Table II.

4. If ordinates are to be drawn to cut off the extreme 10% of the area under the curve, that is the extreme 5% in each tail, where should they be drawn if

a. $n = 3$ $\qquad$ **b.** $n = 16$ $\qquad$ **c.** $n = 500$

5. If ordinates are to be drawn to enclose the middle 80% of the area under the curve, where should they be drawn if

a. $n = 1$ $\qquad$ **b.** $n = 10$ $\qquad$ **c.** $n = 400$

6. If an observed value of t has been found to be 2.8, what is the best reading which Table IX furnishes for $P(t < -2.8 \text{ or } t > 2.8)$ when

a. $n = 1$ $\qquad$ **b.** $n = 3$ $\qquad$ **c.** $n = 500$

Tests About μ when σ Is Unknown. Suppose a sample of 6 cases has $\overline{X} = 12.3$ and $s^2 = 4.8$. It is desired to test the hypothesis $\mu = 15$ with a two-sided test at level $\alpha = .05$. The statistic $s_{\overline{X}} = s/\sqrt{N}$ must be used.

$$t = \frac{(\overline{X} - \mu)\sqrt{N}}{s}$$

will have "Student's" distribution with 5 degrees of freedom. Substituting the given data we have

$$t = \frac{(12.3 - 15)\sqrt{6}}{\sqrt{4.8}} = -3.02$$

To complete the test of significance the observed value of $t = -3.02$ must be compared with tabulated entries in Table IX, where the critical region for the two-sided test with $\alpha = .05$ is seen to be $t < -2.57$ and $t > 2.57$. The observed value falls in this critical region and the hypothesis is rejected.

Confidence Interval for μ.* Formulas for calculating confidence intervals for μ will be developed both for the situation when σ is known and when it is unknown. The confidence coefficient will be taken as $1 - \alpha$ where α is some small value such as .01 or .05, so that $1 - \alpha$ is .99 or .95.

Consider first the situation when σ is known. Then the following relation holds:

$$(7.5) \qquad P\left(z_{\frac{1}{2}\alpha} < \frac{(\overline{X} - \mu)\sqrt{N}}{\sigma} < z_{1-\frac{1}{2}\alpha}\right) = 1 - \alpha$$

when X is normally distributed or when X is not normally distributed but N is large. Simple algebraic manipulation on the inequality in parentheses yields another expression with the same probability:

$$(7.6) \qquad P\left(\overline{X} + z_{\frac{1}{2}\alpha}\frac{\sigma}{\sqrt{N}} < \mu < \overline{X} + z_{1-\frac{1}{2}\alpha}\frac{\sigma}{\sqrt{N}}\right) = 1 - \alpha$$

The inequality within the parentheses provides confidence limits for μ which are appropriate under the conditions stated, namely that X is normally distributed and σ is known. Written with the symbol $\overline{X}$ occurring in the limits of the interval, it is readily understood that μ is a fixed, though usually unknown, value and that it is the limits of the interval which are subject to sampling variation. It should be already understood that the probability given in (7.6) is the probability that $\overline{X}$ for a randomly selected sample will simultaneously satisfy the two inequalities

$$\overline{X} + z_{\frac{1}{2}\alpha}\frac{\sigma}{\sqrt{N}} < \mu \quad \text{and} \quad \overline{X} + z_{1-\frac{1}{2}\alpha}\frac{\sigma}{\sqrt{N}} > \mu.$$

* Before studying this section, the reader may find it profitable to reread the discussion on confidence intervals in Chapter 3.

After a sample has been drawn, $\overline{X}$ computed from it, and the two limits obtained in numerical form, such as, say, 17.3 and 22.5, then the inequality $17.3 < \mu < 22.5$ is either true or not true. The probability of (7.6) does not apply to it. However the probability statement of (7.6) provides us with a measurable degree of confidence that such a pair of values obtained from a sample will contain μ in, say, 95% of all determinations. We may express that degree of confidence by such a statement as

$$C(17.3 < \mu < 22.5) = .95$$

When σ is unknown, a formula analogous to (7.6) is written with s in place of σ, and t in place of z:

$$P\left(\overline{X} + t_{\frac{1}{2}\alpha}\frac{s}{\sqrt{N}} < \mu < \overline{X} + t_{1-\frac{1}{2}\alpha}\frac{s}{\sqrt{N}}\right) = 1 - \alpha \tag{7.7}$$

The number of degrees of freedom associated with t is $N - 1$.

To help the reader develop a more vivid concept of the fluctuation of the interval limits from sample to sample, data from the four samples enumerated on Worksheet I in Chapter 6 have been used to compute four confidence intervals with confidence coefficient .95. These interval estimates are shown in the last column of Table 7.1 under the heading $1 - \alpha = .95$. In this case μ is known to be 121.6 and one can see that it is contained in all four intervals. In the same table are also shown intervals with confidence coefficient .50 made from the same four samples and it may be noted that three of these contain μ and one does not. Intervals with confidence coefficients .95, .90 and .50 from Table 7.1 and intervals with confidence coefficient .10 not in that table are shown graphically in Figure 7–3. In each group the four unbroken lines represent intervals obtained from the four samples with $N = 5$ and the dotted line represents an interval obtained from the composite sample with $N = 20$. The small tick in the middle of each line represents the value of $\overline{X}$. Examining this graph one understands why the confidence coefficient is in practice never taken as a small number such as .10 or even .50.

Examination of Table 7.1 and Figure 7–3 leads to the following interpretations:

1. If N and s are fixed, the narrower the interval the less assurance there is that the population value is contained within it. (Look at the four intervals for any given sample.)

2. If N and the confidence coefficient are fixed, the smaller the value of s the narrower will the interval be. (Look at the four

unbroken lines in any one group, remembering that for these samples $s_3 < s_1 < s_4 < s_2$.)

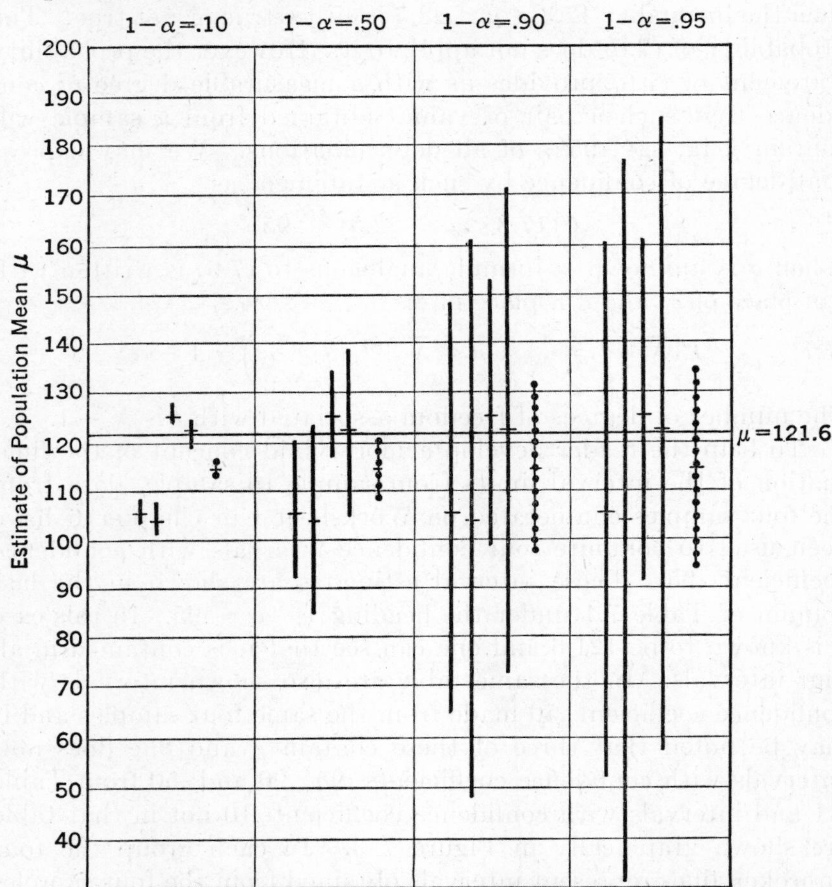

FIG. 7–3. Interval estimates of μ made with confidence coefficients of .10, .50, .90, and .95 from each of the four samples of 5 cases and from the composite sample of 20 cases. (Samples as given on Worksheet I.)

Dotted line is for composite sample. Horizontal tic is mean of sample.

3. As N increases, if the confidence coefficient is fixed, the interval becomes narrower. (In any one group compare the dotted line for $N = 20$ with four unbroken lines for $N = 5$.)

4. Samples of 5 cases provide very unreliable estimates. (Note that when there is high confidence that the population value lies in the interval the intervals are wide and that when intervals are narrow there can be little confidence that the population value lies in them.)

5. The confidence interval for the mean μ is symmetrically placed around the observed mean $\overline{X}$. (The confidence interval for the population variance discussed in the next chapter is not symmetrically placed around the observed variance.)

TABLE 7.1 Interval Estimates with Confidence Coefficients of .50, .90, and .95 Made for the Population Mean μ from the Data of the Four Samples of 5 Cases and of the Composite Sample of 20 Cases on Worksheet I.

Sample	$\overline{X}$	s	$s/\sqrt{N}$	Interval estimate		
				$1-\alpha=.50$	$1-\alpha=.90$	$1-\alpha=.95$
1	106.6	43.7	19.5	$92.2<\mu<121.0$	$65.0<\mu<148.2$	$52.5<\mu<160.7$
2	104.6	59.3	26.5	$85.0<\mu<124.2$	$48.1<\mu<161.1$	$31.0<\mu<178.1$
3	126.2	28.5	12.7	$117.0<\mu<135.4$	$99.1<\mu<153.2$	$90.9<\mu<161.5$
4	122.0	51.7	23.1	$104.9<\mu<139.1$	$72.8<\mu<171.2$	$57.9<\mu<186.1$
Composite	114.85	44.4	9.92	$108.0<\mu<121.7$	$97.7<\mu<132.0$	$94.2<\mu<135.5$

6. If the interval were narrowed to the single point $\mu = \overline{X}$, its confidence coefficient would be zero. If a confidence coefficient of 1.00 were required, the interval would have to be infinitely wide.

EXERCISE 7.3

1. From the samples you obtained in the sampling experiment of Chapter 6 compute a set of interval estimates by Formula (7.7) and draw lines on Figure 7–3 to represent these intervals. You may wish to use the same confidence coefficients employed there and thus increase the number of lines in each group, or to use another coefficient, say .80.

2. By substituting observed values of $\overline{X}$ and μ and values read from tables of "Student's" distribution, verify the interval estimates in Table 7.1 for confidence coefficients of .95 and .90.

3. What proportion of all samples is expected to yield interval estimates that contain μ if $1-\alpha = .95$? Of the 4 interval estimates made from the 4 observed samples how many did contain μ? Answer the same question for $1-\alpha = .90$, .50, and .10.

4. If a sample of 40 cases has a mean $\overline{X} = 27.2$ and a variance $s^2 = 13.6$, what interval estimate can be made for μ at the .99 level of confidence? At the .95 level?

Mean of a Population of Differences between Two Measures for Each Individual. This is a very common situation in research. Sometimes each individual is measured at the beginning and again at the end of an experiment and the gain is then treated as the basic measure to be studied. Sometimes two subjects are paired in such a way that the pair constitutes one individual and the difference between scores for members of the pair becomes the basic measure. An illustration may be taken from Wrightstone's *Appraisal of Newer Elementary School Practices.*[22] In each of six communities he selected two schools one of which he classified as "progressive" and one as "conservative." A test of knowledge of current affairs was given to children in each school and the school mean computed, with results as shown here. X_p and X_c indicate respectively the score of a "progressive" and of a "conservative" school, score for the school being the mean of the scores of all the children studied.

Community	X_p	X_c	$D = X_p - X_c$	D^2
A	32.7	28.2	4.5	20.25
B	33.1	29.1	4.0	16.00
C	35.2	31.9	3.3	10.89
D	36.0	33.1	2.9	8.41
E	36.2	31.4	4.8	23.04
F	39.1	35.3	3.8	14.44
TOTAL	212.3	189.0	23.3	93.03

We must consider a population of communities in each of which there is a "progressive" and a "conservative" school for which a difference score D can be obtained. Such a population is conceptual. It would be an enormously difficult task to enumerate all the communities in this population and take a sample from them. We are interested in the hypothesis that for this conceptual population the expectation of all such differences is zero, $\mu_D = 0$. To test it we shall need the observed mean and standard deviation $\overline{D}$ and s_D for the six communities in the sample and the standard error of $\overline{D}$:

$$\text{(7.8)} \qquad \overline{D} = \frac{\Sigma D}{N}$$

$$\text{(7.9)} \qquad s_D{}^2 = \frac{N\Sigma D^2 - (\Sigma D)^2}{N(N-1)}$$

$$\text{(7.10)} \qquad s_{\overline{D}} = \sqrt{\frac{s_D{}^2}{N}} = \sqrt{\frac{N\Sigma D^2 - (\Sigma D)^2}{N^2(N-1)}}$$

$$t = \frac{\overline{D}}{s_{\overline{D}}} = \frac{\dfrac{\Sigma D}{N}}{\sqrt{\dfrac{N\Sigma D^2 - (\Sigma D)^2}{N^2(N-1)}}}$$

which can be more easily computed by the equivalent formula

$$t = \frac{\Sigma D}{\sqrt{\dfrac{N\Sigma D^2 - (\Sigma D)^2}{N - 1}}} \tag{7.11}$$

By Formula (7.11) $t = \dfrac{23.3}{\sqrt{\dfrac{6(93.03) - (23.3)^2}{5}}} = 13.3$

We find in Table IX on the row for which $n = 5$ that $t_{.9995} = 6.86$, and the observed value of t is very much larger than this tabulated value. Consequently it is almost inconceivable (though not impossible) that the population difference is zero. The statistical analysis does not indicate the cause of the difference but indicates strongly that the difference is positive and should not be attributed to chance and that therefore it has meaning, is significant. Naturally a research worker will examine his procedures carefully to see if any influence other than the one he is studying could have crept into his data and will not assume a significant difference to be due to the experimental factor unless there seems no other reasonable way to account for it.

The quotient $t = \overline{D}/s_{\overline{D}}$ has "Student's" distribution with $N - 1 = 5$ degrees of freedom. Hence an interval estimate at confidence level .99 may be made for the population difference by the general plan of Formula (7.6) as follows:

$$3.88 - (4.032)(.291) < \mu < 3.88 + (4.032)(.291)$$
$$2.71 < \mu < 5.05$$

Therefore the mean advantage enjoyed by the "progressive" school over the "conservative" with respect to knowledge of current affairs on the part of the pupils may be estimated at somewhere between 2.7 and 5.1 points.

Authors do not usually publish the raw scores on which their computations are based, although such data would often be of great value to other persons working in the same field. Suppose a published study gives the mean and variance of a sample at the beginning and at the end of an experimental period and also gives the correlation coefficient between scores at the beginning and at the end but does not give individual scores. The differences $D_i = X_{1i} - X_{2i}$ cannot be computed as was done for the Wrightstone data and so their variance cannot be computed directly. However the mean and variance of these differences can be obtained from the mean and variance of each set of scores and the correlation * between them, as

$$\overline{D} = \overline{X}_2 - \overline{X}_1 \tag{7.12}$$

$$s_D^2 = s_1^2 - 2r_{12}s_1s_2 + s_2^2 \tag{7.13}$$

An illustration may be taken from a study by F. L. Westover.[21] This is a study of three methods of improving reading speed and comprehension among college students. For our present purposes we shall deal with one small aspect of this study only. For the 45 students who were taught by the method of controlled eye movements the mean and standard deviation on an initial test of rate of reading were as given on page 42 of Westover's study:

	$\overline{X}$	s
X_1 = Initial test	39.20	5.97
X_2 = Final test	43.07	7.85
D = Gain	3.87	

The coefficient of correlation between the tests was $r_{12} = .51$.

Then $\quad s_D^2 = (5.97)^2 + (7.85)^2 - 2(.51)(5.97)(7.85) = 49.46$

and $\quad s_{\overline{D}}^2 = \dfrac{49.46}{45} = 1.099$

and $\quad t = \dfrac{3.87}{\sqrt{1.099}} = 3.7$

There can be little doubt that use of this method of instruction results in improved reading when applied to individuals like those in this study.

Test of Hypotheses About $\mu_1 - \mu_2$. *A. When σ_1 and σ_2 are Known.* Assume that a sample of N_1 cases has been drawn from a normal population with mean μ_1 and variance $\sigma^2{}_1$, and another independent sample of N_2 cases has been drawn from a normal population with mean μ_2 and variance $\sigma^2{}_2$. The two sample means $\overline{X}_1$ and $\overline{X}_2$ are distributed with means μ_1 and μ_2 and standard deviations $\sigma_1/\sqrt{N}$ and $\sigma_2/\sqrt{N}$. The mean difference $\overline{X}_1 - \overline{X}_2$ is distributed normally with mean $\mu_1 - \mu_2$ and variance

$$\sigma^2{}_{\overline{X}_1-\overline{X}_2} = \frac{\sigma_1{}^2}{N_1} + \frac{\sigma_2{}^2}{N_2} \tag{7.14}$$

* Readers who have not become at least superficially acquainted with the correlation coefficient in an introductory course might defer this section until they have studied Chapter 10, or might read it now taking the concept of correlation on faith.

Then the quotient

$$(7.15) \qquad z = \frac{\overline{X}_1 - \overline{X}_2 - (\mu_1 - \mu_2)}{\sqrt{\frac{\sigma_1^2}{N_1} + \frac{\sigma_2^2}{N_2}}}$$

has the unit normal distribution.

When the hypothesis tested is that $\mu_1 - \mu_2 = 0$, Formula (7.15) reduces to

$$(7.16) \qquad z = \frac{\overline{X}_1 - \overline{X}_2}{\sqrt{\frac{\sigma_1^2}{N_1} + \frac{\sigma_2^2}{N_2}}}$$

In the special case when the two populations have the same variance, $\sigma_1^2 = \sigma_2^2 = \sigma^2$, the variance of the mean difference becomes

$$(7.17) \qquad \sigma^2_{\overline{X}_1 - \overline{X}_2} = \sigma^2\left(\frac{N_1 + N_2}{N_1 N_2}\right)$$

and the ratio used to test the null hypothesis $\mu_1 - \mu_2 = 0$ can be reduced to the form

$$(7.18) \qquad z = \frac{\overline{X}_1 - \overline{X}_2}{\sigma}\sqrt{\frac{N_1 N_2}{N_1 + N_2}}$$

B. When σ_1 and σ_2 are Unknown but Presumed Equal. In a study which has as its aim the comparison of the means of two populations, both the means and the standard deviations must ordinarily be estimated from the samples. To illustrate the type of data which may be obtained in such a study consider the following unpublished data from scores on a mathematics test obtained from a sample of 12 full-time women students at Barnard College and a sample of 11 part-time women students enrolled in the School of General Studies at Columbia. The means were respectively 82.08 and 72.64, and it is desired to test the hypothesis that the population means are equal, $\mu_1 - \mu_2 = 0$.

Such a test is frequently carried out by using Formula (7.16), substituting sample standard deviations for population standard deviations, and referring the results to a normal probability table. However this substitution produces a statistic in which the denominator as well as the numerator is subject to sampling error.

If the sample variances are not inconsistent with the hypothesis that population variances are equal, the test for which will be described in Chapter 8, a more satisfactory procedure is to estimate this common variance and to replace σ^2 in Formula (7.17) by that estimate. An unbiased estimate of σ^2 based on data from 2 samples is provided by

$$(7.19) \qquad s^2 = \frac{\sum_{i=1}^{N_1} (X_{i1} - \overline{X}_1)^2 + \sum_{i=1}^{N_2} (X_{i2} - \overline{X}_2)^2}{N_1 + N_2 - 2}$$

When raw scores are available, Formula (7.19) may be conveniently reduced to

$$(7.20) \qquad s^2 = \frac{\sum_{i=1}^{N_1} X_{i1}^2 + \sum_{i=1}^{N_2} X_{i2}^2 - \frac{\left(\sum_{i=1}^{N_1} X_{i1}\right)^2}{N_1} - \frac{\left(\sum_{i=1}^{N_2} X_{i2}\right)^2}{N_2}}{N_1 + N_2 - 2}$$

When raw scores are not available but standard deviations or variances are, the formula may be written as

$$(7.21) \qquad s^2 = \frac{(N_1 - 1)s_1^2 + (N_2 - 1)s_2^2}{N_1 + N_2 - 2}$$

These various formulas are algebraically equivalent but if raw scores are at hand it would be obviously inefficient to compute s and insert it in Formula (7.21) because the routine of (7.20) involves less rounding error. After estimating the common population variance by Formula (7.20) or (7.21), the obtained estimate is substituted for σ^2 in Formula (7.17) to obtain an estimate of the variance of the difference between the two means:

$$(7.22) \qquad s^2_{\overline{X}_1 - \overline{X}_2} = s^2\left(\frac{N_1 + N_2}{N_1 N_2}\right)$$

Then when $\mu_1 - \mu_2 = 0$, the formula for t becomes

$$(7.23) \qquad t = \frac{\overline{X}_1 - \overline{X}_2}{\sqrt{s^2 \frac{N_1 + N_2}{N_1 N_2}}} \quad \text{and this}$$

has "Student's" distribution with $N_1 + N_2 - 2$ degrees of freedom.

Now let us return to the problem concerning the comparison of Barnard and general studies students. For each group we need to know the values of N, ΣX and ΣX^2. These data are

	N	ΣX	ΣX^2	$\overline{X}$
Barnard group	12	985	83691	82.08
General studies group	11	799	62149	72.64

Substituting these numbers in Formula (7.20) gives

$$s^2 = \frac{83691 - \frac{(985)^2}{12} + 62149 - \frac{(799)^2}{11}}{12 + 11 - 2} = 331.05$$

From Formula (7.23) we then have

$$t = \frac{82.08 - 72.64}{\sqrt{331.05\left(\frac{23}{(12)(11)}\right)}} = 1.24$$

Since $t = 1.24$ is well within the customary region of acceptance, we accept the hypothesis $\mu_1 = \mu_2$ and say the Barnard students have not been shown to differ from general studies students in respect to scores on this arithmetic test. It must however be noted that when samples are small and variability large, the observed difference must be very large to appear significant. The failure to find a significant difference may be due to the small number of cases examined rather than to the equality of population means.

C. When σ_1 and σ_2 are Unknown but Presumed Unequal and Samples are Large. If the test for equality of the variance to be described in Chapter 8 has been applied and indicates that it is not reasonable to consider the two populations as equally variable, then estimating a common variance as described in the preceding section would be inappropriate. In this situation the choice of the method for estimating the standard error of the mean difference depends upon the size of the samples.

If the samples are not small, say 30 or more cases in each, the standard error of the mean difference may be computed as

(7.24) $$s^2_{\overline{X}_1 - \overline{X}_2} = \frac{s_1^2}{N_1} + \frac{s_2^2}{N_2}$$

(7.25) Then $$t = \frac{\overline{X}_1 - \overline{X}_2 - (\mu_1 - \mu_2)}{\sqrt{\frac{s_1^2}{N_1} + \frac{s_2^2}{N_2}}}$$

may be referred to a table of normal probability because n is so large that the statistic has a distribution approximating the normal.

D. When σ_1 and σ_2 are Unknown but Presumed Unequal and Samples are Small. Suppose samples of size N_1 and N_2 are drawn from normal populations with unknown means and variances, and suppose it appears unreasonable to assume that $\sigma_1 = \sigma_2$. (A test for the hypothesis $\sigma_1 = \sigma_2$ is given in Chapter 8.) To test the hypothesis $\mu_1 = \mu_2$ set $\mu_1 - \mu_2 = 0$ in Formula (7.25) and the resulting statistic has "Student's" distribution with degrees of freedom given by the expression

$$(7.26) \qquad n = \frac{\left(\frac{s_1^2}{N_1} + \frac{s_2^2}{N_2}\right)^2}{\left(\frac{s_1^2}{N_1}\right)^2 \frac{1}{N_1 + 1} + \left(\frac{s_2^2}{N_2}\right)^2 \frac{1}{N_2 + 1}} - 2$$

The value of n given by this formula will seldom be an integer, but usually a good approximation can be obtained by using the nearest integer.

Example: Suppose the sample data are

$N_1 = 10$, $\bar{X}_1 = 35.3$, $s_1^2 = 8$, $\alpha = .05$

$N_2 = 8$, $\bar{X}_2 = 31.1$, $s_2^2 = 24$

Then

$$\frac{s_1^2}{N_1} = .8 \text{ and } \frac{s_2^2}{N_2} = 3.0$$

$$t = \frac{35.3 - 31.1}{\sqrt{3.8}} = \frac{4.20}{1.95} = 2.156$$

$$n = \frac{(.8 + 3)^2}{\frac{(.8)^2}{11} + \frac{(3)^2}{9}} - 2 = 13.6 - 2 = 11.6$$

If n be taken as 11, the region of acceptance is $-2.20 < t < 2.20$; if n be taken as 12, the region of acceptance is $-2.18 < t < 2.18$; and in either case the statistic falls in the region of acceptance. Interpolation is unnecessary to reach a decision.

Formula (7.26) is an approximation to a longer formula given by Welch in the reference at the end of this chapter.

E. When μ_1 and μ_2 are Themselves Differences. Sometimes a research worker has a problem in which he must compare the difference of two means for group *A* with the difference of two similar means for group *B*, the two groups being independent.

If the difference between the two means for one group is based on two measures of the same individual, the difference can be treated in the manner described on page 151. Thus if the problem were to find whether children taught by Method I gained more than children taught by Method II during a specified period, the first step would be to find the gain for each child, as the difference between his initial and final scores. Suppose that difference is called D. Then $\overline{X}_D$ and s_D are computed for each group. The hypothesis $\mu_{D_1} - \mu_{D_2} = 0$ is then tested by the methods described in sections A, B, C, or D, whichever is appropriate.

Consider, however, the situation in which no pairing of scores is possible. Suppose a difference between sexes has been found at one age level and another difference found at another age level. To formalize the statement of the hypothesis, it will be assumed that there are four populations, one at each age level for each sex and that each population is normally distributed. It will be further assumed that each population has the same standard deviation, σ, but that the four means may possibly be different. For convenience we shall call the four populations A, B, C and D as in the adjacent display. Suppose now that a random sample is taken from each population. These samples need not be of the same size. For each sample the statistics ΣX and ΣX^2 are computed, as in the adjacent display.

TABLE 7.2 Statistics Required for Comparison of Two Mean Differences

Population	Population values	Sample statistics required
A. Male, aged 10	μ_A, σ	N_A, ΣX_A, ΣX^2_A
B. Female, aged 10	μ_B, σ	N_B, ΣX_B, ΣX^2_B
C. Male, aged 16	μ_C, σ	N_C, ΣX_C, ΣX^2_C
D. Female, aged 16	μ_D, σ	N_D, ΣX_D, ΣX^2_D

An estimate of σ^2 based on raw data is given by

(7.27)

$$s^2 = \frac{\Sigma X^2_A + \Sigma X^2_B + \Sigma X^2_C + \Sigma X^2_D - \frac{(\Sigma X_A)^2}{N_A} - \frac{(\Sigma X_B)^2}{N_B} - \frac{(\Sigma X_C)^2}{N_C} - \frac{(\Sigma X_D)^2}{N_D}}{N_A + N_B + N_C + N_D - 4}$$

If raw data are not available but the variances are, then the same result can be obtained by

$$\text{(7.28)}\quad s^2 = \frac{(N_A - 1)s^2_A + (N_B - 1)s^2_B + (N_C - 1)s^2_C + (N_D - 1)s^2_D}{N_A + N_B + N_C + N_D - 4}$$

If the hypothesis to be tested is that $(\mu_A - \mu_B) = (\mu_C - \mu_D)$ then the statistic

$$\text{(7.29)}\qquad t = \frac{(\overline{X}_A - \overline{X}_B) - (\overline{X}_C - \overline{X}_D)}{s\sqrt{\frac{1}{N_A} + \frac{1}{N_B} + \frac{1}{N_C} + \frac{1}{N_D}}}$$

has "Student's" Distribution with $N_A + N_B + N_C + N_D - 4$ degrees of freedom.

A comparison of differences of means will be treated in Chapter 14 under the topic of *interaction*.

EXERCISE 7.4

1. Terman and Miles in *Sex and Personality*[19] give masculinity ratings for a group of gifted boys with intelligence quotients of 140 and above and for a control group of unselected boys, as follows:

	N	$\bar{X}$	s
Gifted boys	290	15.22	1.45
Controls	161	14.90	1.49

Do the data give warrant for asserting that gifted boys tend to have higher masculinity ratings than others?

2. In the study by Westover[21] previously quoted the following data were obtained for the 45 students taught by the use of special practice exercises:

	$\bar{X}$	s	
Initial score on vocabulary test	55.96	4.92	$r_{12} = .75$
Final score on vocabulary test	57.44	7.56	

Test the hypothesis that increase in mean score is due to chance.

3. Long[11] reports a study of a comparison of the motor abilities of deaf and hearing children. Deaf subjects were children in residence at the Institution for the Improved Instruction of Deaf Mutes. These were paired with hearing children of the same age and sex. No subjects in either group had known defects other than deafness which might affect motor performance. Seven tests of motor discrimination were given to all subjects and the results analyzed separately for the boys and the girls.

In Table 7.3 is the list of raw scores for 10 out of 37 girl pairs on a test of balance and on a test of grip for the average of the two hands. Scores of deaf children are marked D and scores of hearing children marked H.

TABLE 7.3 Scores on Test of Grip and Test of Balance by 10 Deaf Girls (*D*) and 10 Hearing Girls (*H*) Paired on Basis of Age*

Pair	Score on grip		Score on balance		Pair	Score on grip		Score on balance	
	D	H	D	H		D	H	D	H
1	25	26	2.0	2.3	6	48	51	1.7	4.3
2	22	22	2.0	1.0	7	49	42	2.0	4.7
3	28	29	2.7	3.7	8	54	54	2.0	7.0
4	35	39	2.7	3.3	9	65	77	2.7	3.3
5	37	34	3.0	10.0	10	57	68	1.0	1.7

* Data from Long.[11]

For each trait make the appropriate computations and test the hypothesis that the difference between deaf and hearing girls is zero.

Alternatives to a Hypothetical Mean. Suppose that a population can be assumed to be normal and to have a standard deviation, $\sigma = 10$, but that the mean μ is unknown. Suppose the hypothesis is formulated that $\mu = 50$, and is tested by a sample of 25 observations. The critical region is constructed at a significance level of .05 and the assumption that μ is actually 50. Since $\sigma/\sqrt{N}$ is 2 and $1.96\sigma/\sqrt{N}$ is 3.92 the critical region consists of all values of $\overline{X}$ less than 46.08 or greater than 53.92.

If the hypothesis, $\mu = 50$, is true, the probability is .05 that $\overline{X}$ will have a value in the critical region. But what is the probability that $\overline{X}$ will have a value in the critical region when μ has some value other than 50? Consider the three alternatives $\mu = 48$, $\mu = 52$, and $\mu = 56$. If either of these alternatives is true this alternative will be the actual mean of the distribution of $\overline{X}$. The standard error is unchanged for these alternatives since σ is assumed known. The shaded areas in Figure 7–4 represent the probabilities that $\overline{X}$ will fall in the critical region if each of the

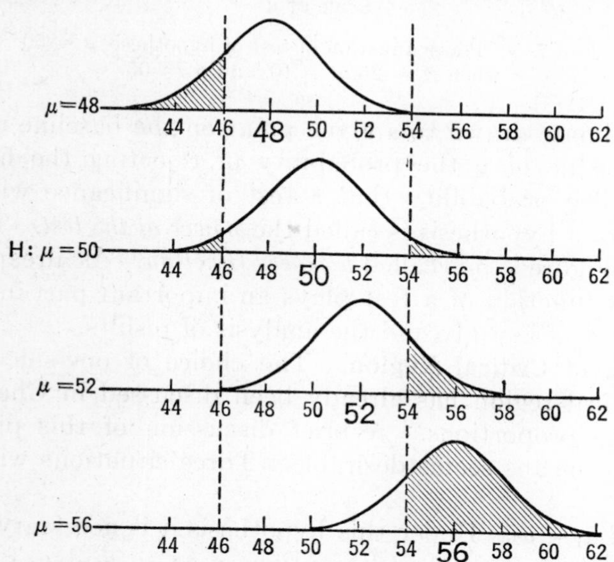

FIG. 7–4. Distribution of $\overline{X}$ when $N = 25$, $\sigma = 10$, and $\mu = 48$, 50, 52, or 56. Under $H: \mu = 50$, critical region with $\alpha = .05$ is $\overline{X} < 46.1$ and $\overline{X} > 53.9$ Shaded area indicates probability that $\overline{X}$ will fall into critical region. This probability is

.17 if $\mu = 48$ .17 if $\mu = 52$
.05 if $\mu = 50$ .85 if $\mu = 56$

alternatives $\mu = 48$, $\mu = 50$, $\mu = 52$, and $\mu = 56$ is true. These probabilities are respectively 17, .05, .17, and .85.

These probabilities suggest that whenever the true value of μ differs greatly from the hypothetical value being tested (which in this case is 50) the probability of rejecting the hypothesis is great but when the true value of μ is not very different from the value stated in the hypothesis tested, the probability of rejection is small. In Figure 7–5 the horizontal axis represents values of μ. The hypothetical value being tested is presumed to be $\mu = 50$.

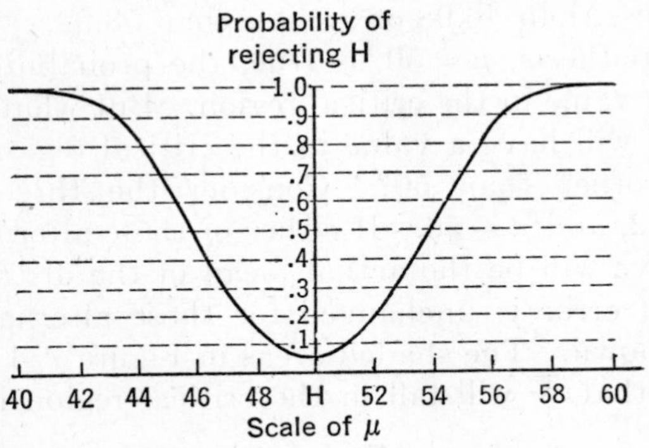

FIG. 7–5. Power function of test of hypothesis $\mu = 50$ when $N = 25$, $\sigma = 10$, and $\alpha = .05$.

An ordinate drawn to a given point on the baseline represents for that value of μ the probability of rejecting the hypothesis $\mu = 50$. The probability that a test of significance will lead to rejection of a hypothesis is called the *power of the test*. The curve shown in Figure 7–5 is called a *power function*. As already stated, the power function of a test plays an important part in planning the conduct of a study and the analysis of results.

Choice of Critical Region. The choice of one-sided or two-sided critical region has already been discussed in Chapter 3 in relation to proportions. A brief discussion of this problem in relation to means seems desirable. Three situations will be considered.

A. $H: \mu_1 = \mu_2$. Under this hypothesis it is necessary to guard oneself against both the alternatives $\mu_1 > \mu_2$ and $\mu_1 < \mu_2$. The risk of being wrong can then be minimized best by using a two-sided critical region, for such a region leads to high probabilities of rejection of the hypothesis both when μ_1 is much greater or much less than μ_2. The critical region is then $t < t_{\frac{1}{2}\alpha}$ and $t > t_{1-\frac{1}{2}\alpha}$.

B. $H: \mu_1 < \mu_2$. This hypothesis means that one is satisfied if μ_1 is less than μ_2 regardless what the difference may be. The alternatives against which it is necessary to guard oneself are $\mu_1 > \mu_2$. The critical region which leads most often to rejection of the hypothesis when it is false is $t > t_{1-\alpha}$.

C. $H: \mu_1 > \mu_2$. By analogous reasoning the critical region for this hypothesis is $t < t_\alpha$.

The Number of Cases Needed to Reject a Hypothesis Concerning μ When Some Alternative Is True. A problem similar in purpose to this one was discussed in Chapter 3 but there the hypothesis related to the population proportion. The decision as to how large a sample shall be taken is always a very fundamental aspect of the plans for an investigation. If a difference actually exists between two population means but the samples taken are too small, the observed difference in the sample means may be nonsignificant. Then all the work of the study is wasted, whereas somewhat larger samples would have produced a positive conclusion. On the other hand, to take samples larger than necessary to establish the mean difference is a waste of time and money which could be better expended otherwise. When an observed difference is nonsignificant, the research worker is usually in a quandary as to how to interpret his findings. Is the real difference zero, or has he used too small a sample to establish a difference which actually exists? He can make a far stronger statement in this situation if he has determined in advance how many cases he would need to find a difference of a predetermined size with a specified risk of error. Having determined the value of N in advance by a little algebra, if he carries out the study as planned and obtains a nonsignificant result, he can dismiss the argument that his sample was too small, and can state, with a specified degree of confidence, that the population difference is less than the predetermined value.

To make the decision as to size of N, practical experience must be relied on for answers to these questions:

1. How large a difference (d) would it be of practical importance to find if it exists in the population? For example, a clinical psychologist may say "If schizophrenics differ from normals by so-and-so much I want to reject the hypothesis that their means are equal; if the difference is less than that amount I do not care whether we find it or not."

2. What estimate can be made for the population variance?

Unless the area of investigation is entirely new, it is often possible to get from previous studies a rough estimate of the variance, or perhaps an estimate that it lies between two specified values.

3. How much risk can be taken of deciding that a difference exists when it really is zero? This decision is the choice of α.

4. How much risk can be taken of deciding that a difference is zero when it really is as large as the predetermined value d? This is β, the risk of error of the second kind.

When these four values (d, σ^2, α, and β) have been chosen on nonstatistical grounds, the statistician can determine the necessary size of N by some easy algebra.

Suppose we wish to test the hypothesis that $\mu = 75$ with a *two-sided test* at .02 significance level. We have some prior knowledge about variability and we hazard a guess that $\sigma = 8$. We decide that if the actual value of μ differs from 75 by 5 points or more in either direction, we wish to detect the existence of a difference d with probability .60, that is, we want β to be no greater than .40 for any alternative outside the range 70 to 80. How large a sample will be required?

The specified values are these:

$\mu_H = 75$ = value under the hypothesis	$d_1 = 80 - 75 = 5$
$\mu_1 = 80$ = one alternative value	$d_2 = 70 - 75 = -5$
$\mu_2 = 70$ = second alternative value	$\alpha = .02,\ \beta = .40,\ \sigma = 8$

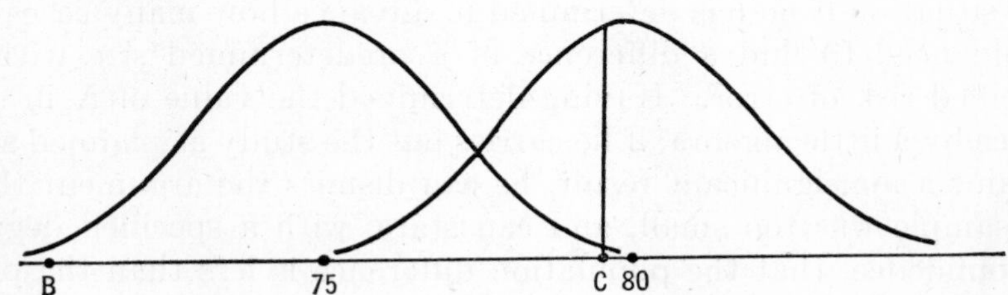

The solution is analogous to that given on page 69 for a hypothesis about a proportion. In the adjacent sketch, the curve with mean $\mu_H = 75$ represents the sampling distribution of $\overline{X}$ under the hypothesis, and the line segment BC is the region of acceptance for $H : \mu = 75$. This region has probability .98. Then

$$C = 75 + z_{.99}\sigma_{\overline{X}} \quad \text{and} \quad B = 75 + z_{.01}\sigma_{\overline{X}}.$$

If $\mu = 80$ instead of 75, the curve on the right represents the actual sampling distribution of $\overline{X}$ and the area under this curve to the left of the ordinate at C is the probability of false acceptance of $H: \mu = 75$ when $\mu = 80$. Since we have said this probability is not to be larger than $\beta = .40$, the point C must be $z_{.40}\sigma_{\overline{X}}$ units from 80, or $C = 80 + z_{.40}\sigma_{\overline{X}}$. As β will always be chosen to be less than .50, z_β will always be negative. If μ is actually larger than 80, β will be even smaller than if $\mu = 80$, and so the requirements of the problem are fulfilled.

Then $\quad C = 75 + z_{.99}\sigma_{\overline{X}}$ and also $C = 80 + z_{.40}\sigma_{\overline{X}}$

Hence $\quad 75 + z_{.99}\sigma_{\overline{X}} = 80 + z_{.40}\sigma_{\overline{X}}$

or $\quad 80 - 75 = \sigma_{\overline{X}}(z_{.99} - z_{.40}) = -\sigma_{\overline{X}}(z_{.01} + z_{.40})$

$$5 = \frac{8}{\sqrt{N}}(2.326 + .253)$$

and $\quad N = (\tfrac{8}{5}(2.326 + .253))^2 = 17.0$

If μ_A should be larger than 80, the curve representing the actual sampling distribution will be farther to the right so β will be less than .40 and the computed value of N will be less than 17. Taking $N = 17$ will then amply satisfy the requirements of the problem.

The argument for $\mu_A = 70$ is similar. The curve representing the actual sampling distribution is to the left and not shown in the diagram.

Then $\quad B = 75 + z_{.01}\sigma_{\overline{X}}$ and $B = 70 + z_{.60}\sigma_{\overline{X}}$

and therefore $\quad 75 + z_{.01}\sigma_{\overline{X}} = 70 + z_{.40}\sigma_{\overline{X}}$

$$75 - 70 = \sigma_{\overline{X}}(z_{.60} - z_{.01})$$

$$5 = \frac{8}{\sqrt{N}}(.253 + 2.326)$$

and $\quad N = (\tfrac{8}{5}(2.579))^2 = 17.0$ as before.

If a *one-sided* test had been used, the only difference would have been in the position of C with respect to μ_H. Its position with respect to μ_A would be unchanged. Then $C = 75 + z_{.98}\sigma_{\overline{X}}$,

and $\quad N = (\tfrac{8}{5}(2.054 + .253))^2 = 14$

In general if $d = \mu_A - \mu_H$ is the departure from hypothesis which it is desired to detect, N may be calculated as follows:

(7.30) For the two-sided test, $N = \left(\frac{\sigma}{d}(z_{\frac{1}{2}\alpha} + z_\beta)\right)^2 = \frac{\sigma^2}{d^2}(z_{\frac{1}{2}\alpha} + z_\beta)^2$

(7.31) and for the one-sided test, $N = \left(\frac{\sigma}{d}(z_\alpha + z_\beta)\right)^2 = \frac{\sigma^2}{d^2}(z_\alpha + z_\beta)^2$

Both formulas indicate that as the discrepancy becomes larger it can be detected with a smaller sample and as d becomes very small only a large sample can cause rejection of the hypothesis when it is false.

Now suppose we do not know the value of σ but we have two or more estimates available, of which σ_1 is the smallest and σ_2 the largest. If we substitute σ_1 for σ in the formula we shall obtain an estimate N_1 of the necessary sample size. If we substitute σ_2 for σ we shall obtain a second estimate N_2 larger than N_1. While it cannot be guaranteed that either sample size will exactly meet the specifications of the problem, these numbers provide estimates which are a vastly better guide to research planning than the blind guess all too often followed.

Suppose there are two populations presumed to have the same variance σ^2 and we wish to test the hypothesis $\mu_1 - \mu_2 = 0$, with α and β chosen arbitrarily as before. How many cases shall be taken in each sample? If the cost of obtaining a single case is the same for each sample, the best procedure is to take samples of the same size, $N_1 = N_2 = N$, and to determine the number of cases in each by the formula

$$(7.32) \qquad N = \frac{2\sigma^2}{d^2}(z_\alpha + z_\beta)^2 \text{ for the one-sided test.}$$

The formula for the two-sided test is similar with $\frac{1}{2}\alpha$ substituted for α.

Suppose the two populations are presumed to have unequal variances and these are estimated to be $\sigma^2{}_1$ and $\sigma^2{}_2$. Again we wish to test the hypothesis $\mu_1 = \mu_2$. If the cost of obtaining a single case is the same for each sample, the best procedure is to make sample size proportional to the standard deviations and to let

$$(7.33) \qquad N_1 = \frac{\sigma^2{}_1 + \sigma_1\sigma_2}{d^2}(z_\alpha + z_\beta)^2$$

$$(7.34) \text{ and} \qquad N_2 = \frac{\sigma_1\sigma_2 + \sigma^2{}_2}{d^2}(z_\alpha + z_\beta)^2$$

for the one-sided test. In the corresponding formula for the two-sided test, $z_{\frac{1}{2}\alpha}$ takes the place of z_α.

By way of illustration, suppose the person planning a research study estimates $\sigma_1 = 5$ and $\sigma_2 = 8$ as a fair approximation for the standard deviations of the two populations, and chooses $\alpha = .01$

and $\beta = .20$. He thinks it important to be able to detect a difference between the means if it is 1.5 or larger. The statistician then estimates that the number of cases to be taken from the two populations should be

$$N_1 = \frac{25 + 40}{2.25}(2.326 + .842)^2 = 290$$

$$N_2 = \frac{40 + 64}{2.25}(2.326 + .842)^2 = 464$$

and verifies that $\frac{290}{464} = \frac{5}{8}$.

If the person paying for the study feels that $N = N_1 + N_2 = 754$ is larger than he can afford, he may revise his choice of α, of β, or of d. The ratio of $\frac{N_1}{N_2}$ will remain $\frac{5}{8}$ in any case.

Verify the following results if $\sigma_1 = 5$, $\sigma_2 = 8$ and a one-tailed test is used:

If $\alpha = .05$, $\beta = .20$ and $d = 1.5$, $N_1 = 179$, $N_2 = 286$ and $N = 465$
If $\alpha = .01$, $\beta = .30$ and $d = 1.5$, $N_1 = 235$, $N_2 = 375$ and $N = 610$
If $\alpha = .01$, $\beta = .20$ and $d = 2$, $N_1 = 163$, $N_2 = 261$ and $N = 424$
If $\alpha = .05$, $\beta = .30$ and $d = 2$, $N_1 = 76$, $N_2 = 122$ and $N = 198$

Standard Error of $\bar{X}$ in Samples from a Finite Population. The formula $\sigma_{\bar{X}} = \frac{\sigma}{\sqrt{N}}$ is correct when the sample is small in comparison with the population. This situation is usually true of experimental studies. In such studies the population which is sampled may not even be entirely in existence at the time of the experiment. Thus, the results of a study on children may be applied to children not yet born at the time of the study. In experimental studies the populations are usually regarded as infinitely large.

Another type of study is one which applies to a well-defined population of finite size. The purpose of the investigation may be to determine the average score of students in a particular college on a scale measuring their attitude toward a current college policy. Suppose the college population consists of M students. If the scale is given to all students then the mean and variance of the scores can be ascertained exactly by the formulas.

(7.35) $$\mu = \frac{\sum_{i=1}^{M} X_i}{M}$$

$$\sigma^2 = \frac{\sum_{i=1}^{M} (X_i - \mu)^2}{M} \tag{7.36}$$

If the purpose of the study is to measure only the attitude of the students actually enrolled in the college the mean in Formula (7.35) provides the answer without sampling error. The standard error of μ is zero. There may, of course, be other errors, such as unreliability of the scale, but sampling error has been eliminated by using the entire population.

It may be uneconomical or otherwise undesirable to apply the scale to all M students. A sample of N may, therefore, be selected at random. An average calculated from this sample is subject to sampling error and a standard error formula is required. It is to be expected that the formula will reflect not only the size of the sample but also this size in relation to the size of the population sampled.

If the sample mean is written

$$\overline{X} = \frac{\sum_{i=1}^{N} X_i}{N}$$

then

$$\sigma_{\overline{X}} = \frac{\sigma}{\sqrt{N}} \sqrt{\frac{M - N}{M - 1}} \tag{7.37}$$

where σ is defined in Formula (7.36). Since σ is not known the sample estimate s is used and

$$s_{\overline{X}} = \frac{s}{\sqrt{N}} \sqrt{\frac{M - N}{M - 1}} \tag{7.38}$$

An examination of Formula (7.37) shows that $\sigma_{\overline{X}} = 0$ when $N = M$, as is to be expected where the sample consists of the entire population. If N is small in comparison to M, the factor $\sqrt{\frac{M - N}{M - 1}}$ is close to 1 and may be disregarded. This leads to the formula for the standard error of a mean from an infinite population.

If M is large, $M - 1$ may be replaced by M, and the factor $\sqrt{\frac{M - N}{M - 1}}$ may be written with close approximation as $\sqrt{1 - \frac{N}{M}}$, where $\frac{N}{M}$ is the fraction of the population included in the sample.

EXERCISE 7.5

1. A mental test has been administered to 1000 students. After the test has been given to the entire group it is decided to estimate the mean score of the 1000 students from a sample of 500 papers. These yield $\overline{X} = 35$ and $s = 5$.

a. What is the estimate of the standard error of $\overline{X}$?

b. What would it be if the number of students in the sample were 100?

c. 900?

Assume that $\overline{X}$ and s are unchanged as sample size changes.

2. Given $s = 5$ as above, what would the standard error be for samples of (a) 500, (b) 100, and (c) 900, if the samples were considered to be drawn from an infinite population? By what proportion is the standard error reduced if finiteness of the population is taken into account?

3. If s is 5 and the population is 1000, what must be the sample size to make the standard error $\frac{1}{2}$ of its value calculated on the basis of an infinite population?

4. Given $N_1 = 6$, $\overline{X}_1 = 29.5$, $s_1^2 = 24$

$N_2 = 5$, $\overline{X}_2 = 25.1$, $s_2^2 = 64$

Compute t to test $H : \mu_1 - \mu_2 = 0$, with two-sided test and $\alpha = .01$

a. Using Formulas (7.21) and (7.22) with $n = 6 + 5 - 2$

b. Using Formula (7.25) with $n = 6 + 5 - 2$

c. Using Formula (7.25) with n as given by (7.26)

Why do the results not agree? Which answer do you consider to be best?

5. As an algebraic exercise, show that if $N_1 = N_2$, the routine of Formula (7.24) will give exactly the same result as Formulas (7.21) and (7.22).

6. As an algebraic exercise, show that if $s^2{}_1 = s^2{}_2$, the routine of Formula (7.24) will give exactly the same result as Formulas (7.21) and (7.22).

7. In a sample of 12 cases, $\overline{X} = 31.8$ and $s = 4.8$.

a. Test $H : \mu = 35$ with $\alpha = .05$ using a two-sided test.

b. Test $H : \mu = 35$ with $\alpha = .05$ using a one-sided test with right tail critical.

c. Test $H : \mu = 35$ with $\alpha = .05$ using a one-sided test with left tail critical.

d. Compute the confidence interval for μ with confidence coefficient .95.

e. Compute the confidence interval for μ with confidence coefficient .99.

8. For each of the following situations a test is to be made of the hypothesis that two population means are equal. Give the number of the formula by which you would compute the standard error for variance of the difference in sample means. After you divide the difference in sample means by its standard error, would you consult the normal probability table or a table of "Student's" distribution? If the latter, with what number of degrees of freedom would you enter the table?

a. 300 pupils in the sixth grade are given a test in speed of reading in September and again in May in order to compare their mean gain with the mean gain for a similar period published as a norm by the author of the test.

b. From each of 6 litters of white rats 2 rats of the same sex and approximately equal weight are selected. One of these is fed diet A and the other diet B. At the end of the experimental period it is desired to test the hypothesis that the diets produce equal gains in weight.

c. For two independent samples the following data are obtained: $N_1 = 325$, $\overline{X}_1 = 52.3$, $s_1^2 = 24.2$, $N_2 = 111$, $\overline{X}_2 = 54.7$, $s_2^2 = 23.6$. A test of $H: \sigma_1^2 = \sigma_2^2$ has been made and the hypothesis accepted.

d. For two independent samples the following data are obtained: $N_1 = 14$, $\overline{X}_1 = 26.3$, $s_1^2 = 18.5$, $N_2 = 19$, $\overline{X}_2 = 25.4$, $s_2^2 = 18.8$. A test of $H: \sigma_1^2 = \sigma_2^2$ has been made and the hypothesis accepted.

e. For two independent samples the following data are obtained: $N_1 = 390$, $\overline{X}_1 = 63.2$, $s_1^2 = 10.3$, $N_2 = 406$, $\overline{X}_2 = 63.2$, and $s_2^2 = 38.3$ A test of $H: \sigma_1^2 = \sigma_2^2$ is made and hypothesis rejected.

f. For two independent samples, the following data are obtained: $N_1 = 5$, $\overline{X} = 19.2$, $s_1^2 = 4.2$, $N_2 = 9$, $\overline{X}_2 = 24.3$, $s_2^2 = 36$. A test of the hypothesis $\sigma_1^2 = \sigma_2^2$ has been made and the hypothesis rejected.

9. A research worker is considering the following plans for a two-sided test of $H: \mu = 70$:

(1) $N = 40$, $\alpha = .01$
(2) $N = 100$, $\alpha = .01$
(3) $N = 200$, $\alpha = .02$
(4) $N = 200$, $\alpha = .05$
(5) $N = 500$, $\alpha = .05$
(6) $N = 500$, $\alpha = .06$

a. Which one will give him the most powerful test?

b. Which will give him the least powerful test?

c. Which will incur the least risk of rejecting the hypothesis if it is true?

d. If he accepts the hypothesis, which will allow him to make the strongest statement?

10. For each of the following requirements, ascertain how many cases should be included in the sample or samples. Use a one-sided test.

1. Hypothesis: $\mu_H = 25$
   Alternative: $\mu_A = 23$
   $\sigma = 12$, $\alpha = .01$, $\beta = .30$
2. Hypothesis: $\mu_1 - \mu_2 = 0$
   Alternative: $\mu_1 - \mu_2 = 3$
   $\sigma_1 = 15, \sigma_2 = 15, \alpha = .02, \beta = .20$
3. Hypothesis: $\mu_1 - \mu_2 = 0$
   Alternative: $\mu_1 - \mu_2 = 2$
   $\sigma_1 = 12, \sigma_2 = 20, \alpha = .05, \beta = .40$
4. Hypothesis: $\mu_1 - \mu_2 = 3$
   Alternative: $\mu_1 - \mu_2 = 6$
   $\sigma_1 = 5, \sigma_2 = 5, \alpha = .02, \beta = .20$
5. Hypothesis: $\mu_1 - \mu_2 = 10$
   Alternative: $\mu_1 - \mu_2 = 5$
   $\sigma_1 = 10, \sigma_2 = 20, \alpha = .05, \beta = .40$

Design of Samples in Surveys. One of the most crucial aspects of a sample survey is the decision as to the number of cases and the methods by which they shall be selected. The answer to this question provides the *design* of the survey. This and other problems related to surveys are discussed by Deming [4] and Yates.[23]

Up to this point, the discussion of sampling error has assumed that each element in the sample is drawn at random from the entire population. This method of sampling is called *unrestricted random* sampling or sometimes *simple sampling*. In some situations, unrestricted random sampling is impossible. In other situations an alternative method may be more advantageous.

The first requirement of any sampling procedure is the avoidance of *bias*. The error which causes a statistic to differ from its parameter may arise partly from random errors in the selection of individuals and partly from bias in their selection. The total of the random errors decreases as sample size increases but the total of errors due to bias does not so decrease. It forms a constant error which on the average is about the same for a large as for a small sample.

The next requirement of a "good" sampling procedure is that it provide as much information about the population as can be obtained at a stipulated cost or that it provide a stipulated amount of information for as low a cost as possible. This requirement raises problems concerning the size of sample, the method of selecting cases, and the allocation of cases. Adequate discussion of these problems would require a large monograph and is outside the scope of this book. Here we shall make brief mention of several alternatives to unrestricted random sampling, and shall give the standard error of the mean and related formulas for two of them.

The advantages of a particular method can be more easily discussed if we first consider the meaning of the terms *frame* and *sampling unit*. The following quotation is from pages 20 and 21 of Yates.[23]

"All rigorous sampling demands a subdivision of the material to be sampled into units, termed *sampling units*, which form the basis of the actual sampling procedure. These units may be natural units of the material, such as individuals in a human population, or natural aggregates of such units, such as households, or they may be artificial units, such as rectangular areas on a map, bearing no relation to the natural subdivisions of the material.

"It is not always necessary to make an actual subdivision of the whole of the material before selection of the sample, provided the selected units can be clearly and unambiguously defined. Thus, with sampling units which are rectangular areas on a map there is no need to demarcate all these areas; they can be defined by co-ordinates, and the selected areas demarcated after selection.

"Clear and unambiguous definition demands the existence or construction of some form of *frame*. In the sampling of a human population, for instance, with households as sampling units, there must be available a list of all households, and this list must be such that any household selected from it can be unambiguously located. In area sampling from maps, the maps must be such that the selected areas can be unambiguously defined on the ground. . . .

"Sampling units may be of the same or differing size. They may contain the same, or approximately the same, number of natural units, or they may contain widely differing numbers. The whole procedure of sampling, including the estimation of the population values and the sampling errors, is simplest when the sampling units are of approximately the same size and contain approximately the same number of natural units. Often, however, the material is such that this condition cannot be conveniently fulfilled. In particular, if the natural units are themselves of widely differing size, variation in size of the sampling units or in the number of natural units they contain is inevitable."

Among the more common alternatives to unrestricted random sampling are these:

A. Conscious selection of "typical" cases. This unsatisfactory method is in widespread use. The literature is full of instances showing bias of one kind or another in such samples. For example, Yates,[23] (p. 12) spread out some 1200 stones on a table and asked 12 observers to select three samples of 20 stones each which should represent as nearly as possible the size distribution of the whole collection. Of the 36 samples, 30 had means larger than the mean of the collection.

B. Systematic selection from a list. A very frequent method of drawing a sample is to take every 10th or every 20th, or in general every rth name, on a list. If the first name is chosen at random from among the first r names, every name has the same opportunity of being included in the sample and that is important. However not all samples are equally likely, in fact some samples would have probability zero. Suppose the list is alphabetical and includes several members of the same family with the same surname. If one of these is selected the others almost certainly will not be, and so observations are not independent. This method is often far less expensive than unrestricted random sampling and it is usually free of bias, unless there are periodic features in the list which coincide with the sampling interval. It is usually not possible to get a proper estimate of the standard error of a statistic from such a sample; the ordinary formulas applicable to unrestricted random sampling may be presumed to overestimate sampling variability.

C. Sampling after stratification of the population. The population is subdivided into a number of groups or "strata" and a random sample selected from each stratum. It is most efficient when the strata are so defined that there is a high degree of uniformity among the units within each stratum and considerable diversity from one stratum to another. It has two purposes: (1) to increase the accuracy of the population estimates and (2) to assure adequate sampling from any subgroup which is of particular interest. The stratification affects the variability of any computed statistics, as indicated on pages 174 and 175.

D. Cluster sampling. Here the sampling units are themselves groups or clusters of natural units. Thus the sampling units might be households composed of individual persons; or city blocks composed of dwelling units; or townships composed of farms; or classes composed of students; or groups of telephone poles erected near each other, and so on. A random sample is taken of all the clusters composing the population and observations are made on all the individuals in the selected clusters. Cluster sampling is discussed further on pages 175–177.

E. Multistage sampling. This term connotes a more complex plan with greater flexibility of pattern than the preceding. The sampling is carried out in successive stages, and any of the preceding plans may be applied at any of the stages. For instance in the first stage a sample of clusters might be chosen at random from the entire population and then in the second stage a sample of individuals be chosen at random from the selected clusters. There are a great many possible variants of multistage sampling and each has its own set of formulas for sampling variability.

Stratified Sampling.* This procedure is possible only when there is some previous information about the population. It is efficient only if the strata or subpopulations can be selected in such

* For a minimum course this and the succeeding sections of this chapter may be omitted without impairing the clarity of subsequent chapters.

a way that the variance of each stratum is smaller than the variance of the entire unstratified population.

Stratification of a community is often on a geographical basis, as when the residents of a city are classified by census tract; or the residents of a state are classified according to whether they live in open country, in villages, or in cities of various specified size. Stratification may be by some easily identified characteristic of individuals which is presumed to be related to the purpose of the inquiry.

Suppose that a finite population has been divided into strata and that

k = the number of strata

M_i = the number of individuals in the ith stratum

$M = \sum_{i=1}^{k} M_i$ = the number of individuals in the population

N_i = the number of individuals in the sample taken from the ith stratum

$N = \sum_{i=1}^{k} N_i$ = the number of individuals in the sample

$\overline{X}_i = \dfrac{\Sigma X_i}{N_i}$ = mean of the observations on the N_i individuals in the sample from the ith stratum

$s_i^2 = \dfrac{\Sigma(X_i - \overline{X}_i)^2}{N_i - 1}$ = variance of the observations on the N_i individuals in the sample from the ith stratum

Then μ, the mean of the population, is estimated by the formula

(7.39) $$\overline{X}_s = \frac{\Sigma M_i \overline{X}_i}{M}$$

and $$\mu = E(\overline{X})$$

The variance of $\overline{X}_s$ is estimated by the formula

(7.40) $$s^2_{\overline{X}_s} = \Sigma \left(\frac{M_i}{M}\right)^2 \cdot \frac{M_i - N_i}{M_i - 1} \cdot \frac{s_i^2}{N_i}$$

Quite often the information sought is not an estimate of the average μ but of the total $M\mu$. That estimate is

(7.41) $$T_s = M\overline{X}_s = \Sigma M_i \overline{X}_i$$

and $M\mu$ is the expected value of T_s. The variance of T_s is estimated as

(7.42)
$$s^2_{T_s} = \Sigma M^2{}_i \cdot \frac{M_i - N_i}{M_i - 1} \cdot \frac{s_i^2}{N_i}$$

Sometimes the information sought is an estimate of the proportion P of individuals in the population possessing some characteristic, say the proportion of homes in a rural area that have central heating, or the proportion of voters who will express a preference for a given presidential candidate. The estimate of P for the entire population is then

(7.43)
$$p_s = \frac{\Sigma M_i p_i}{M}$$

and the variance of p is

(7.44)
$$s^2{}_{p_s} = \Sigma\left(\frac{M_i}{M}\right)^2 \cdot \frac{M_i - N_i}{M_i - 1} \cdot \frac{p_i q_i}{N_i}$$

For large samples the various estimates described above are approximately normally distributed about their respective parameters as mean, with the square root of the indicated variance as standard deviation. Therefore, confidence intervals for the parameters can be obtained by use of tables of the normal distribution.

The problem of how large a sample to take and how to apportion the cases among the strata depends upon such considerations as the amount of money which can be spent on the collection of data, the cost of locating an individual, the cost of making an observation on an individual, the degree of precision required in the estimate and the relative variability of the different strata. Formulas for the optimum allocation of cases to strata will not be presented here because the discussion necessary to safeguard their use requires more space than the scope of this book justifies. A clear presentation of these is given by David.[2] The reader who contemplates making a survey by sampling should also read Cochran, Deming, Hansen, King, Marks, Neyman, Stephan, and Yates. (See references at the end of this chapter.)

Cluster Sampling. For this method the population is divided into many relatively small groups or clusters of individuals and the sample consists of a number of these *clusters chosen at random.*

In the formulas given here it will be assumed that all the individuals are observed in those clusters which are chosen, but this need not be so. It often happens that a number of clusters is selected at random and then out of those selected clusters, a predetermined number of individuals is chosen at random.

Cluster sampling is economical when the cost of measuring an individual is relatively small and the cost of reaching him relatively large. For example, suppose a railroad is making a survey of the ties on which rails rest in order to assess the need for replacements. To take an unrestricted random sample of all the ties in use, would entail heavy costs to travel to the place where the selected ties might be found but very little cost to examine the ties once they are reached. It might cost less and yield more information to measure 100 clusters of 5 ties each than to measure 200 ties chosen individually at random. It would produce more information to measure 100 clusters of 5 ties each than to measure 5 clusters of 100 ties each. The relation of costs to sampling procedure is outside the scope of this text, but it is well worth the careful investigation of any one contemplating a large inquiry by sample.

Cluster sampling is most advantageous when there is great heterogeneity within clusters. If all the individuals in each cluster were exactly alike there would be no advantage in observing more than one of them. The larger the variation within clusters, the smaller the number of individuals which will be required to hold $s_{\overline{X}}$ to a predetermined size.

The formulas for cluster sampling rather than for simple sampling are usually needed in studies that utilize area sampling, as when small areas like city blocks or rural townships are chosen at random and every dwelling in those areas, or every farm, or every individual under consideration, is included in the sample. These formulas would be needed if a population of all the eighth grade pupils in New York City were to be sampled by selecting at random a number of eighth grade classes and making observations on all the pupils in each class.

Let M = the number of clusters in the population

m = the number of clusters in the sample

n_i = the number of individuals in the ith cluster

$$\overline{X}_i = \frac{\Sigma X_i}{n_i} = \text{mean of the } i\text{th cluster}$$

$$\bar{n} = \frac{\sum_{i=1}^{m} n_i}{m} = \text{average number of individuals per cluster}$$

$$N = \Sigma n_i = m\bar{n} = \text{number of individuals in the sample}$$

Then the sample estimate of the population mean μ is

$$(7.45)\qquad \overline{X}_c = \frac{\sum_{i=1}^{m} n_i \overline{X}_i}{\sum_{i=1}^{m} n_i} = \frac{\Sigma\Sigma X_i}{N}$$

and the variance of $\overline{X}_c$ is

$$(7.46)\qquad s^2_{\overline{X}_c} = \frac{M-m}{Mm} \frac{\sum_{i=1}^{m} n_i^2 (\overline{X}_i - \overline{X}_c)^2}{(m-1)(\overline{n})^2}$$

In the special case for which $n_1 = n_2 = \cdots = n_m = n$, Formulas (7.45) and (7.46) can be simplified. Then the estimate of μ is

$$(7.47)\qquad \overline{X}_c = \frac{\sum_{i=1}^{m} \overline{X}_i}{m}$$

and its variance is

$$(7.48)\qquad s^2_{\overline{X}_c} = \frac{M-m}{Mm} \cdot \frac{\Sigma(\overline{X}_i - \overline{X}_c)^2}{m-1}$$

In dealing with proportions in samples obtained by cluster sampling it is only necessary to substitute p_i for $\overline{X}_i$ and P for $\overline{X}_c$ in Formulas (7.45) to (7.48).

The use of cluster sampling in relation to mental testing is discussed by Marks [12] who gives a derivation of the formulas for cluster sampling used above.

REFERENCES

1. Cochran, W. G., "Modern Methods in the Sampling of Human Populations," *American Journal of Public Health*, 41 (1951), 647–653.
2. David, F. N., *Probability Theory for Statistical Methods*, Cambridge, 1949, Cambridge University Press. Chapter XIV, "Sampling Human Populations."
3. Deming, W. Edwards, *Some Theory of Sampling*, New York, 1950, John Wiley and Sons.
4. Deming, W. Edwards, "A Brief Statement on the Uses of Sampling in Censuses of Population, Agriculture, Public Health, and Commerce," United Nations Publications, 1948, XVII, 1.
5. Dixon, W. J. and Massey, F. J., *Introduction to Statistical Analysis*, New York, 1951, McGraw-Hill Book Company.
6. Hansen, M. H. and Hauser, P. M., "Area Sampling — Some Principles of Sample Design," *Public Opinion Quarterly*, (Summer 1945), 183–193.
7. Hansen, M. H. and Hurwitz, W. N., "Relative Efficiencies of Various Sampling Units in Population Inquiries," *Journal of the American Statistical Association*, 37 (1942,) 89–94.

8. Hansen, M. H. and Hurwitz, W. N., "On the Theory of Sampling from Finite Populations," *The Annals of Mathematical Statistics*, 14 (1943), 333–362.
9. Hansen, M. H. and Hurwitz, W. N., "The Problems of Non-Response in Sample Surveys," *Journal of the American Statistical Association*, 41 (1946), 233–236.
10. King A. J. and Jessen, R. J., "The Master Sample of Agriculture," *Journal of the American Statistical Association*, 40 (1945), 38–56.
11. Long, John A., *Motor Abilities of Deaf Children*, New York, 1931, Bureau of Publications, Teachers College, Columbia University.
12. Marks, Eli S., "Selective Sampling in Psychological Research," *Psychological Bulletin*, 44 (1947), 267–275.
13. McNemar, Quinn, *Psychological Statistics*, New York, 1949, John Wiley and Sons.
14. Neyman, Jerzy, "Contribution to the Theory of Sampling Human Populations," *Journal of the American Statistical Association*, 33 (1938), 101–116.
15. Neyman, Jerzy, "On Two Different Aspects of the Representative Method," *Journal of the Royal Statistical Society*, 97 (1934), 558–606.
16. Stephan, Frederick F., "Practical Problems of Sampling Procedure," *American Sociological Review* 1 (1936), 569–580.
17. Stephan, Frederick F., "Stratification in Representative Sampling," *Journal of Marketing*, 6 (1941), 38–47.
18. Stephan, Frederick F., "History of the Uses of Modern Sampling Procedures," *Journal of the American Statistical Association*, 43 (1948), 12–39.
19. Terman, Lewis M. and Miles, Catharine C., *Sex and Personality*, New York, 1936, McGraw-Hill Book Company.
20. Welch, B. L., "The Generalization of 'Student's' Problem when Several Different Population Variances are Involved," *Biometrika*, 34 (1947), 28–35.
21. Westover, F. L., *Controlled Eye Movements versus Practice Exercises in Reading*, New York, 1946, Bureau of Publications, Teachers College, Columbia University.
22. Wrightstone, J. W., *Appraisal of Newer Elementary School Practices*, New York, 1938, Bureau of Publications, Teachers College, Columbia University.
23. Yates, Frank, *Sampling Methods for Censuses and Surveys*, London, 1949, Charles Griffin and Co. Ltd.
24. Yates, Frank, "A Review of Recent Statistical Developments in Sampling and Sampling Surveys," *Journal of the Royal Statistical Society*, 109 (1946), 12–43.

8 Inferences Concerning Variances and Standard Deviations of Normal Populations

Not only do research workers ask questions about means of populations but they ask questions about their variabilities also. What estimate can be made of the unknown variance of a population from the observed variance of a sample? Does a period of study make a class more variable at the end than at the beginning? Less variable? Are boys and girls equally variable in some particular trait? If one sample is drawn from each of several populations, are the observed variances of these samples consistent with the hypothesis that the population variances are all equal?

Such questions are similar to the questions asked concerning means in Chapter 7 and similar logic is used in answering them. However the appropriate statistics are different and will have different sampling distributions. The new issues to be discussed in this chapter therefore will relate to the selection of a statistic, to the identification of the form of the sampling distribution of that statistic, and to the reading of the appropriate probability tables. The general logic of making interval estimates or testing hypotheses on the evidence of such statistics will follow the patterns already established.

Sampling Distribution of the Statistic $(N-1)s^2/\sigma^2$. In the sampling experiment carried out in Chapter 6, each student computed four values of the statistic $\Sigma x^2/\sigma^2$ or $(N-1)s^2/\sigma^2$. (See line 9 of Worksheet II.) In Table 6.1, on page 134, and Figure 6–2, on page 134, the empirical distribution of 125 such computed values is shown. It can be proved mathematically that the statistic $\frac{\Sigma x^2}{\sigma^2} = \frac{(N-1)s^2}{\sigma^2}$ has a χ^2 distribution with $N-1$ degrees of freedom.

If a large number of students draw samples of 5 cases from the data of Table XXIV and compute the variance for each sample, what proportion of these samples would yield a variance of 1500 or more? Since σ^2 is known to be 1380.4 for the population, the relevant statistic is

$$\chi^2 = \frac{4(1500)}{1380.4} = 4.35$$

From Table VIII it may be seen that $4.35 < \chi^2_{.75}$. The expected proportion of samples with $s^2 > 1500$ is therefore greater than .25.

Suppose a student reports that he obtained a variance of $s^2 = 423$ but his computations are not available for checking, should it be assumed that he made a mistake of some sort? His variance is only about a third as large as the population variance. Is the observed variance small enough to arouse suspicions concerning the method of sampling or the correctness of the computations?

$$\chi^2 = \frac{4(423)}{1380.4} = 1.2$$

For 4 degrees of freedom, Table VIII shows $\chi^2_{.10} = 1.1$. Since 10% of random samples of 5 cases from a population in which $\sigma^2 = 1380.4$ would produce χ^2 smaller than 1.1, more than 10% of such samples would show χ^2 smaller than the observed value 1.2. These same samples would of course have s^2 smaller than 423, the observed value from which $\chi^2 = 1.2$ was obtained. Now if more than 10% of samples would by chance produce a variance smaller than the one observed, that variance cannot be considered small enough to excite suspicion as to its correctness. Obviously, however, this absence of suspicion does not demonstrate the correctness of the sampling and computational procedures used.

Interval Estimate for the Variance. The argument here is similar in principle to the argument concerning the interval estimate for the mean developed in Chapter 7. There is probability .05 that $(N-1)s^2/\sigma^2 > \chi^2_{.95}$ and probability .05 that

$$(N-1)s^2/\sigma^2 < \chi^2_{.05}$$

Therefore there is probability .90 that $(N-1)s^2/\sigma^2$ will be neither larger than $\chi^2_{.95}$ nor smaller than $\chi^2_{.05}$. This relation may be expressed in general as

$$P\left\{\chi^2_{\frac{1}{2}\alpha} < \frac{(N-1)s^2}{\sigma^2} < \chi^2_{1-\frac{1}{2}\alpha}\right\} = 1 - \alpha \tag{8.1}$$

What is wanted now is an inequality expressing limits for σ^2. This inequality can be obtained from (8.1) in two steps, or the reader not interested in the algebraic derivation may merely accept Formula (8.2). The first step is to take the reciprocal of each term in (8.1) and reverse the direction of the inequality signs. (By way of illustration one may note that $4 < 8 < 10$ and $\frac{1}{4} > \frac{1}{8} > \frac{1}{10}$ or $\frac{1}{10} < \frac{1}{8} < \frac{1}{4}$. In general $\frac{1}{b} < \frac{1}{a}$ if a and b are positive and $a < b$.) This step produces the inequality

$$\frac{1}{\chi^2_{\frac{1}{2}\alpha}} > \frac{\sigma^2}{(N-1)s^2} > \frac{1}{\chi^2_{1-\frac{1}{2}\alpha}}$$

Each member of this inequality is now multiplied by $(N-1)s^2$. Since $(N-1)s^2$ is a positive number, the direction of the signs is not affected. The result is

$$\frac{(N-1)s^2}{\chi^2_{1-\frac{1}{2}\alpha}} < \sigma^2 < \frac{(N-1)s^2}{\chi^2_{\frac{1}{2}\alpha}}$$

This inequality has probability $1 - \alpha$ or is made with confidence coefficient $1 - \alpha$. In general

$$P\left\{\frac{(N-1)s^2}{\chi^2_{1-\frac{1}{2}\alpha}} < \sigma^2 < \frac{(N-1)s^2}{\chi^2_{\frac{1}{2}\alpha}}\right\} = 1 - \alpha \tag{8.2}$$

Table VIII provides the values of χ^2 needed for obtaining interval estimates made with confidence coefficients of .99, .98, .96, .95, .90, .80, and .50. In a practical problem these values are likely to meet all requirements.

Certain of these values of χ^2 for $n = 4$ are shown in Table 8.1 with the appropriate computations for each of the four samples of Worksheet I. Thus for Sample 1, row 7 of Worksheet I indicates that $(N-1)s^2 = 7635.2$. This number has been multiplied in turn by each of the reciprocals shown in the third column of Table 8.1.

From examination of Table 8.1 and Figure 8–1, interpretations can be made similar to the first four and the sixth interpretation regarding the confidence interval for the mean. However a change must be made in the fifth statement. Whereas the sample mean lies exactly in the middle of the confidence interval for μ, the sample variance lies much nearer to the lower than to the upper end of the confidence interval for σ^2.

If the confidence coefficient were zero the interval would narrow to a point and that point would be at $\sigma^2 = s^2$. If a confidence coefficient of 1.00 were demanded, implying certainty that σ^2 is in the interval, the interval would have to be infinitely wide.

TABLE 8.1 Computation of the Statistic $(N-1)s^2/\chi^2$ for Each of the Four Samples in Worksheet I at Selected Values of Chi-Square.

$n = 4, \quad \sigma^2 = 1380.4$

Symbol for χ^2	Tabulated value of χ^2	Reciprocal of tabulated value	Value of $(N-1)s^2/\chi^2$ for Sample 1 (7635.2)*	2 (14069.2)*	3 (3246.8)*	4 (10696)*
$\chi^2_{.99}$	13.277	.0753	575	1059	244	805
$\chi^2_{.95}$	9.488	.1054	805	1483	342	1127
$\chi^2_{.90}$	7.779	.1286	982	1810	417	1376
$\chi^2_{.80}$	5.989	.1670	1275	2350	542	1786
$\chi^2_{.70}$	4.878	.2050	1565	2884	665	2193
$\chi^2_{.30}$	2.195	.4556	3479	6410	1479	4873
$\chi^2_{.20}$	1.649	.6064	4630	8532	1969	6486
$\chi^2_{.10}$	1.064	.9398	7176	13223	3052	10053
$\chi^2_{.05}$	.711	1.4065	10739	19788	4567	15044
$\chi^2_{.01}$	.297	3.3670	25708	47371	10932	36013

* The observed value of $(N - 1)s^2$ for the sample.

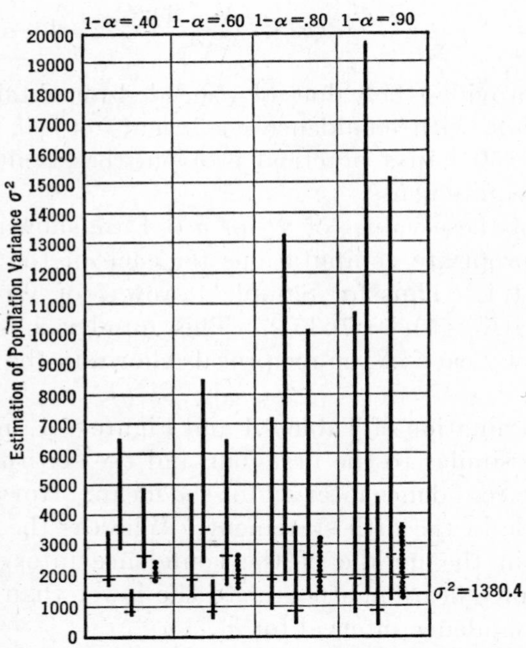

FIG. 8–1. Interval estimates of σ^2 made with confidence coefficients of .40, .60, .80, and .90 from each of four samples of 5 cases and from composite sample of 20 cases. (Samples as given on Worksheet I.) Dotted line is for composite sample. Horizontal tic is s^2 of sample.

EXERCISE 8.1

In Table 8.1

1. Verify those values of χ^2 which are available in Table VIII or in any other table you may have at hand. Values in Table 8.1 are given with more significant digits than can be read from Table VIII.

2. Verify some of the reciprocals in Column 3.

3. Verify some of the values in the last four columns.

4. Verify the intervals for Sample 1:

$$C(575 < \sigma^2 < 25708) = .98$$
$$C(805 < \sigma^2 < 10739) = .90$$
$$C(982 < \sigma^2 < 7176) = .80$$
$$C(1275 < \sigma^2 < 4630) = .60$$
$$C(1565 < \sigma^2 < 3479) = .40$$

5. Verify the intervals shown in Figure 8–1 from the entries in Table 8.1.

6. Compute the intervals for the composite sample and verify them by comparison with the dotted lines in Figure 8–1. The following values of χ^2 for $n = 19$ will be needed:

$$\chi^2_{.95} = 30.144 \qquad \chi^2_{.30} = 15.352$$
$$\chi^2_{.90} = 27.204 \qquad \chi^2_{.20} = 13.716$$
$$\chi^2_{.80} = 23.900 \qquad \chi^2_{.10} = 11.651$$
$$\chi^2_{.70} = 21.689 \qquad \chi^2_{.05} = 10.117$$

7. For samples 2, 3, and 4, obtain confidence intervals similar to those given in question 4 for sample 1.

8. What proportion of all samples is expected to yield interval estimates that actually contain σ^2 when $1 - \alpha = .90$? Of the 4 interval estimates made from the 4 observed samples, how many did contain σ^2? Answer the same questions for confidence coefficients of .80, .60, and .40.

9. If the standard deviation of a population is 15.4, what is the probability that a sample of 18 cases will have a standard deviation at least as large as 20? (*Hint:* Square the standard deviation and work with the corresponding value of the variance.)

10. If a sample of 24 cases has a standard deviation of 5.6, what interval limits can be set for the population standard deviation with confidence of .90?

The Chi-square Distribution When the Number of Degrees of Freedom is Large. The largest value of n found in Table VIII is 30.* How are tests about the variance to be made if $n > 30$? Figure 4–5 has already suggested that as n increases the distribution of χ^2 becomes more symmetrical. The distribution of $\sqrt{\chi^2}$ or χ approaches symmetry much more rapidly than does the dis-

* The volume of statistical tables soon to be published by the *Biometrika* office under the editorship of E. S. Pearson and H. O. Hartley will contain a χ^2 table extending to $n = 40, 50, 60, 70, 80, 90$, and 100.

tribution of χ^2. In fact when $n > 30$, the distribution of χ is approximately normal with mean $\sqrt{n - .5}$ and standard error $\sqrt{.5}$. Then

$$\frac{\chi - \mu}{\sigma_\chi} = \frac{\chi - \sqrt{n - .5}}{\sqrt{.5}} = \frac{\chi\sqrt{2} - \sqrt{2n - 1}}{1}$$

has approximately a unit normal distribution for large n. Changing $\chi\sqrt{2}$ into $\sqrt{2\chi^2}$, this relationship becomes

$$z = \sqrt{2\chi^2} - \sqrt{2n - 1} \tag{8.3}$$

Formula (8.3) can be used to make tests about σ, and consequently also to make tests about σ^2, from a large sample.

Large Sample Estimate for the Standard Deviation. Formula (8.3) can be used for this purpose, substituting $\chi^2 = \frac{(N-1)s^2}{\sigma^2}$ so that $\sqrt{2\chi^2} = \frac{s}{\sigma}\sqrt{2N - 2}$, and $n = N - 1$ so that $\sqrt{2n - 1} = \sqrt{2N - 3}$.

Then

$$P\left\{ z_{\frac{1}{2}\alpha} < \frac{s}{\sigma}\sqrt{2N - 2} - \sqrt{2N - 3} < z_{1-\frac{1}{2}\alpha} \right\} = 1 - \alpha \tag{8.4}$$

By algebraic manipulation of the expression within parentheses this statement may, without changing the probability, be rewritten as

$$P\left\{ \frac{s\sqrt{2N - 2}}{\sqrt{2N - 3} + z_{1-\frac{1}{2}\alpha}} < \sigma < \frac{s\sqrt{2N - 2}}{\sqrt{2N - 3} + z_{\frac{1}{2}\alpha}} \right\} = 1 - \alpha \tag{8.5}$$

The inequality within the parentheses is a confidence interval for σ.

If N is large enough that $\frac{2N - 2}{2N - 3}$ may be considered as 1 and z is small in relation to $\sqrt{2N - 3}$, a simpler inequality giving approximately equal results can be used:

$$P\left\{ s\left(1 + \frac{z_{\frac{1}{2}\alpha}}{\sqrt{2(N - 1)}}\right) < \sigma < s\left(1 + \frac{z_{1-\frac{1}{2}\alpha}}{\sqrt{2(N - 1)}}\right) \right\} = 1 - \alpha \tag{8.6}$$

This is precisely the result which would be arrived at on the assumption that s is normally distributed about σ with standard error $\frac{s}{\sqrt{2(N - 1)}}$, a statement which is sometimes made without the necessary qualification that it holds only for large samples.

Example. Given $N = 308$, $s = 2.15$, to find an interval estimate for σ with confidence coefficient .95. Substituting in the inequality of (8.6) produces the confidence interval

$$2.15\left(1 - \frac{1.96}{\sqrt{614}}\right) < \sigma < 2.15\left(1 + \frac{1.96}{\sqrt{614}}\right)$$

or

$$1.98 < \sigma < 2.32$$

Ratio of the Variances of Two Independent Samples from Populations with the Same Variance. In Chapter 7 on more than one occasion a statement was made that the observed variances of two independent samples were not inconsistent with the hypothesis that the samples came from populations with the same variances, $\sigma_1^2 = \sigma_2^2 = \sigma^2$.

The statistic which is appropriate for testing this hypothesis is the ratio of the two observed variances. In general, if each of two independent statistics has a χ^2 distribution and if each is divided by its appropriate degrees of freedom, the ratio of χ_1^2/n_1 to χ_2^2/n_2 has a distribution called the F distribution * or the variance-ratio distribution. As has already been seen, $(N - 1)s^2/\sigma^2$ has a χ^2 distribution.

Now if $$\chi_1^2 = \frac{(N_1 - 1)s_1^2}{\sigma_1^2} = \frac{n_1 s_1^2}{\sigma_1^2}, \text{ then } \chi_1^2/n_1 = s_1^2/\sigma_1^2$$

and if $$\chi_2^2 = \frac{(N_2 - 1)s_2^2}{\sigma_2^2} = \frac{n_2 s_2^2}{\sigma_2^2}, \text{ then } \chi_2^2/n_2 = s_2^2/\sigma_2^2$$

Then if $$\sigma_1^2 = \sigma_2^2 = \sigma^2$$

$$\frac{\chi_1^2}{n_1}\bigg/\frac{\chi_2^2}{n_2} = \frac{s_1^2}{s_2^2}$$

has an F distribution.

Tables of the *F* Distribution. This distribution is really a family of distributions. The shape changes with n_1 and also with n_2. In Table X values of n_1 or the degrees of freedom associated with the numerator of the variance ratio, are given in the horizontal row across the top of the table. Values of n_2, or the degrees of freedom associated with the denominator of the ratio, are given in the vertical column at the left. Each cell of the table represents a particular combination of n_1 and n_2. For that particular combination there exists a unique probability distribution.

* Named in honor of R. A. Fisher to whom the distribution is due.

In this table only two points on that entire sampling distribution are shown. These are $F_{.95}$ and $F_{.99}$ such that

$$P\{s_1^2/s_2^2 > F_{.95}\} = .05$$

$$P\{s_1^2/s_2^2 > F_{.99}\} = .01$$

In the cell for $n_1 = 4$, $n_2 = 4$, we read $F_{.95} = 6.39$ and $F_{.99} = 15.98$. The position of $F_{.95} = 6.39$ is marked on Figure 6–7 on page 141, but $F_{.99}$ is too far to the right to be shown. Now if $s_i^2/s_j^2 = 6.39$, then $s_j^2/s_i^2 = \frac{1}{6.39} = .16$.

The tables do not show $F_{.05}$ and $F_{.01}$ because these can be readily obtained from the tabulated values with n_2 and n_1 reversed. Values at the lower end of the scale are crowded so close together that they would have to be written with a good many digits to afford adequate precision. It can be shown that $F_\alpha = \frac{1}{F_{1-\alpha}}$ when F_α is based on n_i and n_j degrees of freedom and $F_{1-\alpha}$ is based on n_j and n_i degrees of freedom. Therefore for Figure 6–7, $F_{.05} = 1/6.39 = .16$ and $F_{.01} = 1/15.98 = .06$.

Values of $F_{.80}$, $F_{.90}$ and $F_{.99}$ as well as $F_{.95}$ and $F_{.99}$ are tabulated in Fisher and Yates, *Statistical Tables.*[5] A still more extensive table computed by Merrington and Thompson will be included in the volume of tables soon to be published by the *Biometrika* office.[8]

When the variances of two samples are being compared to test the hypothesis that $\sigma_1^2 = \sigma_2^2 = \sigma^2$, it is just as exceptional for s_i^2/s_j^2 to be less than $F_{.01}$ as it is for s_j^2/s_i^2 to be larger than $F_{.99}$. The proper procedure then is to divide the larger variance by the smaller. If the ratio exceeds $F_{.95}$, the hypothesis of equal variance may be discarded at the .10 level; if the ratio exceeds $F_{.99}$, it is discarded at the .02 level.

In the following chapter, a different manner of reading the tables will be considered, for use in a somewhat different kind of problem requiring a one-sided hypothesis.

From the data on page 156 the variance of scores of 12 Barnard students is found as $s_1^2 = 258.09$ and the variance of 11 general studies students as $s_2^2 = 411.30$. To test the hypothesis

$$\sigma_1^2 = \sigma_2^2 = \sigma^2,$$

we have $F = 411.30/258.09 = 1.59$. In the cell of the F table for which $n_1 = 10$ and $n_2 = 11$, we find that $F_{.95} = 2.86$. The observed

$F < F_{.95}$. Therefore, if samples of this size were drawn repeatedly from populations with equal variance, and the variance ratio computed for every possible pair of such samples, over 10% of such ratios would be more exceptional than the observed ratio. The observations cast no reasonable doubt on the hypothesis of equal variance.

Now let us consider the variances of the four samples of 5 cases listed in Worksheet I on page 128. These provide 12 variance ratios, namely

$s_1^2/s_2^2 = 1908.8/3517.3 = .54$
$s_1^2/s_3^2 = 1908.8/811.7 = 2.35$
$s_1^2/s_4^2 = 1908.8/2674 = .71$
$s_2^2/s_1^2 = 3517.3/1908.8 = 1.84$
$s_2^2/s_3^2 = 3517.3/811.7 = 4.33$
$s_2^2/s_4^2 = 3517.3/2674 = 1.32$

$s_3^2/s_1^2 = 811.7/1908.8 = .426$
$s_3^2/s_2^2 = 811.7/3517.3 = .23$
$s_3^2/s_4^2 = 811.7/2674 = .30$
$s_4^2/s_1^2 = 2674/1908.8 = 1.40$
$s_4^2/s_2^2 = 2674/3517.3 = .76$
$s_4^2/s_3^2 = 2674/811.7 = 3.30$

The sampling distribution of the variance ratio for $n_1 = 4$ and $n_2 = 4$, which are the degrees of freedom associated with these variance ratios, is presented in Figure 6–6. The reader should plot the value of each of the 12 ratios shown above on the base line of Figure 6–6. The largest ratio, with value 4.33 is smaller than the indicated value of $F_{.95}$. The value of $F_{.05}$ is .16 (not marked on the graph) and the smallest of the ratios, with value .23, is larger than $F_{.05}$.

If two independent samples are drawn from populations in which

$$\sigma_1^2 = \sigma_2^2 = \sigma^2$$

then

$$P\ \{F_{.05} < s_i^2/s_j^2 < F_{.95}\} = .90$$
$$P\ \{s_i^2/s_j^2 > F_{.95}\} = .05$$
$$P\ \{s_i^2/s_j^2 < F_{.05}\} = .05$$

EXERCISE 8.2

Reading Tables of the F distribution

1. Verify the following probability statements:

a. Suppose a great many samples of 10 cases each are drawn from one population and a great many samples of 6 cases each from another, and suppose the two populations have the same variance. Now let each sample of 10 cases be paired with a sample of 6 cases in some random fashion and let the ratio of their variances be computed.

Then $P\ \{s_{10}^2/s_6^2 > 4.78\} = .05$ See cell for which $n_1 = 9$, $n_2 = 5$
$P\ \{s_6^2/s_{10}^2 > 3.48\} = .05$ See cell for which $n_1 = 5$, $n_2 = 9$
But $1/4.78 = .209$ and $1/3.48 = .287$
Therefore $P\ \{.287 < s_{10}^2/s_6^2 < 4.78\} = .90$

and $P\{.209 < s_6^2/s_{10}^2 < 3.48\} = .90$

Similarly $P\{.165 < s_{10}^2/s_6^2 < 10.15\} = .98$

$P\{.099 < s_6^2/s_{10}^2 < 6.06\} = .98$

b. A sample of 21 cases has a variance of 25.3 and a sample of 18 cases has a variance of 12.2, the variance ratio being $F = 25.3/12.2 = 2.07$. If the two population variances are equal there is a probability of .05 of drawing samples such that $s^2_{21}/s^2_{18} > 2.23$. Since $F < F_{.95}$, the probability of drawing a pair of samples with variances as dissimilar as these is greater than .10.

2. Fill the blanks in the following:

	N_1	N_2	s_1^2	s_2^2	F	$F_{.95}$	$F_{.99}$	*Probability of at least as exceptional an F*
a.	41	31	6.8	9.4	____	____	____	$P > .10$
b.	12	60	10.4	3.6	____	____	____	$P < .02$
c.	15	120	17.4	30.6	____	____	____	____
d.	25	10	43.5	9.1	____	____	____	____
e.	210	27	33.5	15.3	____	____	____	____

3. From the F table, read values of F for which $n_1 = 1$ and n_2 has the values indicated in the column n below. Enter $F_{.95}$ and $F_{.99}$ on the appropriate lines.

From a table of "Student's" distribution read values of $t_{.975}$ and $t_{.995}$ for the values of n indicated. Enter these in the appropriate lines.

Square the recorded values of $t_{.975}$ and $t_{.995}$ and enter on the appropriate lines. If you have made no mistakes $F_{.95} = t^2_{.975}$ and $F_{.99}, = t^2_{.995}$ except for a possible difference in the last digit due to rounding error.

n_2	$F_{.95}$	$t_{.975}$	$t^2_{.975}$	$F_{.99}$	$t_{.995}$	$t^2_{.995}$
5	____	____	____	____	____	____
7	____	____	____	____	____	____
15	____	____	____	____	____	____
30	____	____	____	____	____	____
∞	____	____	____	____	____	____

4. From the F table, read values of F for which $n_2 = \infty$ and n_1 has the values indicated in the column n below. Enter $F_{.95}$ and $F_{.99}$ on the appropriate lines.

From the χ^2 table, read $\chi^2_{.95}$ and $\chi^2_{.99}$ for the indicated values of n. Enter on the appropriate lines.

Divide each recorded χ^2 by the corresponding value of n and enter on the appropriate line. If you have made no mistakes, $F_{.95} = \chi^2_{.95}/n$ and $F_{.99} = \chi^2_{.99}/n$ except for a possible difference in the last digit due to rounding error.

n_1	$F_{.95}$	$\chi^2_{.95}$	$\chi^2_{.95}/n$	$F_{.99}$	$\chi^2_{.99}$	$\chi^2_{.99}/n$
2	______	______	______	______	______	______
8	______	______	______	______	______	______
10	______	______	______	______	______	______
20	______	______	______	______	______	______
30	______	______	______	______	______	______

5. The values of F for $n_1 = 1$ and $n_2 = \infty$ at several significance levels given below are taken from *Statistical Tables* by Fisher and Yates. Read values of z at the same significance levels from a table of the normal distribution and enter on the appropriate lines. Enter z^2. Compare with the F values. They should agree except for differences due to rounding error.

$F_{.80} = 1.64$	$F_{.90} = 2.71$	$F_{.95} = 3.84$	$F_{.99} = 6.64$	$F_{.999} = 10.83$
$z_{.90} =$ ______	$z_{.95} =$ ______	$z_{.975} =$ ______	$z_{.995} =$ ______	$z_{.9995} =$ ______
$z^2_{.90} =$ ______	$z^2_{.95} =$ ______	$z^2_{.975} =$ ______	$z^2_{.995} =$ ______	$z^2_{.9995} =$ ______

Relation of the F Table to Tables of "Student's" Distribution, the Chi-square Distribution and the Normal Distribution. As has been said before, each cell in the F table represents particular values of n_1 and n_2 to which a unique probability distribution corresponds. Questions 3, 4, and 5 in Exercise 8.2 suggest that for a certain subset of these cells the F distribution is closely related to the chi-square distribution; for another subset it is closely related to "Student's" distribution; for one particular cell it is closely related to the normal distribution.

Consider the cells in the vertical column at the extreme left of the F table. For these cells $n_1 = 1$. Exercise 8.2 has indicated that for these cells $F_{.95} = t^2_{.975}$ and $F_{.99} = t^2_{.995}$, t having n_2 degrees of freedom. Problems utilizing this relationship will be taken up in Chapter 9.

Consider the cells in the last row of the F table, where $n_2 = \infty$. Exercise 8.2 has indicated that for these cells $F_{.95} = \chi^2_{.95}/n$ and $F = \chi^2/n$. Here n is the degrees of freedom for χ^2 and the degrees of freedom for the numerator variance in F. This interesting relationship is easily understood. $F = s_1^2/s_2^2$. When n_2 approaches infinity, s_2^2 approaches σ^2 and F approaches s_1^2/σ^2. But

$$n_1 s_1^2/\sigma^2 = \chi^2 \text{ so } s_1^2/\sigma^2 = \chi^2/n_1.$$

Therefore when n_2 approaches infinity, F approaches χ^2/n.

Consider the single cell in the last row and the left-hand column. In Exercise 8.2, we noted that the entries for $F_{1-\alpha}$ in the probability distribution for this cell are the squares of the entries for $z_{1-\frac{1}{2}\alpha}$ in the normal distribution. Because this cell is in the column in which $n_1 = 1$, we have $F = t^2$. Because it is in the row for which $n_2 = \infty$ we have $F_{1-\alpha} = \chi^2_{1-\alpha}/n = \chi^2_{1-\alpha}/1 = \chi^2_{1-\alpha}$. Then for this single cell, $\chi^2_{1-\alpha} = t^2_{1-\frac{1}{2}\alpha}$, χ^2 having 1 degree of freedom and t having infinite degrees of freedom. This brings us back to a situation noted in Chapter 4. There it was seen that for large values of N it made no difference whether for the double dichotomy $\frac{a \mid b}{c \mid d}$ one computed $\frac{(ad - bc)^2N}{(a + b)(a + c)(b + d)(c + d)}$ and referred it to the χ^2 distribution with 1 degree of freedom or computed $z = \frac{p_1 - p_2}{\sqrt{\frac{p(1 - p)N}{N_1N_2}}}$ and referred it to the normal distribution. In this problem $\chi^2_{1-\alpha} = z^2_{1-\frac{1}{2}\alpha}$.

Comparison of Two Variances Based on Related Scores. Suppose it is desired to compare the variance of a group at the beginning of an experiment with the variance of the same individuals at the end of the experiment in order to test the hypothesis that no genuine change in variance has occurred, that $\sigma_1^2 = \sigma_2^2 = \sigma^2$. The ratio $F = s_1^2/s_2^2$ does not provide a test for this hypothesis because under these circumstances s_1^2 and s_2^2 are based on correlated scores and cannot be regarded as independent variances.

Let σ_1^2 and σ_2^2 be the initial and final variance in the population and ρ_{12} the correlation between initial and final scores for the population.

Let s_1^2, s_2^2 and r_{12} be the corresponding values for the sample. Then if $\sigma_1^2 = \sigma_2^2$, the statistic

$$t = \frac{(s_2^2 - s_1^2)\sqrt{N - 2}}{2s_1s_2\sqrt{1 - r^2_{12}}} \tag{8.7}$$

has "Student's" distribution with $N - 2$ degrees of freedom. An equivalent form of (8.7) which may be more convenient to compute is

$$t = \frac{(\Sigma x_2^2 - \Sigma x_1^2)\sqrt{N - 2)}}{2\sqrt{\Sigma x_1^2 \Sigma x_2^2 - (\Sigma x_1 x_2)^2}} \tag{8.8}$$

An illustration may be drawn from the Westover study previously mentioned.[12] For the 45 freshmen using special practice exercises, the standard deviations of the Total Comprehension Scores at the beginning and end of the remedial period were

$s_1 = 4.05$ and $s_2 = 11.45$. The correlation between initial and final scores was .39. Is this a significant change in variability?

$$t = \frac{\{(11.45)^2 - (4.05)^2\}\sqrt{43}}{2(4.05)(11.45)\sqrt{1 - (.39)^2}} = 8.8$$

The change in variance is so large that no reasonable investigator would claim it was due to chance.

The value $r = .39$ is the value published by Westover as the correlation between initial and final scores for the entire group of 140 subjects. No value for the correlation coefficient was quoted for the 45 students considered in this problem. Knowing that $r = .39$ may be in error one way or the other, we should explore as far as possible the consequences of such error. Suppose the correct value of r is larger than .39. Then $\sqrt{1 - r^2}$ will be even smaller than $\sqrt{1 - (.39)^2}$, the denominator will be smaller than the one we have computed and t will be even larger than 8.8. The final decision to regard the change in variance as due to systematic rather than chance causes would be strengthened even further. Now suppose the correct value is smaller than $r = .39$. Then the numerator would be larger and t smaller than the one computed here. The extreme value in this direction would occur if r were 0. In that case

$$t = \frac{\{(11.45)^2 - (4.05)^2\}\sqrt{43}}{2(4.05)(11.45)} = 8.1$$

and the interpretation is not altered. If t were near $t_{.95}$ an error in the size of r might have serious consequences.

The Variances of Several Samples from Populations Having the Same Variance. When several samples are observed, one often wants to know whether it is reasonable to believe that all their populations have the same mean $\mu_1 = \mu_2 = \cdots = \mu_k = \mu$. That hypothesis will be explored in Chapter 9. One also often wants to know whether it is reasonable to believe that all their populations have the same variance, $\sigma_1^2 = \sigma_2^2 = \cdots = \sigma_k^2 = \sigma^2$. That hypothesis can be considered at this point.

There are several different methods by which this hypothesis can be tested, some of which are described in references.[1,2,4,7,10] We shall describe two of these methods: (A) a method of great simplicity and convenience which can be used when all samples have the same number of cases, but which requires a special probability table, and (B) a method which can be used even when the number of cases is not uniform from sample to sample, which makes use of the chi-square table, but which is arithmetically more laborious than the first.

A. All samples of uniform size. To illustrate this method we may use the data of Table 9.2, page 200. The variances for the three groups of 11 individuals each are as follows:

$$s_A^2 = 1188.97 \qquad s_B^2 = 2837.47 \qquad s_C^2 = 2140.40$$

We wish to test the hypothesis $\sigma_A^2 = \sigma_B^2 = \sigma_C^2 = \sigma^2$. There are 6 possible F ratios among these three variances, and the largest of these ratios is $\dfrac{s_B^2}{s_A^2} = \dfrac{2837.47}{1188.97} = 2.39$. If this largest ratio is not significantly large, none of the others is. Hartley[7] calls this largest F ratio

$$F_{max} = \frac{s^2_{max}}{s^2_{min}} \tag{8.9}$$

Table XI, gives the upper 5% and 1% points for F_{max} in a set of k mean squares all based on n degrees of freedom. In the data of Table 9.2, $k = 3$ and $n = 10$. In the appropriate cell of Table XI we find the entry 4.77, indicating that

$$P\{F_{max} > 4.77\} = .05$$

The critical region is $F > 4.77$. The observed value $F_{max} = 2.39$ does not fall in the critical region and so the hypothesis

$$\sigma_A^2 = \sigma_B^2 = \sigma_C^2$$

is acceptable.

B. Not all samples of uniform size. Harris[6] administered a test of information concerning the social factors of the community to teachers in four St. Louis schools, and found the means and variances to be as follows:

School	N_i	n_i	s_i^2	$\overline{X}$
1. Jefferson	20	19	11.22	12.50
2. Banneker	22	21	10.30	10.40
3. Cole	22	21	6.20	11.91
4. Marshall	15	14	9.79	11.94
	79			

She wanted to know whether the 79 teachers could be combined into a single group or whether these school differences would throw suspicion on the hypotheses

$$\mu_1 = \mu_2 = \mu_3 = \mu_4 = \mu$$

And

$$\sigma_1^2 = \sigma_2^2 = \sigma_3^2 = \sigma_4^2 = \sigma^2$$

Applying the method of section A, we note that the ratio of the largest variance to the smallest is

$$F_{max} = \frac{11.22}{6.20} = 1.81$$

Here $k = 4$ and n varies from 14 to 21. Examination of Table XI indicates that the critical value decreases as n increases. Therefore if for the largest value of n the observed F_{max} is not in the critical region we shall know it would not be in the critical region for a smaller n. Here we find that for

$$k = 4 \text{ and } n = 20, \text{ the critical region is } F_{max} > 3.25$$

and even for

$$k = 4 \text{ and } n = 30, \text{ the critical region is } F_{max} > 2.59$$

Clearly the observed value is not in the critical region and the hypothesis $\sigma_1^2 = \sigma_2^2 = \sigma_3^2 = \sigma_4^2$ is sustained.

If the Hartley test described above had resulted in the decision to reject the hypothesis when Table XI was entered with the largest n and to accept when entered with the smallest n, as might have happened, a different test allowing for variations in n would be needed. The great simplicity of the Hartley test makes its use advisable whenever it gives unambiguous results. In other situations Bartlett's[1] test to be described below may be used.

Let $s_1^2, s_2^2 \cdots s_k^2$ be the variances of k independent samples having respectively $n_1, n_2 \cdots n_k$ degrees of freedom. Then under the hypothesis that $\sigma_1^2 = \sigma_2^2 = \cdots = \sigma_k^2 = \sigma^2$ the estimate of σ^2 obtained by pooling the variances of the k samples is

$$(8.10) \quad s^2 = \frac{n_1 s_1^2 + n_2 s_2^2 + \cdots + n_k s_k^2}{n_1 + n_2 + \cdots + n_k} = \frac{\Sigma n_i s_i^2}{n} \text{ where } n = \Sigma n_i$$

We compute the statistic

$$(8.11) \quad B = \frac{2.3026}{C}\left\{n \left(\log_{10} \sum_{i=1}^{k} n_i s_i^2 - \log_{10} n\right) - \sum_{i=1}^{k} n_i \log_{10} s_i^2\right\}$$

$$= B'/C$$

$$(8.12) \text{ where} \quad C = 1 + \frac{1}{3(k-1)}\left\{\sum_{i=1}^{k} \frac{1}{n_i} - \frac{1}{n}\right\}$$

Even if some of the n_i are quite small, say 5 or more, the statistic B has a chi-square distribution with $k - 1$ degrees of freedom. It is not always necessary to compute C. If B' is not significantly large, B will be even smaller because C is always larger than 1. Therefore C need be computed only if B' appears significantly large.

The procedure known as the *Bartlett test for homogeneity of variance* is shown in Table 8.2 where it is applied to the variances of the same four St. Louis schools discussed at the beginning of this section. The reader who is not familiar with logarithms will need to refer to an algebra text or to reference eleven.

TABLE 8.2 Computation to Test the Homogeneity of Variance of Teachers in 4 St. Louis Schools on a Test of Information about the Community.*

School	N_i	n_i	$n_i s_i^2$	s_i^2	$\log_{10} s_i^2$	$n_i \log_{10} s_i^2$	$\frac{1}{n_i}$
1. Jefferson	20	19	213.2	11.22	1.0500	19.9500	.0526
2. Banneker	22	21	216.3	10.30	1.0124	21.2604	.0476
3. Cole	22	21	130.2	6.20	0.7924	16.6404	.0476
4. Marshall	15	14	137.1	9.79	0.9908	13.8712	.0714
Sum	79	75	696.8		3.8456	71.7220	.2192

$$\log_{10} \Sigma n_i s_i^2 = \log_{10} 696.8 = 2.8431$$
$$\log_{10} \Sigma n_i = \log_{10} 75 = \underline{1.8751}$$
$$0.9680$$

$$B' = 2.3026\ \{75(0.9680) - 71.7220\} = 2.3026(0.8800) = 2.026$$

$$C = 1 + \frac{1}{3(4-1)}\left\{.2192 - \frac{1}{75}\right\} = 1.0229 \quad B = \frac{B'}{C} = \frac{2.026}{1.0229} = 1.98$$

* From Harris, *Teachers' Social Knowledge and its Relation to Pupils' Responses*, page 22.

The statistic $B = 1.98$ is referred to a chi-square table with $k - 1 = 3$ degrees of freedom, where $\chi^2_{.90}$ is found to be 6.3. As $B < \chi^2_{.90}$ the evidence does not refute the hypothesis that

$$\sigma_1^2 = \sigma_2^2 = \sigma_3^2 = \sigma_4^2 = \sigma^2.$$

This conclusion is in agreement with the conclusion previously reached by reference to the Hartley Table.

Cochran [2] has proposed a statistic which is the ratio of the largest of the variances in k independent samples each having n degrees of freedom to the sum of all the variances and has derived its sampling distribution. This statistic is meaningful and simple to compute, but a special table is needed for its sampling distribution. Since this book is not attempting to present all the useful sampling distributions but only those which are needed most often, Cochran's test is mentioned here for the information of the reader, but without necessary tables. These tables may be found on pages 390–391 in *Techniques of Statistical Analysis.* [4]

Bartlett's test is useful to detect lack of homogeneity in general, of any sort. It is not so sensitive as Cochran's test for detecting lack of homogeneity arising because the variance of one population is considerably larger than the variances of the others.

The 5% and 1% significance level of the numerator of Bartlett's statistic have been tabulated by Thompson and Merrington.[10]

REFERENCES

1. Bartlett, M. S., "Properties of Sufficiency and Statistical Tests," *Proceedings of the Royal Society of London*, A, 160 (1937), page 268.
2. Cochran, W. G., "The Distribution of the Largest of a Set of Estimated Variances as a Fraction of their Total," *Annals of Eugenics*, 11 (1941), 47–52.
3. Dixon, W. J. and Massey, F. J., Jr., *Introduction to Statistical Analysis*, New York, 1951, McGraw-Hill Book Company, Inc. See index under "variance."
4. Eisenhart, C., Hastay, M. W., and Wallis, W. A., *Techniques of Statistical Analysis*, New York, 1947, McGraw-Hill Book Company, Inc. Chapter 15, "Significance of the Largest of a Set of Sample Estimates of Variance."
5. Fisher, R. A. and Yates, F., *Statistical Tables for Biological, Agricultural and Medical Research*, New York, 1948, Hafner Publishing Company, 3d Ed.
6. Harris, Ruth, *Teachers' Social Knowledge and its Relation to Pupil's Responses, a Study of Four St. Louis Negro Elementary Schools*, New York, 1941, Bureau of Publications, Teachers College, Columbia University.
7. Hartley, H. O., "The Maximum F-Ratio as a Short-cut Test for Heterogeneity of Variance," *Biometrika*, 37 (December, 1950), 308–312.
8. Merrington, M. and Thompson, C. M., "Tables of Percentage Points of the Inverted Beta (F) Distribution," *Biometrika*, 33 (1943), 73–88.
9. Mood, A. M., *Introduction to the Theory of Statistics*. New York, 1950, McGraw-Hill Book Company, Inc., pages 267–270.
10. Thompson, C. M. and Merrington, M. "Tables for Testing the Homogeneity of a Set of Estimated Variances," *Biometrika*, 33 (June, 1946), 296–304.
11. Walker, H. M., *Mathematics Essential for Elementary Statistics*, New York, 1951, Henry Holt and Company, 2d Ed. Chapter 17, "Logarithms."
12. Westover, F. L., *Controlled Eye Movements Versus Practice Exercises in Reading*, New York, 1946, Bureau of Publications, Teachers College, Columbia University.

9 Analysis of Variance

Methods for testing hypotheses concerning means of *two* populations were considered in Chapter 7. The present chapter will deal with hypotheses concerning the means of *several* populations. The method for testing the hypothesis $\mu_1 = \mu_2$ presented on page 156 will be shown to be a special case of the method for testing the hypothesis $\mu_1 = \mu_2 = \mu_3 = \cdots = \mu_k$ to be presented in the following pages.

Use of Double Subscripts. In a great many statistical problems, in fact in most of those which will be discussed in the remainder of this book, observations need to be classified on two or more variables simultaneously. As the classification becomes more complex it is helpful to have an explicit symbolism to indicate exactly which values contribute to a particular sum or mean or variance. In such situations clarity may be promoted by the use of double (or multiple) subscripts, as in the following rectangular arrangement.

$$\begin{matrix} X_{11} & X_{12} & X_{13} & X_{14} & X_{15} & X_{16} & X_{17} \\ X_{21} & X_{22} & X_{23} & X_{24} & X_{25} & X_{26} & X_{27} \\ X_{31} & X_{32} & X_{33} & X_{34} & X_{35} & X_{36} & X_{37} \end{matrix}$$

Each entry here represents a numerical score. The symbol X_{23} is read "X two three" or "X sub two three," *not* "X twenty-three." If the arrangement represents the scores of 7 persons on 3 tests, the entries in any one vertical column are the 3 scores made by one person, the scores in any one horizontal row are the scores of 7 persons on one test. If this arrangement represents 3 samples of 7 individuals each, the entries in the first column represent the scores of the first individual drawn in each sample, the entries in the first row represent the scores of the 7 individuals of the first sample. Innumerable other interpretations might be made of such an arrangement. A rectangular arrangement of numbers is called a *matrix*.

Assuming that the arrangement represents the scores of 7 persons on 3 tests, study the following parallels:

X_{26} represents a score on Test 2 made by the sixth person

X_{i3} represents a score made by person 3 on *one of the tests,* on an unspecified test

X_{2j} represents a score on Test 2 made by some person, an unspecified person

X_{ij} represents a score on one of the tests made by one of the persons, neither test nor person being specified.

Then the sum of the scores

in the first row is $\sum_{j=1}^{7} X_{1j}$ and in *some* row is $\sum_{j=1}^{7} X_{ij}$

in the first column is $\sum_{i=1}^{3} X_{i1}$ and in *some* column is $\sum_{i=1}^{3} X_{ij}$

The sum of all 21 scores is

$$\sum_{i=1}^{3} \sum_{j=1}^{7} X_{ij} = \sum_{j=1}^{7} \sum_{i=1}^{3} X_{ij}$$

The first letter or digit in the subscript customarily indicates the row; the second letter or digit indicates the column. In situations such as these omission of the variable subscripts and limits of summation begets confusion. If one wrote ΣX for data from this matrix there would be no way of telling whether the expression means the sum for a row (and which row?), the sum for a column (and which column?), or the sum for the entire matrix.

We also need a symbolism which will permit us to distinguish between the mean of the 2d row which is $\frac{1}{7}\sum_{j=1}^{7} X_{2j}$ and the mean of the 2d column which is $\frac{1}{3}\sum_{i=1}^{3} X_{i2}$. The important aspect of this symbolism is to be able to distinguish whether 2 is the first subscript or the second. To make this point clear it is customary to write $\overline{X}$ with subscripts similar to the subscripts for X in the summation but with a dot replacing the variable subscript over which summation has taken place. Thus in general

$\frac{1}{10}\sum_{i=1}^{10} X_{i3}$ would be $\overline{X}_{.3}$ $\qquad$ $\frac{1}{r}\sum_{i=1}^{r} X_{ij}$ would be $\overline{X}_{.j}$

$\frac{1}{40}\sum_{j=1}^{40} X_{7j}$ would be $\overline{X}_{7.}$ $\qquad$ $\frac{1}{c}\sum_{j=1}^{c} X_{ij}$ would be $\overline{X}_{i.}$

$$\frac{1}{rc}\sum_{i=1}^{r} \sum_{j=1}^{c} X_{ij} \text{ would be } \overline{X}$$

If the meaning is clear without it, the dot should be omitted.

A similar convention may be applied to the variance and the standard deviation. Thus

$$\frac{1}{9}\sum_{i=1}^{10} (X_{i3} - \overline{X}_{.3})^2 \text{ would be written } s^2{}_{.3}$$

$$\frac{1}{39}\sum_{j=1}^{40} (X_{7j} - \overline{X}_{7.})^2 \text{ would be written } s^2{}_{.7}$$

$$\frac{1}{r-1}\sum_{i=1}^{r} (X_{ij} - \overline{X}_{.j})^2 \text{ would be written } s^2{}_{.j}$$

$$\sqrt{\frac{1}{c-1}\sum_{j=1}^{c} (X_{ij} - \overline{X}_{i.})^2} \text{ would be written } s_{i.}$$

$$\sqrt{\frac{1}{rc-1}\sum_{i=1}^{r}\sum_{j=1}^{c} (X_{ij} - \overline{X}_{..})^2} \text{ would be written } s_{..}$$

Often $\overline{X}_{..}$, $s^2{}_{..}$ and $s_{..}$ are written merely as $\overline{X}$, s^2 and s when omission of the .. creates no confusion.

EXERCISE 9.1

Write out all entries for a matrix of 4 rows and 3 columns, using X with appropriate subscripts for each entry.

Write the expression for each row total in the matrix just written, that for the first row being $\sum_{j=1}^{3} X_{1j}$.

Write the expression for each column total in the matrix, that for the first column being $\sum_{i=1}^{4} X_{i1}$.

Write the expression for the total for all 12 entries.

Write an expression for each row mean, the mean for the first row being $\overline{X}_{1.} = \frac{1}{3}\sum_{j=1}^{3} X_{1j}$.

Write an expression for each column mean, the mean for the first column being $\overline{X}_{.1} = \frac{1}{4}\sum_{i=1}^{4} X_{i1}$.

Write an expression for the mean of the entire matrix.

Write an expression for the variance of each row, the variance for the first row being $s^2{}_{1.} = \frac{1}{2}\sum_{j=1}^{3} (X_{1j} - \overline{X}_{1.})^2$.

Write an expression for the variance of each column, the variance for the first column being $s^2{}_{.1} = \frac{1}{3}\sum_{i=1}^{4} (X_{i1} - \overline{X}_{.1})^2$.

Write an expression for the variance of all 12 entries.

Write expressions for the mean and the variance of an unspecified row, the mean and the variance of an unspecified column.

Check what you have written against the symbols recorded in Table 9.1.

TABLE 9.1 Symbols for Mean and Variance of a Subgroup

	Individual Scores			Row total	Row mean	Row variance
	X_{11}	X_{12}	X_{13}	$\sum_{j=1}^{3} X_{1j}$	$\overline{X}_{1.} = \frac{\sum_{1}^{3} X_{1j}}{3}$	$s^2_{1.} = \frac{\sum_{j=1}^{3} (X_{1j} - \overline{X}_{1.})^2}{2}$
	X_{21}	X_{22}	X_{23}	$\sum_{j=1}^{3} X_{2j}$	$\overline{X}_{2.} = \frac{\sum_{j=1}^{3} X_{2j}}{3}$	$s^2_{2.} = \frac{\sum_{j=1}^{3} (X_{2j} - \overline{X}_{2.})^2}{2}$
	X_{31}	X_{32}	X_{33}	$\sum_{j=1}^{3} X_{3j}$	$\overline{X}_{3.} = \frac{\sum_{j=1}^{3} X_{3j}}{3}$	$s^2_{3.} = \frac{\sum_{j=1}^{3} (X_{3j} - \overline{X}_{3.})^2}{2}$
	X_{41}	X_{42}	X_{43}	$\sum_{j=1}^{3} X_{4j}$	$\overline{X}_{4.} = \frac{\sum_{j=1}^{3} X_{4j}}{3}$	$s^2_{4.} = \frac{\sum_{j=1}^{3} (X_{4j} - \overline{X}_{4.})^2}{2}$
Column total	$\sum_{i=1}^{4} X_{i1}$	$\sum_{i=1}^{4} X_{i2}$	$\sum_{i=1}^{4} X_{i3}$			
Column mean	$\overline{X}_{.1} = \frac{\sum_{i=1}^{4} X_{i1}}{4}$	$\overline{X}_{.2} = \frac{\sum_{i=1}^{4} \overline{X}_{i2}}{4}$	$\overline{X}_{.3} = \frac{\sum_{i=1}^{4} X_{i3}}{4}$			
Column variance	$s^2_{.1} = \frac{\sum_{i=1}^{4} (X_{i1} - \overline{X}_{.1})^2}{3}$	$s^2_{.2} = \frac{\sum_{i=1}^{4} (X_{i2} - \overline{X}_{.2})^2}{3}$	$s^2_{.3} = \frac{\sum_{i=1}^{4} (X_{i3} - \overline{X}_{.3})^2}{3}$			

Row total for an unspecified row $= \sum_{j=1}^{3} X_{ij}$

Column total for an unspecified column $= \sum_{i=1}^{4} X_{ij}$

Sum of column totals $= \sum_{j=1}^{3} \sum_{i=1}^{4} X_{ij}$ Sum of row totals $= \sum_{i=1}^{4} \sum_{j=1}^{3} X_{ij}$

$$\text{Mean of entire group} = \overline{X} = \frac{\sum_{i=1}^{4} \sum_{j=1}^{3} X_{ij}}{12} = \frac{\sum_{j=1}^{3} \sum_{i=1}^{4} X_{ij}}{12} = \frac{\Sigma\Sigma X_{ij}}{12}$$

$$\text{Variance of entire group} = s^2 = \frac{\sum_{i=1}^{4} \sum_{j=1}^{3} (X_{ij} - \overline{X})^2}{11} = \frac{\Sigma\Sigma(X - \overline{X})^2}{11}$$

Sum of row totals = sum of column totals.

Comparison of Three Means. As an illustration of a problem in which the means of three populations are to be compared, consider an experiment carried out by Schroeder [3] to study factors influencing performance in archery. The standard "Round" in archery consists of sets of 6 shots at each of three ranges, 30, 40, and 50 yards, shot in that order. One of the goals of Schroeder's study was to find out whether order of shooting the different ranges has an effect on performance. If the ranges are shot in non-standard order will the scores be comparable with scores obtained from the standard series?

TABLE 9.2 Archery Scores at the 50-Yard Range Made by 33 College Women.*

Group	Individual scores	$\Sigma X = T$	$\bar{X}$	ΣX^2	$(\Sigma X)^2/N = T^2/N$	$\Sigma(X - \bar{X})^2$
A	99, 114, 51, 78 134, 71, 66, 33 146, 80, 105	977	88.82	98665	86775.3	11889.7
B	104, 26, 136, 87 187, 34, 106, 63 155, 68, 29	995	90.45	118377	90002.3	28374.7
C	41, 83, 61, 189 88, 80, 141, 112 141, 112, 173	1221	111.0	156935	135531.0	21404.0
Sum		3193		373977	312308.6	61668.4
Entire group		3193	96.76	373977	308946.9	65030.1

* Data from Schroeder.[3]

A sample of 33 subjects was chosen and divided randomly into 3 equal subsamples. Each group of 11 subjects was given 6 lessons in archery, the order of shooting the ranges being changed from lesson to lesson. (Note that there are 6 possible orders, because the number of arrangements of 3 things is 6.) Now consider the performance at the 50-yard range when this range was shot first by Group *A*, second by *B*, and third by *C*. Table 9.2 presents the resulting scores, each score there being the sum of the performance scores of one individual in two lessons. The means of the three groups seem to suggest that the range shot last has the advantage. However before concluding that the advantage is real, existing in the population of all possible observations, it is necessary to determine that the variation among the three observed means is too great to be attributed to the chance effects of sampling.

Note that if the study had been set up to compare scores made on the range shot last with scores on either of the other ranges, it would be satisfactory to combine the scores of Group A and B into one group of 22 cases, which for convenience we may call D, and to test the hypothesis that $\mu_C = \mu_D$ by the methods of Chapter 7. However the experiment was not set up to test that hypothesis but to test the hypothesis $\mu_A = \mu_B = \mu_C$. *When observation of the data suggests a new hypothesis, that new hypothesis can never be satisfactorily tested on the data from which it was obtained* but requires a new set of observations.

Mathematical Model. To specify the mathematical population (that is to provide a mathematical model), we shall assume that each of the three samples is drawn at random from a normal population and that all three populations have the same variance but not necessarily the same mean.

Population	Mean	Variance
A	μ_A	σ^2
B	μ_B	σ^2
C	μ_C	σ^2

For precision, the assumption that all three samples were drawn from normal populations with the same variance needs to be investigated. Application of the tests of normality described in Chapter 5 indicates that the assumption of normality may be accepted. (Usually it is satisfactory to look at the grouped frequency distribution of scores and to decide more or less intuitively that the distribution appears fairly normal.) The assumption of equality of variance can be tested by comparing the three sample variances by the method described in Chapter 8. This test indicates that the assumption of equality of variance may also be accepted.

Hypothesis to be Tested. The hypothesis to be tested is

$$\mu_A = \mu_B = \mu_C = \mu$$

If this hypothesis is true and the assumption of normal populations with equal variance is justified, then the 33 scores may be regarded as random observations from a single normal population with mean μ and variance σ^2. The means of the three samples would then be random observations from a normal population of sample means for which $E(\overline{X}) = \mu$ and $\sigma_{\overline{X}}^2 = \dfrac{\sigma^2}{N} = \dfrac{\sigma^2}{11}$, as explained in Chapter 7.

The unknown variance σ^2 can be estimated from the variation among the three sample means. It can also be estimated from the variation among the archers within groups. The ratio of these two estimates of σ^2 provides the statistic by means of which the hypothesis can be tested.

Estimate of σ^2 from Variation Among Means. The value of $\sigma_{\overline{X}}^2 = \frac{\sigma^2}{N}$, which in this problem is $\frac{\sigma^2}{11}$, can be estimated by computing the variance of the means shown in Table 9.1 around the mean of the entire group. These three means may be treated as a sample of three individuals, so that their variance has $3 - 1 = 2$ degrees of freedom. Then

$$s_{\overline{X}}^2 = \frac{(\overline{X}_1 - \overline{X})^2 + (\overline{X}_2 - \overline{X})^2 + (\overline{X}_3 - \overline{X})^2}{2} = \frac{\sum_{j=1}^{3} (\overline{X}_j - \overline{X})^2}{2}$$

is an unbiased estimate of $\sigma_{\overline{X}}^2 = \frac{\sigma^2}{11}$, and therefore

$$11 s_{\overline{X}}^2 = \frac{11 \sum_{j=1}^{3} (\overline{X}_{.j} - \overline{X})^2}{2} = \frac{11 \sum_{j=1}^{3} (\overline{X}_j - \overline{X})^2}{2}$$

is an unbiased estimate of σ^2 if the population means are equal.

In general if there are k samples of N cases each,

$$(9.1) \qquad N s_{\overline{X}}^2 = \frac{N \sum_{j=1}^{k} (\overline{X}_{.j} - \overline{X}_{..})^2}{k - 1} = \frac{N \sum_{j=1}^{k} (\overline{X}_j - \overline{X})^2}{k - 1}$$

is the estimate of σ^2 obtained from *variation among the means.* It is usually called the "mean square between group means," or the "mean square for variation between means" or the "mean square between groups" or "mean square for means."

The numerator of Formula (9.1) is the *sum of squares between groups.* The denominator is the number of degrees of freedom.

Applying Formula (9.1) to the data of Table 9.2 we obtain

$$\begin{aligned} 11 s_{\overline{X}}^2 &= \tfrac{11}{2}[(88.82 - 96.76)^2 + (90.45 - 96.76)^2 + (111.0 - 96.76)^2] \\ &= \tfrac{3362}{2} = 1681. \end{aligned}$$

Computing routines which are algebraically equivalent to that of Formula (9.1) but which demand less arithmetic labor and produce smaller rounding errors are furnished by Formulas (9.2) and (9.3).

$$Ns_{\bar{X}}^2 = \frac{\frac{1}{N}\sum_{j=1}^{k}(\sum_{i=1}^{N}X_{ij})^2 - \frac{1}{Nk}(\sum_{j=1}^{k}\sum_{i=1}^{N}X_{ij})^2}{k-1} \tag{9.2}$$

$$= \frac{\frac{1}{N}\sum_{j}(\sum_{i}X)^2 - \frac{1}{Nk}(\Sigma\Sigma X)^2}{k-1}$$

$$Ns_{\bar{X}}^2 = \frac{k\sum_{j}(\sum_{i}X)^2 - (\Sigma\Sigma X)^2}{Nk(k-1)} \tag{9.3}$$

Applying these formulas to the data of Table 9.2 we have

by (9.2) $$Ns_{\bar{X}}^2 = \frac{\frac{(977^2 + 995^2 + 1221^2)}{11} - \frac{(3193)^2}{33}}{2} = 1680.8$$

and by (9.3)

$$Ns_{\bar{X}}^2 = \frac{3(977^2 + 995^2 + 1221^2) - 3193^2}{11(3)(2)} = 1680.8$$

Estimate of σ^2 from Variation within Groups. Formula (8.10) was stated on page 193 as providing an estimate of σ^2 based upon the pooled variance of several groups. In the present problem the estimate of σ^2 thus obtained would be

$$\frac{(N_1 - 1)s_1^2 + (N_2 - 1)s_2^2 + (N_3 - 1)s_3^2}{N_1 + N_2 + N_3 - 3} = \frac{10s_1^2 + 10s_2^2 + 10s_3^2}{11 + 11 + 11 - 3}$$

This is usually called the "mean square within groups." In general if there are k groups of N cases each, σ^2 is estimated as

$$s^2 = \frac{(N-1)(s_1^2 + s_2^2 + \cdots + s_k^2)}{Nk - k} = \frac{\sum_{j=1}^{k}\sum_{i=1}^{N}(X_{ij} - \bar{X}_j)^2}{Nk - k} \tag{9.4}$$

The numerator of (9.4) is the *sum of squares within groups.* The denominator is the number of degrees of freedom.

Computing routines which are equivalent to that of Formula (9.4) but which involve less arithmetic and less rounding error are provided by Formulas (9.5) and (9.6).

$$s^2 = \frac{\sum_{j=1}^{k}\sum_{i=1}^{N}X^2_{ij} - \frac{1}{N}\sum_{j=1}^{k}(\sum_{i=1}^{N}X_{ij})^2}{Nk - k} \tag{9.5}$$

$$= \frac{\sum_{j}\sum_{i}X^2 - \frac{1}{N}\sum_{j}(\sum_{i}X)^2}{(N-1)k}$$

(9.6) $$s^2 = \frac{N\sum_j \sum_i X^2 - \sum_j (\sum_i X)^2}{N(N-1)k}$$

Applying Formula (9.4) to the data of Table 9.2 we have

$$s^2 = \frac{11889.7 + 28374.7 + 21404.0}{33 - 3} = \frac{61668.4}{30} = 2055.6$$

This computation is simple only because the numerator had already been worked out in Table 9.2. Applying Formulas (9.5) and (9.6) we have

$$s^2 = \frac{373977 - \frac{1}{11}(977^2 + 995^2 + 1221^2)}{(10)(3)} = 2055.6$$

and $$s^2 = \frac{11(373977) - (977^2 + 995^2 + 1221^2)}{11(10)(3)} = 2055.6$$

The Variance Ratio. We have found two estimates of σ^2, namely 1681 and 2056. Estimates computed in this way have the property that they are independently distributed. See page 208 for further discussion of this property. A third estimate of σ^2 may be obtained from the deviations of all 33 scores around the grand mean $\overline{X}$ but this estimate is not distributed independently of either of the other estimates and therefore cannot be used in the F ratio about to be described.

In Chapter 8 it was said that any ratio of the form $(N-1)s^2/\sigma^2$ or ns^2/σ^2 has a chi-square distribution with $n = N - 1$ degrees of freedom. It was also said in that chapter that if s_1^2/s_2^2 are two independent estimates of the same variance σ^2, the ratio s_1^2/s_2^2 has an F distribution with n_1 degrees of freedom for the numerator and n_2 for the denominator. Now since

$$\frac{n_1 s_1^2}{\sigma^2} \text{ may be called } \chi_1^2 \text{ and } \frac{n_2 s_2^2}{\sigma^2} \text{ called } \chi_2^2,$$

$$\frac{s_1^2}{\sigma^2} \text{ may be called } \frac{\chi_1^2}{n_1} \text{ and } \frac{s_2^2}{\sigma^2} \text{ called } \frac{\chi_2^2}{n_2}.$$

Then $$\frac{s_1^2}{s_2^2} = \frac{\chi_1^2/n_1}{\chi_2^2/n_2} = \frac{\chi_1^2}{\chi_2^2} \cdot \frac{n_2}{n_1},$$

and any expression which can be reduced to this form has an F distribution if χ_1^2/n_1 and χ_2^2/n_2 come from independent estimates of the same variance. Therefore in the problem under consideration the ratio of the mean square between group means to the mean square within groups is distributed as F with 2 degrees of freedom for the numerator and 30 for the denominator, or in general with $k - 1$ degrees of freedom for the numerator and $Nk - k$ for the denominator:

$$(9.7) \qquad F = \frac{\text{mean square between group means}}{\text{mean square within groups}}$$

$$= \frac{\text{sum of squares between groups}}{\text{sum of squares within groups}} \cdot \frac{Nk - k}{k - 1}$$

$$(9.8) \text{ or } \qquad F = \frac{N\Sigma(\overline{X}_{.j} - \overline{X})^2}{\Sigma\Sigma(X_{ij} - \overline{X}_{.j})^2} \cdot \frac{Nk - k}{k - 1}$$

Analysis of the Archery Data. The computations already made from the data of Table 9.2 may now be summarized in Table 9.3, which is in the general form customarily used for such problems. Usually the value read from an F table with which the observed F is to be compared would also be included in the table, but as that has not yet been discussed it will not be shown here. Interpretation of the value $F = .82$ depends upon the selection of a critical region and will be discussed in the following section.

TABLE 9.3 Analysis of Variance of 33 Archery Scores

Source of variation	Sum of squares	Degrees of freedom	Mean square	F
Total group	65030	32		
Between group means	3362	2	1681	.82
Among archers within groups	61668	30	2056	

Critical Region. From Table X in the Appendix, a critical region with either $\alpha = .05$ or $\alpha = .01$ can be obtained. For testing the hypothesis under consideration, the variance ratio has two degrees of freedom for the numerator mean square ($n_1 = 2$) and 30 for the denominator ($n_2 = 30$). The corresponding cell of the table contains the entries 3.32 and 5.39. From these it is to be understood that

$$P(F > 3.32 \mid n_1 = 2, n_2 = 30) = .05$$
$$P(F > 5.39 \mid n_1 = 2, n_2 = 30) = .01$$

or

$$P(F < 3.32 \mid n_1 = 2, n_2 = 30) = .95$$
$$P(F < 5.39 \mid n_1 = 2, n_2 = 30) = .99$$

or

$$F_{.95} = 3.32 \quad \text{and} \quad F_{.99} = 5.39$$

Thus for $\alpha = .05$ the region of acceptance is $F < 3.32$ and the region of rejection is $F \geqq 3.32$; while for $\alpha = .01$ the region of acceptance is $F < 5.39$ and the region of rejection is $F \geqq 5.39$. It may be assumed that values precisely 5.39 and 3.32 will never occur, but values equal to these within a given margin of rounding error may appear. The research worker should make up his mind before he sees the results of his computations whether he will consider that such shall be considered to fall in the region of acceptance or of rejection. If he decides to place them in the region of rejection, he would define such as $F \geqq 5.39$ for $\alpha = .01$, and similarly for $\alpha = .05$.

The observed value $F = .82$ falls well within the region of acceptance and one must conclude that the data are consistent with the hypothesis that scores obtained at the 50-yard range are not influenced by the order in which that range is shot within the round.

In the present test the critical region has been placed in the upper tail of the distribution while for the problems considered in Chapter 8 it was in both tails. The difference in the logic of the two situations needs to be examined.

In Chapter 8 the values of s_1^2 and s_2^2 used in the variance ratio were obtained from two independent samples which by hypothesis came from populations having the same variance. Too great a discrepancy between s_1^2 and s_2^2 is damaging to that hypothesis regardless of which variance is larger. Therefore the critical region must include both tails of the distribution so that the hypothesis will be rejected if

either $\quad s_1^2/s_2^2$ is very small $\quad$ or $\quad s_1^2/s_2^2$ is very large

and this is the same as if

s_2^2/s_1^2 is very large $\quad$ or $\quad s_2^2/s_1^2$ is very small

The procedure is to place the *larger variance in the numerator* and to consider the probabilities associated with the two-sided critical region to be not α but 2α. Significance levels read from Table X for such problems will be .02 and .10. The study of Figures 9–2 and 9–3 on pages 208 and 209 will further clarify this point.

In the problem under consideration in the present chapter, the two variances are obtained from *the same sample.* The variance within groups estimated by Formulas (9.4), (9.5), or (9.6), is an unbiased estimate of σ^2 whether the hypothesis tested is true or not. If the hypothesis that $\mu_1 = \mu_2 = \cdots = \mu_k = \mu$ is true, the variance between groups is also an unbiased estimate of σ^2. However if the groups have different means in the population, the mean square between groups will have an expectation *larger than* σ^2.

Form of the *F* Distribution. As this curve has a different form for every possible pair of numbers n_1 and n_2, the attempt to visualize it is not very rewarding. It is always skewed with range from 0 to infinity. Negative values of F cannot occur because both numerator and denominator are necessarily positive. The highest point on the F curve occurs at $F = \dfrac{n_2(n_1 - 2)}{n_1(n_2 - 2)}$ but that fact is not very important. Its mean is at $F = \dfrac{n_2}{n_2 - 2}$, which is slightly above 1.0. Falsity of the hypothesis $\mu_1 = \mu_2 = \cdots = \mu_k$ cannot possibly make the mean square between means smaller than σ^2 and must make it greater. Therefore in problems of this type the mean square *between* groups is always placed in the numerator and the mean square *within* groups in the denominator regardless of which is the larger. Then very large values of F throw doubt on the hypothesis but very small ones do not. As large values of F occur in the upper or right-hand tail of the sampling distribution of F, the critical region is in the right tail only. Significance levels obtained from Table X will be .01 and .05.

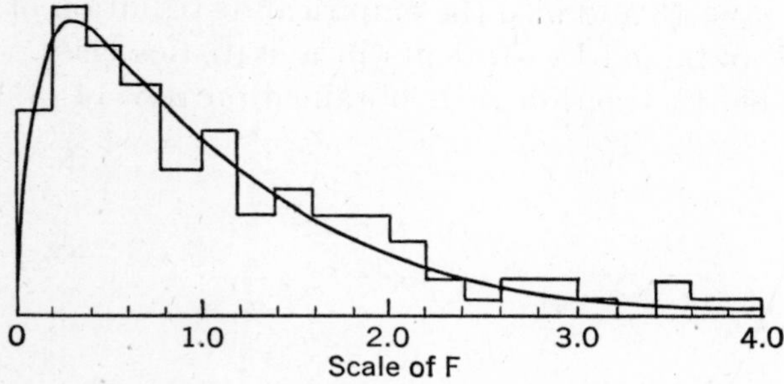

FIG. 9–1. Sampling distribution of F when $n_1 = 3$ and $n_2 = 16$ with empirical distribution of the 34 samples values.

One may ask what can produce a very small F, since failure of the hypothesis cannot make it small. When a suspiciously small F occurs one asks if computations are correct, if the cases were selected at random, if the data were in any sense artificial or improperly gathered. For example, instructors have been known to make up examples from artificial data yielding F's that are improbably small. If there appears to be nothing wrong with the data or the computation, one merely ascribes the situation to chance. When $F < 1$, it is customary to say at once that the hypothesis is accepted without referring to probability tables.

However, if F is very small one may suspect that it represents a non-chance situation and may wish to make a test of significance. The procedure then is to take the reciprocal of F and to compare it with the tabular entry for which n_2 is the degrees of freedom for the numerator and n_1 for the denominator. For example for the Schroeder data $F = .82$, so $1/F = 1.22$. In the cell for which $n_1 = 30$ and $n_2 = 2$ we find $F_{.95} = 19.46$, and $F_{.99} = 99.47$. If, therefore, we had the complete distribution for the variance ratio with $n_1 = 2$ and $n_2 = 30$, it would show us that

$$F_{.01} = 1/99.47 = .01005, \quad F_{.05} = 1/19.46 = .0514,$$
$$F_{.95} = 3.32 \qquad F_{.99} = 5.39$$

while the complete distribution for the variance ratio with $n_1 = 30$ and $n_2 = 2$ would show

$$F_{.01} = \frac{1}{5.39} = .19, \quad F_{.05} = \frac{1}{3.32} = .301, \quad F_{.95} = 19.46, \quad F_{.99} = 99.47$$

It may interest the reader to see pictures of the curve for selected values of n_1 and n_2. Figure 6–6 on page 139 shows the form of the curve for $n_1 = 4$ and $n_2 = 4$. Figure 9–1 shows the form for $n_1 = 3$ and $n_2 = 16$ and also the empirical distribution of 34 sample values of F obtained by students in a statistics class. These are the values of the fraction A/B obtained on row 14 of Worksheet

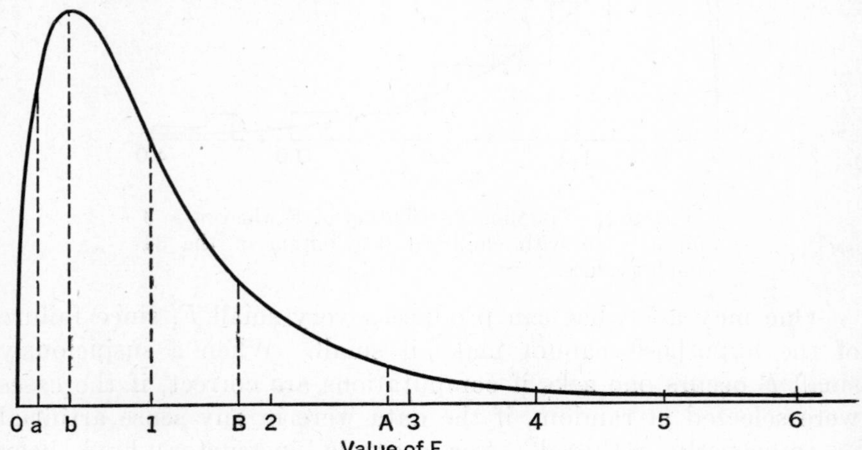

FIG. 9–2. Sampling distribution of F when $n_1 = 4$ and $n_2 = 20$.

5% of area lies above $F = 2.87$, at A
5% of area lies below $F = .17$, at a — Mode $= .45$
20% of area lies above $F = 1.65$, at B — Mean $= 1.11$
20% of area lies below $F = .41$, at b — Median $= .9$
57% of area lies below $F = 1$.

III in Chapter 6.

Figure 9–2 shows the curve for $n_1 = 4$ and $n_2 = 20$ while Figure 9–3 shows the curve for $n_1 = 20$, and $n_2 = 4$. These two curves may now be studied together. If 9–2 represents the distribution of $F = s_i^2/s_j^2$ then 9–3 represents the distribution of $F' = 1/F = s_j^2/s_i^2$. Either curve alone shows the probability for every possible value of the ratio between the two variances. However ratios smaller than 1 would be closely crowded on the base line between 0 and 1 and would have to be given in the table with a large number of decimal places in order to distinguish probability levels. The segment of the horizontal axis in Figure 9–2 to the right of the point 1 represents the same situations as the segment of the horizontal axis of 9–3 to the left of 1 and vice versa. Together the two segments to the right of 1 represent all possible situations. Therefore it is satisfactory to tabulate only the right-hand segment of each curve, and this is the reason that Table X contains no entries smaller than 1.

Independence of the Components of the Sum of Squares. The two components into which the sum of squares has been analyzed have the surprising property of being independently distributed. This property of independence holds in spite of the fact that the two components are based on the same measures. As these two

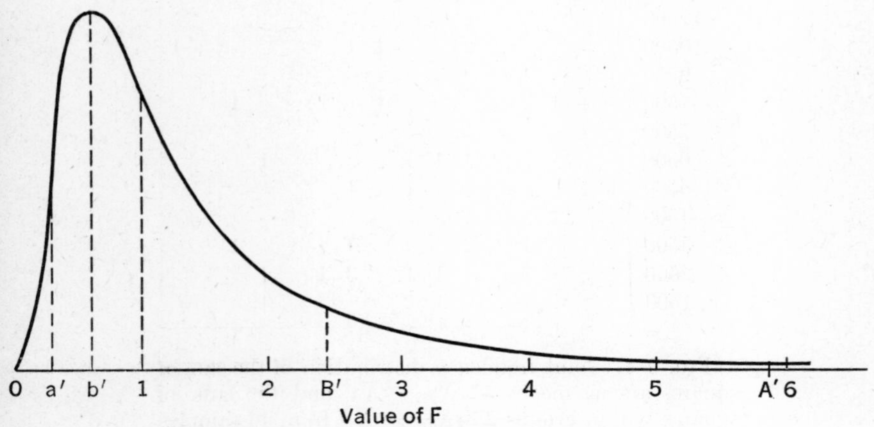

FIG. 9–3. Sampling distribution of F when $n_1 = 20$ and $n_2 = 4$.

5% of area lies above $F = 5.80$, at A′
5% of area lies below $F = .35$, at a′ — Mode = .6
20% of area lies above $F = 2.45$, at B′ — Mean = 2.0
20% of area lies below $F = .61$, at b′ — Median = 1.1
43% of area lies below $F = 1$.

components of the sum of squares are proportional to the two estimates of the variance, those estimates also are independently distributed. The word "independent" implies that if many samples of the same size from the same population are examined, the value of one of these components in a sample is in no way predictive of the value of the other. By way of illustration, there are available computations made by 46 students of the variance between means of 4 samples of 5 cases and the variance among individuals in these same samples.

These two components have been distributed in a scatter diagram in Figure 9–4. The correlation is $r = -.05$, a value which is not significantly different from zero by the test described in Chapter 10.

Unless the two components of variance are independent, the ratio of the related variances does not have an F distribution. The algebraic relationship of Formula (9.9) holds for all samples regardless of the population from which they were obtained but this is a relationship within a sample and does not establish independence from sample to sample.

Value of $\Sigma\Sigma(X_{ij} - \overline{X}_j)^2$ (columns); Value of $5\Sigma(\overline{X}_j - \overline{X})^2$ (rows)

	9000	11000	13000	15000	17000	19000	21000	23000	25000	27000	29000	31000	33000	35000	37000	39000
12500											1	1				
11500																
10500						2			1	1						1
9500				1												
8500		1	1						1					1		
7500		1														
6500						1	1	1					1			
5500	1	1				1		1		1						
4500	1		1			1						1				
3500				1		2				4		1		1		
2500			1	1			1	1		3	1		1			
1500							1						1			

Fig. 9–4. Joint frequency distribution of the sum of squares among means $5\Sigma(\overline{X}_j - \overline{X})^2$ and the sum of squares within groups $\Sigma\Sigma(X_{ij} - \overline{X}_j)$ from 46 samples of 5 cases. $r = -.05$.

Algebraic Relations in Analysis of Variance. While the computing procedure described in the preceding pages can be carried out when numbers in the subsamples are equal, slight modifications are necessary if those numbers are unequal. Moreover certain algebraic relations among the sums of squares can be used to simplify the computations considerably. Those relations will be described in the following paragraphs.

The double subscript notation described at the beginning of this chapter is particularly useful for analysis of variance. Let X_{ij} represent the ith observation in group j, or subsample j. Because the formulas look rather long and imposing, though they are not essentially difficult, we shall introduce the symbol T as sum or total of a set of scores.

$$\sum_{i=1}^{N_1} X_{j1} = T_1 \text{ and } \overline{X}_1 = T_1/N_1$$

$$\sum_{i=1}^{N_j} X_{ij} = T_j \text{ and } \overline{X}_j = T_j/N_j$$

$$\sum_{j=1}^{k} N_j = N$$

$$\sum_{j=1}^{k}\sum_{i=1}^{N_j} X_{ij} = T \text{ and } \overline{X} = T/N$$

Then for any one subsample, say the jth, the sum of the squares of the deviations of individual observations from the subsample mean is

$$\sum_{i=1}^{N_j} (X_{ij} - \overline{X}_j)^2 = \sum_{i=1}^{N_j} X^2_{ij} - \frac{T_j^2}{N_j}.$$

For brevity this expression will be called the *sum of squares.*

The total sum of squares can be partitioned as follows:

$$(9.9) \quad \sum_{j=1}^{k}\sum_{i=1}^{N_j}(X_{ij} - \overline{X})^2 = \sum_{j=1}^{k}\sum_{i=1}^{N_j}(X_{ij} - \overline{X}_j)^2 + \sum_{j=1}^{k} N_j(\overline{X}_j - \overline{X})^2$$

Equation (9.9) is very important, is in fact the basic relationship underlying the process of "analysis of variance" described in this chapter. The total variation described by the sum of squares of all N cases around the total mean has been broken up into two components each of which is expressive of a type of variation. Thus it is the sum of squares rather than the variance which is analyzed. The sum of squares can be analyzed into meaningful components in a number of different ways, some to be described here and some in subsequent chapters. In Formula (9.9) the component $\sum_{j=1}^{k}\sum_{i=1}^{N_j}(X_{ij} - \overline{X}_j)^2$ represents variation among individuals within groups. It would be zero only if all individuals in each group had the same score. The component $\sum_{j=1}^{k} N_j(\overline{X}_j - \overline{X})^2$ represents variation between group means. It would be zero only if all samples had the same mean.

Some additional algebraic relationships are useful to simplify calculations.

A. When the number of cases is the same for all groups, so that $N_1 = N_2 = \cdots = N_k = M$, Formulas (9.10), (9.11), and (9.12) may be used for the sums of squares:

(9.10) Total: $$\sum_{j=1}^{k}\sum_{i=1}^{M}(X_{ij} - \overline{X})^2 = \sum_{j=1}^{k}\sum_{i=1}^{M}X^2_{ij} - \frac{T^2}{kM}$$

(9.11) Between * means: $$M\sum_{j=1}^{k}(\overline{X}_j - \overline{X})^2 = \frac{1}{M}\sum_{j=1}^{k}T_j^2 - \frac{T^2}{kM}$$

(9.12) Within groups: $$\sum_{j=1}^{k}\sum_{i=1}^{M}(X_{ij} - \overline{X}_j)^2 = \sum_{j=1}^{k}\sum_{i=1}^{M}X^2_{ij} - \frac{1}{M}\sum_{j=1}^{k}T_j^2$$

B. When the number of cases differs from group to group, Formulas (9.13), (9.14), and (9.15) will be needed for the sums of squares.

(9.13) Total: $$\sum_{j=1}^{k}\sum_{i=1}^{N_j}(X_{ij} - \overline{X})^2 = \sum_{j=1}^{k}\sum_{i=1}^{N_j}X^2_{ij} - \frac{T^2}{N}$$

(9.14) Between means: $$\sum_{j=1}^{k}N_j(\overline{X}_j - \overline{X})^2 = \sum_{j=1}^{k}\frac{T_j^2}{N_j} - \frac{T^2}{N}$$

(9.15) Within groups: $$\sum_{j=1}^{k}\sum_{i=1}^{N_j}(X_{ij} - \overline{X}_j)^2 = \sum_{j=1}^{k}\sum_{i=1}^{N_j}X^2_{ij} - \sum_{j=1}^{k}\frac{T_j^2}{N_j}$$

Computation Procedures Applicable when Subgroups are not of Uniform Size. Data from a study by Harrington [1] provide an illustration. He made a study of the recommendations written for a selected group of applicants for teaching positions in different high school subjects, to determine what characteristics of these recommendations, if any, are associated with success in obtaining a position. The number of recommendations varied from candidate to candidate. "Successful" candidates were those who were

* Whenever the authors can remember to do so, they are using the phrase "between groups" or "between means" whether there are two groups or more than two. This flouting of usual grammatical convention regarding "between" and "among" is deliberate. Experience indicates that use of the phrase "between means" when there are two samples and "among means" when there are more than two introduces a verbal complexity which causes some students to confuse the latter phrase with the phrase "among individuals within groups."

elected to the position for which they made application. "Unsuccessful" candidates were those not elected to these same positions, although they might subsequently have been elected to other positions. In all, 59 independent similar positions were available, providing 59 successful and 134 unsuccessful candidates, for whom there were 1144 recommendations.

The recommendations were scored on a large number of traits. The data presented here relate to length of recommendation, a score being the "number of items commented on not unfavorably" in the recommendation. Table 9.4 shows the basic data for the 6 successful candidates and Table 9.6 for the 14 unsuccessful candidates, selected from the entire group to illustrate procedures.

TABLE 9.4 Scores on Length of Recommendations Written for 6 Successful Candidates for Teaching Positions.*

Candidate	Recommendation scores							N	ΣX	ΣX^2
1	9	12	9	19	6			5	55	703
2	10	12	7	12	6			5	47	473
3	4	6	5	5	8			5	28	166
4	4	5	11	9	14	10	10	7	63	639
	8	17	8	19				4	52	778
6	5	6	13	3				4	27	239
TOTAL								30	272	2998

$$\frac{T^2}{N} = \frac{(272)^2}{30} = 2466.13$$

Total sum of squares = 2998 − 2466.13 = 531.87

Sum of squares between means $= (55)^2/5 + (47)^2/5 + (28)^2/5 + (63)^2/7 + (52)^2/4 + (27)^2/4 - \frac{T^2}{N} = 2628.85 - 2466.13 = 162.72$

Sum of squares within groups = 531.87 − 162.72 = 369.15

* Data from Harrington.[1]

TABLE 9.5 Analysis of Variance of Scores on Length of Recommendations for 6 Successful Candidates for Teaching Positions

Source of variation	Sum of squares	Degrees of freedom	Mean square	F	$F_{.95}$
Total	531.87	29			
Between means	162.72	5	32.54	2.12	2.62
Within groups	369.15	24	15.38		

Since the F obtained in Table 9.5 is less than $F_{.95}$ the hypothesis that the means of recommendation scores do not differ among the 6 successful candidates may be accepted.

Recommendation scores for 14 unsuccessful candidates are shown in Table 9.6. The student should complete the analysis and should verify that $F = 1.31$ and that $F_{.95} = 1.9$. Hence the hypothesis that the mean length of recommendations does not differ among unsuccessful candidates may be accepted.

TABLE 9.6 Scores on Length of Recommendations Written for 14 Unsuccessful Candidates for Teaching Positions

Candidate	Recommendation scores									N	ΣX	ΣX^2
1	12	5	20	11	24							
2	7	11	14									
3	9	3	6	6	20	4	8	6				
4	23	10	7	8	13	6						
5	8	7	17									
6	2	5	8	8	7							
7	10	14	7	10	6	11	6	9				
8	4	15	4	15	8							
9	7	8	5	10	7	9	8	4	6			
10	6	9	10	4								
11	5	4	6	23	9	15						
12	24	20	9	9								
13	5	17	5	5	7	5	10					
14	4	5	22	7								
Total										77	723	9009

The information just obtained about successful and unsuccessful candidates may be used to advantage in pursuing one of the purposes of Harrington's study, namely to determine whether successful candidates differ from unsuccessful in mean length of recommendation. Since we accept the hypothesis that the means of candidates within the groups are equal all recommendations of each group can be regarded as coming from a single population. Hence the problem of testing the hypothesis that the mean recommendation length of successful candidates is equal to the mean recommendation length of unsuccessful may be reduced to a problem in analysis of variance with two populations. The data may now be treated as consisting of two subsamples, one of 30 and one of 77 recommendations. The calculation follows:

$$\frac{T^2}{N} = \frac{(272 + 723)^2}{30 + 73} = \frac{(995)^2}{107} = 9252.57$$

$$\text{Total sum of squares} = (2998 + 9009) - 9252.57 = 2754.43$$

Sum of squares between means

$$= (272)^2/30 + (723)^2/77 - 9252.57 = 2.25$$

Sum of squares within groups = 2754.43 − 2.25 = 2752.18

As we are now testing the hypothesis that the means of two populations are equal, the t test for comparing the means of two independent samples might have been used. The value of t obtained by Formula (7.23), page 156, would be $\sqrt{.086} = .29$ since $t = \sqrt{F}$ when F has 1 degree of freedom in the numerator.

The calculation of F is usually simpler than that for obtaining t directly. However, the F table shows values for $F_{.95}$ and $F_{.99}$ only while the table of t gives a greater range of values. It is a satisfactory procedure when comparing the means of *two* independent samples, to compute F, take its square root, and refer the result to the table of "Student's" distribution.

TABLE 9.7 Analysis of Variance for Comparing Length of Recommendations of 6 Successful and 14 Unsuccessful Candidates

Source of variation	Sum of squares	Degrees of freedom	Mean square	F	$F_{.05}$
Total	2754.43	106			
Between means	2.25	1	2.25	.086	3.94
Within groups	2752.18	105	26.21		

The observed value of $F = .086$ is so small that one is justified in questioning whether the selection of candidates was really random. As a matter of fact it was not. Harrington supplied the figures to illustrate his procedures and at that time there was no intention to use them for any purpose other than to examine his methodology.

It is of interest, however, that even for his entire group Harrington did not find mean length of recommendation significantly different for persons who secured positions and for their unsuccessful competitors. By a process too long to be described here, he obtained a quality score for each recommendation. These quality scores differentiated the candidates whereas length had not done so. For variation between 183 candidates the mean square was 76.48/182 = .420. For variation of 1035 recommendation scores around the candidate means the mean square was

$$208.70/(1035 - 183) = .245.$$

Therefore $F = .420/.245 = 1.71$. With 182 degrees of freedom for the numerator and 852 for the denominator, $F_{.99} = 1.28$. The candidates cannot be treated as having the same means of quality scores.

Comparison of Means of Several Measures of the Same Individuals. Let us return now to the problem of the effect of varying the order with which ranges of different length are used in lessons of archery. When this problem was discussed at the beginning of this chapter three *independent* groups were used, each group shooting at the 50-yard range in a different order from the other two. An objection to that form of experimental design is that the sample differences were based not only on order of shooting, but also on differences in skill among the groups, so that difference between orders is *confounded* with difference between groups.

One way of eliminating group differences from the design is to compare the scores on the *same* group of subjects. For simplicity in illustration we will present scores for 11 subjects even though data are available for all 33 subjects. For all 11 subjects scores made at the 50-yard range when this range was shot first, second and third are presented in Table 9.8.

TABLE 9.8 Scores of 11 Archery Students at the 50-yard Range for Varying Order of Shooting*

Subject	First order	Second order	Third order	Sum	Mean
1	114	182	123	419	139.67
2	99	121	119	339	113
3	51	100	35	186	62
4	78	144	72	294	98
5	134	125	201	460	153.33
6	71	38	49	158	52.67
7	66	67	107	240	80
8	33	89	51	173	57.67
9	146	159	157	462	154
10	80	101	83	264	88
11	105	113	113	331	110.33
Sum	977	1239	1110	3326	
Mean	88.82	112.64	100.91		100.79

* Data from Schroeder.[3]

It is important to notice the difference between the scores in Table 9.1 and those in Table 9.8. In the former the scores in any column can be rearranged in any arbitrary manner without changing the meaning of the data. In the latter any interchange of scores in a column must be accompanied by a corresponding interchange in every other column since the three scores in any row are linked by the fact that they belong to a given person. This difference plays an important part in determining the statiscal model which is to be used in the analysis of the data.

We shall suppose that each observation in Table 9.8 is derived from a normal population with a mean which depends both on the order of shooting the range and the person doing the shooting. Consider all the possible scores which might be made by the ith person shooting this range in the jth order to be a population and let the mean of that population be called μ_{ij}. The single score recorded for that person at that order is a random deviate from μ_{ij}. Thus each cell in Table 9.8 has its own population mean and each of the 33 scores recorded there is a random deviate from the population mean of the cell in which it stands. As both order and person may influence the mean, it is conceivable that the 33 observations in the table come from 33 different means. These 33 possible population means, together with certain row and column averages are displayed in Table 9.9. In this table

$$\mu_{1.} = \tfrac{1}{3}(\mu_{11} + \mu_{12} + \mu_{13})$$

and in general $\mu_{i.} = \frac{1}{3}(\mu_{i1} + \mu_{i2} + \mu_{i3})$. Similarly

$$\mu_{.1} = \tfrac{1}{11}(\mu_{11} + \mu_{21} + \mu_{31} + \cdots + \mu_{11,\,1}) \text{ and } \mu_{.j} = \tfrac{1}{11}\sum_{i=1}^{11}\mu_{ij}.$$

The total mean μ is a mean of the 33-cell means, also of the 11-row means, and also of the 3-column means.

$$\mu = \tfrac{1}{33}\sum_{i=1}^{11}\sum_{j=1}^{3}\mu_{ij} = \tfrac{1}{11}\sum_{i=1}^{11}\mu_{i.} = \tfrac{1}{3}\sum_{j=1}^{3}\mu_{.j}$$

or in general, if there are r rows and c columns

$$\text{(9.16)} \qquad \mu = \frac{1}{rc}\Sigma\Sigma\mu_{ij} = \frac{1}{r}\sum_{i}\mu_{i.} = \frac{1}{c}\sum_{j}\mu_{.j}$$

The row and column means are expressive of the physical aspects of the problem. The mean $\mu_{i.}$ is the skill of the ith person regardless of order of shooting. The mean $\mu_{.j}$ is the mean of jth order regardless of subject. The mean μ is the average of all effects. The difference $\mu_{i.} - \mu$ may be regarded as the person component or the deviation of the skill of the ith person from the skill of all 11 persons. Similarly the difference $\mu_{.j} - \mu$ is the order component.

TABLE 9.9 Population Means of Scores in Table 9.8

Subject	Order			Mean of row means
	First	Second	Third	
1	μ_{11}	μ_{12}	μ_{13}	$\mu_{1.}$
2	μ_{21}	μ_{22}	μ_{23}	$\mu_{2.}$
3	μ_{31}	μ_{32}	μ_{33}	$\mu_{3.}$
4	μ_{41}	μ_{42}	μ_{43}	$\mu_{4.}$
5	μ_{51}	μ_{52}	μ_{53}	$\mu_{5.}$
6	μ_{61}	μ_{62}	μ_{63}	$\mu_{6.}$
7	μ_{71}	μ_{72}	μ_{73}	$\mu_{7.}$
8	μ_{81}	μ_{82}	μ_{83}	$\mu_{8.}$
9	μ_{91}	μ_{92}	μ_{93}	$\mu_{9.}$
10	$\mu_{10,\,1}$	$\mu_{10,\,2}$	$\mu_{10,\,3}$	$\mu_{10.}$
11	$\mu_{11,\,1}$	$\mu_{11,\,2}$	$\mu_{11,\,3}$	$\mu_{11.}$
Mean of column means	$\mu_{.1}$	$\mu_{.2}$	$\mu_{.3}$	μ

To obtain information about the 33 unknown parameters of Table 9.9 from the 33 observations of Table 9.8 is a hopeless task unless the statistical model can be simplified in some way so that the number of parameters is smaller than the number of observations. We must make some assumption that will reduce the number of unknown parameters. An assumption useful for this purpose is that each cell mean μ_{ij} is the sum of the general mean, μ, the component for the ith person, and the component for the jth order, that is

$$\mu_{ij} = \mu + (\mu_{i.} - \mu) + (\mu_{.j} - \mu) = \mu_{i.} + \mu_{.j} - \mu. \tag{9.17}$$

This assumption allows us to describe the 33 population means as in Table 9.10, which presents the statistical model that will be used in the analysis of the archery data in Table 9.8.

The reader may verify that the entries in the right-hand column are means of the entries in the corresponding rows and that the entries in the lowest row are means of the column entries. Another point to note in the table is that although 15 parameters appear in Table 9.10 only 13 of these are independent. One restriction is introduced by the fact that μ is the mean of the 11 row means or the mean of the 3-column means. Another restriction is introduced by the fact that the mean of the row means equals the mean of the column means. Since we have now only 13 parameters instead of 33 the problem is manageable.

To complete the statistical model we shall assume that each

TABLE 9.10 Revised Population Means of Scores in Table 9.8

Subject	Order			Mean of row means
	First	Second	Third	
1	$\mu_{1.} + \mu_{.1} - \mu$	$\mu_{1.} + \mu_{.2} - \mu$	$\mu_{1.} + \mu_{.3} - \mu$	$\mu_{1.}$
2	$\mu_{2.} + \mu_{.1} - \mu$	$\mu_{2.} + \mu_{.2} - \mu$	$\mu_{2.} + \mu_{.3} - \mu$	$\mu_{2.}$
3	$\mu_{3.} + \mu_{.1} - \mu$	$\mu_{3.} + \mu_{.2} - \mu$	$\mu_{3.} + \mu_{.3} - \mu$	$\mu_{3.}$
4	$\mu_{4.} + \mu_{.1} - \mu$	$\mu_{4.} + \mu_{.2} - \mu$	$\mu_{4.} + \mu_{.3} - \mu$	$\mu_{4.}$
5	$\mu_{5.} + \mu_{.1} - \mu$	$\mu_{5.} + \mu_{.2} - \mu$	$\mu_{5.} + \mu_{.3} - \mu$	$\mu_{5.}$
6	$\mu_{6.} + \mu_{.1} - \mu$	$\mu_{6.} + \mu_{.2} - \mu$	$\mu_{6.} + \mu_{.3} - \mu$	$\mu_{6.}$
7	$\mu_{7.} + \mu_{.1} - \mu$	$\mu_{7.} + \mu_{.2} - \mu$	$\mu_{7.} + \mu_{.3} - \mu$	$\mu_{7.}$
8	$\mu_{8.} + \mu_{.1} - \mu$	$\mu_{8.} + \mu_{.2} - \mu$	$\mu_{8.} + \mu_{.3} - \mu$	$\mu_{8.}$
9	$\mu_{9.} + \mu_{.1} - \mu$	$\mu_{9.} + \mu_{.2} - \mu$	$\mu_{9.} + \mu_{.3} - \mu$	$\mu_{9.}$
10	$\mu_{10.} + \mu_{.1} - \mu$	$\mu_{10.} + \mu_{.2} - \mu$	$\mu_{10.} + \mu_{.3} - \mu$	$\mu_{10.}$
11	$\mu_{11.} + \mu_{.1} - \mu$	$\mu_{11.} + \mu_{.2} - \mu$	$\mu_{11.} + \mu_{.3} - \mu$	$\mu_{11.}$
Mean of column means	$\mu_{.1}$	$\mu_{.2}$	$\mu_{.3}$	μ

of the 33 populations is normal, with mean as indicated by its position in Table 9.10, and that all of these populations have the same variance σ^2.

The observations and their row and column means may be designated by symbols as in Table 9.11. Thus each cell of the table has an observed value X_{ij} and an unknown population mean

TABLE 9.11 Symbolism for Observations and Their Means for 3 Scores on Each of 11 Subjects

Subject	Order			Mean for row	Sum for row
	First	Second	Third		
1	X_{11}	X_{12}	X_{13}	$\overline{X}_{1.}$	$T_{1.}$
2	X_{21}	X_{22}	X_{23}	$\overline{X}_{2.}$	$T_{2.}$
3	X_{31}	X_{32}	X_{33}	$\overline{X}_{3.}$	$T_{3.}$
4	X_{41}	X_{42}	X_{43}	$\overline{X}_{4.}$	$T_{4.}$
5	X_{51}	X_{52}	X_{53}	$\overline{X}_{5.}$	$T_{5.}$
6	X_{61}	X_{62}	X_{63}	$\overline{X}_{6.}$	$T_{6.}$
7	X_{71}	X_{72}	X_{73}	$\overline{X}_{7.}$	$T_{7.}$
8	X_{81}	X_{82}	X_{83}	$\overline{X}_{8.}$	$T_{8.}$
9	X_{91}	X_{92}	X_{93}	$\overline{X}_{9.}$	$T_{9.}$
10	$X_{10,1}$	$X_{10,2}$	$X_{10,3}$	$\overline{X}_{10.}$	$T_{10.}$
11	$X_{11,1}$	$X_{11,2}$	$X_{11,3}$	$\overline{X}_{11.}$	$T_{11.}$
Mean of column	$\overline{X}_{.1}$	$\overline{X}_{.2}$	$\overline{X}_{.3}$	$\overline{X}$	
Sum of column	$T_{.1}$	$T_{.2}$	$T_{.3}$		T

$\mu_{ij} = \mu_{i.} + \mu_{.j} - \mu$. Each row has an observed mean $\overline{X}_{i.}$ and an unknown population mean $\mu_{i.}$. Each column has an observed mean $\overline{X}_{.j}$ and an unknown population mean $\mu_{.j}$. The table as a whole has an observed mean $\overline{X}$ and an unknown population mean μ.

The sample estimate for μ_{ij} is $\overline{X}_{i.} + \overline{X}_{.j} - \overline{X}$. The expression $X_{ij} - \mu_{ij}$ is a random deviate. Therefore

$$X_{ij} - (\overline{X}_{i.} + \overline{X}_{.j} - \overline{X}) = X_{ij} - \overline{X}_{i.} - \overline{X}_{.j} + \overline{X}$$

is the best sample estimate of the error in X_{ij}. Expressions for sample variances which will be needed in testing hypotheses will now be given.

Estimate of σ^2 Based on Error. This estimate of σ^2 is obtained from the sample estimate of the error in X_{ij}. It measures the effect of random deviation of observed scores X_{ij} from values expected on the basis of row and column means. If each X_{ij} was exactly equal to μ_{ij} this error variance would be zero. We shall denote this estimate by the letter E. If $\mu_{ij} = \mu_{i.} + \mu_{.j} - \mu$, E is an unbiased estimate of σ^2 regardless of the values of the row and column means in the population.

In general, if there are r rows and c columns,

$$(9.18) \qquad E = \frac{\sum_{i=1}^{r} \sum_{j=1}^{c} (X_{ij} - \overline{X}_{i.} - \overline{X}_{.j} + \overline{X})^2}{(r-1)(c-1)}$$

It is more easily computed by equivalent formula
(9.19)

$$E = \frac{\sum_{i=1}^{r} \sum_{j=1}^{c} X^2_{ij} - \frac{1}{r} \sum_{j=1}^{c} (\sum_{i=1}^{r} X_{ij})^2 - \frac{1}{c} \sum_{i=1}^{r} (\sum_{j=1}^{c} X_{ij})^2 + \frac{1}{rc} (\sum_{i=1}^{r} \sum_{j=1}^{c} X_{ij})^2}{(r-1)(c-1)}$$

or

$$(9.20) \qquad E = \frac{\Sigma\Sigma X^2_{ij} - \frac{1}{r} \sum_j T_j^2 - \frac{1}{c} \sum_i T_i^2 + \frac{1}{rc} T^2}{(r-1)(c-1)}$$

Estimate of σ^2 Obtained from Variation between Row Means. In this problem, each row mean is the average of 3 scores made by one of the 11 persons shooting at the target. The variance among these 11 means is given by the expression $\dfrac{\sum_{i=1}^{11} (\overline{X}_{i.} - \overline{X})^2}{10}$, which is an estimate of $\frac{\sigma^2}{3} + \frac{\sum_{i=1}^{11} (\mu_{i\cdot} - \mu)^2}{10}\cdot$ Here $\frac{\sigma^2}{3}$ is the variance of means of 3 scores if these scores are chosen at random from the same population, with mean μ and variance σ^2, while $\frac{\sum_{i=1}^{11} (\mu_{i\cdot} - \mu)^2}{10}$ is a component due to variation among population means of rows. The hypothesis $\mu_{1\cdot} = \mu_{2\cdot} = \cdots = \mu_{11\cdot} = \mu$ would in this case be the hypothesis that the 11 archers have equal skill. Under that hypothesis this second component is zero and so $\frac{1}{10} \sum_{i=1}^{11} (\overline{X}_{i\cdot} - \overline{X})^2$ is an unbiased estimate of $\sigma_{\overline{X}}^2 = \frac{\sigma^2}{3}\cdot$ Therefore under this hypothesis an unbiased estimate of σ^2 is provided by

$$\tfrac{3}{10} \sum_{i=1}^{11} (\overline{X}_{i\cdot} - \overline{X})^2$$

This is the *mean square among row means.* For convenience we shall denote it R. In general, if there are r rows and c columns and one score in each cell, an unbiased estimate of σ^2 is provided by

$$R = \frac{c \sum_{i=1}^{r} (\overline{X}_{i\cdot} - \overline{X})^2}{r - 1} \tag{9.21}$$

if the hypothesis $\mu_1 = \mu_2 = \cdots = u_r = \mu$ is true.

A more convenient routine for computing R is

$$R = \frac{\frac{1}{c} \sum_i T_i^2 - \frac{T^2}{N}}{r - 1} \tag{9.22}$$

The numerator of (9.21) and of (9.22) is the *sum of squares for rows* and the denominator is the corresponding degrees of freedom.

Estimate of σ^2 Obtained from Variation between Column Means. In this problem a column mean is the average score made by all 11 archers on one particular order of shooting. The variance among the three-column means is

$$\frac{1}{2} \sum_{j=1}^{3} (\overline{X}_{\cdot j} - \overline{X})^2, \text{ which is an estimate of } \frac{\sigma^2}{11} + \frac{\sum_{j=1}^{3} (\mu_{\cdot j} - \mu)^2}{2}.$$

Here $\frac{\sigma^2}{11}$ is the variance of means of 11 scores if these are taken at random, while $\frac{1}{2}\sum_{j=1}^{3}(\mu_{.j}-\mu)^2$ is a component due to variation among population means of columns. Under the hypothesis that the three column means are equal ($\mu_{.1} = \mu_{.2} = \mu_{.3} = \mu$) this component is zero and so $\frac{1}{2}\sum_{j=1}^{3}(\overline{X}_{.j}-\overline{X})^2$ is an unbiased estimate of $\sigma_{\overline{X}}^2 = \sigma^2/11$. Therefore under this hypothesis an unbiased estimate of σ^2 is provided by

$$\frac{11}{2}\sum_{j=1}^{3}(\overline{X}_{.j}-\overline{X})^2$$

This is the *mean square among column means* which will be denoted C. In general, for r rows and c columns,

$$C = \frac{r\sum_{j=1}^{c}(\overline{X}_{.j}-\overline{X})^2}{c-1} \tag{9.23}$$

A more convenient routine for computing C is

$$C = \frac{\frac{1}{r}\sum_{j} T_{j}^2 - \frac{T^2}{N}}{c-1} \tag{9.24}$$

The numerator of (9.23) and of (9.24) is the *sum of squares for columns* and the denominator is the corresponding degrees of freedom.

Hypotheses and Procedure for Testing Them. An important characteristic of the sample mean squares E, R, and C is that under the assumptions of normality and equality of variance in the population, these three statistics are independently distributed. Hence the F test may be used to test hypotheses.

Usually two separate hypotheses are formulated, the hypothesis concerning row means:

$$H_r : \mu_{.1} = \mu_{2.} = \cdots = \mu_r = \mu$$

and the hypothesis concerning column means:

$$H_c : \mu_{.1} = \mu_{.2} = \cdots = \mu_c = \mu$$

These hypotheses may be tested separately and one may be rejected without the other.

To test hypothesis H_r
that row means are equal, the ratio $F_r = R/E$ is calculated.
To test hypothesis H_c
that column means are equal, the ratio $F_c = C/E$ is calculated.

It is instructive to carry out the calculations indicated by Formulas (9.18), (9.21), and (9.23) directly, although far simpler procedures are available and will be described below. Students do not always correctly understand the meaning of the error term E so Table 9.12 has been set up to list in detail the numbers (for the data of Table 9.8) whose squares are added to obtain the error sum of squares which is the numerator of E. Each entry in Table 9.12 is a *residual*, the amount by which the observed value X_{ij} differs from the estimate of that value based on row mean, column mean and total mean.

$$E = \frac{(-13.70)^2 + (30.48)^2 + \cdots + (2.55)^2}{(10)(2)} = \frac{12530.909}{20} = 626.55.$$

$$R = \tfrac{3}{10}\{(139.67 - 100.79)^2 + (113 - 100.79)^2 + \cdots + (110.33 - 100.79)^2\} = 4087.4$$

$$C = \tfrac{11}{2}\{(88.82 - 100.79)^2 + (112.64 - 100.79)^2 + (100.91 - 100.79)^2\} = 1560.5$$

TABLE 9.12 Value of $X_{ij} - (\bar{X}_{i.} + \bar{X}_{.j} - \bar{X})$ for each Entry in Table 9.8

Subject	First order	Second order	Third order	Sum
1	− 13.70	30.48	− 16.79	− .01
2	− 2.03	− 3.85	5.88	.00
3	.97	26.15	− 27.12	.00
4	− 8.03	34.15	− 26.12	.00
5	− 7.36	− 40.18	47.55	.01
6	30.30	− 26.52	− 3.79	− .01
7	− 2.03	− 24.85	26.88	.00
8	− 12.70	19.48	− 6.79	− .01
9	3.97	− 6.85	2.88	.00
10	3.97	1.15	− 5.12	.00
11	6.64	− 9.18	2.55	.01
Sum	.00	− .02	.01	− .01

$F_r = \dfrac{R}{E} = \dfrac{4087.4}{626.55} = 6.52.$ The error mean square is always placed in the denominator and the critical region is in the right tail of the F curve. For $n_1 = 10$ and $n_2 = 20$, $F_{.99} = 3.37$. The observed value 6.52 clearly falls in the region of rejection for $\alpha = .01$, and consequently the hypothesis that individuals do not differ in skill must be rejected.

$$F_c = \frac{C}{E} = \frac{1560.5}{626.55} = 2.49. \quad \text{For } n_1 = 2 \text{ and } n_2 = 20, \; F_{.95} = 3.49.$$

The observed value 2.49 falls in the region of acceptance with $\alpha = .05$, hence there is no reason to reject the hypothesis that performance is independent of order of shooting, no reason to suppose that higher scores are to be expected when the 50-yard range is shot in one order than another.

Additive Nature of Component Sums of Squares. For each X_{ij} the following identity holds

$$X_{ij} - \overline{X} = (\overline{X}_{i.} - \overline{X}) + (\overline{X}_{.j} - \overline{X}) + (X_{ij} - \overline{X}_{i.} - \overline{X}_{.j} + \overline{X})$$

When this identity is squared we get

$$\begin{aligned}(X_{ij} - \overline{X})^2 = {} & (\overline{X}_{i.} - \overline{X})^2 + (\overline{X}_{.j} - \overline{X})^2 + (X_{ij} - \overline{X}_{i.} - \overline{X}_{.j} + \overline{X})^2 \\ & + 2[(\overline{X}_{i.} - \overline{X})(\overline{X}_{.j} + \overline{X}) + (\overline{X}_{i.} - \overline{X})(X_{ij} - \overline{X}_{i.} - \overline{X}_{.j} + \overline{X}) \\ & + (\overline{X}_{.j} - \overline{X})(X_{ij} - \overline{X}_{i.} - \overline{X}_{.j} + \overline{X})]\end{aligned}$$

When the sum is taken over all rows and all columns, the sum of each expression inside the square brackets is found to be identically zero, so the cross product terms vanish, leaving

$$(9.25) \quad \sum_{j=1}^{c}\sum_{i=1}^{r} (X_{ij} - \overline{X})^2$$

$$= c\sum_{i=1}^{r} (\overline{X}_{i.} - \overline{X})^2 + r\sum_{j=1}^{c} (\overline{X}_{.j} - \overline{X})^2 + \sum_{j=1}^{c}\sum_{i=1}^{r} (X_{ij} - \overline{X}_{i.} - \overline{X}_{.j} + \overline{X})^2$$

$$\text{or } \left\{\begin{array}{c}\text{Total}\\ \text{sum of}\\ \text{squares}\end{array}\right\} = \left\{\begin{array}{c}\text{sum of}\\ \text{squares}\\ \text{for}\\ \text{rows}\end{array}\right\} + \left\{\begin{array}{c}\text{sum of}\\ \text{squares}\\ \text{for}\\ \text{columns}\end{array}\right\} + \left\{\begin{array}{c}\text{sum of}\\ \text{squares}\\ \text{for}\\ \text{error.}\end{array}\right\}$$

The three additive component sums of squares are independently distributed with $r - 1$ degrees of freedom among row means, $c - 1$ degrees of freedom among column means, and $(r - 1)(c - 1)$ degrees of freedom for error. These degrees of freedom together make up the $rc - 1$ degrees of freedom for the total sum of squares. When each of the component sums is divided by its degrees of freedom, the results are the mean squares R, C, and E.

Formula (9.25) may be rewritten in equivalent form as

$$\Sigma\Sigma X^2 - \frac{T^2}{N} = \left(\frac{1}{c}\sum T_{i.}^2 - \frac{T^2}{N}\right) + \left(\frac{1}{r}\sum_j T_{.j}^2 - \frac{T^2}{N}\right) + \left(\Sigma\Sigma X^2 - \frac{1}{c}\sum_i T_{i.}^2 - \frac{1}{r}\sum_j T_{.j}^2 + \frac{T^2}{N}\right) \tag{9.26}$$

where the quantities in parentheses are the numerators of Formulas (9.22), (9.24), and (9.20) respectively. An easy way to obtain the sum of squares due to error is expressed schematically as follows:

Error = Total − Rows − Columns

Table 9.13 shows computations for obtaining the three component sums of squares by the routine of Formula (9.26) for the

TABLE 9.13 Computation of Sums of Squares for Data of Table 9.8

Subject	X_{i1}	X_{i2}	X_{i3}	$T_{i.}$	$T_{i.}^2$	$\sum_{j=1}^{3} X_{ij}^2$
1	114	182	123	419	175561	61249
2	99	121	119	339	114921	38603
3	51	100	35	186	34596	13826
4	78	144	72	294	86436	32004
5	134	125	201	460	211600	73982
6	71	38	49	158	24964	8886
7	66	67	107	240	57600	20294
8	33	89	51	173	29929	11611
9	146	159	157	462	213444	71246
10	80	101	83	264	69696	23490
11	105	113	113	331	109561	36563
$T_{.j}$	977	1239	1110	3326		
$T_{.j}^2$	954529	1535121	1232100			
$\sum_{i=1}^{11} X_{ij}^2$	98665	156231	136858			391754

$T^2/N = (3326)^2/33 = 335220.5$

$\frac{\Sigma T_{i.}^2}{3} = \frac{1128308}{3} = 376102.7$

$T^2/N = 335220.5$

Sum of squares for rows $= 40882.2$

$\frac{\Sigma T_{.j}^2}{11} = \frac{3721750}{11} = 338340.9$

$T^2/N = 335220.5$

Sum of squares for columns $= 3120.4$

$\Sigma\Sigma X_{ij}^2 = 391754$

$T^2/N = 335220.5$

Total sum of squares $= 56533.5$

$40882.2 + 3120.4 = 44002.6$

Sum of squares for error $= 12530.9$

archery scores of Table 9.8. The results of this computation are shown in Table 9.14.

TABLE 9.14 Analysis of Variance of Data from Table 9.8

Source of variation	Sum of squares	Degrees of freedom	Mean square	F	$F_{.95}$	$F_{.99}$
Total group	56533.5	32				
Between means of individuals	40882.2	10	4088.22	6.53		3.37
Between order means	3120.4	2	1560.2	2.49	3.49	
Error	12530.9	20	626.5			

In general the analysis of variance computations may be summarized as in Table 9.15.

TABLE 9.15 General Summary of Analysis of Variance Components for Data with r Rows and c Columns and One Score in Each Cell

Source of variation	Sum of squares	d. f.	Expectation
Total	$\Sigma\Sigma X^2_{ij} - \dfrac{T^2}{N}$	$rc - 1$	
Between row means	$\dfrac{1}{c}\sum_1^r T_{i.}{}^2 - \dfrac{T^2}{N}$	$r - 1$	$\sigma^2 + \dfrac{c\Sigma(\mu_{i.} - \mu)^2}{r - 1}$
Between column means	$\dfrac{1}{r}\sum_1^c T_{.j}{}^2 - \dfrac{T^2}{N}$	$c - 1$	$\sigma^2 + \dfrac{r\Sigma(\mu_{.j} - \mu)^2}{c - 1}$
Error	$\Sigma\Sigma X_{ij}{}^2 - \dfrac{1}{c}\Sigma T_{i.}{}^2 - \dfrac{1}{r}\Sigma T_{.j}{}^2 + \dfrac{T^2}{N}$	$(r-1)(c-1)$	σ^2

Computations When Original Scores are not Available. Sometimes one wishes to apply the test described on pages 216 to 226 to published data for which the original scores are not available. It would then be impossible to use any of the formulas which have been presented in this chapter, but if for each subgroup the computed mean and variance or standard deviation are given and the number of cases, the formulas can be adapted as follows:

(9.27) Mean of total group, $\overline{X} = \dfrac{\sum_{j=1}^{k} N_j \overline{X}_j}{\Sigma N_j} = \dfrac{\Sigma N_j \overline{X}_j}{N}$

(9.24) Sum of squares within groups, $\sum_{j=1}^{k} (N_j - 1)s_j{}^2$

(9.29) Sum of squares among means,

$$\sum_{j=1}^{k} N_j(\overline{X}_j - \overline{X})^2 = \Sigma N_j \overline{X}_j^2 - N\overline{X}^2$$

A difficulty often encountered in trying to use published data in this way is that the original computer may not have retained enough digits to have any significant digits in the sum of squares among means. Another difficulty is that one cannot always be sure whether N or $N - 1$ was used as denominator in the original computation of the variance.

Factors Influencing *F*. In order to assist the student in recognizing the general kinds of situations in which the mean square for means is typically less than, equal to, or greater than the mean square for individuals within groups let us consider a hypothetical situation. Imagine that 500 names have been taken at random from the list of registered voters in New York City, and that a card has been made out for each of the 500 persons, containing such information as age, sex, marital status, number of children, occupation, number of years of schooling completed, height, weight, index of physical strength, party ticket voted in preceding presidential election, score on a mental test, score on a test of public affairs, voting precinct. Obviously such data would be difficult to obtain, but they are real enough to the imagination to serve as a good illustration.

A. Now let the 500 cards be thoroughly shuffled and dealt into 20 random piles of 25 each. For the mental test scores, let the mean square among groups and the mean square within groups be computed and the F ratio obtained and recorded. Then let the cards be shuffled again and again dealt into 20 random piles of 25 cards each and F ratio computed. Let this be done many times. Sometimes the mean square between groups will be larger and sometimes smaller than the mean square within groups. The distribution of the obtained values of F will approximate a smooth F curve with $n_1 = 19$ and $n_2 = 480$.

If instead of score on mental test, score on test of public affairs had been used, both mean squares might have been very different from those obtained in A but the theoretical F distribution would be the same because its form depends upon the number of degrees of freedom and not upon the nature of the physical variate studied.

Suppose the same procedure were carried through with the data on income, or on number of years of schooling completed. These variates probably have a very skewed distribution and the assumption of normality in the trait measured, which is basic to the F test, would not be met. Certain other traits named such as index of physical strength, height, or weight, might have a bimodal distribution if both men and women are in the group studied. However, if the distribution of the trait does not depart too radically from the normal, the distribution of the variance ratio will resemble the F distribution under the experimental conditions described above.

B. Now let the same 500 cards be sorted on the basis of voting precinct, and let us suppose 20 precincts are represented. For several of the variates we have mentioned, a group of persons living in the same neighborhood and consequently registered in the same precinct would be more homogeneous than a group obtained by random selection from the entire city. Hence in this situation the mean square within groups is almost certain to be reduced and that between groups increased in comparison with situation *A*. Consider income or years of schooling completed. One feels a rather strong conviction that group means will vary more from precinct to precinct than in *A* and that individual scores will vary less from person to person in the same precinct than in *A*. Consequently, the numerator of the variance ratio would tend to be larger than the denominator, though not necessarily larger in every sample. Also, if the cards were sorted on the basis of occupation or sex, the income data might be expected to show a mean square between groups in general larger than that within groups, and therefore the variance ratio would not conform to the F distribution but would have fewer small values of F and more large values than would be expected under situation *A*. Here the various groups are in reality samples of different populations.

C. Now let the same 500 cards be sorted as before by precincts, but instead of keeping the cards from a given precinct together we shall distribute them so that each group receives approximately 1/20 of the cards from each precinct. Now if the mean precinct score on any given trait such as income varies greatly from precinct to precinct, this new sorting will have the effect of making the mean square between means in general less than in either *A* or *B*. If the mean square between means is reduced that within groups must be increased for the total mean square has not been affected by the manner of sorting the cards. Therefore in such a case F would tend to be smaller than 1.

EXERCISE 9.2

1. In each of the following situations state the number of degrees of freedom with which the F table should be entered and the corresponding value of $F_{.95}$.

a. A comparison of the means of 5 groups in which $N_1 = 12$, $N_2 = 30$, $N_3 = 6$, $N_4 = 13$, $N_5 = 8$.

b. A comparison of the means of two groups each having 25 cases.

c. There are 5 test scores for each of 20 subjects. We want to test the hypothesis that the scores do not distinguish the subjects, that all subjects have the same mean.

d. There are 5 test scores on each of 20 subjects. We want to test the hypothesis that the tests are equally difficult, that they all have the same mean.

2. Complete the analysis of the data in Table 9.6.

3. In a study [2] of the amount of community information possessed by 79 elementary school teachers in St. Louis, Harris constructed a social information test and administered it to teachers in four schools. These schools were located in districts that differed markedly as to socio-economic status, Jefferson being at one extreme and Banneker at the other. However, if the differences among the means are no greater than might readily occur by chance, it would be inappropriate to seek for any other explanation of their origin. From the data reported on page 192, test the hypothesis that $\mu_1 = \mu_2 = \mu_3 = \mu_4$.

REFERENCES

1. Harrington, Wells, *Recommendation Quality and Placement Success*, Psychological Monograph, 55 (1943).
2. Harris, Ruth M., *Teachers' Social Knowledge and Its Relation to Pupils' Responses*, New York, 1941, Teachers College, Columbia University, Bureau of Publications.
3. Schroeder, Elinor M., *On Measurement of Motor Skills*, New York, 1945, King's Crown Press.

10 Linear Regression and Correlation

In this chapter, methods of statistical inference will be applied to *bivariate* data, that is to data in which each individual receives a score on *two variables*, two scaled traits. In Chapter 13 the work of the present chapter will be extended to situations in which each individual receives a score on more than two variables (multivariate analysis). In Chapter 11 there will be a discussion of methods of measuring relationship between two traits when for some reason the methods of the current chapter are not applicable.

Although many readers of this chapter will have studied regression and correlation in an earlier course, a brief review of the principles, formulas and computing procedures may be helpful to some. Such a review will be presented in the first part of this chapter.

Linear Regression. Regression is the estimation, or prediction, of unknown values of one variable from known values of another variable. An example of such use of regression is the prediction of grades at the end of a course from grades in a prognostic test given prior to the beginning of the course.

Let X be a variable for which the value is known for each individual in a study. This is commonly called the independent variable. Let Y be a variable for which the value is to be estimated for some individuals. This is commonly called the dependent variable. Let X_α and Y_α be scores for the αth individual. The reader should note that this is a new use of the letter α, differing from its use to designate the size of a region of rejection. The letter α will be used in both senses from this point on, but its meaning will be readily apparent from context. From this point on, many problems will involve summing over rows, over columns, and also over individuals within cells, and formulas may require three, or sometimes more, subscripts. The use of English letters to denote the categories and the Greek letter α to denote the individual within the category makes the meaning of a formula more obvious. Thus $\sum_{\alpha} X_{ij\alpha}$ can be understood at once as the sum for all individuals in the ijth class, while $\sum_{k} X_{ijk}$ might mean different things in different problems and would require a specific definition to state whether all three letters indicated categories or one of them referred to individuals. Let $\tilde{Y}$ be the estimate of an individual's unknown Y from his known X. It is called "regression Y," "estimated Y," "predicted Y," "tilde $\tilde{Y}$," and sometimed "curlicue Y." The meaning of Y_α as an observed value and $\tilde{Y}_\alpha$ as the best linear estimate based on knowledge of X_α must never be confused. (For an account of the origin of the term "regression" see reference 11.)

The relation between $\tilde{Y}$ and X is called the regression equation and, for linear regression, is given by the formula

$$\tilde{Y}_\alpha = \overline{Y} + b_{yx}(X_\alpha - \overline{X}) \tag{10.1}$$

In this formula $\tilde{Y}_\alpha$ and X_α vary from individual to individual, while $\overline{Y}$, b_{yx} and $\overline{X}$ are constant for all individuals to whom the formula is applied.

The statistic b_{yx} may be expressed in terms of deviations from the means as

$$b_{yx} = \frac{\sum_{\alpha=1}^{N} (X_\alpha - \overline{X})(Y_\alpha - \overline{Y})}{\sum_{\alpha=1}^{N} (X_\alpha - \overline{X})^2} \tag{10.2}$$

The computing routine suggested by this and Formulas (10.3) to (10.5) would be unnecessarily laborious and would incur large rounding errors. Equivalent formulas that are more convenient to use will be found in later sections where machine computation and computation from a scatter diagram are treated. There is a very large number of equivalent formulas which are useful to know. The efficient computer understands the algebraic relations among them and makes use of whichever one appears to offer the simplest routine for the data in hand. In order to keep the development simple, only the most necessary formulas are presented in the chapter but a longer list is given in an Appendix to the chapter.

The reason for heading this section "Linear regression" is that the graph of Formula (10.1) is a straight line. This formula is appropriate to use when the mean value of Y for each given value of X lies near a straight line. If these means depart considerably from the straight regression line, a curvilinear regression line is more appropriate. Curvilinear regression will not be taken up here. It is treated in Chapter 23 of reference 1, in Chapter 6 of reference 5, and in Chapter 12 of reference 8.

If a graph of Formula (10.1) were plotted on a chart of the XY distribution the constant b_{yx} would represent the slope of the line, and the line would pass through the point $(\overline{X}, \overline{Y})$. The reader who does not understand the relation between an equation and its graph will find Chapter 10 of reference 10 helpful.

The difference $Y_\alpha - \tilde{Y}_\alpha$ between an individual's observed Y score and the regression estimate for that score is called a *residual* or *residual error*. The sum of the squares of the residuals for all N individuals is

$$(10.3) \qquad \Sigma(Y - \tilde{Y})^2 = \Sigma(Y - \overline{Y})^2 - \frac{[\Sigma(X - \overline{X})(Y - \overline{Y})]^2}{\Sigma(X - \overline{X})^2}$$

This sum has $N - 2$ degrees of freedom because there are N observations from which two constants, the mean of Y and the slope of the regression line, have been obtained.

The equation in Formula (10.3) may be read as follows: The sum of squares of deviations of individual Y scores from the regression estimates corresponding to these scores is less than the sum of squares of the deviations from the mean, $\overline{Y}$, for all these scores by the quantity

$$\frac{[\Sigma(X - \overline{X})(Y - \overline{Y})]^2}{\Sigma(X - \overline{X})^2}$$

If only Y scores are available, $\overline{Y}$ is the best estimate of an unknown Y. For a given sample size the quantity $\Sigma(Y - \overline{Y})^2$ is a measure of the precision of estimate obtained from $\overline{Y}$. If an X score is known for an individual, but the Y score is not, then $\tilde{Y}_\alpha$ calculated from the known X_α is the best estimate of Y. For a given sample size the precision of an estimate of Y obtained from a known X is given by $\Sigma(Y - \tilde{Y})^2$. The quantity

$$\frac{[\Sigma(X - \overline{X})(Y - \overline{Y})]^2}{\Sigma(X - \overline{X})^2}$$

measures the improvement in precision of estimating Y obtained by using X over the precision in not using X. Clearly, the larger this quantity is, the greater is the improvement in estimating Y by using X.

The Correlation Coefficient. We may write Formula (10.3) as

$$\Sigma(Y - \tilde{Y})^2 = (1 - r^2)\Sigma(Y - \overline{Y})^2 \tag{10.4}$$

if we define r by the formula

$$r = \frac{\Sigma(X - \overline{X})(Y - \overline{Y})}{\sqrt{\Sigma(X - \overline{X})^2\Sigma(Y - \overline{Y})^2}} \tag{10.5}$$

It becomes obvious that the value of r measures the gain in precision of estimate of an unknown Y from a known X. If r is zero, $\Sigma(Y - \tilde{Y})^2$ is the same as $\Sigma(Y - \overline{Y})^2$ and there is no gain in precision. If r is near $+1$ or near -1 the gain in precision is great, for then $\Sigma(Y - \tilde{Y})^2$ is much less than $\Sigma(Y - \overline{Y})^2$.

The quantity r defined in Formula (10.5) is called the *coefficient of linear correlation.* The word "linear" is included because of its relationship to straight line regression. This coefficient is often called the product moment coefficient because the quantity $\Sigma(X - \overline{X})(Y - \overline{Y})$ is a product moment. It is also called Pearson r because of the important contributions of Karl Pearson.[11]

In some problems interest centers on the estimation of scores by means of a regression equation; other problems are concerned chiefly with the mutual interrelationship between two variables as measured by the coefficient of correlation. In some problems both regression equations

$$\tilde{Y} = \overline{Y} + b_{yx}(X - \overline{X})$$

and

$$\tilde{X} = \overline{X} + b_{xy}(Y - \overline{Y})$$

are of interest, in others only one. Thus there would be practical value in predicting college achievement from a prognostic test but little value in estimating prognostic test scores from measures of college achievement. In a regression equation the relationship is from known scores to estimated scores and is not reversible. In correlation the relationship is mutual, and

$$r_{xy} = \sqrt{b_{yx}b_{xy}} \tag{10.6}$$

The order of letters in the subscript for r is immaterial, $r_{xy} = r_{yx}$. For b the order is important and in general $b_{xy} \neq b_{yx}$.

Machine Computation of b_{yx} and r_{xy} Without the Use of a Scatter Diagram. To illustrate the way in which data may be organized so that adequate checks are obtained when a computing machine is used, a problem will be set up using a relatively small number of cases. The members of a class in first term statistics were given several prognostic tests at the first meeting of the course. One of these, which is here called X, was a specially constructed test in *artificial language.* The criterion variable Y, is the semester grade in the course. The X and Y scores for a part of the class are listed in Table 10.1, the number of cases having been reduced because it does not seem likely that readers of this text will learn any more from working with a long series of data than with a short one. The $X - Y$ and $X + Y$ columns are utilized for checks.

In machine work there is no need to keep numbers small and therefore gross scores (X and Y) are used instead of deviations ($X - \overline{X}$ and $Y - \overline{Y}$ or $X - A_x$ and $Y - A_y$). Less work is involved and greater accuracy secured if division and square root, which usually involve rounding error, are performed as late in the process as possible. The following formulas for b_{yx} and r_{xy} meet these criteria and are equivalent to Formulas (10.2) and (10.5):

$$(10.7) \qquad b_{yx} = \frac{N\Sigma XY - (\Sigma X)(\Sigma Y)}{N\Sigma X^2 - (\Sigma X)^2}$$

$$(10.8) \text{ and } \qquad r = \frac{N\Sigma XY - (\Sigma X)(\Sigma Y)}{\sqrt{[N\Sigma X^2 - (\Sigma X)^2][N\Sigma Y^2 - (\Sigma Y)^2]}}$$

On certain machines it is possible to enter X, Y, X^2, Y^2 and XY in a single setting of the machine, and thus to obtain ΣX, ΣY, ΣX^2, ΣY^2 and ΣXY in one process (see K. Pease [9]). Even with a machine, some check on the correctness of the results is essential. One possible check is to cumulate the XY products as a separate operation. If the result agrees with ΣXY previously obtained it is unlikely that there is an error in the sums found, but this check does not guarantee correctness. A foolproof check can be obtained from the sums and sums of squared entries in $X - Y$ and $X + Y$ columns. If the five sums named above have already been found by the method described by Pease, use of $X - Y$ column alone would provide a complete check. Any of these formulas may be used to check the sums:

$$(10.9) \qquad \Sigma X + \Sigma Y = \Sigma(X + Y)$$

$$(10.10) \qquad \Sigma X - \Sigma Y = \Sigma(X - Y)$$

$$(10.11) \qquad \Sigma(X + Y) + \Sigma(X - Y) = 2\Sigma X$$

$$(10.12) \qquad \Sigma(X + Y) - \Sigma(X - Y) = 2\Sigma Y$$

TABLE 10.1 Marks of Students in First Term Statistics Course (Y) and Scores on an Artificial Language Test (X) used To Predict Term Marks

Student	X	Y	$X - Y$	$X + Y$
1	52	62	− 10	114
2	57	50	7	107
3	56	57	− 1	113
4	30	32	− 2	62
5	47	55	− 8	102
6	49	43	6	92
7	60	59	1	119
8	56	57	− 1	113
9	53	55	− 2	108
10	55	56	− 1	111
11	54	55	− 1	109
12	53	56	− 3	109
13	58	57	1	115
14	57	48	9	105
15	45	36	9	81
16	46	57	− 11	103
17	60	63	− 3	123
18	37	47	− 10	84
19	24	43	− 19	67
20	43	57	− 14	100
21	47	57	− 10	104
22	50	47	3	97
23	48	47	1	95
24	42	49	− 7	91
25	59	51	8	110
26	40	48	− 8	88
27	41	58	− 17	99
28	47	63	− 16	110
29	43	56	− 13	99
30	57	50	7	107
31	32	46	− 14	78
32	53	43	10	96
33	46	39	7	85
34	54	47	7	101
35	49	48	1	97
36	58	55	3	113
37	55	47	8	102
38	14	35	− 21	49
39	50	62	− 12	112
40	41	59	− 18	100
41	14	29	− 15	43
42	46	54	− 8	100
Sum of scores	1978	2135	− 157	4113
Sum of squares of scores	98232	111399	3937	415325

These formulas may be used to check sums of squares and sums of products:

(10.13) $\Sigma(X + Y)^2 + \Sigma(X - Y)^2 = 2\Sigma X^2 + 2\Sigma Y^2$

(10.14) $\Sigma XY = \frac{1}{4}[\Sigma(X + Y)^2 - \Sigma(X - Y)^2]$

The checks of Formulas (10.9) to (10.13) all hold for the data of Table 10.1. Then we may compute ΣXY by (10.14) as

$$\tfrac{1}{4}[415325 - 3937] = 102847$$

The following values have now been obtained:

$$N = 42 \qquad \Sigma XY = 102847 \qquad \Sigma X^2 = 98232$$
$$\Sigma X = 1978 \qquad \Sigma Y = 2135 \qquad \Sigma Y^2 = 111399$$
$$\overline{X} = 47.10 \qquad \overline{Y} = 50.83$$

From these the following computations are made:

$$N\Sigma xy = N\Sigma XY - (\Sigma X)(\Sigma Y) = 42(102847) - (1978)(2135) = 96544$$
$$N\Sigma x^2 = N\Sigma X^2 - (\Sigma X)^2 = 42(98232) - (1978)^2 = 213260$$
$$N\Sigma y^2 = N\Sigma Y^2 - (\Sigma Y)^2 = 42(111399) - (2135)^2 = 120533$$

$$b_{yx} = \frac{96544}{213260} = .453$$

$$r_{xy} = \frac{96544}{\sqrt{(213260)(120533)}} = .602$$

$$\tilde{Y} = 50.83 + .453\,(X - 47.10)$$
$$\tilde{Y} = .453X + 29.5$$

To see the effect of the regression equation we may apply it to the X scores of the first 5 cases in Table 10.1 to see what Y score would have been estimated for them if that Y score had happened to be unknown.

Student	X	$\tilde{Y}$	Y	$Y - \tilde{Y}$	$Y - \overline{Y}$
1	52	53.1	62	8.9	11.2
2	57	55.3	50	− 5.3	− .8
3	56	54.9	57	2.1	6.2
4	30	43.1	32	− 11.1	− 18.8
5	47	50.8	55	4.2	4.2

In no case did the estimate of Y based on X agree precisely with the obtained Y; the *residual error* $Y - \tilde{Y}$ was sometimes positive and sometimes negative. On the whole the deviation of Y from the regression value $(Y - \tilde{Y})$ seems to be smaller than its deviation from the mean $(Y - \overline{Y})$. A method of measuring the efficiency of prediction will be discussed on page 244.

Computation of b_{yx} and r_{xy} from a Scatter Diagram. Even when a machine is available many statisticians prefer to work from a scatter diagram in order that they may have a general impression of the linearity of the relationship. Those who prefer to work directly from the list of raw scores sometimes need to compute when no machine is available, and then they usually make use of a scatter diagram. Coding the scores reduces the size of the numbers involved and thus cuts down on labor.

To code scores, an arbitrary origin is taken at the midpoint of some interval. This interval is usually either the lowest interval in the distribution so that all deviations will be positive or it is near the middle of the distribution so that deviations will be numerically small. This arbitrary origin will be called A, and when more than one variable is being studied it will have a subscript as A_x, A_y, or A_z. Then if X_j and Y_j are the midpoints of the class intervals, we may define the coded scores as

$$(10.15) \qquad x_j' = \frac{X_j - A_x}{i_x} \quad \text{and} \quad y_j' = \frac{Y_j - A_y}{i_y}$$

The actual process of coding is merely to label one interval as 0, successive intervals above it as 1, 2, 3 . . . and successive intervals below it, if there are such, as -1, -2, -3 . . ..

The symbol f_{xy} will denote the frequency in a cell in the body of the scatter diagram, f_x a marginal frequency in an interval of the horizontal variable, f_y a marginal frequency in an interval of the vertical variable.

The formulas for r and b_{yx} based upon coded scores are

$$(10.16) \qquad b_{yx} = \frac{i_y}{i_x} \cdot \frac{N\Sigma f_{xy}x'y' - (\Sigma f_x x')(\Sigma f_y y')}{N\Sigma f_x(x')^2 - (\Sigma f_x x')^2}$$

$$(10.17) \text{ and } r_{xy} = \frac{N\Sigma f_{xy}x'y' - (\Sigma f_x x')(\Sigma f_y y')}{\sqrt{[N\Sigma f_x(x')^2 - (\Sigma f_x x')^2][N\Sigma f_y(y')^2 - (\Sigma f_y y')^2]}}$$

There are many different routines by which to compute the sums of scores, sums of squared scores, and sums of products which enter into Formulas (10.16) and (10.17). The method shown in Table 10.2 has the advantages of celerity, directness, and partial checks. The values

$$N = \Sigma f_x = \Sigma f_y \qquad C = \Sigma f_x x'$$
$$A = \Sigma f_y y' \qquad D = \Sigma f_{xy}x'y'$$

are computed twice and so their accuracy is beyond doubt. The values of $\Sigma f_y(y')^2$ and $\Sigma f_x(x')^2$ are not checked by this method.

TABLE 10.2 Computation of Correlation and Regression Coefficients from a Scatter Diagram

	15	18	21	24	27	30	33	36	39	42	45	48	51	54	57	60	f_y	y'	$f_y y'$	$f_y(y')^2$	$\Sigma x'$	$y'\Sigma x'$
62												1	2			1	4	11	44	484	50	550
59										2						1	3	10	30	300	33	330
56										2	1	2		4	4		13	9	117	1053	158	1422
53											1						1	8	8	64	10	80
50										1					2	1	4	7	28	196	52	364
47							1	1	1			2	1	2	1		9	6	54	324	95	570
44				1								1		1			3	5	15	75	27	135
41																		4				
38											1						1	3	3	9	10	20
35	1										1						2	2	4	8	10	30
32						1											1	1	1	1	5	5
29	1																1	0				
																	42		304	2514	450	3506
																			A	B	C	D

	15	18	21	24	27	30	33	36	39	42	45	48	51	54	57	60	
f_x	2			1		1	1	1	1	5	4	6	3	7	7	3	
x'	0	1	2	3	4	5	6	7	8	9	10	11	12	13	14	15	
$f_x x'$				3		5	6	7	8	45	40	66	36	91	98	45	450 C
$f_x(x')^2$				9		25	36	49	64	405	400	726	432	1183	1372	675	5376 E
$\Sigma y'$	2			5		1	6	6	6	45	22	46	28	53	56	28	304 A
$x'\Sigma y'$	0			15		5	36	42	48	405	220	506	336	689	784	420	3506 D

$$\Sigma y' = A = 304$$
$$\Sigma(y')^2 = B = 2514$$
$$\Sigma x' = C = 450$$
$$\Sigma(x')^2 = E = 5376$$
$$\Sigma x'y' = D = 3506$$
$$N = 42$$
$$i_x = 3$$
$$i_y = 3$$

$$b_{yx} = \frac{9}{9} \cdot \frac{10452}{23292} = .449$$

$$b_{xy} = \frac{9}{9} \cdot \frac{10452}{13172} = .794$$

$$r = \frac{10452}{\sqrt{(23292)(13172)}}$$
$$= .597$$

$$\tilde{Y} = .449X + 29.5$$

$$\overline{X} = 15 + \frac{3(450)}{42} = 47.14$$

$$\overline{Y} = 29 + \frac{3(304)}{42} = 50.71$$

$$N\Sigma xy = i_x i_y(ND - AC) = 9(10452)$$
$$N\Sigma x^2 = i_x^2(NE - C^2) = 9(23292)$$
$$N\Sigma y^2 = i_y^2(NB - A^2) = 9(13172)$$

For a large-scale enterprise, the authors recommend that computations be made by I B M machines. For a smaller study when a scatter diagram is to be used, they recommend using one of the various published charts which provides for a complete check at every step, such as the Durost-Walker Chart published by the World Book Company.

Grouping scores into class intervals tends to produce a slight increase in variance and so a slight decrease in r. The error thus created is negligible if there are 12 or more intervals for each variable and N is large. The error is likely to be greater when N is small and when intervals are broad. In the present problem such grouping error accounts for the discrepancy between $r = .602$ when computed directly from raw scores and $r = .597$ when computed from data grouped into class intervals.

A Mathematical Model for Linear Regression. The mathematical model which is commonly used in dealing with regression estimates of Y is one in which the values of X are the same for all possible samples as they are for the observed sample. Therefore the population mean of X is $\overline{X}$ as this quantity is calculated from the sample of observations. The X's are sometimes called *known parameters.*

$$\overline{X} = \mu_x$$

The Y's, however, are random variables. For each observed X, the population distribution of Y is normal with a mean which depends on X and a variance which is the same for each X. The population mean of Y for a given X is written

(10.18) $$\mu_{y.x} = \mu_y + \beta_{yx}(X - \overline{X})$$

The constants μ, β and $\overline{X}$ are to be estimated from the sample. Of these $\overline{X}$ is fully determined from the sample as the mean of X's, and this mean is not an estimate of a parameter but is in fact that parameter. The remaining constants are *unknown* parameters which are merely estimated from the sample. The estimate of μ_y is $\overline{Y} = \frac{\Sigma Y}{N}\cdot$ The estimate of β_{yx} is b_{yx}, as defined in Formula (10.2).

The variance of Y for a fixed X is

(10.19) $$\sigma^2_{y.x} = \sigma_y^2(1 - \rho^2)$$

where σ_y^2 and ρ are the variance and the correlation coefficient in the population. The standard deviation of Y for a fixed X,

(10.20) $$\sigma_{y.x} = \sigma_y\sqrt{1 - \rho^2},$$

is commonly called the *standard error of estimate* of Y on X. It is the standard deviation in the population of the residual errors $Y_\alpha - \mu_{y.x}$.

The best sample estimate of $\sigma^2_{y.x}$ is

$$s^2_{y.x} = \frac{1}{N-2}\sum_{\alpha=1}^{N}(Y_\alpha - \tilde{Y}_\alpha)^2 \tag{10.21}$$

$$= \frac{N-1}{N-2}s_y^2(1-r^2) \tag{10.22}$$

The symbol $s_{y.x}$ had been used by statisticians a long time before they began to take the idea of degrees of freedom seriously, and had been defined as $s_{y.x} = s_y\sqrt{1-r^2}$. However $s_y^2(1-r^2)$ is a biased estimate of $\sigma_y^2(1-\rho^2)$ and multiplication by the fraction $\dfrac{N-1}{N-2}$ corrects the bias. Unless N is small, $\dfrac{N-1}{N-2}$ is so near unity that the traditional definition is nearly as good as the correct one.

A convenient formula for computing $s_{y.x}$ is

$$s_{y.x} = \sqrt{\frac{\Sigma x^2\Sigma y^2 - (\Sigma xy)^2}{(N-2)\Sigma x^2}} \tag{10.23}$$

Sampling Distributions of Statistics in Linear Regression. The distributions of the statistics $\overline{Y}$, b_{yx}, and $s^2_{y.x}$ must be known in order to test hypotheses or make interval estimates for the parameters μ_y, β_{yx}, and $\sigma^2_{y.x}$. These distributions can be derived mathematically from the mathematical model for regression. The constant $\overline{X}$ being by assumption the same for all samples is a parameter which has no variability and no sampling distribution.

1. The mean $\overline{Y}$. Imagine a total population from which repeated samples of N cases are drawn by unrestricted random sampling. As was stated in Chapter 7, the distribution of $\overline{Y}$ would then be normal with mean μ and standard error $\dfrac{\sigma_y}{\sqrt{N}}$, and the statistic

$$t = \frac{(\overline{Y} - \mu_y)\sqrt{N}}{s_y}$$

would have "Student's" distribution. This is a familiar relation. However, the value of $\overline{Y}$ which occurs in the regression equation is the mean of Y values in a sample *which has a particular fixed set of X values*, and μ_y is the value of the mean of a subpopulation which includes *individuals with those X values and no others.* Therefore it is reasonable that if Y is related to X the $\overline{Y}$ in the regression equation would have a standard error smaller than $\sigma_y/\sqrt{N}$. The subscript x may be used, writing $\overline{Y}_x$ for the mean of a sample with fixed set of X values and μ_y for the corresponding population value. Then $\overline{Y}_x$ is normally distributed around μ_y with standard error

(10.24) $$\sigma_{\overline{Y}_x} = \frac{\sigma_{y.x}}{\sqrt{N}} = \sigma_y\sqrt{\frac{1-\rho^2}{N}}$$

(10.25) The statistic $$t = \frac{(\overline{Y}_x - \mu_y)\sqrt{N}}{s_{y.x}}$$

has "Student's" distribution with $N - 2$ degrees of freedom.

2. The regression coefficient b_{yx}. The sample regression coefficient b_{yx} is normally distributed around β_{yx}. The sample estimate of its standard error is

(10.26) $$s_{b_{yx}} = \frac{s_{y.x}}{s_x\sqrt{N-1}}$$

(10.27) and $$t = \frac{b_{yx} - \beta_{yx}}{s_{b_{yx}}} = \frac{(b_{yx} - \beta_{yx})s_x\sqrt{N-1}}{s_{y.x}}$$

has "Student's" distribution with $N - 2$ degrees of freedom.

To test $H : \beta_{yx} = 0$, the t ratio reduces to

(10.28) $$t = \frac{r\sqrt{N-2}}{\sqrt{1-r^2}}$$ which is equal to

(10.29) $$t = \frac{\Sigma xy\sqrt{N-2}}{\sqrt{\Sigma x^2\Sigma y^2 - (\Sigma xy)^2}}$$

3. The standard error of estimate $s_{y.x}$. The statistic

(10.30) $$\frac{(N-2)s^2_{y.x}}{\sigma^2_{y.x}} = \frac{(N-2)[\Sigma x^2\Sigma y^2 - (\Sigma xy)^2]}{\Sigma x^2\sigma^2_{y.x}}$$

has the chi-square distribution with $N - 2$ degrees of freedom.

Confidence Interval for μ_y, β_{yx}, $\sigma^2_{y.x}$ and $\mu_{y.x}$. Interval estimates can readily be developed from Formulas (10.25), (10.27), and (10.30). If $1 - \alpha$ is the confidence coefficient, these estimates are

(10.31) $$\overline{Y}_x + \frac{s_{y.x}}{\sqrt{N}}\, t_{\frac{1}{2}\alpha} < \mu_y < \overline{Y}_x + \frac{s_{y.x}}{\sqrt{N}}\, t_{1-\frac{1}{2}\alpha}$$

(10.32) $$b_{yx} + \frac{s_{y.x}}{s_x\sqrt{N-1}}\, t_{\frac{1}{2}\alpha} < \beta_{yx} < b_{yx} + \frac{s_{y.x}}{s_x\sqrt{N-1}}\, t_{1-\frac{1}{2}\alpha}$$

(10.33) $$\frac{s^2_{y.x}(N-2)}{\chi^2_{1-\frac{1}{2}\alpha}} < \sigma^2_{y.x} < \frac{s^2_{y.x}(N-2)}{\chi^2_{\frac{1}{2}\alpha}}$$

(10.34) $$\tilde{Y}_x + t_{\frac{1}{2}\alpha}s_{y.x}\sqrt{\frac{1}{N} + \frac{(X-\overline{X})^2}{(N-1)s_x^2}} < \mu_{y.x} < \tilde{Y}_x + t_{1-\frac{1}{2}\alpha}s_{y.x}\sqrt{\frac{1}{N} + \frac{(X-\overline{X})^2}{(N-1)s_x^2}}$$

For each value of X the confidence interval for

$$\mu_{y.x} = \mu_y + \beta_{yx}(X - \overline{X})$$

is a pair of points given by formula (10.34). These points lie on two curved lines, one of which is above and one below the sample line of regression. These curved lines are closest to the sample line when $X = \overline{X}$ and depart further from it as X departs from $\overline{X}$. The t-table is entered with $N - 2$ degrees of freedom.

EXERCISE 10.1

Use the data from Table 10.1 (p. 235) to answer questions 1 and 2.

1. Test these hypotheses: (a) $\beta_{yx} = 0$; (b) $\beta_{yx} = .6$; (c) $\mu_y = 52$.

2. With $\alpha = .05$ find an interval estimate (a) for β_{yx}, (b) for μ_y, (c) for $\sigma^2_{y.x}$, (d) for $\mu_{y.x}$ for an individual whose X score is 39.

3. The following data are made artificially simple in order to enable you to make the necessary computations very easily and concentrate your attention on the method.

$N = 27$ $\quad \Sigma x'y' = -83 \quad i_x = 5 \quad A_x = 32.5$

$\Sigma x' = -45 \quad \Sigma y' = 81 \quad i_y = 3 \quad A_y = 60$

$\Sigma(x')^2 = 219 \quad \Sigma(y')^2 = 412$

(a) Find $\overline{X}$ and $\overline{Y}$

(b) Find b_{yx}

(c) Find the regression equation to predict Y from X

(d) Find $s^2_{y.x}$

(e) With confidence coefficient .99, what is the interval estimate for (1) β_{yx}, (2) μ_y, (3) $\sigma^2_{y.x}$

(f) Test the hypothesis (1) $\beta_{yx} = 0$, (2) $\beta_{yx} \leqq 0$, (3) $\beta_{yx} = .65$, all at significance level .01.

Component Sums of Squares in Regression. The Y score of any given individual (Y_α) is the sum of three components: (1) the mean of the entire Y distribution ($\overline{Y}$); (2) a regression estimate ($\tilde{Y}_\alpha - \overline{Y}$) of his deviation from that mean made on the basis of his deviation from the mean of X; and (3) the deviation of his score from the regression estimate, or the residual error ($Y_\alpha - \tilde{Y}_\alpha$). In symbols

$$Y_\alpha = (\overline{Y}) + (\tilde{Y}_\alpha - \overline{Y}) + (Y_\alpha - \tilde{Y}_\alpha)$$

or $$Y_\alpha - \overline{Y} = (\tilde{Y}_\alpha - \overline{Y}) + (Y_\alpha - \tilde{Y}_\alpha)$$

Therefore

$$(Y_\alpha - \overline{Y})^2 = (\tilde{Y}_\alpha - \overline{Y})^2 + 2(\tilde{Y}_\alpha - \overline{Y})(Y_\alpha - \tilde{Y}_\alpha) + (Y_\alpha - \tilde{Y}_\alpha)^2$$

When this expression is summed for all individuals in the sample, the cross product term is found to be identically equal to zero. Then we have the very important relation

$$(10.35) \qquad \sum_{\alpha=1}^{N} (Y_\alpha - \overline{Y})^2 = \sum_{\alpha=1}^{N} (\tilde{Y}_\alpha - \overline{Y})^2 + \sum_{\alpha=1}^{N} (Y_\alpha - \tilde{Y}_\alpha)^2$$

which may be put into words as follows:

The sum of the squares of the deviations of the observations from the mean of all observations is equal to the sum of the squares of the deviations of the regression estimates from the mean of all observations and the sum of the squares of the deviations of the observations from their regression estimates.

The left-hand member of Formula (10.35) is already well known as equal to $(N - 1)s_y^2$. The two expressions on the right can be reduced to expressions in s^2 and r:

$$(10.36) \qquad \sum_{\alpha=1}^{N} (\tilde{Y}_\alpha - \overline{Y})^2 = (N - 1)s_y^2 r^2$$

$$(10.37) \text{ and } \qquad \sum_{\alpha=1}^{N} (Y_\alpha - \tilde{Y}_\alpha)^2 = (N - 1)s_y^2(1 - r^2)$$

The algebra which leads to these results will not be reproduced here but it consists in substituting for $\tilde{Y}$ its value from Formulas (10.1) and (10.2), squaring the binomial, summing and combining similar terms. Then

$$(10.38) \qquad (N - 1)s_y^2 = (N - 1)r^2 s_y^2 + (N - 1)(1 - r^2)s_y^2$$

$$(10.39) \text{ and } \qquad s_y^2 = r^2 s_y^2 + (1 - r^2)s_y^2$$

This is an important relationship leading to an interpretation of r. The total variance among the Y scores s_y^2 has been divided into two components. The component $r^2 s_y^2$ comes from variation of $\tilde{Y}_\alpha$ about $\overline{Y}$ and so is the portion due to regression. The component $(1 - r^2)s_y^2$ comes from the variation of Y_α about $\tilde{Y}_\alpha$, that is the variation of scores about the regression line, and is variation due to some source other than regression on X. Therefore

r^2 is the proportion of the Y variance attributable to the relation of Y to X

$1 - r^2$ is the proportion of the Y variance not attributable to the relation of Y to X.

The relationship in (10.38) may be regarded as a partition of the sum of squares of the same general nature as the partition described in Chapter 9 as analysis of variance. This partition is displayed in Table 10.3.

TABLE 10.3 Analysis of Variance in Regression

Source of variation	Degrees of freedom	Sum of squares	Mean square
Regression estimates around $\bar{Y}$	1	$(N-1)r^2s_y^2$	$(N-1)r^2s_y^2$
Observations around regression estimates	$N-2$	$(N-1)(1-r^2)s_y^2$	$\frac{N-1}{N-2}(1-r^2)s_y^2$
Observations around $\bar{Y}$	$N-1$	$(N-1)s_y^2$	s_y^2

From the two components of the sum of squares an F ratio can be obtained to test the hypothesis that the regression coefficient is zero in the population, so X is of no value at all in estimating Y.

$H: \beta_{yx} = 0$

$$F = \frac{(N-1)r^2s_y^2}{1} \Big/ \frac{(N-1)(1-r^2)s_y^2}{N-2}$$

(10.40) or $$F = \frac{r^2(N-2)}{1-r^2}$$

Since F has 1 degree of freedom for the numerator variance and $N - 2$ for the denominator,

(10.28) $$t = \sqrt{F} = r\frac{\sqrt{N-2}}{\sqrt{1-r^2}} \quad \text{with } N-2 \text{ degrees of freedom.}$$

Thus the formula already given as (10.28) on page 241 has now been reached again by analysis of variance.

This partition of the sum of squares shows the effect of the size of the correlation coefficient upon the precision of estimate. If r is large, most of the variance in the y scores can be attributed to the information contributed by the regression equation. If r is small, little information is contributed by this equation. The variation must then be explained by other means if at all. The

F test may be used to determine whether the information yielded by the regression study makes any contribution at all.

Sometimes F is to be computed directly from original data and the value of r is not needed for any other purpose. In that case, ease of computation and desire to minimize the effect of rounding errors make it expedient to use Formula (10.41) which is equivalent to (10.40) and closely related to (10.28).

$$(10.41) \qquad F = \frac{r^2(N-2)}{1-r^2} = \frac{(\Sigma xy)^2(N-2)}{\Sigma x^2 \Sigma y^2 - (\Sigma xy)^2}$$

Test for Linearity of Regression. If regression is truly linear in the population, the mean μ_j of all values of Y which are associated with a particular X_j will lie precisely on the population regression line: $\mu_{y.x} = \mu_y + \beta_{yx}(X - \overline{X})$. In this case, $\mu_j - \mu_{y.x} = 0$ for every j. However, even when regression is linear in the population, the sample values of $\overline{Y}_j$ will not agree precisely with the population values of μ_j and will not all lie on the sample regression line $\tilde{Y} = \overline{Y} + b_{yx}(X - \overline{X})$. It is apparent that a test of the hypothesis $\mu_j - \mu_{y.x} = 0$ should involve the sum of squares of the sample differences $\overline{Y}_j - \tilde{Y}_j$.

To simplify the formulas needed we shall use these additional symbols:

T' = sum of all y' scores in table $= \sum_{\alpha=1}^{N} y_\alpha'$

$T_j' = \sum_{\alpha=1}^{N_j} y_\alpha'$ = sum of all y' scores associated with X_j

C = sum of squares of Y scores about regression $= \sum_{j=1}^{k} \sum_{\alpha=1}^{N_j} (Y_{j\alpha} - \tilde{Y}_j)^2$

W = sum of squares of Y scores about column means

$$(10.42) \qquad W = \sum_{j=1}^{k} \sum_{\alpha=1}^{N_j} N_j(Y_{j\alpha} - \overline{Y}_j)^2$$

M = sum of squares of Y means about regression line

$$(10.43) \qquad M = \sum_{j=1}^{k} N_j(\overline{Y}_j - \tilde{Y}_j)^2$$

As W and M are independently distributed, they can be used with their degrees of freedom in an F test, and $W + M = C$,

C has $N - 2$ degrees of freedom
W has $N - k$ degrees of freedom
and M has $k - 2$ degrees of freedom

The statistic

$$F = \frac{M/(k-2)}{W/(N-k)} = \frac{M}{W} \cdot \frac{N-k}{k-2} \tag{10.44}$$

provides a test for the hypothesis of linearity. Formulas to facilitate the computation of M and W from an arbitrary origin are needed.

$$C = \Sigma y^2 - \frac{(\Sigma xy)^2}{\Sigma x^2} \tag{10.45}$$

Where x and y are deviations from means, not from arbitrary origins.

$$W = i_y^2 \left[\sum_{j=1}^{k} \sum_{\alpha=1}^{N_j} (y'_{j\alpha})^2 - \sum_{j=1}^{k} \frac{(T_j')^2}{N_j} \right] \tag{10.46}$$

$$M = C - W \tag{10.47}$$

These formulas will now be applied to the data in Table 10.2.

$$N\Sigma y^2 = 9(13172)$$
$$N\Sigma x^2 = 9(23292)$$
$$N\Sigma xy = 9(10452)$$

$$C = \tfrac{1}{42}\left[9(13172) - \frac{81(10452)^2}{9(23292)}\right] = 1817.53$$

$$\Sigma \frac{(T_j')^2}{N_j} = \frac{2^2}{2} + \frac{5^2}{1} + \frac{1^2}{1} + \cdots + \frac{56^2}{7} + \frac{28^2}{3} = 2386.62$$

$$W = 9(2514 - 2386.62) = 1146.42$$

$$M = 1817.53 - 1146.42 = 671.11$$

$$F = \frac{671.11}{13-2} \bigg| \frac{1146.42}{42-13} = \frac{671.11}{1146.42} \cdot \frac{29}{11} = 1.54$$

$$F_{.95} = 2.14$$

Bivariate Population Model. The regression model described on page 239 is appropriate to use when interest centers around the problem of estimating one unknown variable from another known variable. In problems about the *mutual* relationship of two variables or in problems in which it is necessary to find an estimate of *either* variable from the other, that model will not suffice. For example, suppose two tests, X and Y, have been given to a group of subjects on different days, a few subjects being absent on one day and a few on the other. It is for some reason not feasible to obtain the missing scores by administering the test again. From the subjects for whom both scores are available, *two* regression equations are computed, one to estimate the missing scores in X from observed scores in Y and the other to estimate the missing scores in Y from observed scores in X.

In the mathematical model used for problems of this sort each individual is a *pair of observations*. A sample is then a sample of pairs from the population of paired observations. In this model both X's and Y's vary randomly from sample to sample, whereas in the regression model previously described the X's are fixed for all samples and only the Y's vary. A population of this type is called *bivariate.*

The probability distribution of a population on a single continuous variate, that is a univariate population, was discussed in Chapter 5. That distribution consists of all the points on a line segment (which may or may not extend to infinity) and probabilities corresponding to specified intervals on that line. Those probabilities are represented by the areas under the probability curve between two ordinates.

For a continuous bivariate population, the scales of the two traits will be represented by two coordinate axes, and each pair of scores for one individual will locate a point in the plane of those axes. The bivariate probability distribution then consists of all points in a portion of this plane (which portion may or may not extend to infinity) and the appropriate probability values. These probability values are represented by volumes. The probability that $a < X < b$ and simultaneously $c < Y < d$ is written

$$P\{a < X < b, c < Y < d\}$$

This probability is a volume within a solid figure whose base and 4 sides are planes but whose top may not be a plane. The X, Y scales, the intervals and probability are shown in Figure 10–1. The probabilities of the type shown in the figure may all be described as volumes under a surface which has a mathematical form.

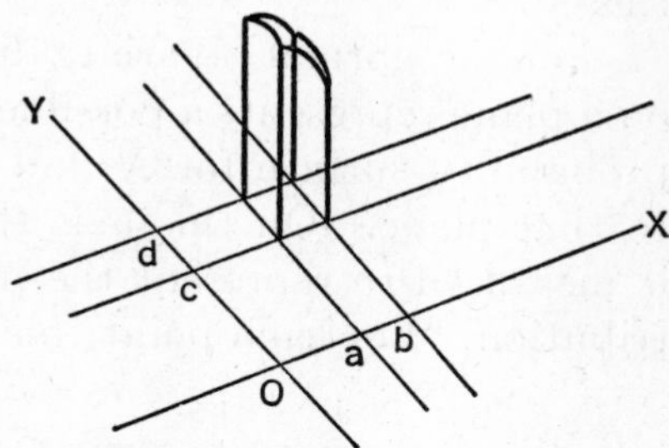

FIG. 10–1. Segment of volume representing the probability $P\{a < X < b, c < Y < d\}$ in a bivariate distribution.

In any bivariate population, each variable has its own moments and so the probability distribution involves the four parameters μ_x, μ_y, σ_x, and σ_y. In addition the bivariate population has a product moment which is the expectation $E(X - \mu_x)(Y - \mu_y)$. This product moment is also called the *covariance*. The correlation coefficient of X and Y in the population is defined as

$$\rho_{xy} = \frac{E[(X - \mu_x)(Y - \mu_y)]}{\sigma_x \sigma_y} \tag{10.48}$$

Normal Bivariate Population. In this chapter we shall be concerned with only one type of bivariate population, namely the *normal bivariate*, which is an extension of the univariate normal population to the bivariate situation. The tests of significance described in the remainder of this chapter are based on the assumption of such a population and do not necessarily apply if the population differs too greatly from that form.

For the normal univariate distribution of X, every point on a line represents a possible value of X. To set up the probability curve for X, an axis is drawn perpendicular to the scale of X. On this axis the ordinate (which we shall call u) is measured to represent the *probability density* of X. Then as already discussed in Chapter 5,

$$u = \frac{1}{\sigma_x \sqrt{2\pi}} e^{-\frac{1}{2}\frac{(X-\mu_x)^2}{\sigma_x^2}} \tag{10.49}$$

This curve has two parameters, μ_x and σ_x. The ordinate u is not a probability because probability would be represented by the area under the normal curve between two ordinates, but it may be thought of as something like the average height of such an area when its base is very small so that the two ordinates are nearly the same.

For the normal bivariate distribution of X and Y, every point on a plane represents a possible pair of values. To set up the joint probability surface for X and Y, an axis is drawn perpendicular to that plane. On this axis the ordinate (which we shall call u) is measured to represent the probability density of the X, Y distribution. For each point this ordinate is

$$u = \frac{1}{2\pi\sigma_x\sigma_y\sqrt{1-\rho^2}} e^{-\frac{1}{2(1-\rho^2)}\left\{\frac{(X-\mu_x)^2}{\sigma_x^2} - \frac{2\rho(X-\mu_x)(Y-\mu_y)}{\sigma_x\sigma_y} + \frac{(Y-\mu_y)^2}{\sigma_y^2}\right\}} \tag{10.50}$$

This probability surface has 5 parameters, μ_x, μ_y, σ_x, σ_y, and ρ. The ordinate u is not a probability because probability is represented by a volume, but it may be thought of as something like the average height of such a volume when the area of its base is very small, so that all the ordinates are nearly the same.

When the parameters are given definite values, u is defined for each point (X, Y), and varies from point to point. Populations with different parameters will have different probability distributions.

The normal bivariate probability distribution is traditionally spoken of as having the form of a "cocked hat." The marginal distributions for X and for Y are both normal. Furthermore, if the three dimensional solid is cut by *any* plane perpendicular to the (X, Y) plane, the intersection is a normal curve.

If any bivariate probability distribution, whether normal or not, is cut by a plane parallel to the X, Y plane, the intersection will be a kind of contour line marking out those points in the plane which have equal probability densities, that is points at which the ordinates are equal. For the normal bivariate distribution all such contour lines are ellipses with their center at the point

$$(X = \mu_x,\ Y = \mu_y)$$

All such ellipses for one distribution have the same axes so they do not intersect each other.

Each normal surface has its own set of ellipses. These ellipses are of particular interest because when a sample from a normal bivariate population is plotted on a scatter diagram the distribution of tallies is concentrated about the point representing the sample means in accordance with the form of the ellipses obtained from the distribution. This phenomenon is familiar to all persons who have worked with scatter diagrams and corresponds to the concentration of tallies about the mean of a univariate normal population. Figure 10–2 shows how these ellipses change as the parameters of the distribution are changed.

Distribution of the Correlation Coefficient. One difficulty in problems of statistical inference in relation to the correlation coefficient arises because the range of this coefficient is -1 to $+1$ both for r and ρ. Hence r can never have a truly normal distribution regardless of the form of the population sampled. When the population is bivariate normal and $\rho = 0$ the distribution of r is symmetrical and when the number of cases is large the distribution of r can be reasonably approximated by the normal curve.

When ρ differs from zero the sample r's cluster about the population value as may be expected. But now there is less space

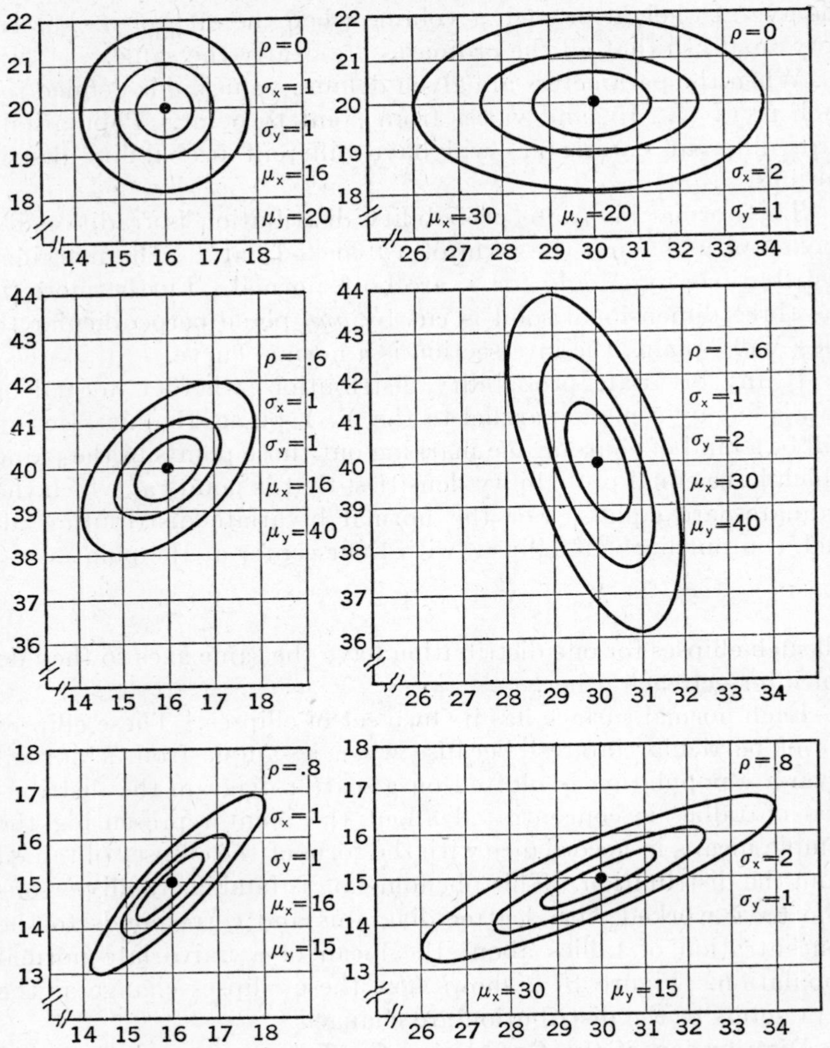

Fig. 10–2. Ellipses of equal probability density for normal bivariate surfaces having different values of the five parameters, μ_x, μ_y, σ_x, σ_y, ρ_{xy}.

on one side of ρ than on the other. Hence the clustering is denser on one side than on the other, and the distribution of r is skewed.

A mathematical formula which describes the distribution of r for any value of ρ was derived by R. A. Fisher in a classic paper which ushered in a new way of thinking about statistical distributions (see reference 6), but it is very complicated, involving ρ and N as well as r. This exact formula for the sampling distribution of r is seldom used but as substitute there are several approximations which are valid under certain assumptions and give results accurate enough for all practical purposes. The exact distribution of r has been published by David with a discussion of the accuracy of approximation of the various substitute methods for testing the significance of r.[2]

When $N = 2$, r can take only the values $+1$ and -1 and so the distribution consists merely of an ordinate at each of these points. When $N = 3$ and $\rho = 0$ the distribution of r is U-shaped, that is, symmetrical but lower in the center than at the ends. As N increases the distribution becomes higher in the center and lower at the ends until for $N = 30$ or more, its form is approximately normal.

Tests of the Hypothesis that Correlation is Zero in the Population. When a normal bivariate population has the parameter $\rho = 0$, the statistic

$$F = \frac{r^2(N-2)}{1-r^2}$$

has the F distribution with 1 degree of freedom for the numerator and $N - 2$ for the denominator. Consequently $\sqrt{F} = t$, and the statistic

$$t = \frac{r\sqrt{N-2}}{\sqrt{1-r^2}} \tag{10.28}$$

has "Student's" distribution with $N - 2$ degrees of freedom. This is an exact distribution and applies to samples of 3 or more. (Obviously correlation is meaningless in a sample of 2 cases because r could have only the values $+1$ and -1 unless both values of one variate were alike and then r would be indeterminate.) The reader should notice that while r ranges only from -1 to $+1$, t ranges from $-\infty$ to $+\infty$.

Formula (10.28) has already appeared as providing a test for the hypothesis $\beta_{yx} = 0$. But when $\rho = 0$, $\beta_{yx} = 0$ and when $\beta_{yx} = 0$, $\rho = 0$, so the hypotheses $\rho = 0$ and $\beta = 0$ are really the same.

Table XI shows for varying values of $n = N - 2$ the value of r such that the critical region for rejection of the hypothesis $\rho = 0$ consists of all values of r *numerically* greater than the tabulated value of r.

A second test of the hypothesis $\rho = 0$ is available when the sample is not small, say $N = 30$ or more. This test is obtained from the fact that if $\rho = 0$ and N is not small the distribution of r is approximately normal with mean zero and standard error $1/\sqrt{N-1}$. Therefore, under these circumstances

$$\frac{r}{\sigma_r} = r\sqrt{N-1} \tag{10.51}$$

has approximately the unit normal distribution.

Warning. A formula which is widely but incorrectly used should be mentioned in order that the student may understand why it is no longer in good repute. This formula is sometimes written $\sigma_r = \dfrac{1-r^2}{\sqrt{N}}$ and sometimes $s_r = \dfrac{1-r^2}{\sqrt{N-1}}$. The standard error of r is correctly given by the formula

$$\sigma_r = \frac{1-\rho^2}{\sqrt{N-1}} \tag{10.52}$$

But this involves the unknown ρ. If $\rho = 0$, this formula becomes

$$\sigma_r = \frac{1}{\sqrt{N-1}} \tag{10.53}$$

as previously stated. There is no justification for substituting r for ρ in (10.52) to produce the incorrect formulas quoted at the beginning of this paragraph and to do so sometimes produces results that are extremely misleading.

Another incorrect practice which is so common that it cannot be passed over in silence is that of computing a probable error of r as $.6745(1-r^2)/\sqrt{N-1}$ and attaching it to r, as for example, $r = .65 \pm .03$. A "probable error" has meaning only in a normal distribution and so is obviously out of place in this connection.

EXERCISE 10.2

Compute both $r\sqrt{N-2}/\sqrt{1-r^2}$ and $r\sqrt{N-1}$ for $r = .06$, $.20$ and $.60$ and $N = 5$, 26, 82, 102, and 401. Examine the results to see whether the two formulas appear to be in closer agreement when N is large or N is small. Is there anything in the foregoing explanation which would account for this apparent tendency? Do the two formulas appear to agree more closely for large or for small r? Can you account for this tendency?

Tests that ρ is Some Value Other than Zero. When ρ is different from zero, the distribution of r is skewed and neither of the tests described in the previous section can be used. To obtain the data of Figures 10–3 and 10–4 samples were drawn from the data of Table XXIV, for which ρ was .58. The distribution of r in samples of 5 cases as shown in Figure 10–3 is very skewed. For samples of 20 cases, as shown in Figure 10–4, the distribution

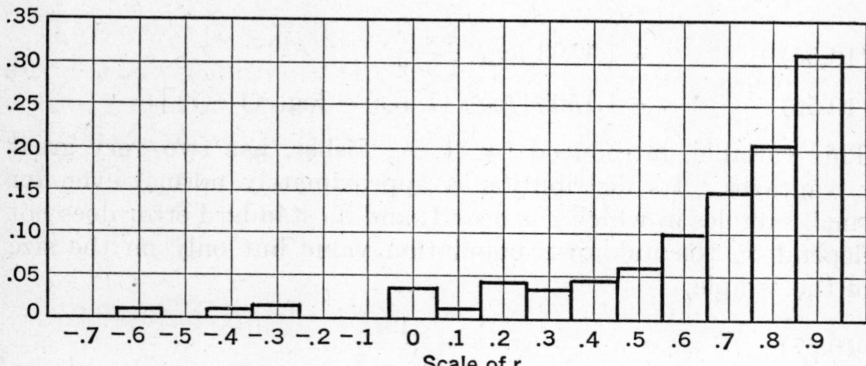

FIG. 10–3. Distribution of r in samples of 5 cases from a population in which $\rho = .58$.

is markedly less skewed though still far from normal. As N increases the distribution of r becomes more nearly symmetrical so that for extremely large samples with ρ not too near $+1$ or -1 treating $\frac{r - \rho}{\sigma_r}$ as normally distributed would give fairly satisfactory results. However a much better procedure is available which does not depend upon the dubious assumption of normality for r.

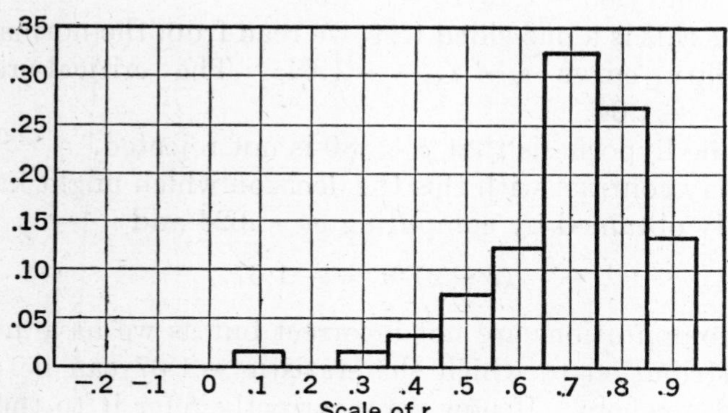

FIG. 10–4. Distribution of r in samples of 20 cases from a population in which $\rho = .58$.

A variable, which is usually called z but which we shall call z_r in order to distinguish it from the other variables which have already been denoted by that letter, is related to r by the formula

$$z_r = \frac{1}{2} \log_e \frac{1+r}{1-r} \tag{10.54}$$

$$= 1.1503 \log_{10} \frac{1+r}{1-r} \tag{10.55}$$

$$= 1.1503 [\log_{10} (1+r) - \log_{10} (1-r)] \tag{10.56}$$

This variable, introduced by R. A. Fisher, has two very great advantages. Its distribution is approximately normal even for small samples in which ρ is near 1, and its standard error does not depend on the unknown population value but only on the size of the sample,

$$\sigma_{z_r} = \frac{1}{\sqrt{N-3}} \tag{10.57}$$

If ζ is the population value corresponding to ρ, then $(z_r - \zeta)\sqrt{N-3}$ may be treated as a normally distributed variable.

The transformation of r to z_r and vice versa can be made easily by reference to Table XII.

Suppose we have $r = .76$ for $N = 228$, and we wish to test the hypothesis that $\rho \geqq .80$ with $\alpha = .05$. A correct procedure would be as follows:

(1) From Table XII we find that if $r = .76$, $z_r = 1.00$
(2) From Table XII we find that if $\rho = .80$, $\zeta = 1.10$
(3) $\sqrt{N-3} = 15$
(4) Then $(1.00 - 1.10)15 = -1.50$
(5) As this is a one-sided test, we read from the normal probability curve $z_\alpha = z_{.05} = -1.64$. The critical region is $z < -1.64$.
(6) The hypothesis that $\rho \geqq .80$ is not rejected.

We may contrast with this the decision which might have been incorrectly obtained by computing $\sigma_r = .024$ and

$$(r - \rho)/\sigma_r = -1.67.$$

The computations are not incorrect but as we have no probability distribution to which the statistic -1.67 can be referred, they lead nowhere. If now we incorrectly refer it to the normal probability distribution and reject the hypothesis $\rho \geqq .80$ because $-1.67 < z_{.05}$, we shall make an incorrect decision.

Confidence Interval for ρ. The z-transformation is useful in obtaining a confidence interval for ρ. The procedure is as follows:

(1) In Table XII find the value of z_r corresponding to the sample value of r

(2) Compute a confidence interval for the population value ζ by the formula

$$C\left(z_r + \frac{z_{\frac{1}{2}\alpha}}{\sqrt{N-3}} < \zeta < z_r + \frac{z_{1-\frac{1}{2}\alpha}}{\sqrt{N-3}}\right) = 1 - \alpha \tag{10.58}$$

Here one must remember that z_r and z_α are two quite different values represented by the same letter only because of tradition and the brevity of our alphabet.

(3) In Table XII read the value of ρ corresponding to each of the bounding values of ζ. From these form the interval for ρ.

Thus suppose we have obtained $r = .65$ in a sample of 40 cases and we want an interval estimate for ρ with confidence coefficient .95. From Table XII we read $z_r = .78$. From the normal probability table we find

$$z_{.025} = -1.96 \text{ and } z_{.975} = 1.96. \quad \sqrt{N-3} = \sqrt{37}.$$

Then $$.78 - \frac{1.96}{\sqrt{37}} < \zeta < .78 + \frac{1.96}{\sqrt{.37}} \text{ or } .46 < \zeta < 1.10$$

and $$.43 < \rho < .80$$

Notice that because of the skewness in the distribution of r the confidence limits for ρ are not symmetrically placed about the observed r, but $.80 - .65 = .15$ while $.65 - .43 = .22$

David's *Tables of the Correlation Coefficient* [2] show the complete cumulative distribution for r in samples from populations for which ρ is 0, .1, .2, .3, .4, .5, .6, .7, .8, or .9 and $3 \leqq N \leqq 25$, $N = 50$, 100, 200 or 400. She also presents confidence belts for r for samples of the sizes listed, with $\alpha = .10$, $\alpha = .05$, $\alpha = .02$ and $\alpha = .01$. The chart for $\alpha = .05$ has been reproduced as Chart XIV in the Appendix.

Test of the Hypothesis That Two Independent Populations Have the Same Correlation. If a sample is drawn from each of two independent, normal bivariate populations the difference $r_1 - r_2$ should fluctuate around $\rho_1 - \rho_2$. If each r is transformed to z, the difference $z_1 - z_2$ will also fluctuate around $\zeta_1 - \zeta_2$ as mean and will have as standard deviation

$$\sqrt{\frac{1}{N_1 - 3} + \frac{1}{N_2 - 3}}$$

Then

$$\frac{z_1 - z_2 - (\zeta_1 - \zeta_2)}{\sqrt{\frac{1}{N_1 - 3} + \frac{1}{N_2 - 3}}} \tag{10.59}$$

may be treated as a normal deviate. If the hypothesis that $\zeta_1 = \zeta_2$ is rejected, the hypothesis $\rho_1 = \rho_2$ must also be rejected. If the hypothesis $\zeta_1 = \zeta_2$ is sustained, the hypothesis $\rho_1 = \rho_2$ must also be sustained.

In his research concerning *Children's Collecting Activity* [3] Durost studied the collections made by 50 boys and 50 girls between the ages of 10 and 14. Among the correlations obtained was a correlation between mental age and the average rating of the child's collections (each of the collections of each child being rated as to quality and the average taken for the child). For boys this correlation was .31 and for girls .06. Do these figures provide evidence that the relation between mental maturity and quality of collections made is higher for boys than for girls?

	r	z_r	$N - 3$	$\frac{1}{N-3}$
Boys	.31	.3205	47	.021277
Girls	.06	.0601	47	.021277
		$z_B - z_G = .2604$		$.042554 = \sigma^2_{z_B} + \sigma^2_{z_G}$

$$z = \frac{.2604}{\sqrt{.0426}} = \frac{.2604}{.206} = 1.26$$

With so small a value of z, it would be inappropriate to assume that the relationship is higher for boys than for girls.

Test of the Hypothesis That $\rho_{yz} = \rho_{xz}$ When Computed for the Same Population. This situation is quite different from that of the preceding section though often confused with it. There we had measures on the same two variates X and Y for two *different populations*. Here we have for *one population* measures on three variates, X, Y, and Z, and we wish to know whether Z is more highly correlated with X than with Y, or vice versa. This question is particularly important when two predictors are available but the one showing the higher correlation with the criterion is more expensive, more time-consuming, or more difficult to apply. For example, suppose that a prognostic test, long and rather difficult to administer, has yielded a correlation of .56 with Freshman college marks, while a shorter test, less costly to administer, has yielded a correlation of .43, the two correlations being obtained from the same 100 subjects. If the tests were equally costly the one yielding the higher correlation would be chosen regardless of whether the difference in the r's was significant or not. Still better, both tests would be used, and prediction made from a multiple regression equation. However let us suppose the college authorities have decided to use only one test and to use the more costly test only if its correlation with marks is significantly higher than that of the other test. If the hypothesis $\rho_{yz} = \rho_{xz}$ proves tenable, they have decided to use only the shorter test.

Let X = score on the longer test
Y = score on the shorter test
Z = average mark at end of first semester

Hotelling [7] has given a solution of the problem of the significance of the difference between r_{yz} and r_{xz} without making any assumption as to the form of distribution of X or of Y in the population, but with the limitation that generalization is only to a subpopulation of all possible samples for which X and Y have exactly the same set of values as those in the observed sample. It is assumed that Z has a normal distribution for each value of X and for each value of Y, with common variance.

(10.60) Then $$t = (r_{xz} - r_{yz})\sqrt{\frac{(N-3)(1+r_{xy})}{2(1 - r^2_{xy} - r^2_{xz} - r^2_{yz} + 2r_{xy}r_{xz}r_{yz})}}$$

has "Student's" distribution with $N - 3$ degrees of freedom.

Obviously it is necessary to know the correlation between the two tests before the question can be answered. Assume that $r_{xy} = .52$.

Then $$t = (.56 - .43)\sqrt{153.10} = 1.61$$

In view of this small value of t it would be difficult to make a strong case for the use of the longer test if only one test is to be used. It is of course easy to show that the predictive value of $r = .43$ is too low to be of much practical use.

EXERCISE 10.3

1. (a) In the problem of the preceding paragraph, test the significance of $r_{xz} - r_{yz}$ if $N = 100$ and $r_{xz} = .56$, $r_{yz} = .43$ as before but $r_{xy} = .20$.

(b) If $r_{xy} = .70$.

Regression Equations in the Normal Bivariate Population. In the normal bivariate population each of the variates may be regarded as independent and as related to the other by a linear regression relationship. The two equations are defined in the population as

$$(10.61) \qquad \mu_{y.x} = \mu_y + \beta_{yx}(X - \mu_x) \quad \text{and} \quad \mu_{x.y} = \mu_x + \beta_{xy}(Y - \mu_y).$$

The corresponding standard errors of estimate are

$$(10.62) \qquad \sigma_{y.x} = \sigma_y\sqrt{1 - \rho^2} \quad \text{and} \quad \sigma_{x.y} = \sigma_x\sqrt{1 - \rho^2}$$

The corresponding regression equations for the sample have this form

$$(10.63) \qquad \tilde{Y} = \overline{Y} + b_{yx}(X - \overline{X}) \quad \text{and} \quad \tilde{X} = \overline{X} + b_{xy}(Y - \overline{Y})$$

and the corresponding standard errors are

$$(10.64) \qquad s_{y.x} = s_y\sqrt{\frac{N-1}{N-2}(1 - r^2)} \quad \text{and} \quad s_{x.y} = s_x\sqrt{\frac{N-1}{N-2}(1 - r^2)}$$

EXERCISE 10.4

1. A prognostic test in mathematics was given to 98 students who were about to begin a course in elementary statistics. The results of this test were examined in relation to scores on the final examination. The pairs of scores are not given below but data derived from the scores are shown. In the following, X is a score on the prognostic test and Y the score on the final examination. The sums of scores, sums of squares and cross-products obtained by machine computation follow:

$\Sigma X = 3075 \quad \Sigma Y = 4817 \quad \Sigma X^2 = 101581 \quad \Sigma XY = 154468 \quad \Sigma Y^2 = 245381$

a. Compute $\overline{X}$, $\overline{Y}$, b_{yx}, s_x, s_y, r_{xy}, $s_{y.x}$

b. Find the regression equation to predict Y from X

c. What proportion of the variance of Y is independent of variation in X?

d. Test the hypothesis $H: \rho = 0$

e. What Y value would you predict for a student with $X = 62$? $X = 38$? $X = 54$?

f. What interval estimate would you make with confidence coefficient .95

(1) for $\mu_{y.x}$ when $X = 42$ (2) for β_{yx} (3) for ρ (4) for $\sigma^2_{y.x}$

2. Suppose a study has yielded data as follows:

$N = 122,$	$\Sigma x' = 94,$	$\Sigma(x')^2 = 990$	$i_x = 3,$	$A_x = 45$
$\Sigma x'y' = 420,$	$\Sigma y' = -35,$	$\Sigma(y')^2 = 598,$	$i_y = 5,$	$A_y = 60$

a. What is the equation to estimate Y from X?

b. What is the equation to estimate X from Y?

c. Find a confidence interval for ρ with confidence coefficient .99

d. Test the hypothesis that $\rho = .60$

e. Test the hypothesis that $\beta_{xy} = 1.25$

3. In each of the following situations there is some inconsistency, some reason why real data would not yield these figures unless a mistake had been made. Explain what is wrong in each case.

a. $\tilde{Y} = .96X + 13.3$ and $\tilde{X} = 1.42Y - 12.5$

b. $\Sigma xy = 1543$, $\Sigma x^2 = 1136$, and $\Sigma y^2 = 1560$

c. $r = .65$, $b_{yx} = -.24$, $b_{xy} = -.72$

d. $r = .60$, $b_{yx} = .80$, $b_{xy} = .90$

e. $r = .60$, $s_y = 12$, $s_{y.x} = 7.2$

f. $r = -.20$, $b_{yx} = .80$, $b_{xy} = .50$

g. $\tilde{Y} = -.9X + 5$, $\tilde{X} = -.6Y + 4$, $r = .43$

h. $r = .5$, $s_x = 4$, $s_y = 10$, $b_{yx} = .25$

i. $r = .5$, $s_x = 6$, $s_y = 3$, $\tilde{y} = x$, $\tilde{x} = .25y$

4. In a sample of 203 cases from population A a correlation coefficient of .66 has been found. In a sample of 153 cases from population B, a coefficient of .70 has been found. Test H: $\rho_A = \rho_B$.

Additional formulas often useful in computations for correlation and regression:

$$\Sigma xy = \left(\Sigma x'y' - \frac{(\Sigma x')(\Sigma y')}{N}\right) i_x i_y$$

$$= \Sigma XY - \frac{(\Sigma X)(\Sigma Y)}{N}$$

$$2\Sigma xy = \Sigma x^2 + \Sigma y^2 - \Sigma(x - y)^2$$

$$= \Sigma(x + y)^2 - \Sigma x^2 - \Sigma y^2$$

$$= i_x i_y \left(\Sigma(x')^2 + \Sigma(y')^2 - \Sigma(x' - y')^2 - \frac{2(\Sigma x')(\Sigma y')}{N}\right)$$

$$= \Sigma X^2 + \Sigma Y^2 - \Sigma(X - Y)^2 - \frac{2(\Sigma X)(\Sigma Y)}{N}$$

$$N\Sigma xy = i_x i_y (N\Sigma x'y' - (\Sigma x')(\Sigma y'))$$

$$= N\Sigma XY - (\Sigma X)(\Sigma Y)$$

$$2N\Sigma xy = N\Sigma X^2 + N\Sigma Y^2 - N\Sigma(X - Y)^2 - 2(\Sigma X)(\Sigma Y)$$

$$\Sigma y^2 = i_y{}^2\left(\Sigma(y')^2 - \frac{(\Sigma y')^2}{N}\right)$$

$$= \Sigma Y^2 - \frac{(\Sigma Y)^2}{N}$$

$$N\Sigma y^2 = i_y{}^2(N\Sigma(y')^2 - (\Sigma y')^2)$$

$$= N\Sigma Y^2 - (\Sigma Y)^2$$

$$b_{yx} = \frac{\Sigma xy}{\Sigma x^2} \quad \text{and} \quad b_{xy} = \frac{\Sigma xy}{\Sigma y^2}$$

$$r_{xy} = \frac{\Sigma xy}{\sqrt{\Sigma x^2 \Sigma y^2}}$$

$$t = \frac{(\overline{Y}_x - \mu_y)\sqrt{N}}{s_{y.x}} = (\overline{Y}_x - \mu_y)\sqrt{\frac{N(N-2)\Sigma x^2}{\Sigma x^2 \Sigma y^2 - (\Sigma xy)^2}}$$

$$= \frac{(\overline{Y}_x - \mu_y)}{s_y\sqrt{1 - r^2}} \sqrt{\frac{N(N-2)}{N-1}}$$

$$s^2_{b_{yx}} = \frac{\Sigma x^2 \Sigma y^2 - (\Sigma xy)^2}{(\Sigma x^2)^2(N-2)}$$

$$\frac{b^2_{yx}}{s^2_{b_{yx}}} = \frac{(\Sigma xy)^2(N-2)}{\Sigma x^2 \Sigma y^2 - (\Sigma xy)^2}$$

REFERENCES

1. Croxton, F. E. and Cowden, D. J., *Applied General Statistics,* New York, Prentice Hall, 1940.
2. David, F. N., *Tables of the Correlation Coefficient,* Cambridge, England, Cambridge University Press, 1938.
3. Durost, Walter N., *Children's Collecting Activity Related to Social Factors,* New York, Teachers College, Columbia University, Bureau of Publications, 1932.
4. Dwyer, Paul, *Linear Computations,* New York, John Wiley and Sons, 1951.
5. Ezekiel, M., *Methods of Correlation Analysis,* New York, John Wiley and Sons, 1930, 1941.
6. Fisher, R. A., "Frequency Distribution of the Values of the Correlation Coefficient in Samples from an Indefinitely Large Population," *Biometrika,* 10 (1915), 507.
7. Hotelling, Harold, "The Selection of Variates for Use in Prediction, with some Comments on the General Problem of Nuisance Parameters," *Annals of Mathematical Statistics,* 11 (1940), 271–283.
8. Mills, F. C., *Statistical Methods,* New York, Henry Holt and Company, 1938.
9. Pease, Katherine, *Machine Computation of Elementary Statistics,* New York, Chartwell House Inc., 1949.
10. Walker, H. M., *Mathematics Essential for Elementary Statistics,* New York, Henry Holt and Company, 1952.
11. Walker, H. M., *Studies in the History of Statistical Method,* Baltimore, The Williams and Wilkins Company, 1929.
12. Waugh, Albert E., *Elements of Statistical Method,* New York, McGraw-Hill, 1938.

11 Other Measures of Relationship

This chapter will take up methods of measuring relationship in situations where the assumptions specified in Chapter 10 are not wholly met and in considering the appropriate tests of significance. It will also deal with certain problems related to the use of the product moment correlation in special situations.

Biserial Correlation. When one of two traits is scored on a continuous scale and the other on a scale having only two values, the resulting correlation is called a *biserial* correlation. The scale with only two values is called dichotomous. This situation arises very often in statistical studies. A vocational counselor is concerned to know the relationship of some measured trait or traits to such a dichotomous trait as employment status (employed or unemployed), success on the job (fired or not fired), sex (male or female), liking for a type of work or activity (liking, disliking), technical training for a job (trained, untrained), and the like. A test writer needs to analyze the items in a test to retain those which have a high correlation with respect to some criterion and to reject those which have a low correlation. If the criterion is a scaled trait and the item is dichotomous, a biserial correlation is called for. The item scores are dichotomous if only two answers are possible (such as "true" or "false"), or if several possible answers are classified into those which are acceptable and those which are not acceptable. In an attempt to discover measures which could be used to predict success in a professional school, one might use "survival" as a criterion, classifying students into groups, those who drop out and those who complete the course. A biserial coefficient of correlation is used in a very wide variety of situations of which the foregoing are illustrative.

Two different coefficients of biserial correlation will be discussed, the point biserial coefficient for which we shall use the symbol r_{pb}, and the biserial coefficient for which we shall use the symbol r_{bis}. These symbols are not standardized, r_{bis} is in fairly wide use but there is no generally accepted symbol for the point biserial.

The Point Biserial Coefficient of Correlation. This coefficient provides a very simple solution to the problem of biserial correlation. Arbitrary numbers are assigned to the two classes of the dichtomous variable. The outcome will be the same no matter what numbers are chosen but the use of 0 and 1 holds computational labor to a minimum and so these are commonly chosen. Each individual then has a pair of scores, one which is based on a continuous scale and one which is either 0 or 1. The correlation coefficient may then be computed by the formulas of Chapter 10. This is a product moment correlation. It can be used in combination with other product moment coefficients in a multiple regression equation. It has the same range of values as other product moment r's, from -1 to $+1$. Its significance is tested in similar fashion.

However the general formula can be reduced to a very simple formula for computing the point biserial coefficient. Suppose N individuals have been measured, and of these N_1 fall in the category which is arbitrarily scored $X = 1$ while N_0 fall into the class which is arbitrarily scored $X = 0$. Let the means of the scaled trait for these two classes be $\overline{Y}_1$ and $\overline{Y}_0$. For the entire group $N = N_1 + N_0$, and mean is $\overline{Y} = \frac{1}{N}(N_1\overline{Y}_1 + N_0\overline{Y}_0)$ and

$$s_y^2 = \frac{\Sigma(Y - \overline{Y})^2}{N - 1}$$

Then the point biserial correlation is

$$r_{pb} = \frac{\overline{Y}_1 - \overline{Y}_0}{s_y}\sqrt{\frac{N_1N_0}{N(N-1)}} \tag{11.1}$$

and will be positive if $\overline{Y}_1$ is larger than $\overline{Y}_0$. If $N_1/N = p$ and $N_0/N = q$, the formula may be conveniently written as

$$r_{pb} = \frac{\overline{Y}_1 - \overline{Y}_0}{\sqrt{\Sigma y^2}}\sqrt{Npq} \tag{11.2}$$

If a number of biserial coefficients are to be computed from the same data, the work is reduced by using a formula involving $\overline{Y}$ (which can be computed from the entire group and remains constant from one correlation to another) and either $\overline{Y}_1$ or $\overline{Y}_0$ but not both. If N_0 is smaller the formula involving $\overline{Y}_0$ is used; if N_1 is smaller, the formula involving $\overline{Y}_1$.

$$r_{pb} = \frac{\overline{Y}_1 - \overline{Y}}{\sqrt{\Sigma y^2}}\sqrt{\frac{N_1N}{N_0}} \qquad = \frac{\overline{Y} - \overline{Y}_0}{\sqrt{\Sigma y^2}}\sqrt{\frac{N_0N}{N_1}} \tag{11.3}$$

or

$$(11.4) \quad r_{pb} = \frac{\overline{Y}_1 - \overline{Y}}{s_y}\sqrt{\frac{N_1 N}{N_0(N-1)}} = \frac{\overline{Y} - \overline{Y}_0}{s_y}\sqrt{\frac{N_0 N}{N_1(N-1)}}$$

Only very simple algebra is needed to demonstrate the equivalence of these formulas and their derivation from the more general formula for the product moment coefficient.

If N is very large so that $\frac{N-1}{N}$ may be treated as 1, the formula reduces to any of the following forms:

$$(11.5) \quad r_{pb} = \frac{\overline{Y}_1 - \overline{Y}_0}{s_y}\sqrt{pq}$$

$$(11.6) \quad = \frac{\overline{Y}_1 - \overline{Y}}{s_y}\sqrt{\frac{p}{q}} = \frac{\overline{Y}_1 - \overline{Y}}{s_y}\sqrt{\frac{N_1}{N_0}}$$

$$(11.7) \quad = \frac{\overline{Y} - \overline{Y}_0}{s_y}\sqrt{\frac{q}{p}} = \frac{\overline{Y} - \overline{Y}_0}{s_y}\sqrt{\frac{N_0}{N_1}}$$

The use of point biserial correlation may be illustrated by data gathered by Spaney.[17] A battery of tests was administered to 308 student nurses shortly after their admission to nursing school. Among the measures obtained was a rating of the student nurses on the trait steadiness-emotionality, and these ratings may be treated as a continuous scale. Six months later, at the end of the preclinical period, 29 students had withdrawn. The mean steadiness-emotionality rating for the 29 withdrawals was

$$\overline{Y}_0 = 35.07$$

and for the 279 who stayed on it was $\overline{Y}_1 = 30.00$. For the entire group of 308 the standard deviation was $s_y = 11.62$. Hence the point biserial coefficient was

$$r_{pb} = \sqrt{\frac{(29)(279)}{(308)(307)}} \cdot \frac{30.00 - 35.07}{11.62} = -.13$$

Since the scale is so arranged that a high score indicates steadiness and a low score emotionality, the correlation suggests a slight tendency for those staying on to be, in general, less steady, more emotional than those withdrawing. The correlation is significantly different from zero according to the test discussed in a subsequent section, but the correlation is so low that rating could not be used to furnish any useful prediction as to whether an individual student is or is not likely to withdraw.

Table 11.1 presents the kind of data commonly assembled by a test technician making an item analysis, except that he would have more subjects and more items. Since $\overline{Y} = 43.4$ for every

TABLE 11.1 Point Biserial and Biserial Correlation Coefficients Obtained for 20 Subjects on each of 5 Items

Subject	Y Criterion Score	Item 1	Item 2	Item 3	Item 4	Item 5
1	50	1	1	1	0	0
2	46	1	1	0	0	1
3	37	0	0	0	0	1
4	48	1	1	1	0	0
5	47	1	1	1	0	0
6	40	0	0	0	1	1
7	39	0	0	0	0	1
8	43	1	1	0	1	1
9	42	0	1	0	1	1
10	46	1	1	1	0	0
11	42	0	1	0	0	1
12	41	0	1	0	0	1
13	43	0	1	0	1	1
14	43	0	1	0	1	1
15	44	1	1	1	0	0
16	42	0	1	0	0	1
17	41	0	0	0	1	1
18	45	1	0	0	0	0
19	46	1	1	0	0	0
20	43	1	0	0	1	1
N_1		10	14	5	7	13
N_0		10	6	15	13	7
ΣY_1		458	623	235	295	542
ΣY_0		410	245	633	573	326
$\overline{Y}_1$		45.8	44.5	47.0	42.1	41.7
$\overline{Y}_0$		41.0	40.83	42.2	44.1	46.6
r_{pb}		.78	.54	.67	$-$ .31	$-$ .75
r_{bis}		.95	.71	.89	$-$ .39	$-$ .95

$\sum_1^{20} Y = 868$

$\overline{Y} = 43.40$

$\Sigma Y^2 = 37862$

$(868)^2/20 = \underline{37671.2}$

$\sum_1^{20} y^2 = 190.8$

$s_y = 3.17$

item, the use of Formula (11.3) would make it unnecessary to compute both $\overline{Y}_1$ and $\overline{Y}_0$, so the experienced test technician might compute only the one based on the smaller number of cases. For item 3, the computation of point biserial would in this case be

$$r_{pb} = \frac{47.0 - 43.4}{3.17} \sqrt{\frac{(5)(20)}{(15)(19)}} = .67$$

Test of Significance for Point Biserial Correlation. It will be assumed that in the population the distribution of Y scores can be described by two normal curves, one curve for the Y scores paired with $X = 0$ and one for the Y scores paired with $X = 1$. These two curves have the same standard deviation $\sigma_y\sqrt{1 - \rho^2_{pb}}$, where ρ_{pb} is the point biserial coefficient for the population. The mean for the Y scores paired with $X = 0$ is $\mu_0 = \mu_y + \rho_{pb}\dfrac{\sigma_y}{\sigma_x}(0 - \overline{X})$ and the mean of Y scores paired with $X = 1$ is $\mu_1 = \mu_y + \rho_{pb}\dfrac{\sigma_y}{\sigma_x}(1 - \overline{X})$.

These are the same assumptions of normality of distribution and homogeneity of variance which were made in Chapter 7 for testing the hypothesis that the means of two populations are equal.

To test the hypothesis that $\rho_{pb} = 0$, the statistic

$$(11.8) \qquad t = \frac{r_{pb}\sqrt{N-2}}{\sqrt{1 - r^2_{pb}}} \text{ may be used as in Chapter 10.}$$

It has "Student's" distribution with $N - 2$ degrees of freedom. If $\rho_{pb} = 0$, then $\mu_1 = \mu_0 = \mu_y$, and the test that $\rho_{pb} = 0$ is also the test that the two normal distributions have the same mean. If any of the formulas for r_{pb} is substituted in (11.8) the latter can be reduced identically to the familiar formula first presented in Chapter 7 for comparing the means of two independent populations with equal variance:

$$(11.9) \quad t = \frac{\overline{Y}_1 - \overline{Y}_0}{s_{\overline{Y}_1 - \overline{Y}_0}} = \frac{\overline{Y}_1 - \overline{Y}_0}{\sqrt{\dfrac{\Sigma\Sigma Y^2 - (\Sigma Y_1)^2/N_1 - (\Sigma Y_2)^2/N_2}{N_1 + N_2 - 2} \cdot \dfrac{N_1 + N_0}{N_1 N_0}}}$$

For the correlation obtained for item 3 of Table 11.1, Formula (11.8) would give

$$t = \frac{.673\sqrt{18}}{\sqrt{1 - (.673)^2}} = \frac{2.853}{\sqrt{.5471}} = 3.86$$

while Formula (11.9) would give

$$t = \frac{47.0 - 42.2}{\sqrt{\dfrac{37862 - (235)^2/5 - (633)^2/15}{18} \cdot \dfrac{20}{5 \times 15}}} = \frac{4.8}{\sqrt{1.546}} = 3.86$$

Confidence limits for ρ_{pb} can be obtained by an application of the *non-central t* distribution. This is the distribution of t when the mean of t, $E(t)$, is not equal to zero. "Student's" distribution may be regarded as *central* since it is the distribution of t when

$E(t) = 0$. Applications of non-central t including tables for its use have been given by Johnson and Welch (see reference 7).

When $\rho_{pb} = 0$ the mean of $t = \frac{r_{pb}\sqrt{N-2}}{\sqrt{1-r^2_{pb}}}$ is zero, hence t has "Student's" distribution. When $\rho_{pb} \neq 0$ the mean of $t = \frac{r_{pb}\sqrt{N-2}}{\sqrt{1-r^2_{pb}}}$ is not zero but depends on ρ_{pb}, hence the distribution is non-central. For each value of ρ_{pb}, t has a separate distribution. If a value of r has been observed the set of non-central distributions make possible the calculation of confidence limits. (For a fuller discussion, see reference 12.)

When the Johnson-Welch tables are not available, and when N is not less than 20, an approximation using tables of normal probability will give fairly satisfactory results. Suppose an interval with confidence coefficient $1 - \alpha$ is sought.

First compute $$t = \frac{r_{pb}\sqrt{N-2}}{\sqrt{1-r^2_{pb}}}.$$

Then compute

(11.10) $$d_1 = t + z_{\frac{1}{2}\alpha}\sqrt{\frac{t^2}{2N-4}+1}$$

(11.11) and $$d_2 = t + z_{1-\frac{1}{2}\alpha}\sqrt{\frac{t^2}{2N-4}+1}$$

Then the required interval is

(11.12) $$\frac{d_1}{\sqrt{N+d_1^2}} < \rho_{pb} < \frac{d_2}{\sqrt{N+d_2^2}}$$

The reader should be warned that the approximation becomes inaccurate if confidence coefficients of less than .95 are used. However the Johnson-Welch tables make it possible to obtain confidence intervals at a variety of levels.

From the point biserial correlation of $-.13$ obtained for 308 student nurses, previously described, we shall now make an interval estimate for ρ_{pb}.

$$t = \frac{-.13\sqrt{306}}{\sqrt{1-(.13)^2}} = -2.29$$

Since t has "Student's" distribution with 306 degrees of freedom when $\rho_{pb} = 0$, it is clear that the hypothesis $\rho_{pb} = 0$ may be rejected.

To calculate confidence limits with $1 - \alpha = .95$ we have

$$d_1 = -2.29 - 1.96\sqrt{1 + \frac{(-2.29)^2}{612}} = -4.26$$

$$d_2 = -2.29 + 1.96\sqrt{1 + \frac{(-2.29)^2}{612}} = -.32$$

Then
$$\frac{-4.26}{\sqrt{308 + (-4.26)^2}} < \rho_{pb} < \frac{-.32}{\sqrt{308 + (-.32)^2}}$$

or
$$-.236 < \rho_{pb} < -.018$$

The Biserial Coefficient of Correlation. A different approach to biserial correlation was made by Karl Pearson (reference 15). His method depends on the assumption that the dichotomous variable is actually continuous. Call this variable X and assume further with Pearson that the distribution of X is unit normal, that the regression of the continuous variable Y, on X is linear and that for each X the variance of Y is the same as for every other X. A further assumption will be made below that the joint distribution of X and Y is normal bivariate.

Suppose that in the dichotomous variable a proportion p of the cases in the sample are in one class, and a proportion $q = 1 - p$ are in the other. The corresponding situation on the continuous variable X is represented by locating a point A on the X scale such that an ordinate drawn at A divides the hypothetical normal distribution of the dichotomous variable into two areas with proportions p and q. We suppose that each individual in the sample has a value on the X scale, but that the only information available about an X value is that it is greater than or less than A.

To illustrate this situation, suppose that we wish to compute the relationship between response to an objective test item and the total score on the test. For each person we know whether he answered the item correctly or incorrectly, and know his total test score. Under the assumptions made above, the person's actual knowledge about the subject matter tested by the item has some value on the scale of the continuous variable X, but the only information available about his knowledge is that it exceeds, or is less than, the value of X at some point A on the X scale. That point can be determined by the proportion of persons who answer the item correctly and the tables of the normal curve. In actual practice the score corresponding to A is not needed, as will be shown in the following discussion.

In practice, we find the coordinates of two points on the line of regression of Y on X and use this information to estimate the correlation between the variables. One of these points has coordinates $\overline{X}_1$ and $\overline{Y}_1$, which are the means for the two variables of those persons who answered the item incorrectly. Let q be the proportion and qN the number of such persons. Then q is represented by the area under the normal curve to the left of A. The X mean of that part of the normal distribution is given by the formula

$$\overline{X}_1 = \frac{u}{q} \tag{11.13}$$

where u is the ordinate * of the unit normal probability curve at the point A. This ordinate can be read from Table III if the table is entered with the area between ordinates A and at the mean. The value of $\overline{Y}_1$ is computed directly from the Y scores of the qN persons in this subgroup.

The second point has coordinates $\overline{X}_2$ and $\overline{Y}_2$. $\overline{X}_2$ is the mean of that portion of the unit normal curve to the right of A. This portion has area p and mean

$$\overline{X}_2 = \frac{u}{p} \tag{11.14}$$

The value of $\overline{Y}_2$ is computed directly from the scores of the pN persons who answered the item correctly.

The two points which determine the regression line are therefore the points $\left(-\frac{u}{q}, \overline{Y}_1\right)$ and $\left(\frac{u}{p}, \overline{Y}_2\right)$. The line passing through these two points is the regression line and its slope is

$$b_{bis} = \frac{\overline{Y}_2 - \overline{Y}_1}{\frac{u}{p} - \left(-\frac{u}{q}\right)} = (\overline{Y}_2 - \overline{Y}_1)\frac{pq}{u} \tag{11.15}$$

The slope of the regression line is also given by the expression

$$b_{bis} = r_{bis}\frac{s_y}{s_x} \tag{11.16}$$

Since the distribution of X has been taken to be unit normal $s_x = 1$ and so $b_{bis} = r_{bis}s_y$. Equating the two expressions for the slope we have

$$(\overline{Y}_2 - \overline{Y}_1)\frac{pq}{u} = r_{bis}s_y$$

* Most texts use the letter z for this ordinate, but we have already used z to represent an abscissa of a normal curve.

Therefore we have the formula

$$(11.17) \qquad r_{bis} = \frac{\overline{Y}_2 - \overline{Y}_1}{s_y} \cdot \frac{pq}{u}$$

Under the assumption that the joint distribution of X and Y is normal bivariate r_{bis} is an estimate of ρ. It can be regarded as an appropriate estimate only when the sample is large.

We can also write r_{bis} in the form

$$(11.18) \qquad r_{bis} = \frac{\overline{Y}_1 - \overline{Y}}{s_y} \cdot \frac{p}{u} = \frac{\overline{Y} - \overline{Y}_2}{s_y} \cdot \frac{q}{u}$$

For item 3 of Table 11.1, $p = .25$ and $u = .3177$

$$r_{bis} = \frac{47.0 - 42.2}{3.17} \cdot \frac{(.25)(.75)}{.3177} = .89$$

An interesting — and disconcerting — aspect of biserial r is that its value may be numerically larger than 1. In fact, the range of its values is unbounded in either direction.

Sampling Theory of the Biserial Correlation Coefficient. The exact sampling distribution for r_{bis} is not known. Karl Pearson derived a formula for its standard error, but that formula involves the unknown parameter ρ and substitution of r_{bis} for ρ is not satisfactory.

An extensive study of biserial coefficients has recently been completed by R. F. Tate.[19] One valuable outcome of his study is a transformation for r_{bis} similar in purpose to Fisher's logarithmic transformation of r to z in Table XII. When the dichotomous cut is so made that in the population $P = Q = 0.5$ (approximately) and when N is large, and r_{bis} is not close to -1 or $+1$, Tate shows that a quantity z^* (read "z star") has a normal distribution with standard error

$$(11.19) \qquad \sigma_{z^*} = \frac{1}{\sqrt{N}}$$

The relation of z^* to r_{bis} is

$$(11.20) \quad z^* = 1.0297\{\log_{10}(1 + .8944r_{bis}) - \log_{10}(1 - .8944r_{bis})\}$$

The corresponding formula for the population is

$$(11.21) \quad \zeta^* = 1.0297\{\log_{10}(1 + .8944\rho) - \log_{10}(1 - .8944\rho)\}$$

Table XII giving the transformation of r to z may be used instead of making the direct computation from logarithms. To utilize this table we use the following transformations:

(11.22) $$r = .8944r_{bis} \text{ or } r_{bis} = 1.118r$$

(11.23) $$z = \tfrac{1}{2}\{\log_e(1+r) - \log_e(1-r)\}$$

(11.24) $$z^* = .8944z \text{ or } z = 1.118z^*$$

Procedure for obtaining an interval estimate for ρ from r_{bis}:

(1) Multiply r_{bis} by .8944.
(2) Read z corresponding to $.8944r_{bis}$ from the table.
(3) Multiply this value by .8944 to obtain z^*.
(4) Make whatever test of hypothesis or interval estimate is required for ζ^*.
(5) If an interval estimate has been made for ζ^* and the corresponding interval is required for ρ, multiply the upper and lower limits of the obtained interval by .8944 for values with which to reenter the table.
(6) Using the values obtained in step (5) read the corresponding values of r from the table.
(7) Multiply these values of r by 1.118 to obtain the limits for ρ.

Example. Given $r_{bis} = .72$ when $N_2 = 163$ and $N_1 = 185$. Find an interval estimate for ρ with .95 confidence coefficient. Since

$$p = 185/348 = .5316,$$

it may be assumed that P is near enough to 0.5 to justify using the method.

(1) $.8944r_{bis} = .6440$
(2) If $r = .6440$, $z = .765$
(3) $z^* = .8944(.765) = .684$
(4) $\sigma_{z^*} = 1/\sqrt{348} = .0536$
$.684 - 1.96(.0536) < \zeta^* < .684 + 1.96(.0536)$
$.579 < \zeta^* < .789$
(5) $1.118(.579) = .647$
$1.118(.789) = .882$
(6) If $z = .647$, $r = .570$
If $z = .882$, $r = .707$
(7) $1.118(.570) = .637$
$1.118(.707) = .790$
Then $.637 < \rho < .790$

Another aspect of the statistic r_{bis} which Tate investigated is its *efficiency* or the degree to which r_{bis} approximates ρ. The approximation is good when $\rho = 0$ and increasingly poorer as it approaches -1 or $+1$. The approximation is good when $P = .5$ and increasingly poorer as P is removed from 0.5.

Comparison of Biserial (r_{bis}) and Point (r_{pb}) Coefficients. The following general comment is taken from Tate[19]: "It would seem from the evidence presented that point biserial r is in most cases the better coefficient to use." The two coefficients may now be compared on several points.

a. The statistical model. For r_{bis} a normal bivariate universe is assumed. If this is the case, then the distribution of Y cannot be normal within the separate categories. For r_{pb} no assumption is made as to the distribution of the dichotomous variable, but generalization is made only to a universe of samples of size N having the same fixed number of cases N_0 and N_1 in the dichotomous categories. For r_{pb} it is assumed that Y is normally distributed within each X category and that the two Y distributions have the same variance. The validity of this assumption can be ascertained by testing the two distributions for equality of variance and testing, possibly only by inspection, the normality of each distribution.

b. Range of values of r. For point biserial the range is from -1 to $+1$. For biserial r the range is unlimited.

c. Sampling distribution and tests of significance. The exact sampling distribution of biserial r is unknown and significance can be tested only if the transformation to z^* can be made. This is defensible only when P is near 0.5, N is large and ρ_{bis} is not near 1 or -1. The exact sampling distribution of point biserial is known and tests of significance and confidence intervals can be obtained for any value of ρ and any size of N.

d. Use with other r's in a regression equation. For biserial r such use is very dubious, for point biserial legitimate.

e. Position of dichotomous cut. For either coefficient, better results are obtained when $N_0 = N_1$ than when they differ in size.

Fourfold Correlation. A measure of relationship may be needed in a problem where *both traits* are scored dichotomously. The chi-square test may be used in this situation to test for complete lack of relationship between the two traits, as was done in Chapter 4. However when the chi-square test indicates a significant relationship it does not itself provide a measure of the strength of that relationship.

In Spaney's study of the prediction of success of students in schools of nursing,[17] students entering a school of nursing were asked to mark items in a personality inventory and their responses were studied in relation to their subsequent completion of the course or withdrawal before the end of the course. Responses to the item "Do you like performing on the radio" may be used as an illustration.

	Withdrawing	Not withdrawing	Total
Some liking for performing on radio	29	126	155
No liking for performing on radio	9	15	24
Total	38	141	179

$\chi^2 = 4.38$ $\sqrt{\chi^2} = 2.09$

The chi-square test indicates that at the .05 level we must reject the hypothesis of independence between liking for performing on the radio and remaining in a school of nursing. If then the traits are not to be assumed independent, how strong is the relationship between them?

Two methods of correlating dichotomously scored traits will be discussed. These methods are parallel to the two biserial coefficients.

The Phi Coefficient. As for the dichotomous trait in the point biserial coefficient, arbitrary values may be assigned to the two categories into which the X-scale is divided and also to the two categories into which the Y-scale is divided. For this purpose any numbers whatever may be used and the final outcome will be the same, but the work is minimized by using 0 and 1, as was done for the point biserial r. Let a, b, c and d represent frequencies, as in the formula for chi-square. The application of

	0	1	
1	b	a	$a+b$
0	d	c	$c+d$
	$b+d$	$a+c$	

the product moment formula gives the correlation between the two traits as

$$\phi = \frac{ad - bc}{\sqrt{(a+b)(c+d)(a+c)(b+d)}} \tag{11.25}$$

Thus for the Spaney data, $\phi = .157$.

$$\chi^2 = N\phi^2 \tag{11.26}$$

where χ^2 is the statistic already given by Formula (4.7). Hence the significance of ϕ is tested by referring $N\phi^2$ to a chi-square table with 1 degree of freedom or by referring $\sqrt{N\phi^2} = \phi\sqrt{N}$ to a table of normal probability. In other words, if the null hypothesis for χ^2 is justified, the null hypothesis for ϕ is justified and vice versa.

No way of finding confidence limits for ϕ is known.

Yates' correction should be applied to the numerator of ϕ whenever it is needed for the numerator of χ^2.

In order to have the positive value of ϕ indicate a positive relationship, the table should be so set up that a and d represent the frequencies of individuals who possess both traits or neither trait while b and c represent the frequencies of individuals who possess one trait and not the other. (If a and d are used to represent frequencies of individuals possessing one trait and not the other, then the numerator of ϕ should be written $bc - ad$.)

The ϕ coefficient is a product moment correlation.

In making item analyses it is often convenient to divide the criterion group into two equal parts, so that $a + c = b + d = \frac{1}{2}N$. This arrangement reduces the formula for χ^2 and for ϕ to very simple special formulas which permit considerable saving of time when each of many dichotomous items is to be related to the same dichotomous criterion. Under these circumstances

$$(11.27) \qquad \phi = \frac{a - b}{\sqrt{(a + b)(c + d)}} = \frac{d - c}{\sqrt{(a + b)(c + d)}}$$

$$(11.28) \text{ and } \chi^2 = \frac{N(a - b)^2}{(a + b)(c + d)} = \frac{N(d - c)^2}{(a + b)(c + d)}$$

where $c + d$ is the number of individuals failing the item, $a + b$ is the number passing the item, a is the number in the upper criterion group who pass the item and b is the number in the lower criterion group who pass the item, d is the number in the lower criterion group who fail the item, and c is the number in the upper criterion groups who fail the item.

Tetrachoric Correlation. This coefficient is developed on the assumption that both variables are continuous and that the joint distribution of the variables is normal bivariate. From this point of view the fourfold may be regarded as a scatter diagram divided into four quadrants by lines parallel to the coordinate axes. The specific X and Y values of the observations are unknown, all that is known is the frequency, or number of observations, in each of the four quadrants. From these frequencies the value of ρ in the normal bivariate population is estimated.

In his original paper on the tetrachoric coefficient of correlation Karl Pearson[14] derived some extremely complex formulas for computation of this coefficient. These formulas will not be reproduced here. However, some approximations also derived by Pearson will be presented.

When both variables are split approximately at the median, that is when $a + b = c + d$ and $a + c = b + d$ approximately, then r_t the tetrachoric coefficient is given approximately by the formula

$$r_t = \sin\left\{90° \cdot \frac{(a + d - b - c)}{N}\right\} \tag{11.29}$$

Formula (11.29) is exact when the relations $a + b = c + d$ and $a + c = b + d$ hold exactly.

Under other circumstances an approximation to r_t is obtainable from the formula

$$r_t = \cos\left\{180° \cdot \frac{\sqrt{bc}}{\sqrt{ad} + \sqrt{bc}}\right\} \tag{11.30}$$

A series of very useful diagrams from which the value of tetrachoric r could be read by graphical interpolation were published by Chesire, Saffir and Thurstone but are now out of print.

Comparison of Phi and Tetrachoric *r*. Since phi and tetrachoric r are both used to compute relationships in a fourfold, or doubly dichotomous, distribution some discussion of the relative merits of the two methods is called for.

The phi coefficient is preferred:

1. Because phi can easily be computed for all distributions. Tetrachoric r has meaning only for large samples. It is difficult to compute r_t when one of the marginal proportions such as $\frac{a + b}{N}$ is small.

2. Because the phi coefficient readily provides a test for the hypothesis of independence through χ^2. Use of r_t for this purpose presents almost insurmountable difficulties.

3. When the traits are logically dichotomous rather than continuous.

The tetrachoric coefficient is preferred:

1. When the traits involved in the relationship may logically be assumed to be continuous.

2. Because tetrachoric r provides an estimate of ρ. Phi is not an estimate of a parameter.

3. Because tetrachoric r ranges from -1 to $+1$ regardless of the marginal frequencies. On the other hand, the values of phi are restricted by the marginal frequencies. Consider, for example, the fourfold distribution with marginal frequencies 100, 100, 160, 40. For this fourfold, r_t can take values from -1 to $+1$, whereas phi is restricted to the range $-\frac{1}{2}$ to $+\frac{1}{2}$. A situation such as that indicated in the fourfold may arise in correlating responses to an item with test scores using high-low halves. The range of phi is always restricted when the ratio of marginal frequencies for one variable differs from this ratio in the other variable.

Estimating Correlation from the Tails of the Distribution. A time-saving method devised by Flanagan [4] is useful for estimating relationship when one variable is dichotomous and the other continuous. Such a situation arises in correlating a test item with scores on a test. The scores on the test are arranged in order of size and the upper and lower 27% are selected for further computation. The middle 46% are put aside. From the proportion of correct responses in each of the high and low 27% groups a measure of relationship is obtained.

The coefficient calculated in this way is an estimate of ρ in a bivariate normal population. The dichotomous trait is assumed to be actually continuous. However, the only information available is that given by the frequencies in the four corners of the hypothetical scatter diagram. The estimate of ρ obtained in this way has been shown by Kelley [9] and by Mosteller,[13] to be more efficient than tetrachoric r, at least when ρ is zero. Though biserial r can be used in this situation Flanagan's method is very much faster.

Table XIII (prepared by Flanagan) provides a ready means of computing the correlation coefficient when the percentages in the upper and lower 27% groups are known. In analyzing test items it is convenient, when possible, to select a sample of $N = 370$ cases because 27% of 370 = 100. The upper 100 and lower 100 of the papers in the sample are then used for further computation. For each item the per cents correct in the two selected groups are used for estimation of ρ.

In Chapter 16 a method analogous to the one just described is used for estimating ρ when both variables are continuous. Though this method is less efficient than product moment r it is much faster to use; so it is sometimes advisable to use a larger sample and an inefficient method of estimation.

The Correlation Ratio. The correlation ratio is a measure of relationship which is useful in two circumstances:

1. When both variables are continuous but the regression is not linear. This situation is illustrated in the relationship between age and IQ in Table 11.2, page 279.

2. When one variable is continuous and the other is discrete. Problems of this sort were considered in Chapter 9 under the heading of analysis of variance.

The development of a formula for the correlation ratio is similar to its development for the product moment coefficient r in Chapter 10. By simple algebra the following relationship can be derived from Formula (10.4)

$$(11.31) \qquad r^2 = 1 - \frac{\Sigma(Y - \tilde{Y})^2}{(N-1)s_y^{\,2}} = 1 - \frac{\Sigma(Y - \tilde{Y})^2}{\Sigma(Y - \overline{Y})^2}$$

In this formula $\tilde{Y}$ is given by a linear regression equation. When linear regression cannot be assumed the estimate $\tilde{Y}$ is no longer applicable. Instead, the mean of a column of the scatter diagram is the best estimate of the scores in that column. Call the mean of the jth column $\overline{Y}_j$ and replace $\tilde{Y}$ in Formula (11.31) by $\overline{Y}_j$. Designating the *correlation ratio* of Y on X by E_{yx}, we then obtain the formula

$$(11.32) \qquad E^2{}_{yx} = 1 - \frac{\sum_{j=1}^{k}\sum_{\alpha=1}^{Nj}(Y_{j\alpha} - \overline{Y}_j)^2}{\sum_{j=1}^{k}\sum_{\alpha=1}^{Nj}(Y_{j\alpha} - \overline{Y})^2}$$

If both variables are continuous, there are *two* correlation ratios which in general are not equal. By analogy the correlation ratio of X on Y is E_{xy}, where

$$(11.33) \qquad E^2{}_{xy} = 1 - \frac{\sum_{j=1}^{k}\sum_{\alpha=1}(X_{j\alpha} - \overline{X}_j)^2}{\sum_{j=1}^{k}\sum_{\alpha=1}^{Nj}(X_{j\alpha} - \overline{X})^2}$$

Here $\overline{X}_j$ is the mean of the jth row, and k is the number of rows, which is not necessarily the same as the number of columns.

From the definition of the correlation ratio the following characteristics of this coefficient can be determined.

1. If the means of all columns are equal to each other, and therefore to the general mean, $E^2{}_{yx} = 1 - 1 = 0$.

2. If the means differ greatly from each other and the observations within a column are very close to the mean of the column E^2_{yx} is close to one.

3. The square root of E^2_{yx} is always taken positively, therefore E_{yx} ranges from zero to one.

An alternative formula for E^2_{yx} is obtainable through the subdivision of sum of squares as in analysis of variance.

$$(11.34) \quad \sum_{j=1}^{k} \sum_{\alpha=1}^{Nj} (Y_{j\alpha} - \overline{Y})^2 = \sum_{j=1}^{k} \sum_{\alpha=1}^{Nj} (Y_{j\alpha} - \overline{Y}_j)^2 + \sum_{j=1}^{k} N_j(\overline{Y}_j - \overline{Y})^2$$

Appropriate substitution in Formula (11.32) leads to the formula for E^2_{yx}

$$(11.35) \qquad E^2_{yx} = \frac{\Sigma N_j(\overline{Y}_j - \overline{Y})^2}{(N-1)s_y^2} = \frac{\Sigma N_j(\overline{Y}_j - \overline{Y})^2}{\Sigma\Sigma(Y_{j\alpha} - \overline{Y})^2}$$

From Formula (11.35) it can be seen that E^2_{yx} is the ratio which the sum of squares of column means around the total mean bears to the total sum of squares of scores around the total mean. A convenient formula for computing E^2_{yx} is

$$(11.36) \qquad E^2_{yx} = \frac{\sum_{j=1}^{k} \frac{T_j^2}{N_j} - \frac{T_y^2}{N}}{(N-1)s_y^2}$$

where $\quad T_j = \sum_{\alpha=1}^{Nj} Y_{j\alpha}$ and $T_y = \sum_{j=1}^{k} T_j$

If data are grouped in the form of a scatter diagram and scores are coded, Formula (11.35) is modified by use of the following notation:

N_{ij} is the frequency in a cell in the ith row and jth column.

N_i is the total frequency in the ith row.

N_j is the total frequency in the jth column.

N is the total number of cases in the sample.

x' and y' are coded X and Y scores as explained in Chapter 10.

$T_i' = \sum_{j=1}^{k} N_{ij}x_j'$ is the sum of x' scores in the ith row, each multiplied by its appropriate frequency.

$T_j' = \sum_{i=1}^{h} N_{ij}y_i'$ is the sum of the y' scores in the jth column, each multiplied by the appropriate frequency, and h is the number of rows.

$$T_x' = \Sigma T_i' \qquad T_y' = \Sigma T_j'$$

Then we have the following formulas

$$(11.37) \qquad E^2_{yx} = \frac{\Sigma \dfrac{(T_j')^2}{N_j} - \dfrac{(T_y')^2}{N}}{\Sigma N_i(y_i')^2 - \dfrac{(T_y')^2}{N}}$$

and

$$(11.38) \qquad E^2_{xy} = \frac{\Sigma \dfrac{(T_i')^2}{N_i} - \dfrac{(T_x')^2}{N}}{\Sigma N_j(x_j')^2 - \dfrac{(T_x')^2}{N}}$$

Computation of E^2_{xy} is illustrated in Table 11.2 which shows the joint frequency distribution for age and intelligence quotient of 109 pupils in a fourth grade. The arbitrary origin for age has been placed at 96 months, with step intervals of 5 months. The arbitrary origin for intelligence quotient has been placed at 66 with step interval of 7.

The population values of the correlation ratios are indicated by the symbols η_{yx} and η_{xy}. (η is the small Greek letter eta.) A test for the hypothesis $\eta_{yx} = 0$ is given by the F ratio

$$(11.39) \qquad F = \frac{E^2_{yx}}{1 - E^2_{yx}} \cdot \frac{N - k}{k - 1}$$

with $n_1 = k - 1$ and $n_2 = N - k$ degrees of freedom. This is identical with the F test for the hypothesis $\mu_1 = \mu_2 = \cdots = \mu_k$ described in Chapter 9. This is logical, for $\eta_{yx} = 0$ if the column means are equal in the population.

The test for linearity of regression is the test that $\eta_{yx} = \rho$ and is made by computing the ratio

$$(11.40) \qquad F = \frac{E^2_{yx} - r^2}{1 - E^2_{yx}} \cdot \frac{N - k}{k - 2}$$

with degrees of freedom $n_1 = k - 2$ and $n_2 = N - k$. This test is derived from the analysis of the total variance into three independent components shown as follows together with the degrees of freedom.

$$(11.41) \qquad \begin{aligned} s_y^2 &= r^2 s_y^2 + (E^2_{yx} - r^2)s_y^2 + (1 - E^2_{yx})s_y^2 \\ N - 1 &= 1 \quad + (k - 1 - 1) \quad + (N - k) \end{aligned}$$

Rearranging the order of columns has no effect on E_{yx}, but of course may change r strikingly. Similarly rearranging the order of rows has no effect on E_{xy}.

Correlation Among Ranks. There are two situations in which it may be expedient to work with ranks rather than scores and to

TABLE 11.2 Computation of the Correlation Ratio of Age on Intelligence Quotient for 109 Fourth Grade Children

Age to Nearest Month

Intelligence Quotient	94–98	99–103	104–108	109–113	114–118	119–123	124–128	129–133	134–138	139–143	144–148	149–153	154–158	N_i	y'	T_i'	$(T_i')^2/N_i$
147–153		1												1	12	1	1.00
140–146			3	1										4	11	9	20.25
133–139			2	2										4	10	10	25.00
126–132		1	4	4	1									10	9	25	62.50
119–125	2	1	4	7	6									20	8	54	145.80
112–118		1	4	5	5	1								16	7	49	150.06
105–111			3	5	6		1							15	6	51	173.40
98–104				3	5	4	1	2						15	5	69	317.40
91– 97			1	2	2	1	1	1	1					9	4	42	196.00
84– 90				1	1	2		1						5	3	24	115.20
77– 83				1			3	1		1				6	2	37	228.17
70– 76													1	1	1	12	144.00
63– 69										1	1	1		3	0	30	300.00
N_j	2	4	21	31	26	8	6	5	1	2	1	1	1	109		413	1878.78
x'	0	1	2	3	4	5	6	7	8	9	10	11	12				
$N_j x'$	0	4	42	93	104	40	36	35	8	18	10	11	12	413			
$N_j(x')^2$	0	4	84	279	416	200	216	245	64	162	100	121	144	2035			

$$E^2_{xy} = \frac{1878.78 - \dfrac{(413)^2}{109}}{2035 - \dfrac{(413)^2}{109}} = \frac{(1878.78)(109) - (413)^2}{(2035)(109) - (413)^2} = .668$$

$$E_{xy} = \sqrt{.668} = .817$$

$$r_{xy} = -\ .723$$

seek a measure of relationship among ranks. The first situation arises when there is no satisfactory device for scoring the trait in question but the individuals can be placed in a rank order in respect to the degree of the trait they exhibit. In this situation it is possible to say for any two individuals which one is higher on the scale for this trait but not possible to say how much higher. The reader will readily think of many situations of this kind, as e.g. the attempt to place in order of merit the performances of a number of contestants for an award in an area where the criteria cannot easily be reduced to quantitative terms, or to place individuals in order in respect to their possession of some intangible such as, "attractiveness," "sense of responsibility," "courtesy," and the like. If the group is large, determining the order of individuals becomes very difficult, so the rank order correlation is obviously more useful for small samples.

A second situation arises when traits which can be measured on a scale are recorded as ranks instead. The chief occasion for doing this is when the distribution of scores is obviously not normal and a measure of relationship is sought which does not depend for its validity upon the assumption of a normal bivariate universe. The advantage of the rank order correlation coefficient in this situation is worthy of considerable attention.

Nearly all the tests of significance commonly used are derived on the assumption that sampling is from a normal universe. In the case of the mean, those tests are still valid even when the universe is far from normal for the distribution of the mean rapidly becomes normal as N increases (except for a very special case which the theoretical statistician likes to talk about but which is not at all likely to be encountered in practice). The sampling distribution of the variance and of the correlation coefficient are seriously disturbed by lack of normality. If a population is bivariate normal, the standard error of r is $\sigma_r = \dfrac{1 - \rho^2}{\sqrt{N}}$ but if it is not bivariate normal that standard error may be quite different, but how much different is usually unknown.

The formula for rank order correlation, given originally by Spearman[18] is

$$R = 1 - \frac{6\Sigma d^2}{N(N^2 - 1)} \tag{11.42}$$

where N is the number of individuals ranked and d is the difference in the ranks assigned to the same individual. In the computation, a useful check is provided by the fact that $\Sigma d = 0$. This formula is derived by applying the usual product moment formula to the ranks (see reference 6).

Suppose 12 cakes submitted in a competition at a country fair have been ranked by two judges with results as shown in Table 11.3. Then

$$R = 1 - \frac{6(40)}{12(144 - 1)} = \frac{123}{143} = .86$$

TABLE 11.3 Computation of Coefficient of Correlation Among Ranks Assigned to 12 Cakes

Cake	Rank Assigned by Judge I	Rank Assigned by Judge II	d	d^2
A	7	6	1	1
B	8	4	4	16
C	2	1	1	1
D	1	3	− 2	4
E	9	11	− 2	4
F	3	2	1	1
G	12	12	0	0
H	11	10	1	1
I	4	5	− 1	1
J	10	9	1	1
K	6	7	− 1	1
L	5	8	− 3	9
			$\Sigma d^2 =$	40

$$R = 1 - \frac{6(40)}{12(143)} = 1 - \frac{20}{143} = \frac{123}{143} = .86$$

Now let the ranks assigned by Judge I be denoted X and those assigned by Judge II be denoted Y. Then

$$\Sigma X = 78 \qquad \Sigma Y = 78$$

$$\Sigma X^2 = 650 \qquad \Sigma Y^2 = 650$$

$$\Sigma x^2 = 650 - \frac{78^2}{12} = 143 \qquad \Sigma y^2 = 650 - \frac{78^2}{12} = 143$$

$$\Sigma XY = 630 \qquad \Sigma xy = 630 - \frac{(78)(78)}{12} = 123$$

and $$r = \frac{123}{\sqrt{(143)(143)}} = \frac{123}{143} = .86$$

This computation illustrated the fact that the rank order coefficient and the product moment coefficient applied to the ranks are identical. However, if scores are transformed to ranks — a procedure which Hotelling calls uniformizing the distribution — the product moment correlation of the ranks (which is the rank order coefficient) is almost certain to be different from the product moment coefficient of the original scores[5, 6].

Test of Significance for Rank Order Coefficient. For very small samples from a bivariate population in which the variables X and Y are uncorrelated so that $\rho_{xy} = 0$, the exact distribution of the rank order coefficient can be obtained by direct enumeration of the number of permutations of the ranks which would produce each possible value of the correlation. The distribution of R is discrete and is bimodal in small samples. A table obtained in this way, giving the probability distribution, not for R, but for Σd^2 has been computed by Kendall[10, 11] with $N \leqq 8$. Obviously, the work of direct enumeration, while possible, becomes very laborious for larger values of N. (For $N = 8$ the number of permutations is $8! = 40320$. For $N = 9$ it would be $9! = 362880$.) Using this table the values of R required for significance at a given level, from samples of a given size, may be computed. Such values are given in Table XVI in the Appendix.

Comparison of the entries in Table XVI with the corresponding entries in Table XI (where $N = n + 1$) shows (at least for these small values of N) that the rank order correlation must be larger than the product moment correlation to achieve the same level of significance.

For larger samples, an approximation is needed. If $\rho = 0$, the standard error is

$$\sigma_R = \frac{1}{\sqrt{N - 1}} \tag{11.43}$$

and the sampling distribution of R approaches the normal form as N increases. If N is as large as 25,

$$z = R\sqrt{N - 1} \tag{11.44}$$

may be safely referred to tables of normal probability. How to deal with samples larger than 8 and smaller than 25 is still a problem. For this situation the coefficient τ mentioned later in the chapter may be used. How to test hypotheses other than $\rho = 0$ is also not known.

Estimation of Product Moment Coefficient from Rank Order Coefficient. The relation between the product moment correlation and the rank order coefficient was derived by Karl Pearson and later confirmed by Hotelling.[5] It is

$$\tilde{r} = 2 \sin \frac{\pi}{6} R \tag{11.45}$$

Then

$$\sigma_{\tilde{r}}^2 = \frac{\pi^2}{9(N - 1)} \tag{11.46}$$

is the variance of $\tilde{r}$. Since the sampling variance of the product moment r is $\sigma_r^2 = \frac{1}{N-1}$, when $\rho = 0$, the variance of $\tilde{r}$ is

$$\sigma_{\tilde{r}}^2 = \frac{\pi^2}{9}\sigma_r^2 = 1.097\sigma_r^2 \tag{11.47}$$

The meaning of this formula is that if in a sample of 100 cases from a normal bivariate population, the product moment coefficient is significant, it will require a sample of 110 cases to achieve the same degree of significance for the rank order coefficient. Hence the rank order coefficient has efficiency $\frac{1}{1.097} = .91$.

Formula (11.45) has often been used to "convert the rank order coefficient to a product moment coefficient." Unfortunately, it cannot perform that magic and its usefulness is somewhat dubious. A continuous variate is really not susceptible to ranking. If scores are available, the procedure of transforming them to ranks, computing the coefficient of rank order correlation, and then applying Formula (11.45) to attempt to estimate what the product moment coefficient might have been had it been computed, has nothing whatever to recommend it. Usually it does not even save time.

Relation Among Ranks Given by Several Judges. Suppose that 8 individuals have been ranked by 4 different judges who may be called P, Q, R, and S as in Table 11.4. A single measure of the

TABLE 11.4 Computation of the Coefficient of Concordance from Ranks Assigned to 8 Subjects by 4 Judges

Subject	Rank Given by				Sum of Ranks	Square	Judges	R
	P	Q	R	S				
A	1	4	3	3	11	121	P, Q	$\frac{34}{42} = .762$
B	2	1	4	1	8	64	P, R	$\frac{30}{42} = .714$
C	3	3	2	6	14	196	P, S	$\frac{31}{42} = .738$
D	4	2	1	2	9	81	Q, R	$\frac{31}{42} = .738$
E	5	5	7	5	22	484	Q, S	$\frac{34}{42} = .810$
F	6	6	5	4	21	441	R, S	$\frac{26}{42} = .610$
G	7	8	6	7	28	784	Sum	$\frac{186}{42} = 4.381$
H	8	7	8	8	31	961	Mean	$\frac{31}{42} = .730$
					144	3132		

$$S = 3132 - \frac{(144)^2}{8} = 540 \qquad W = \frac{12(540)}{16(8)(63)} = \frac{45}{56} = .804$$

$$\overline{R} = \frac{4(\frac{45}{56}) - 1}{3} = \frac{31}{42} = .730$$

general agreement among all four judges is desired. Probably it would occur to most persons that the correlation of each judge with every other judge might be found and the average of all such coefficients taken. This has been done for the four judges of Table 11.4, with results recorded at the right of that table. The mean of the six rank order coefficients is $\overline{R} = .730$. If there are m judges the number of the coefficients which must be computed in order to find $\overline{R}$ is $m(m-1)/2$.

Kendall has proposed a *coefficient of concordance* among rankings and has obtained an approximation to its sampling distribution [10, 11]. This coefficient of concordance has a linear relation to $\overline{R}$.

The steps in the computation of the coefficient of concordance are as follows:

1. Find the sum of the ranks given by the m judges to each subject. In Table 11.4 these sums are in column 6.

2. Verify that the sum of these sums-of-ranks is $mN(N+1)/2$. In Table 11.4 this is $4(8)(9)/2 = 144$.

3. Find the mean of these sums-of-ranks. Here this is 18.

4. Obtain the sum of the squares of the deviations of the m sums-of-rank around their mean and call it S. For the data under consideration, the deviations of the entries in the sixth column from 18 which is their mean, are respectively

$$-7, -10, -4, -9, 4, 3, 10, 13$$

and the sum of the squares of these eight deviations is 540.

Alternatively, $$3132 - \frac{(144)^2}{8} = 540.$$

If agreement among the ranks were perfect, the value of S would be $\frac{m^2N(N^2-1)}{12}$. The student can verify this by writing down a set of ranks, duplicating it several times, and computing S. The measure W is defined as the ratio of the observed S to the value S would have if there were perfect agreement among the several rankings:

$$W = \frac{12S}{m^2N(N^2-1)} \tag{11.48}$$

is the *coefficient of concordance.* It may have values ranging from 0 to 1 but it cannot be negative. For the data under discussion,

$W = \frac{45}{56} = .804$. Then R, the average rank order coefficient among all possible pairings of the judges, is related to W by the formula

$$\bar{R} = \frac{mW - 1}{m - 1} \tag{11.49}$$

For these data $\bar{R} = \dfrac{4(\frac{45}{56}) - 1}{3} = \dfrac{31}{42} = .730$ which agrees perfectly with the value obtained previously as mean of six computed coefficients.

For small values of m (the number of judges) and N (the number of subjects judged) the exact probability distribution of S can be obtained by enumerating all possible permutations of the N ranks for the m judges. Kendall has done this and furnishes a table (page 412 of his Volume I) showing the probability that a given S will be attained or exceeded for $N = 3$ and $m = 2, 3, \ldots 10$. He also gives a table for $N = 4$, $m = 2, 3, 4, 5$, or 6, and for $N = 5$, $m = 3$. For larger values of N and m the F test may be used:

$$F = \frac{(m - 1)W}{1 - W} \tag{11.50}$$

with degrees of freedom $n_1 = N - 1 - \dfrac{2}{m}$

and $$n_2 = (m - 1)\left(N - 1 - \frac{2}{m}\right)$$

If N and m are small, the correction for continuity should be made by subtracting 1 from S and increasing the divisor of W by 2, so that

$$W' = \frac{S - 1}{\dfrac{m^2N(N^2 - 1)}{12} + 2} = \frac{12(S - 1)}{m^2N(N^2 - 1) + 24} \tag{11.51}$$

For the data of Table 11.5, the test of significance would be

$$W' = \frac{12(540 - 1)}{16(8)(63) + 24} = .7997$$

and $$F = \frac{3W'}{1 - W'} = 11.97 \text{ has } n_1 = 6\tfrac{1}{2},\ n_2 = 19.5$$

Reference to the F table for $n_1 = 6$, or $n_1 = 7$ and $n_2 = 19$ or $n_2 = 20$ shows that the largest of the values in the four cells indicated is $F_{.99} = 3.94$. The observed F is even larger than that value so that interpolation is needless. There can be no hesitancy in stating that the four sets of ranks show agreement far beyond what might be produced by sampling variance.

For such data what is the "best estimate" of the "true ranking"? These data have shown a significant concordance. Let it be assumed that the relations among the rankings reflect the true ranking, which of course may not be the case. Then the ranking of the sum of the ranks is the "best" ranking in the least square sense (see page 421 of reference 10). For the data considered, this would make the "best ranking" *B, D, A, C, F, E, G, H*. If the data had not shown significant concordance among the various rankings, then no composite ranking could be considered meaningful.

The Tau Coefficient. Kendall (see references 10 and 11) has proposed a coefficient called τ (tau) which provides an alternative method of measuring relationship between ranks. While not quite so simple to compute as Spearman's coefficient of Formula (11.42), τ has the great advantage that its sampling distribution is known, especially in that area for moderate sized values of N larger than 10 and too small for use of the normal approximation, where there is no very good method of testing the rank order coefficient. This measure will not be described here because to test its significance the tables Kendall has computed are needed, when N is small.

Relation Between Two Traits Expressed in Qualitative Categories. The *existence* of relation can be tested by the chi-square test, but its *measurement* is not always possible without additional assumptions. The case in which there are just two categories for each trait has been discussed in an earlier section of this chapter. If for each trait the qualitative categories can be placed in a meaningful order, it may be possible to assign numerical scores to the categories and compute a product moment correlation with these scores. One assumption which might be used to obtain such scores if it appears reasonable is that the various categories are spaced at equal intervals along a scale, so that the numbers 0, 1, 2, 3, 4, . . . may be assigned to the categories. Another is that each trait has a normal distribution. Ranks may then be normalized as described in Chapter 17.

If the categories for either variable do not have a meaningful order there is no satisfactory way of measuring relationship, although χ^2 can be computed to test the hypothesis that no relationship exists. If the categories for both variables can be arranged in meaningful order and if χ^2 is large, so that the hypothesis of independence of the two variables is rejected, the research worker is likely to feel an intense need of some measure of relationship. For this situation Karl Pearson [14] proposed the coefficient of contingency

$$C = \sqrt{\frac{\chi^2}{\chi^2 + N}}.$$

This is not a very satisfactory measure of relationship but under the circumstances no better measure is available. If $\chi^2 = 0$, then $C = 0$, but that situation very seldom occurs. C cannot be negative. Its maximum value for a table of k rows and k columns is $\sqrt{\frac{k-1}{k}}$. Imagine 200 cases distributed in 4 rows and 4 columns with 50 cases in each diagonal cell and all other cells empty. The 200 scores could not be distributed in a way to indicate higher relationship. For this table

$$\chi^2 = 600 \text{ and } C = \sqrt{\frac{600}{600 + 200}} = \sqrt{\frac{3}{4}} = .87 \text{ not } 1.00$$

REFERENCES

1. DuBois, Philip H., "A Note on the Computation of Biserial r in Item Validation," *Psychometrika*, 7 (June 1942), 143–147.
2. Dunlap, Jack W., "Note on the Computation of Tetrachoric Correlation," *Psychometrika*, 5 (June 1940), 137–140.
3. Dunlap, Jack W., "Note on Computation of Biserial Correlations in Item Evaluation," (Including Table of p and p/z, basic data sheet, and nomograph), *Psychometrika*, 1 (June 1936), 51–60.
4. Flanagan, John C., "General Considerations in the Selection of Test Items and a Short Method of Estimating the Product-Moment Coefficient from the Tails of the Distribution," *Journal of Educational Psychology*, 30 (1939), 674–680.
5. Hotelling, Harold and Pabst, Margaret Richards, "Rank Correlation and Tests of Significance Involving no Assumption of Normality," *The Annals of Mathematical Statistics*, 7 (March 1936), 29–43.
6. Jackson, Dunham, "The Algebra of Correlation," *The American Mathematical Monthly*, 31 (March 1924), 110–121.
7. Johnson, N. L. and Welch, B. L., "Applications of the Non-Central t-Distribution," *Biometrika*, 31 (1940), 362.
8. Kelley, Truman L., *Fundamentals of Statistics*, Cambridge, 1947, Harvard University Press. (See Index for references to many topics treated in this chapter.)
9. Kelley, Truman L., "The Selection of Upper and Lower Groups for the Validation of Test Items," *Journal of Educational Psychology*, 30 (1939), 17–24.
10. Kendall, Maurice G., *The Advanced Theory of Statistics*. Vol. I. Philadelphia, 1943, J. B. Lippincott Company.
11. Kendall, Maurice G., *Rank Correlation Methods*, London, 1948, Charles Griffin and Company, Ltd.

12. Lev, Joseph, "The Point Biserial Coefficient of Correlation," *Annals of Mathematical Statistics*, 20 (1949), 125–126.
13. Mosteller, Frederick, "On Some Useful Inefficient Statistics," *Annals of Mathematical Statistics*, 17 (1946), 377–408.
14. Pearson, Karl, "On the Correlation of Characters Not Quantitatively Measurable," *Philosophical Transactions*, Series A, Vol. 195, (1901) 1–47.
15. Pearson, Karl, "On a New Method for Determining the Correlation Between a Measured Character A and a Character B, of Which only the Percentage of Cases wherein B Exceeds (or falls short of) a Given Intensity is Recorded for Each Grade of A," *Biometrika*, 7 (1909), 96–105.
16. Pitman, E. J. G., "Significance Tests which may be Applied to Samples from any Populations, Part II, The Correlation Coefficient Test," *Journal of the Royal Statistical Society*, Supplement 4, 255.
17. Spaney, Emma, "Personality Tests and the Selection of Nurses," *Nursing Research*, 1 (Feb. 1953) 4–26. (Data used here were taken from the original manuscript of which this paper is an abridgement.)
18. Spearman, Charles, "The Proof and Measurement of Association Between Two Things," *American Journal of Psychology*, 15 (1904), 72–101.
19. Tate, R. F., "The Biserial and Point Correlation Coefficients," Institute of Mathematical Statistics, University of North Carolina, Mimeographed Series #14, (for limited distribution). A special report of research under Office of Naval Research Project N R 042031.
20. Wallis, W. A., "The Correlation Ratio for Ranked Data," *Journal of the American Statistical Association*, 34 (1939), 533–538.

12 The Statistics of Measurement

All measurement is infested with error. The physicist, the engineer, the astronomer, the surveyor, as well as the educator and the psychologist are vividly aware of this liability in their data and aware of the importance of holding measurement error to a minimum and of estimating the effects of such error as cannot be controlled. In the preceding chapters of this book we have apparently assumed that observations could be taken at their face value and could be treated as perfectly accurate measures of individuals on whatever traits they purport to measure. The discussion in earlier chapters of this text has proceeded almost as though the only important uncertainties in statistical studies were uncertainties about population parameters when these are estimated from sample statistics. However, in the social sciences the variance due to errors in measuring the individuals selected is often larger than the variance due to sampling errors in selecting individuals. Furthermore while sampling errors have a random effect upon the statistics computed, measurement errors affect certain statistics in a systematic not a random fashion, and so cannot be safely disregarded. If measurement error has remained unnoticed in the preceding chapters that has been done for the sake of the reader, to allow him to grasp one thing at a time.

The discussion in the present chapter will be directed toward answering such questions as the following. If the same individuals take two forms of a mental test and the correlation between the two sets of scores is found to be only, say, .60, will the test be useful in a situation where predictions are to be made concerning the performance of individuals? Will it be useful in a study concerning group performance? How does the variability among scores on one test form condition the answers to these questions? If the test can be lengthened, how will that affect the correlation between forms? Is it feasible to make the test long enough to yield a correlation of .90 between two forms? What is the difference in the information provided by the correlation between the results of giving the same test twice, of giving two test forms on two different days, of giving two test forms on the same day, of giving one test form and correlating scores on chance halves? If the correlation between two test forms is low, how will that fact affect a test of significance employing that test as a measure of the trait concerned?

Symbols. In this chapter we shall be concerned with multiple measures made on more than one trait for many individuals. It will be necessary to distinguish the trait, to distinguish the individual, to distinguish the measure. In order to be unambiguous the symbolism must be explicit, and consequently somewhat cumbersome.

The letters, X, Y, Z, W will be used to name the traits (the variates). Thus tests on American history might be denoted X and vocabulary tests denoted Y.

$X_{h\alpha}$ will indicate the score on trial h for individual α. The first subscript will represent the test form used or the repetition made. Thus X_{37} might mean the score made by individual 7 on the third form of test X, or it might mean the score made by individual 7 on the third trial of task X.

In Table 12.1 are displayed the symbols for mN scores of N individuals on m forms (or m trials) of test X, together with the various means and variances. For the sample of N individuals the means and variances of the different test forms present no new concept. The set of m trials furnishes a sample of m observations of the performance of each individual with mean and variance as indicated.

The student should note that the word "test" as used in the present discussions connotes some measure of an individual and is not related to "test of significance" as used elsewhere in the text.

For the universe of individuals the mean for trial h is the expected value of $X_{h\alpha}$ summed over individuals. This concept is thoroughly familiar but the subscript α will now be attached to the symbol E to indicate that summation is over individuals not trials, thus

$$\mu_h = E_\alpha(X_{h\alpha}) \tag{12.1}$$

For the universe of trials for individual α the mean is the expected value of $X_{h\alpha}$ summed over the trials. This value will be denoted "tau sub alpha."

$$\tau_\alpha = E_h(X_{h\alpha}) \tag{12.2}$$

TABLE 12.1 Symbolic Representation of Scores and Statistics on *X* for Many Individuals on Many Trials

Trial or Test Form	Individual				Sample of N individuals		Population of individuals	
	1	2	·	N	Mean	Variance	Mean	Variance
1	X_{11}	X_{12}	·	X_{1N}	$\overline{X}_{1.}$	$s^2_{1.} = \frac{1}{N-1}\sum_{\alpha=1}^{N}(X_{1\alpha} - \overline{X}_{1.})^2$	μ_1	$\sigma^2_{1.} = E_\alpha(X_{1\alpha} - \mu_1)^2$
2	X_{21}	X_{22}	·	X_{2N}	$\overline{X}_{2.}$	$s^2_{2.} = \frac{1}{N-1}\sum_{\alpha=1}^{N}(X_{2\alpha} - \overline{X}_{2.})^2$	μ_2	$\sigma^2_{2.} = E_\alpha(X_{2\alpha} - \mu_2)^2$
·	·	·	·	·	·	·	·	·
m	X_{m1}	X_{m2}	·	X_{mN}	$\overline{X}_{m.}$	$s^2_{m.} = \frac{1}{N-1}\sum_{\alpha=1}^{N}(X_{m\alpha} - \overline{X}_{m.})^2$	μ_m	$\sigma^2_{m.} = E_\alpha(X_{m\alpha} - \mu_m)^2$
Sample of m trials								
Mean	$\overline{X}_{.1}$	$\overline{X}_{.2}$	·	$\overline{X}_{.N}$				
Variance	$s^2_{.1}$	$s^2_{.2}$	·	$s^2_{.N}$				
Universe of trials								
Mean	τ_1	τ_2	·	τ_N				
Variance	$\sigma^2_{.1}$	$\sigma^2_{.2}$	·	$\sigma^2_{.N}$				
					$\overline{X}_{.\alpha} = \frac{1}{m}\sum_{h=1}^{m} X_{h\alpha}$		$\tau_\alpha = E_h(X_{h\alpha})$	
					$s^2_{.\alpha} = \frac{1}{m-1}\sum_{h=1}^{m}(X_{h\alpha} - \overline{X}_{.\alpha})^2$		$\sigma^2_{.\alpha} = E_h(X_{h\alpha} - \tau_\alpha)^2$	

the subscript h being used to indicate that summation is over the trials not the individuals.

For the universe of individuals the variance on test form h, or trial h, will be denoted

$$\sigma_h^2 = E_\alpha(X_{h\alpha} - \mu_h)^2 \tag{12.3}$$

while for the universe of trials for individual α the variance will be denoted

$$\sigma_\alpha^2 = E_h(X_{h\alpha} - \tau_\alpha)^2 \tag{12.4}$$

The score on test form h (or trial h) made by individual α may be described by the equation

$$X_{h\alpha} = \tau_\alpha + e_{h\alpha} \tag{12.5}$$

Here $e_{h\alpha}$ is an error made in measuring individual α on test form h and τ_α is the expectation of $X_{h\alpha}$ for the individual, or the value around which the various measures of that individual fluctuate as they are affected by different kinds of measurement error. τ_α is not amenable to direct observation but is surrounded by a kind of haze of measurement error in the same way that an inaccessible population parameter is shrouded in a haze of sampling error.

The variance of $X_{h\alpha}$ from individual to individual is denoted $\sigma^2{}_{h.}$ for the population, and $s^2{}_{h.}$ for the sample, and is called an *observed variance*, being the variance of observed scores. If the different test forms are truly comparable measures of the same trait it may be assumed that they all have equal variance, so that

$$\sigma^2{}_{1.} = \sigma^2{}_{2.} = \cdots = \sigma^2{}_{h.} = \sigma^2 \tag{12.6}$$

where σ^2 is the expectation of the variance of all possible scores of all individuals around the population mean μ.

Even when Equation (12.6) holds, the variance of the different test forms need not be equal for a particular sample,

$$s^2{}_{1.} \neq s^2{}_{2.} \neq s^2{}_{3.} \neq \cdots \neq s^2{}_{h.}$$

The variance of τ from individual to individual, called σ_τ^2 for the population and s_τ^2 for the sample, is the *true variance* among individuals. It is that component of the observed variance which is due to genuine differences among individuals

$$\sigma_\tau^2 = E_\alpha(\tau_\alpha - \mu)^2 \tag{12.7}$$

There is no way to compute σ_τ^2 or s_τ^2 directly, as τ cannot be measured directly. Methods of inferring σ_τ^2 or s_τ^2 indirectly will be discussed later in the chapter.

Components of an Observed Score. The error component indicated as $e_{h\alpha}$ in Equation (12.5) can be considered as arising from several different sources. The performance of any individual fluctuates from time to time partly because of changes in the individual himself, and partly because of changes in the environment. There are errors in the observer so that the same observer varies in his judgment from time to time and the judgments of different observers on the same performance are not uniform. The measuring instrument itself may be inconsistent.

In some situations it is possible to make separate estimates of the variance due to each of the three kinds of error. However, in most situations they are hopelessly confounded and their effects cannot be disentangled. Each of them may involve either random or systematic error, or both. In practical problems it is essential that the investigator try in advance of gathering his data to foresee what will be the chief sources of error, not only in order that he may control them as much as possible, but also in order that he may use the appropriate method of measuring the effect of such error on the reliability of his observations. Therefore, before going further, it will be well to consider some of the most common causes which play upon the "real" component τ and the error component e of an observed score.

If the individual is a person taking a psychological test, τ is affected by the level of his general ability, by his familiarity with such tests and his general ability to understand instructions, by his knowledge of the pertinent subject matter or his skill in the function tested, and the like. If the individual is a rat running a maze, τ is affected by his learning ability, his maturity, his physical vigor, the keenness of his senses, his testwiseness, and the like. If the individual is a pipe, the internal diameter of which, is to be found, or a cement mixture tested for the pressure it will bear, τ represents the average of all the large number of measurements which could be made, measurements which will differ one from the other because the object measured is not completely uniform, the measuring instrument is not completely reliable, and the person making the measurement has certain human frailties of touch, vision, etc., which make his measurements not absolutely dependable.

One component of error is due to the observer. If a test performance is to be timed, no human observer can be completely consistent in his timing even with the most accurate of stopwatches. Moreover, some observers will show a systematic leniency in timing, others a systematic tendency to call time a split-second too soon. When judgment of quality enters into the process of scoring, this component of error is never negligible and is seldom entirely random. Observer error is never wholly absent from reading a gauge such as a thermometer or pressure gauge, and it varies with the type of instrument. Observer error is at a minimum and perhaps wholly eliminated from scores on an objective test of the pencil and paper type.

Another component of error is due to fluctuation in the individual measured or in the environment. Since a person is never precisely the same at two different moments in time, temporary states of physical well being, emotional tension, preoccupation with other matters may affect his performance favorably or unfavorably as compared with his typical performance. Attention fluctuates continually and a momentary lapse of attention or memory may affect his performance. Distractions occur during the testing period, a pencil breaks, a fire siren sounds nearby, a neighbor sneezes disconcertingly. Conditions preceding the testing period are never uniform for all participants, and are usually unknown to the examiner. Individuals do not completely shed their worries or their excitements when they begin a test. In certain kinds of tests the amount of recent practice on specific skills may affect the score. If the individual is a person, this component of error is always large. If it is an inanimate object this component is likely to be relatively smaller but not necessarily absent. Materials expand and contract and wear out. Materials are not completely uniform and samples cut from different parts of a piece of cloth or different points on a metal rod do not test alike. Machines do not perform with complete consistency at all times.

Another sort of error comes from inconsistencies in the measuring instrument. This component is of paramount importance in pencil and paper tests for which a limited number of items has been selected out of a large pool of items. If different sets are randomly selected, they will not be equally difficult for all individuals measured, but one set will favor some individuals and penalize others. This error is really a chance error produced by sampling of items. It is the only error inherent in the test itself and the only one affecting that which can properly be called *the reliability of the test* while *the reliability of the observations* is affected by other random errors as well.

If test items are not selected at random (and they usually are not) there may be a consistent or systematic error as well as a random error in any particular set. Such consistent errors affect the *validity of the test.* This validity is affected not only by consistent errors in the test items but by consistent errors of the observer and of the individual measured.

Over and above all the preceding, there are certain chance errors such as those related to luck in guessing the right answer on partial information, or no information. These may well be absorbed into one or the other of the preceding components of error.

Effect of Measurement Error on the Mean. Random errors have a negligible effect upon the mean of a sample, because positive and negative errors tend to cancel each other. However, because they increase the variability of the sample, as described in the next section, they increase the standard error of the mean and consequently decrease the reliability of the mean. Random errors may even completely obscure a genuine difference between two or more means. Therefore, when a sample has shown a nonsignificant difference between means the research worker is always obliged to consider the possibility that a real difference exists but that his observations are too unreliable to reveal it. For this purpose (as well as for other purposes) he needs to study the reliability of his observations.

If all possible measures of each individual were taken, then the mean of $X_{h\alpha}$ would be identical with the mean of τ_α for the sample as well as for the population. Even so the variance of X_h would be larger than the variance of τ_α. However one never has all possible measures of individuals, but usually has only one or two measures for each. Then the sample mean of X_h is not necessarily identical with the sample mean of τ_α, though the discrepancy is negligible if errors are random.

If only one or two measures are available for each individual and if in these there is a systematic error, one has no assurance that the effect of errors on the mean is small and no assurance that errors increase the variance. Bias in the observer, an abnormally easy or abnormally difficult test form, some aspect of the testing situation which served to distract the attention of all individuals tested, or the like, might depress or raise all scores on a particular trial or might depress or raise the scores of some individuals and not of all. Under such circumstances errors are not random and their effect may be almost anything. It is not usually possible to make a statistical test to discover whether errors are random or not, and therefore a careful logical scrutiny of the experimental situation is particularly important.

Let $e_{h\alpha}$ and $e_{j\alpha}$ represent the errors in the score of individual α on test forms h and j. Since only two forms are postulated, we can say nothing about the expected values obtained from all possible test forms as indicated at the bottom of Table 12.1. The expected values obtained by averaging $X_{h\alpha}$ over all individuals in the population may be considered. If $X_{h\alpha}$ is a measure which differs from τ_α only because of random error, then the expectation of such error is zero and so

$$E_\alpha(e_{h\alpha}) = 0$$

(12.8) and $$E_\alpha(X_{h\alpha}) = E_\alpha(\tau_\alpha + e_{h\alpha}) = E_\alpha(\tau_\alpha) + E_\alpha(e_{h\alpha}) = E_\alpha(\tau_\alpha)$$

By the same argument if errors are random because items have been assigned to test forms at random the expectation of scores on any other test form is also equal to the expectation of τ_α. Consequently if errors are random, the expectation of scores on any one form is equal to the expectation of scores on any other, and each is equal to the population mean.

(12.9) $$E_\alpha(X_{h\alpha}) = E_\alpha(X_{j\alpha}) = \cdots = E_\alpha(X_{m\alpha}) = E_\alpha(\tau_\alpha) = \mu$$

and

(12.10) $$E_\alpha(X_{h\alpha} - \mu) = E_\alpha(X_{h\alpha}) - \mu = \mu - \mu = 0$$

and

(12.11) $$E_\alpha(\tau_\alpha - \mu) = E_\alpha(\tau_\alpha) - \mu = 0$$

For any particular sample, random errors may produce slight discrepancies among the means of different forms. If errors are not random, the test forms may be of unequal difficulty so that the expectation of errors is not zero over the population and therefore two test forms do not have the same population mean.

Effect of Measurement Error on the Variance. Random errors of measurement consistently inflate the variance so that the variance of observed scores is larger than the variance of "true" scores. Because people who think intuitively rather than algebraically often assume that random errors might sometimes increase and sometimes decrease the variance, recourse must be made to the formula. By squaring $X_{h\alpha} - \mu = (\tau_\alpha - \mu) + e_{h\alpha}$ and taking the expectation of each term for the population of individuals, the following formula is obtained:

(12.12) $$\sigma_x^2 = \sigma_\tau^2 + \sigma_e^2 + 2\rho_{\tau e}\sigma^\tau\sigma_e$$

If errors of measurement are uncorrelated with "true" scores, the last term disappears leaving

$$\sigma_x^2 = \sigma_\tau^2 + \sigma_e^2 \tag{12.13}$$

The assumption that $\rho_{\tau e} = 0$ appears to be reasonable in very many research situations. For the sample, $r_{\tau e}$ will usually not be precisely zero.

As will be seen later, this inflation of the variance by random errors of measurement presents a serious hazard in tests of significance, for unless it is possible to obtain fairly reliable observations the hypothesis that two or more means are equal can be refuted only when differences among the means are very great.

Indirect Estimate of the "True" Variance σ_τ^2. Suppose two forms of a measure X are available, which may be called X_1 and X_2, or X_h and X_j if greater generality is desired.

$$X_{1\alpha} = \tau_\alpha + e_{1\alpha} \quad \text{and} \quad X_{2\alpha} = \tau_\alpha + e_{2\alpha}$$

The correlation between X_1 and X_2 is usually called the *reliability coefficient* of the measure. It may be designated ρ_{xx} for the population and r_{xx} for a sample.

Since X_1 and X_2 are comparable measures, it may be assumed that errors are equally variable

$$\sigma^2_{e_1} = \sigma^2_{e_2} = \sigma_e^2 \tag{12.14}$$

and errors are equally correlated with τ

$$\rho_{e_1\tau} = \rho_{e_2\tau} = \rho_{e\tau} \tag{12.15}$$

If errors are random, $\rho_{\tau e}$ may be assumed to be zero. This is usually the case. However, if a test might conceivably be so designed or so administered that persons with low standing tended to incur consistently greater or consistently smaller measurement errors than persons with high standing it would not be zero. If (12.14) and (12.15) hold, then

$$\sigma^2_{x_1} = \sigma^2_{x_2} = \sigma_x^2.$$

The correlation ρ_{xx} may be found by substituting $X_{1\alpha} - \mu = (\tau_\alpha - \mu) + e_{1\alpha}$ for x and $X_{2\alpha} - \mu = \tau_\alpha - \mu + e_{2\alpha}$ for y in the formula $\rho_{xy} = \dfrac{E(xy)}{\sqrt{E(x^2)E(y^2)}}$, taking the expectation, and reducing the result by the application of Formulas (12.14) and (12.15). By this procedure it may be found that

$$\rho_{xx} = \frac{\sigma_\tau^2 + 2\rho_{\tau e}\sigma_\tau\sigma_e + \rho_{e_1e_2}\sigma_e^2}{\sigma_x^2} \tag{12.16}$$

Now, if errors are random $\rho_{\tau e} = 0$ and $\rho_{e_1e_2} = 0$. In that case

(12.17) $$\rho_{xx} = \frac{\sigma_\tau^2}{\sigma_x^2}$$

and for the sample, approximately,

(12.18) $$r_{xx} \cong \frac{s_\tau^2}{s_x^2}.$$

Formulas (12.17) and (12.18) constitute an important interpretation of the reliability coefficient. *If two measures differ from each other only because of random errors of measurement, the correlation between the two is the ratio of the variance of true scores to the variance of observed scores.*

Solving (12.17) for σ_τ^2 and (12.18) for s_τ^2 gives the formulas

(12.19) $$\sigma_\tau^2 = \sigma_x^2\rho_{xx} \quad \text{or} \quad \sigma_\tau = \sigma_x\sqrt{\rho_{xx}}$$

(12.20) $$s_\tau^2 \cong s_x^2 r_{xx} \quad \text{or} \quad s_\tau \cong s_x\sqrt{r_{xx}}$$

which provide a method of indirectly estimating the variability of the "true scores."

Indirect Estimate of the Error Variance. By Formula (12.13) the total observed variance was partitioned into two portions, the variance of true scores plus the variance of errors of measurement,

$$\sigma_x^2 = \sigma_\tau^2 + \sigma_e^2.$$

As an estimate for σ_τ^2 has now been found to be $\sigma_x^2\rho_{xx}$, an estimate for σ_e^2 can be found by substitution. Then

(12.21) $$\sigma_e^2 = \sigma_x^2 - \sigma_x^2\rho_{xx} = \sigma_x^2(1 - \rho_{xx})$$

(12.22) $$\sigma_e = \sigma_x\sqrt{1 - \rho_{xx}}.$$

At this point the student may profitably look again at Formula (10.20) and compare it with (12.22) noting that the former involves ρ^2 and the latter ρ. The error e may be thought of as a residual error incurred in predicting a true score τ from an observed score X by the regression equation

$$\tilde{\tau}_\alpha = X_{h\alpha} \text{ with } \tau_\alpha - \tilde{\tau}_\alpha = e_{h\alpha}$$

Then σ_e^2 is the variance of residual errors corresponding to $\sigma^2_{y.x}$ of Chapter 10.

The corresponding formulas for the sample are reasonable approximations if N is not too small. If N is small, $r_{\tau e}$ may differ considerably from zero and $N - 2$, which is the appropriate denominator for s_e^2 may be rather different from $N - 1$, which is the denominator for s_x^2. With these reservations, however, we may state the sample formulas as

(12.23) $$s_e^2 \cong s_x^2(1 - r_{xx})$$

and

(12.24) $$s_e \cong s_x\sqrt{1 - r_{xx}}$$

Effect of Measurement Error on a Coefficient of Correlation. Let us suppose that X_1 and X_2 are two measures of trait X and that Y_1 and Y_2 are two measures of trait Y, and that

(12.25) $$\begin{aligned} X_{1\alpha} &= \tau_\alpha + e_{1\alpha} \qquad & Y_{1\alpha} &= \upsilon_\alpha + d_{1\alpha} \\ X_{2\alpha} &= \tau_\alpha + e_{2\alpha} \qquad & Y_{2\alpha} &= \upsilon_\alpha + d_{2\alpha} \end{aligned}$$

where τ_α and υ_α (upsilon) are the measures of those traits for individual α without measurement errors and e and d are the respective errors. Then $\rho_{\tau\upsilon}$ is the "true" correlation between X and Y, that is the correlation which would exist if there were no errors of measurement, while ρ_{xy} is the correlation between observed, fallible measures.

We have seen that

$\mu_x = \mu_\tau$ and $\overline{X}$ approximates $\overline{\tau}$

$\sigma_x > \sigma_\tau$ and s_x tends to be larger than s_τ

What is the relation of ρ_{xy} to $\rho_{\tau\upsilon}$, and of r_{xy} to $r_{\tau\upsilon}$?

To answer this question, we shall assume that

$$\sigma_{e_1} = \sigma_{e_2}, \quad \sigma_{d_1} = \sigma_{d_2}, \quad E(e_1) = E(e_2) = E(d_1) = E(d_2) = 0$$

$$\rho_{\tau e_1} = \rho_{\tau e_2}, \quad \rho_{\upsilon d_1} = \rho_{\upsilon d_2}$$

The student should paraphrase each of these statements in words. We have already seen in Formula (12.19) that $\sigma_\tau^2 = \sigma_x^2\rho_{xx}$

Similarly $$\sigma_\upsilon^2 = \sigma_y^2\rho_{yy}$$

and $$E(X - \mu_x)(Y - \mu_y) = \rho_{\tau\upsilon}\sigma_\tau\sigma_\upsilon + \rho_{e\upsilon}\sigma_e\sigma_\upsilon + \rho_{d\tau}\sigma_d\sigma_\tau + \rho_{ed}\sigma_e\sigma_d$$

But

(12.26) $$\rho_{xy} = \frac{E(X - \mu_x)(Y - \mu_y)}{\sigma_x\sigma_y}$$

(12.27) $$\rho_{xy} = \frac{\rho_{\tau\upsilon}\sigma_\tau\sigma_\upsilon + \rho_{e\upsilon}\sigma_e\sigma_\upsilon + \rho_{d\tau}\sigma_d\sigma_\tau + \rho_{ed}\sigma_e\sigma_d}{\sigma_x\sigma_y}$$

If errors are random they are uncorrelated with true scores so $\rho_{e\upsilon} = 0$ and $\rho_{d\tau} = 0$, and they are uncorrelated with each other so $\rho_{ed} = 0$. In that case

(12.28) $$\rho_{xy} = \frac{\rho_{\tau\upsilon}\sigma_\tau\sigma_\upsilon}{\sigma_x\sigma_y} = \rho_{\tau\upsilon}\sqrt{\rho_{xx}}\sqrt{\rho_{yy}}$$

and therefore

$$\rho_{\tau v} = \frac{\rho_{xy}}{\sqrt{\rho_{xx}\rho_{yy}}} \tag{12.29}$$

The sample formula corresponding to (12.27) is obtained by summing over N cases instead of taking the expectation. It holds precisely:

$$r_{xy} = \frac{r_{\tau v}s_\tau s_v + r_{ev}s_e s_v + r_{\tau d}s_\tau s_d + r_{ed}s_e s_d}{s_x s_y} \tag{12.30}$$

Even if errors are random, the correlations r_{ev}, $r_{\tau d}$ and r_{ed} would usually be only approximately and not precisely zero for a sample. Therefore, the sample formulas analogous to (12.28) and (12.29) must be considered as approximations only:

$$r_{xy} \cong r_{\tau v}\sqrt{r_{xx}}\sqrt{r_{yy}} \tag{12.31}$$

$$r_{\tau v} \cong \frac{r_{xy}}{\sqrt{r_{xx}}\sqrt{r_{yy}}} \tag{12.32}$$

The preceding formulas indicate that when measurement error is random, the correlation of observed scores X and Y is numerically smaller than the correlation of "true" scores τ and v. This lowering or *attenuation* of the correlation coefficient is inescapable since the correlation coefficients r_{xx} and r_{yy} for the sample as well as ρ_{xx} and ρ_{yy} for the population are less than 1. Formulas (12.29) and (12.32), which give an estimate of the correlation between scores freed from measurement error, are called *the correction for attenuation.*

It must be noted that the correction for attenuation was obtained on the assumption that three of the four terms in the numerator of (12.27), or of (12.30), were zero. This assumption is almost impossible to verify empirically, but the research worker will find it instructive to think about situations in which it is unreasonable on *a priori* grounds. Two illustrations will be given. The possible variety of such is almost inexhaustible.

Suppose that one form of test X and one form of test Y are given on the same day, and that a few individuals are suffering from some unusual strain which adversely affects their performance on both. Then r_{ed} is likely to be not zero, but positive. Consequently, the right-hand member of (12.30) is likely to be larger than the right-hand member of (12.31) and so Formula (12.32) will overestimate $r_{\tau v}$.

• Suppose only one form of test X is available and r_{xx} is the correlation between two applications of the same test form. Then it cannot be assumed that $r_{e_1e_2} = 0$ since the errors an individual makes on one application of the test will not be unrelated to those made on the other. If $r_{e_1e_2}$ is positive, r_{xx} is larger than s_τ^2/s_x^2 and $r_{\tau v}$ is *overestimated* by Formula (12.32).

The correction for attenuation, if applicable under the assumptions, becomes a sort of ceiling indicating the highest value to which the correlation between two measures could be pushed by improving the reliability of measurement. Suppose two forms of an arithmetic reasoning test have shown an intercorrelation of $r_{xx} = .66$, and two forms of a verbal reasoning test an intercorrelation of $r_{yy} = .71$. The correlations between a single form of the arithmetic and a single form of the verbal test are variously $r_{xy} = .55$, .49, .54, and .51. Is it conceivable that the two tests are actually measuring the same function and correlations between them are less than unity only because we have imperfect measures of each? In order to apply Formula (12.32) some average of the four values of r_{xy} is needed. Strictly speaking we should average the four covariances but no data are given concerning the covariances or the standard deviations. (The covariance of x and y is defined as $E(X - \mu_x)(Y - \mu_y) = \rho_{xy}\sigma_x\sigma_y$.) The arithmetic mean of the four correlations is $\frac{1}{4}(.55 + .49 + .54 + .51) = .5225$. The geometric mean is $[(.55)(.49)(.54)(.51)]^{\frac{1}{4}} = .522$. If each of the 4 values of r is converted to z, the z's averaged and the average of the z's is converted back to r, the result is .52. Obviously the method of averaging will have little effect on the outcome.

Then
$$r_{\tau v} = \frac{.52}{\sqrt{(.66)(.71)}} = .76$$

In interpretation it may be said in passing that reliability coefficients of .66 and .71 make the tests of little value as instruments for measuring individuals.

The correlation between the two traits could not be expected to rise higher than about .76 even if all errors of measurement could be eliminated. The functions measured by the two tests cannot be held to be identical.

The Coefficient of Reliability. If two measures of trait X differ only by random errors of measurement,

$$\rho_{xx} = \frac{\sigma_\tau^2}{\sigma_x^2} = 1 - \frac{\sigma_e^2}{\sigma_x^2} \qquad (12.33)$$

With the qualifications stated on page 300 the analogous formula for the sample holds approximately,

$$r_{xx} \cong \frac{s_T^2}{s_x^2} \cong 1 - \frac{s_e^2}{s_x^2} \tag{12.34}$$

These formulas will be considered as a definition of the *coefficient of reliability*, or the *reliability coefficient* of measure X.

The question of how to obtain r_{xx} from data will be discussed in a later section. It presents certain difficulties about which a great deal has been written. Within the scope of the present book only the major problems can be considered.

Effect on the Coefficient of Reliability of Changing the Length of the Test. Sometimes when the coefficient of reliability is unsatisfactorily low, the test maker wishes to know how much it might be increased if the test forms were lengthened by the addition of a specified amount of similar material, or how much material would need to be added to the tests in order to produce a reliability coefficient of a given size. Conversely, he may feel that the test requires more testing time than can be justified and he may wish to estimate how much the reliability coefficient would be decreased if the test were shortened.

To answer any of these questions one must assume a homogeneous body of material from which test items are chosen at random so that errors due to selection of test material are random errors. One must also assume that errors due to variation within the individual tested, or to variation in the administration of the test, are random errors. Then it can be assumed that the covariance for any two forms is the same as for any other two forms, or

$$E(X_k - \mu)(X_j - \mu) = \rho_{xx}\sigma_x^2$$

for any k and j. Assumptions which are intuitively clearer though somewhat more restrictive are

(1) all forms are equally variable, so $\sigma^2_{x_1} = \sigma^2_{x_2} = \ldots = \sigma_x^2$ and and (2) all correlations between forms are the same, so

$$\rho_{x_1x_2} = \ldots = \rho_{x_kx_j} = \rho_{xx}$$

Now let ${}_2\rho_{xx}$ be the correlation between $(X_1 + X_2)$ and $(X_3 + X_4)$ and
${}_3\rho_{xx}$ be the correlation between $(X_1 + X_2 + X_3)$ and $(X_4 + X_5 + X_6)$
and ${}_p\rho_{xx}$ be the correlation between $(X_1 + \cdots + X_p)$
and $(X_{p+1} + \cdots + X_{2p})$

(12.35) Then $${}_{2}\rho_{xx} = \frac{2\rho_{xx}}{1 + \rho_{xx}}$$

(12.36) and approximately $${}_{2}r_{xx} = \frac{2r_{xx}}{1 + r_{xx}}$$

(12.37) also $${}_{p}\rho_{xx} = \frac{p\rho_{xx}}{1 + (p - 1)\rho_{xx}}$$

(12.38) and approximately $${}_{p}r_{xx} = \frac{pr_{xx}}{1 + (p - 1)r_{xx}}$$

Formula (12.38) is commonly called the *Spearman-Brown Prophecy Formula.* The names of Charles Spearman and William Brown are both attached to it because papers by these men appeared simultaneously in the same issue of the same journal [1, 9].

Illustrations.

A. A test with reliability coefficient .52 requires 15 minutes to administer. If it could be increased in length to require 60 minutes, how much increase might be hoped for in the reliability coefficient? Here $p = \frac{60}{15} = 4$. Then

$${}_{4}r_{xx} = \frac{4(.52)}{1 + 3(.52)} = \frac{2.08}{2.56} = .78$$

Actual experience in lengthening the test and giving it to a new group is of course necessary, because the added material may not be entirely comparable to the original items, and individuals may work either more or less effectively in the longer period.

B. If a reliability coefficient of .90 were required for the purpose in hand, how long would the test need to be? Now p is the unknown to be found from the equation

$$.90 = \frac{p(.52)}{1 + (p - 1)(.52)}$$

Solving this equation gives $p = 8.3$ so the time presumably required would be (8.3)(15) minutes or 125 minutes. If that appears to be more testing time than can be suitably allowed, the test maker may consider whether he can tolerate a lower reliability, or whether by changing the type of item he can secure greater reliability in less testing time. He will have discovered without laborious writing of new items that sheer lengthening of the test by addition of similar material is not likely to achieve the desired result.

Effect on the Correlation between Two Measures of Changing their Reliabilities. *A. When the data are given in terms of reliability coefficients.* (1) Suppose $r_{xy} = .55$ when $r_{xx} = .65$ and $r_{yy} = .75$.

If each reliability coefficient could be made .85, what value of r_{xy} could be anticipated? Let r'_{xy} designate the value of r_{xy} to be anticipated when the two reliability coefficients are $r'_{xx} = .85$, and $r'_{yy} = .85$.

By Formula (12.32) $$r_{TV} \cong \frac{.55}{\sqrt{(.65)(.75)}}$$

and also $$r_{TV} \cong \frac{r'_{xy}}{\sqrt{(.85)(.85)}}.$$

Therefore $$\frac{r'_{xy}}{\sqrt{(.85)(.85)}} \cong \frac{.55}{\sqrt{(.65)(.75)}}$$

and so $$r'_{xy} \cong \frac{.55(.85)}{\sqrt{(.65)(.75)}} = .67$$

Generalizing this procedure, we may write

(12.39) $$r'_{xy} \cong \frac{r_{xy}\sqrt{r'_{xx}r'_{yy}}}{\sqrt{r_{xx}r_{yy}}}$$

(2) Suppose $r_{xy} = .55$ when $r_{xx} = .65$ and $r_{yy} = .75$. If measures of X could be made completely reliable without any change in the reliability of Y, what value of r'_{xy} might be anticipated? The question implies that $r'_{xx} = 1.00$ and $r'_{yy} = r_{yy}$ and that r'_{xy} is really to be r_{Ty} because measures of X are to be free of error. When these values are substituted, Formula (12.39) becomes

(12.40) $$r_{Ty} \cong \frac{r_{xy}}{\sqrt{r_{xx}}}$$

and similarly $$r_{xV} \cong \frac{r_{xy}}{\sqrt{r_{yy}}}$$

Then $$r_{Ty} \cong \frac{.55}{\sqrt{.65}} = .68$$

B. When the data are given in terms of the proportionate change in length of tests. Suppose it is desired to find the correlation between $(X_1 + \cdots X_p)$ and $(Y_1 + \cdots + Y_q)$ where it is assumed that $X_1, \ldots X_p$ are p comparable measures of X and $Y_1 \ldots Y_q$ are q comparable measures of Y. Let this correlation be designated ${}_{pq}\rho_{xy}$. We speak here as though p and q were integers but the resultant formulas apply even when p and q are fractions. Let either one of the following sets of assumptions be made:

(1) The covariance of any two measures of X is $\rho_{xx}\sigma_x^2$
The covariance of any two measures of Y is $\rho_{yy}\sigma_y^2$

The covariance of any measure of X and any measure of Y is $\rho_{xy}\sigma_x\sigma_y$

(2) All measures of X have the same variance, σ_x^2
All measures of Y have the same variance σ_y^2
The correlation between any two measures of X is ρ_{xx}
The correlation between any two measures of Y is ρ_{yy}
The correlation between any measure of X and any measure of Y is ρ_{xy}.

On the basis of these assumptions

$$(12.41) \qquad {}_{pq}\rho_{xy} = \frac{pq\rho_{xy}}{\sqrt{p + p(p-1)\rho_{xx}}\sqrt{q + q(q-1)\rho_{yy}}}$$

and approximately

$$(12.42) \qquad {}_{pq}r_{xy} \cong \frac{pqr_{xy}}{\sqrt{p + p(p-1)r_{xx}}\sqrt{q + q(q-1)r_{yy}}}$$

Suppose r_{xy} has been found to be .35 when $r_{xx} = .58$ and $r_{yy} = .65$. It is decided that the test for X can be made twice as long and that for Y three times as long as at present. What correlation might be anticipated between X and Y? Here $p = 2$ and $q = 3$. Then

$${}_{23}r_{xy} = \frac{6(.35)}{\sqrt{2 + 2(.58)}\sqrt{3 + 6(.65)}} = \frac{2.10}{\sqrt{(3.16)(6.90)}} = \frac{2.10}{4.67} = .45$$

It is interesting to note that Formulas (12.32), (12.36), (12.38), and (12.40) are special cases of (12.42) and can be derived from it by appropriate substitutions for p and q.

Effect of Measurement Error on a Regression Coefficient. Random errors of measurement have been seen to reduce the correlation coefficient and to increase the standard deviation. What effect do these errors have upon the regression coefficients

$$\beta_{v\tau} = \frac{E(v - \mu_v)(\tau - \mu_\tau)}{E(\tau - \mu_\tau)^2} \quad \text{and} \quad b_{v\tau} = r_{v\tau}\frac{s_v}{s_\tau}?$$

How do these coefficients to predict v from τ compare with the corresponding coefficients to predict y from x?

The question is easily answered by comparing the formulas

$$\beta_{v\tau} = \frac{E(v - \mu_v)(\tau - \mu_\tau)}{E(\tau - \mu_\tau)^2} \quad \text{and} \quad \beta_{yx} = \frac{E(Y - \mu_y)(X - \mu_x)}{E(X - \mu_x)^2}$$

Errors in Y, which is the dependent or predicted variable, can obviously have no effect on the denominator. Random errors in X, which is the independent variable, have already been seen to make $E(X - \mu_x)^2 = \sigma_x^2$ larger than $E(\tau - \mu_\tau)^2 = \sigma_\tau^2$. See Formula (12.13).

Random errors in either X or Y have no effect upon the numerator. If errors are uncorrelated with each other and with true scores, then

$$\begin{aligned} E(X - \mu_x)(Y - \mu_y) &= E(\tau - \mu_\tau + e)(v - \mu_v + d) \\ &= E(\tau - \mu_\tau)(v - \mu_v) + E(\tau - \mu_\tau)d \\ &\qquad + E(v - \mu_v)e + E(ed) \\ &= E(\tau - \mu_\tau)(v - \mu_v) + 0 + 0 + 0 \end{aligned}$$

Similar statements hold *approximately* for the sample coefficients $b_{v\tau}$ and b_{yx}.

Therefore it may be stated that random errors in the predicted or dependent variable have no effect upon a regression coefficient and that random errors in the independent variable reduce the coefficient.

Effect of Measurement Error on Tests of Significance. In general, random errors of measurement make the null hypothesis appear more tenable than it would be if true measures could have been used.

In an earlier section of this chapter it was shown that random errors of measurement have no effect on the mean of a *population*, so that $\mu_x = \mu_\tau$. Their chief effect on the mean of a *sample* is to increase its sampling variability. As σ_τ^2 is increased by measurement error to $\sigma_x^2 = \sigma_\tau^2 + \sigma_e^2$, than $\sigma_{\bar{x}}^2$ is increased from

$$\frac{\sigma_\tau^2}{N} \quad \text{to} \quad \frac{\sigma_x^2}{N} = \frac{\sigma_\tau^2 + \sigma_e^2}{N}$$

When several means are to be compared by use of an F ratio, random errors of measurement may raise or lower any of the means slightly, but the effect on the numerator of the F ratio is small and may be such as to make the means either more alike or less alike. However, the denominator sum of squares is consistently increased by random errors and so the F ratio is reduced by them. The t ratio of the difference between two means to its standard error is similarly reduced by random errors. When an investigator has accepted the hypothesis that two or more means are equal in the population he must always keep in mind the possibility that a very real difference has been obscured by the measurement error present in his data. This is one of the reasons why some evidence concerning the reliability of the data should be sought.

The F test of significance for r is affected in the same direction by unreliability of the scores. As r is attenuated by error,

$$F = \frac{r^2(N-2)}{1-r^2}$$

is also reduced in size. In general, the greater the measurement error, the less likely is it that any statistical test will prove significant.

Method of Estimating a Reliability Coefficient from Data. Although the reliability coefficient has been defined by the formulas

$$\rho_{xx} = \frac{\sigma_\tau^2}{\sigma_x^2} = 1 - \frac{\sigma_e^2}{\sigma_x^2} \quad \text{and} \quad r_{xx} = \frac{s_\tau^2}{s_x^2} = 1 - \frac{s_e^2}{s_x^2},$$

and some aspects of its meaning have been discussed, there has as yet been no discussion of how to obtain it from data. The reader has probably noticed this omission and attributed it to oversight. The omission has been deliberate. Because every possible method of estimating a reliability coefficient from data has certain drawbacks, it has seemed better not to identify the concept with a particular experimental procedure at too early a stage in the reader's thinking.

There is no direct way to measure either τ or e but only $X = \tau + e$. Consequently there is no direct way to compute s_τ^2 or s_e^2. If two measures of τ can be obtained such that they differ only by random errors of measurement, $X_1 = \tau + e_1$ and $X_2 = \tau + e_2$ then the correlation and variance of observed measures can be used to estimate s_τ^2 as $r_{x_1x_2}s_x^2$. The difficulty is to set up an experimental situation in which X_1 and X_2 actually conform to this assumption. There are four principal experimental procedures commonly used, each of which has some advantages and involves some serious drawbacks. These are: (A) correlating scores from two comparable but different tests given on two different occasions; (B) correlating scores on a single test given twice with a time interval between the repetitions; (C) correlating scores on two tests given on the same occasion, or scores on two halves of a single application of a single test; and (D) analyzing the variance among items on a single application of a single test. In considering the appropriateness of each of these four procedures, the essential requirements are (1) that τ shall be a measure of the trait it is desired to measure and shall not change from one form to another, or from one occasion to another, and (2) that e_1 and e_2

shall be random errors due to variation of the kind it is desired to appraise. It is therefore especially important to make an *a priori* analysis of the four procedures. We shall now discuss the *statistical aspects* of these four procedures. For practical advice as to how to construct tests which are likely to conform to the assumptions made, the reader should consult a treatise on test construction [2, 8, 11].

A. Correlating scores on two different test forms given on two different occasions. Suppose a large pool of test items is available, each of which has been constructed to conform to specifications drawn up for the test. Then let items be drawn at random from this pool and assigned at random to the two test forms. Under such a plan, the two forms should measure the same τ and differences between them should be due to random errors in the sampling of items. If items are not assigned at random to the two test forms, these may be either more alike or less alike than under random assignment of items. If they are more alike, s_e^2 is underestimated and r_{xx} is overestimated. If they are less alike, s_e^2 is overestimated and r_{xx} is underestimated. In many situations, some of which are discussed by Thorndike and by Cronbach in the references cited, it is impossible to secure a large pool of items or to construct comparable test forms. If the two test forms are not of equal difficulty, or if the items are of two different types (say one test is a completion test and one a multiple-choice test on the same subject matter), or if the subject matter differs from test to test, then the two forms are not measuring the same τ.

The purpose of allowing a time interval to elapse between the administration of the two tests is to permit temporary states of attention, fatigue, well-being and the like in the subjects, and accidental advantages or disadvantages in the environment to register differences in the scores. Therefore, the time interval should not be great enough for the real abilities of the subjects to undergo a change, for in that case the two scores would not be representing the same τ. If the second test is given immediately after the first, temporary states of well-being of the subjects will have similar effect on both scores, s_e^2 will be underestimated and r_{xx} overestimated.

If two comparable test forms are available and if it is administratively feasible to allow time for testing on two different days, this procedure appears to give the most satisfactory estimate of r_{xx}. The error variance then represents variation due both to selection of test items and to fluctuation in performance of subjects.

B. Correlating scores on repetitions of the same test form. In this procedure the task is precisely the same on the two administrations. Therefore, if the sampling of test items favors a particular subject unduly on one occasion they do so on both, and departures from his true score because of sampling of test items does not show up in the error variance but works to increase r_{xx} unduly. In this procedure the error variance is due to differences in the performance of the subjects on two occasions, so r_{xx} is measuring the *stability of the subjects' performance* rather than the reliability of the test. If in the interval between repetitions, some of the subjects have had more practice than others in the function tested or have had some experience which changed them in respect to that function, the corresponding changes in score will appear as errors when actually they represent changes in τ. Then s_e^2 will be overestimated and r_{xx} underestimated.

Sometimes the only error in which the investigator is interested is performance error. For example, consider the archery data presented in Chapters 9 and 14. The essential task is uniform, shooting at a uniform target under conditions as nearly standard as they can be made. The stability of performance of the subjects is properly the aspect of reliability to be studied. In measures of posture, of metabolism, of reaction time, or in general of physical states or simple skills, the essential kind of error is performance error in the subject and perhaps also in the person administering the test. No sampling of test items is called for.

In measures of knowledge, achievement, temperament, attitude, opinion, and the like, repetition of the same test form usually greatly underestimates s_e^2 and overestimates r_{xx}. Errors in measuring an individual because the test items are a sample out of all possible items should contribute to s_e^2 but cannot do so when the same test form is repeated. Furthermore, there is the risk that some memory of answers given on the first test may affect answers on the second, thus further reducing s_e^2 and fallaciously increasing r_{xx}.

C. Correlating scores on two test forms given on the same occasion. (a) *When two distinct test forms are available.* The first paragraph of the discussion under A applies here also. The error variance includes variance due to the sampling of test items. Variance due to instability of performance of individual subjects does not appear as error but as part of the measure of τ in both tests thus raising the estimate of r_{xx}. (b) *When only one test form is available and two scores are obtained from it by subdivision of the items.* This procedure is very widely used. Perhaps there is no second form of the test. Perhaps time is not available for administering two complete forms. Perhaps a test maker is developing an instrument and needs a preliminary estimate of its reliability before he carries out the work of standardizing two comparable forms. The single test form is administered, its items are in some manner divided so as to form two half-tests, and the scores on these half-tests are correlated. Then the Spearman-Brown Prophecy Formula, Formula (12.36) is applied,

$$_2r_{xx} = \frac{2r_{xx}}{1 + r_{xx}}$$

with the correlation between the half-tests used as r_{xx}. The resulting value of $_2r_{xx}$ is then assumed to be the correlation which would have been obtained between scores on two full test forms had such been available. Certain comments on the method should be made.

(1) The error variance takes account of the sampling of test items but not of the variation in subjects' performance from time to time.

(2) Sometimes it is impossible to subdivide a test into comparable halves. Such is the case when success on one item is conditioned by success on previous items, or when speed plays an important role. If a test is to be timed, the half-tests should be constructed in advance, and each half-test given independently with its own time limits. Suppose a test consists of four blocks of questions. For example, suppose a reading test consists of 4 long passages with several questions on each. If half the passages and all the questions on each of them are placed in one form, the correlation between the two forms may be low. The application of the Prophecy Formula will in that case suggest the increase in reliability to be expected if the test is increased by the *addition of new passages.* If half the questions on every passage are placed in one form, the correlation may be quite high. The application of the Prophecy Formula can in this case be used only to estimate the correlation between two test forms obtained by the *addition of new questions based on the same set of passages.* As it is usually not possible to find a large number of new and equally good

questions, and as one is more likely to want to generalize to a universe of passages than to a universe of questions about a fixed set of passages, this second method of subdividing items has little to recommend it.

(3) The number of ways in which the items of a test can be subdivided to produce two half-tests is very large, and each of them produces a different correlation between the test halves. If, for example, a test contains 20 items, the number of ways in which the items can be assigned to the two half-tests is 92378.

(4) The Spearman-Brown Prophecy Formula is derived from rather restrictive assumptions (stated earlier in this chapter) to which the practical situation may not conform.

D. Measuring the internal consistency of a test. The preceding section referred to the great variety of ways in which a test can be subdivided to form two half-tests and the consequent indeterminacy of the estimate of the reliability coefficient obtained by correlating scores on the halves. This indeterminacy has caused research workers to look for a method which is independent of any particular split up of items. A formula which serves this purpose was developed by Kuder and Richardson.[7] The symbols used here are slightly different from those in the original presentation.

N = number of individuals taking the test.

m = number of items in the test.

p_i = proportion of individuals answering the ith item correctly.

Np_i = number of individuals answering the ith item correctly.

$q_i = 1 - p_i$ = proportion of individuals not answering the ith item correctly.

Nq_i = number of individuals not answering the ith item correctly.

s_x^2 = variance of the test scores of the N individuals if each score is the number of items answered correctly by the individual.

(12.43) Then $$r_{xx} = \frac{m}{m-1}\left(1 - \frac{N\sum_{i=1}^{m} p_i q_i}{(N-1)s_x^2}\right)$$

(12.44) $$= \frac{m}{m-1}\left(1 - \frac{N(\Sigma p_i - \Sigma p_i^2)}{(N-1)s_x^2}\right)$$

(12.45) $$= \frac{m}{m-1}\left(1 - \frac{\Sigma(Np_i)(Nq_i)}{N(N-1)s_x^2}\right)$$

Formulas (12.43), (12.44), and (12.45) are equivalent. They provide a measure of the internal consistency of the items in the test. If data come to the computer in terms of the *proportion* of persons answering an item correctly, Formula (12.44) provides a convenient routine for machine computation since Σp and Σp^2 can be obtained simultaneously. If the *number* of persons answering each item correctly is available, Formula (12.45) should be used because it involves less computational labor and less error from rounding.

These formulas provide a kind of average of the various reliability coefficients which could be obtained from all the possible ways of subdividing the m test items, but that fact is not immediately obvious and requires more algebra for its development than it seems appropriate to introduce here.

The variance of scores, s_x^2, can be written as the sum of all item covariances and variances if each correct item is scored 1 and each incorrect item 0. In such scoring the variance of an item is $Npq/(N-1)$. Hence $\Sigma Np_iq_i/(N-1)$ is the sum of item variances in the sample. In formula (12.43) the quantity $N\Sigma p_iq_i/(N-1)s_x^2$ is the sum of item variances divided by the sum of item variances and covariances, each covariance being based on a pair of items.

If the sum of all the covariances were zero, the numerator and denominator would be equal, the quantity in parentheses would be zero and r would be zero. However this situation is very unlikely for it is almost inconceivable that a test maker would put together a set of wholly unrelated items. It is still less likely that he would formulate a test in which many of the inter-item correlations would be negative.

If the items are all measures of the same variable they should show positive correlations. If these inter-item correlations are high and positive, the inter-item covariances are large and positive, and the denominator s_x^2 which is the sum of variances and covariances is much larger than the numerator $N\Sigma p_iq_i/(N-1)$ which is the sum of variances only. Then the fraction $\dfrac{N\Sigma p_iq_i}{(N-1)s_x^2}$ is small (though it cannot be zero) and r_{xx} is near to 1. In this case the items are highly consistent with each other.

Kuder and Richardson [7] have given several variations of Formula (12.43) under different assumptions. Other proofs have been given by Jackson [6] and by Hoyt.[4]

As an application, consider a test of 12 items given to 9 subjects, each item being scored 1 if answered correctly and 0 if answered incorrectly as in Table 12.2. A genuine problem would be likely to involve a far greater number of subjects, but the pattern of procedure is the same, and the reader will learn as much from a small computation as from a long one.

TABLE 12.2. Record of 9 Subjects on 12 Items

Item	Record on Item i Made by Subject α									Np_i	Nq_i	p_i
	1	2	3	4	5	6	7	8	9			
1	1	0	0	0	1	1	0	1	1	5	4	.556
2	1	0	0	0	0	1	1	1	1	5	4	.556
3	1	0	1	1	1	1	1	1	0	7	2	.778
4	1	1	1	1	1	1	1	0	1	8	1	.889
5	1	1	1	1	1	1	1	0	0	7	2	.778
6	1	0	1	0	1	1	0	0	0	4	5	.444
7	1	1	1	0	1	1	1	0	1	7	2	.778
8	1	1	0	0	1	1	0	1	1	6	3	.667
9	1	1	1	0	1	1	1	0	1	7	2	.778
10	1	1	1	0	1	1	1	0	0	6	3	.667
11	1	0	1	0	0	1	1	1	1	6	3	.667
12	1	0	0	0	0	0	1	1	1	4	5	.444
X_α	12	6	8	3	9	11	9	6	8	72	36	8.002

Summing the columns of Table 12.2 produces the scores of the subjects, X_α. For these 9 scores,

$$\Sigma(X - \overline{X})^2 = (N - 1)s_x^2 = 60.$$

Summing the rows produces the item scores Np_i. Subtracting each Np_i from $N = 9$ produces Nq_i. As a check we note that

$$\sum_1^{12} Np_i = 72 = \sum_1^{9} X,$$

that

$$\Sigma Nq_i = 36,$$

and that

$$\Sigma Np_i + \Sigma Nq_i = 108 = 9 \times 12.$$

If the computation is completed by Formula (12.45) we first find $\Sigma(Np_i)(Nq_i) = 20 + 20 + 14 + 8 + \cdots + 18 + 20 = 198$ and

$$r_{xx} = \frac{12}{11}\left(1 - \frac{198}{9(60)}\right) = .69$$

If the computation is completed by Formula (12.44), we obtain the column p_i by dividing the Np_i column by $N = 9$. It is necessary to carry these values out to several decimal places to reduce the effect of rounding error. Then $\Sigma p_i = 8.002$ is checked against the expected value $\frac{72}{9} = 8$. $\Sigma p_i^2 = 5.559$.

$$r = \frac{12}{11}\left(1 - \frac{9(8.002 - 5.559)}{60}\right) = .69$$

REFERENCES

1. Brown, William, "Some Experimental Results in the Correlation of Mental Abilities," *British Journal of Psychology,* 3 (1910), 296–322.
2. Cronbach, Lee J., *Essentials of Psychological Testing,* New York, Harper Brothers, 1949.
3. Gulliksen, Harold, *Theory of Mental Tests,* New York, John Wiley and Sons, 1950.
4. Hoyt, Cyril, "Test Reliability Obtained by Analysis of Variance," *Psychometrika,* 6 (1941), 153–160.
5. Jackson, Robert W. B., *Application of the Analysis of Variance and Covariance Method to Educational Problems,* Bulletin No. 11, Department of Educational Research, University of Toronto, 1940.
6. Jackson, Robert W. B. and Ferguson, George A., *Studies on the Reliability of Tests,* Bulletin No. 12 of the Department of Educational Research, University of Toronto, 1941.
7. Kuder, G. F. and Richardson, M. W., "The Theory of the Estimation of Test Reliability," *Psychometrika,* 2 (1937), 151–160.
8. Lindquist, E. F., *Educational Measurement,* Washington, D.C., American Council on Education, 1951.
9. Spearman, Charles, "Correlation Calculated from Faulty Data," *British Journal of Psychology,* 3 (1910), 271–295.
10. Stouffer, Samuel A., *et al., Measurement and Prediction* (Studies in Social Psychology in World War II, Vol. 4), Princeton, N.J., Princeton University Press, 1950.
11. Thorndike, Robert S., *Personnel Selection; Test and Measurement Techniques,* New York, John Wiley and Sons, 1949.

13 Multiple Regression and Correlation

Methods of using scores on *one* variable to predict scores on another related variable were discussed in Chapter 10, and tests of significance for the correlation coefficient and the regression coefficient were given there. In this chapter scores on *two or more* variables will be combined to predict scores on another variable called the criterion and the following questions will be considered: What weight should be assigned to each of the predictor variables in order to obtain the best estimate of the criterion variable? How good is that "best estimate"? What computational routines are economical and efficient? How can significance tests be made for the coefficients in the prediction equation and for the coefficient of multiple correlation?

In this chapter it will be assumed that all correlation coefficients are product moment coefficients as defined in Chapter 10.

Prediction of Semester Grade in a First Course in Statistics. In order to estimate in advance the amount of difficulty students were likely to have in an introductory course in statistical methods, three prognostic tests were administered at the first session. One of these was a 45-minute test in reading difficult material. One was a specially constructed test of simple arithmetic and algebraic relationships of the sort most often encountered in statistical problems. One was an artificial language test involving unfamiliar symbols in logical systems of operation. Three class sections were available. Sections I and III met at the same evening period for a total of 3 hours a week. Students with good mathematical preparation and high scores on the prognostic tests were assigned to Section I while students who anticipated difficulty because of poor preparation and who had low scores on the tests were assigned to Section III, which was considerably smaller than Section I. Section II met in the morning for a total of 4 hours a week, and included students with widely varying background. The three sections were taught by three different teachers. When these

TABLE 13.1 Scores Made by Students in a First Course in Statistical Methods Subject Matter of the Course, and the Semester Grade (*indicates a women

Code number of student	Section	Prognostic Test Score: Reading	Prognostic Test Score: Artificial language	Prognostic Test Score: Arithmetic test	Criterion Score: Mid-term test	Criterion Score: Final exam	Criterion Score: Semester grade
1	III	33	51	33	58	65	62
2	III	39	50	36	53	51	52
3	I	38	38	39	52	53	53
4	I	23	27	29	47	42	45
*5	I	44	40	41	61	50	56
*6	I	45	54	38	47	53	50
7	I	48	57	42	64	64	64
8	II	38	39	35	64	54	59
9	II	32	46	23	58	50	54
*10	II	28	45	37	44	45	45
11	II	33	53	28	62	63	63
12	II	40	43	25	52	50	51
13	II	34	55	38	50	56	58
14	II	34	57	36	71	68	70
15	II	35	46	37	62	65	64
16	I	32	43	39	52	59	56
17	II	34	44	38	59	57	58
18	II	42	51	35	53	60	57
19	I	32	55	36	62	56	59
*20	III	24	34	17	37	43	40
21	I	39	52	34	55	53	54
22	I	34	25	29	30	42	36
23	II	44	58	35	61	56	59
24	III	27	29	26	49	40	45
25	II	34	52	30	43	38	41
26	II	40	53	29	61	54	58
27	I	37	34	26	47	57	52
28	III	22	40	33	47	50	49
29	I	30	54	40	56	47	52
*30	I	36	58	25	52	39	45
31	I	35	43	40	49	37	43
32	I	39	58	32	49	37	43
33	II	37	28	14	43	36	40
34	II	38	51	26	40	42	41
35	II	36	55	31	59	52	56
36	I	46	52	39	61	63	62
37	II	44	57	32	46	53	50
38		40	56	32	64	49	57
39	III	38	30	18	25	38	32
40	I	50	47	32	58	52	55
41	II	16	49	26	52	36	43
42	I	46	60	43	61	57	59
43	I	42	56	40	59	54	57
*44	III	27	53	26	62	48	55
45	III	33	55	25	55	57	56
46	II	40	54	34	52	57	55
47	I	46	53	37	62	49	56
*48	I	46	58	39	58	56	57

on Three Prognostic Tests given at Beginning of Term, Two Examinations in student.)

Code number of student	Section	Prognostic Test Score			Criterion Score		
		Reading	Artificial language	Arithmetic test	Midterm test	Final exam	Semester grade
*49		25	57	24	46	49	48
*50	III	26	45	18	47	25	36
*51	I	42	46	31	58	56	57
*52	I	34	60	33	62	64	63
53	III	28	37	8	47	46	47
54	II	21	24	16	44	41	43
55	I	44	43	35	58	55	57
56	I	38	47	28	58	56	57
57	III	16	50	27	47	47	47
58	III	40	48	35	56	38	47
59	III	33	42	25	52	46	49
*60	II	35	59	25	52	49	51
61	III	33	40	28	49	47	48
62	III	30	41	30	56	59	58
63	I	38	47	39	62	63	63
*64	III	36	43	26	61	50	56
*65	I	45	57	35	53	46	50
66	III	32	32	21	50	41	46
67	III	36	53	27	49	34	43
*68	III	21	46	39	44	33	39
69	II	30	54	34	47	46	47
70	II	34	49	27	50	44	48
71	II	41	58	39	53	57	55
72	I	44	55	38	47	46	47
*73	II	36	14	20	30	40	35
74	I	58	50	38	68	55	62
75	II	36	41	30	62	56	59
76	III	31	14	18	27	30	29
77	III	40	46	36	58	50	54
78	I	44	60	43	71	45	58
*79	III	36	36	23	49	43	46
80	I	44	51	36	53	47	50
*81	I	34	46	37	43	49	46
*82	I	38	56	36	64	61	63
*83	I	38	52	33	50	56	53
84	I	38	51	33	50	48	49
85	I	46	51	40	62	54	58
86	III	30	42	22	37	33	34
*87	III	26	44	28	58	48	53
*88	I	36	58	42	59	69	64
89	I	36	43	42	46	44	45
*90	III	32	59	36	61	55	58
*91	III	30	23	28	38	38	38
*92	I	31	58	31	44	51	48
93	II	44	34	32	55	49	52
*94	III	14	16	18	40	33	37
95	III	44	26	30	37	19	28
*96	I	30	58	37	61	56	59
97	I	39	34	33	41	46	44
98	I	32	56	30	65	51	58

tests were first given, only more or less intuitive speculation could be used to indicate how scores might be interpreted to predict success in the course as no criterion was then available. At the end of the semester, scores on a midterm test and on a final test and the average of these two tests recorded as the semester mark provided criteria against which the effectiveness of the prognostic tests could be studied. A formula thus developed to estimate one or the other of these criteria from the three placement tests could then be used in giving advice to similar classes in subsequent terms.

The data for all students who had scores on every test are shown in Table 13.1. An asterisk attached to a code number indicates a woman student. The figures in this table can be analysed in a variety of ways. In this chapter we shall consider problems related to the prediction of a criterion score from the three prognostic test scores.

Simplified Problem with Two Predictors. In order to help the student gain clear concepts of the procedure and the meaning of estimating one variable from several others and the residual errors involved in that process, a very small problem will now be worked out with only two predictors and a small number of cases selected at random from the data of Table 13.1. For this problem we shall predict score on the midterm test (Y) from score on the reading test (X_1) and score on the artificial language test (X_2).

Multiple Regression Equation with Two Predictors. To combine the two predicting variables (also called the independent variables) a *multiple regression equation* is used. For two predictors, the general form of this equation is

$$\tilde{Y}_\alpha = A + b_{y1.2}X_{1\alpha} + b_{y2.1}X_{2\alpha} \tag{13.1}$$

The notation of this equation is to be interpreted as follows:

$X_{1\alpha}$ and $X_{2\alpha}$ are observed scores for the αth individual.

A is a number to be computed from the sample data.

$b_{y1.2}$ is a number to be computed from the sample data indicating the weight given to X_1 in the regression equation. It is called a partial regression coefficient.

$b_{y2.1}$ is a number to be computed from the sample data. It is the partial regression coefficient which expresses the weight given to X_2 in the regression equation.

$\tilde{Y}_\alpha$ is the value of Y estimated from $X_{1\alpha}$ and $X_{2\alpha}$, by the regression equation

The formulas for $b_{y1.2}$, $b_{y2.1}$, and A will now be given without justification and the rationale will be developed in a later section.

(13.2) $$b_{y1.2} = \frac{r_{y1} - r_{y2}r_{12}}{1 - r^2_{12}} \cdot \frac{s_y}{s_1} \quad \text{and} \quad b_{y2.1} = \frac{r_{y2} - r_{y1}r_{12}}{1 - r^2_{12}} \, \frac{s_y}{s_2}$$

(13.3) $$A = \overline{Y} - b_{y1.2}\overline{X}_1 - b_{y2.1}\overline{X}_2$$

In order to display vividly the relations involved, 10 cases were chosen at random from the 98 cases of Table 13.1 and computations carried through for these 10 cases.

The mean and standard deviation of each trait are shown in the lower part of Table 13.2, also the three correlation coefficients. When these values are substituted in Formula (13.2) the values of the two regression coefficients are found to be

$$b_{y1.2} = -.006 \qquad\qquad b_{y2.1} = .134$$

Substitution of the means and $b_{y1.2}$ and $b_{y2.1}$ in Formula (13.3) gives

$$A = 51.2 + (.006)(34.1) - (.134)(49.2) = 44.9$$

The regression equation is therefore $\tilde{Y} = 44.9 - .006X_1 + .134X_2$ This equation should now be applied in turn to each of the ten individuals listed in Table 13.2, estimating his midterm test score Y on the basis of his two observed prognostic scores. These predictions are listed in the column headed $\tilde{Y}$ and the student should verify some of them. Errors of estimate are listed in the column $Y - \tilde{Y}$ and should be verified by the student.

When the variables are expressed in standard score form, we shall attach a star to the symbol for the regression coefficient. In this case the constant A disappears from the equation leaving it

(13.4) $$\frac{\tilde{Y}_\alpha - \overline{Y}}{s_y} = b^*_{y1.2} \frac{X_{1\alpha} - \overline{X}_1}{s_1} + b^*_{y2.1} \frac{X_{2\alpha} - \overline{X}_2}{s_2}$$

(13.5) where $$b^*_{y1.2} = \frac{r_{y1} - r_{y2}r_{12}}{1 - r^2_{12}}$$

$$b^*_{y2.1} = \frac{r_{y2} - r_{y1}r_{12}}{1 - r^2_{12}}$$

For the data of Table 13.2 therefore $b^*_{y1.2} = -.0084$ and $b^*_{y2.1} = .165$.

Thus b^*'s like the r's are pure numbers which do not involve the scale of measurement of the traits while the b's are affected by the scale of measurement. For all work in which a regression equation is used to predict scores the b's must be used unless all variables are in standard score form. For almost all other problems, including tests of significance, it is more convenient to use the b^*'s. In later sections of this chapter several such problems

TABLE 13.2 Scores for Ten Cases Selected at Random from Table 13.1 and Certain Statistics Derived from Those Scores

Case	X_1 Reading	X_2 Artificial language	Y Mid-term test	$\tilde{Y}$ Predicted value	$Y - \tilde{Y}$ Residual	$(Y)(\tilde{Y})$
32	39	58	49	52.34	− 3.34	2564.66
16	32	43	52	50.39	1.61	2620.28
66	32	32	50	48.93	1.07	2446.50
46	40	54	52	51.80	.20	2693.60
22	32	55	62	51.98	10.02	3222.76
41	16	49	52	51.29	.71	2667.08
28	22	40	47	50.06	− 3.06	2352.82
47	46	53	62	51.63	10.37	3201.06
34	38	51	40	51.41	− 11.41	2056.40
37	44	57	46	52.17	− 6.13	2399.82
Sum	341	492	512	512.00	0	26224.98
Sum of squares	12429	24838	26626	26224.95	400.99	———
$\frac{(\text{Sum})^2}{10}$	11628.1	24206.4	26214.4	26214.4	0	———
Sum of squares of deviations	800.9	631.6	411.6	10.55	400.99	———

$\Sigma X_1X_2 = 17130$	$r_{12} = .496$	$\overline{X}_1 = 34.1$	$s_1^2 = 88.99$	$s_1 = 9.43$
$\Sigma X_1Y = 17501$	$r_{1y} = .073$	$\overline{X}_2 = 49.2$	$s_2^2 = 70.18$	$s_2 = 8.38$
$\Sigma X_2Y = 25272$	$r_{2y} = .160$	$\overline{Y} = 51.2$	$s_y^2 = 45.73$	$s_y = 6.76$

$$b^*_{y1.2} = \frac{r_{y1} - r_{y2}r_{12}}{1 - r^2_{12}} = -.00843 \qquad b_{y1.2} = -.008\frac{s_y}{s_1} = -.00604$$

$$b^*_{y2.1} = \frac{r_{y2} - r_{y1}r_{12}}{1 - r^2_{12}} = .165 \qquad b_{y2.1} = .164\frac{s_y}{s_2} = .134$$

will be considered. The symbol β is in fairly general use for the value here denoted as b^*, having been used before there was any general recognition of the desirability of using different symbols for population parameters and sample statistics. In this text β^* represents the population value corresponding to the sample value b^* and β the population value corresponding to b.

Effectiveness of Prediction by a Multiple Regression Equation. A multiple regression equation may involve a large number of terms and a great deal of computation and still be relatively useless. Two different questions have probably occurred to the reader before now: (1) How effective was this equation in estimating midterm scores for these ten students? (2) If applied to another random sample out of the 98 students or if applied to another class another term, how effective would the predictions be?

Unless the equation is effective with the group on which it was obtained it cannot be expected to be useful with another group. However it may give very close estimations for the group on which it was obtained and be much less effective with a new group. The two issues must be considered separately.

Intuitively one might say that a regression equation gives a satisfactory estimation for the group on which it was obtained if there is a high correlation between observed and estimated scores, or if most of the variation of observed scores can be ascribed to regression and very little to errors of estimate. These two interpretations will now be considered in relation to the data of Table 13.2 and will be seen to be really the same interpretation.

Multiple Correlation. The coefficient of correlation between observed scores on some trait and scores predicted for that trait by a multiple regression equation is called a *coefficient of multiple correlation* or a *multiple correlation coefficient.* For the data of Table 13.2 this would be the correlation between scores in the columns Y and $\tilde{Y}$. From the final column in that table $\Sigma Y\tilde{Y} = 26224.98$. Since the mean of $\tilde{Y}$ is the same as $\overline{Y}$,

$$\Sigma y\tilde{y} = 26224.98 - (512)^2/10 = 10.58$$

and

$$r_{y\tilde{y}} = \frac{\Sigma Y\tilde{Y} - (\Sigma Y)^2/N}{\sqrt{\left(\Sigma Y^2 - \dfrac{(\Sigma Y)^2}{N}\right)\left(\Sigma \tilde{Y}^2 - \dfrac{(\Sigma Y)^2}{N}\right)}} = \frac{10.58}{\sqrt{(411.6)(10.55)}} = .16$$

The symbol for this multiple correlation will be written $R_{y.12}$. The single primary subscript standing to the left of the dot names the variable whose observed and estimated scores are being correlated. The two secondary subscripts to the right of the dot name the variables used as predictors in the regression equation. Other symbols sometimes used with the same meaning as $R_{y.12}$ are

$$R_{y(12)},\quad r_{y.12},\quad r_{y(12)},\quad r_{0.12},\quad \text{and}\quad R_{0.12}.$$

The direct computation described above was employed only for the purpose of making vivid to the student the concept of what a multiple r means. Several formulas algebraically equivalent to that process are available for obtaining $R_{y.12}$ more economically. Of these one of the most convenient to use is

$$R_{y.12} = \sqrt{r_{y1}b^*_{y1.2} + r_{y2}b^*_{y2.1}} \tag{13.6}$$

Substitution of $r_{y1} = .073$, $r_{y2} = .160$, $b^*_{y1.2} = -.0084$, and $b^*_{y2.1} = .165$ as already found, yields $R_{y.12} = \sqrt{.0256} = .16$ which agrees with the result previously obtained by more laborious computation.

Partition of the Sum of Squares. Reference to the lower portion of Table 13.2 shows the following sums of squares:

Sum of squares of regressed values about $\overline{Y}$,	$\Sigma(\tilde{Y} - \overline{Y})^2 =$	10.555
Sum of squares of residual errors,	$\Sigma(Y - \tilde{Y})^2 =$	400.995
		411.550
Total = Sum of squares of scores about $\overline{Y}$,	$\Sigma(Y - \overline{Y})^2 =$	411.6

This partition of the total sum of squares is reminiscent of similar relations encountered in Chapters 9 and 10. It may be described by the formula

$$\Sigma(Y - \overline{Y})^2 = R^2_{y.12}\Sigma(Y - \overline{Y})^2 + (1 - R^2_{y.12})\Sigma(Y - \overline{Y})^2 \tag{13.7}$$

For these data

$$\begin{aligned}\Sigma(Y - \overline{Y})^2 &= (.0256)(411.6) + (1 - .0256)(411.6)\\ &= 10.54 \qquad\qquad + 401.06\end{aligned}$$

Except for rounding errors, the result of substituting $R_{y.12}$ and $\Sigma(Y - \overline{Y})^2$ in Formula (13.7) agrees with the sums of squares read from Table 13.2. The partition of the sum of squares may now be interpreted in two ways.

A. Interpretation as to effectiveness of prediction for observed group. From Formula (13.7) it appears that for this group

$R^2_{y.12}$ = proportion of the sum of squares of midterm marks which can be ascribed to variation in prognostic score

= proportion of variation (measured as sum of squares) of midterm marks which might be eliminated if all cases were selected to have the same prognostic test score

$1 - R^2_{y.12}$ = proportion of variation in midterm marks which is independent of variation in prognostic test scores and so must be ascribed to other sources of variation

= proportion of variation in midterm marks which would remain even in a group uniform as to prognostic test score.

The question of whether the regression equation does or does not provide effective prediction may now be answered in terms of a value judgment as to how much unexplained variation can be tolerated in the particular circumstances in which one is working. Anyone who thinks realistically about achievement of students on a college course would think of many sources of variation unrelated to scores on any prognostic test, as, for example, differences in motivation and interest, in study habits, in time available for study, in other abilities such as mathematical background and general level of intelligence not measured by these tests, in personal vicissitudes during the term. He would also think of sources of measurement error affecting scores on the criterion and on the prognostic tests such as differences in previous experience of the student with such tests, his state of mind and body on the day the tests were given, the brevity of the tests and the particular selection of material in them, and so on. All such sources of error contribute to the proportion of variation $1 - R^2_{y.12}$. The person using the regression equation must decide whether the reduction in variation represented as $R^2_{y.12}$ represents an increase of information sufficient to justify the time required for giving the tests, scoring them, and analyzing results. For the present data of course it must be presumed that inclusion of the third prognostic test in the regression equation, as is done later in this chapter, will improve the predictions. For the ten cases considered here, the proportional reduction in variance of .0256 is too slight to be worth the trouble of giving and scoring the tests. However, it will presently be seen that for 98 cases the multiple correlation is much higher, in fact .66. This sample, which was actually drawn at random, happened to be an extreme deviate.

B. Interpretation in terms of sampling significance. The partition of the sum of squares leads to a test of significance for the multiple correlation coefficient. The sum of squares of regressed values $\dfrac{\Sigma(\tilde{Y} - \overline{Y})^2}{\sigma^2} = R^2_{y.12} \dfrac{\Sigma(Y - \overline{Y})^2}{\sigma^2}$ is distributed as χ^2 with 2 degrees of freedom. The sum of squares of residual errors

$\frac{\Sigma(Y - \tilde{Y})^2}{\sigma^2} = (1 - R^2_{y.12}) \frac{\Sigma(Y - \overline{Y})^2}{\sigma^2}$ is distributed as χ^2 with $N - 3$ degrees of freedom. The two sums of squares are independently distributed. Under the hypothesis that $\rho_{y.12} = 0$, the two ratios $\frac{\Sigma(\tilde{Y} - \overline{Y})^2}{2}$ and $\frac{\Sigma(Y - \tilde{Y})^2}{N - 3}$ are estimates of the same variance σ^2. Therefore the quotient

$$(13.8) \qquad F = \frac{R^2\Sigma(Y - \overline{Y})^2}{2} \bigg/ \frac{(1 - R^2)\Sigma(Y - \overline{Y})^2}{N - 3} = \frac{R^2}{1 - R^2} \cdot \frac{N - 3}{2}$$

has the F distribution with $n_1 = 2$ and $n_2 = N - 3$. This expression gives a test of the hypothesis that in the population the multiple correlation coefficient is zero.

For the 10 cases of Table 13.2, $F = \frac{.0256}{.9744} \cdot \frac{7}{2} = .09$. It is apparent from *interpretation A* that the two tests under consideration — difficult reading and artificial language — did not furnish a usable prediction of midterm mark for the 10 cases observed and it is apparent by *interpretation B* that the sample of 10 cases does not contradict the hypothesis that in the population there is no correlation between midterm mark and a weighted combination of the two tests. The size of the sample affects the second interpretation but not the first.

If there had been k predictor variables instead of 2 the ratio

$$(13.9) \qquad F = \frac{R^2}{1 - R^2} \cdot \frac{N - k - 1}{k}$$

would be distributed as F with $n_1 = k$ and $n_2 = N - k - 1$.

The Normal Equations. In order to generalize the regression equation with two predictors to a regression equation with any number of predictors it will be helpful to explore the rationale more carefully. Such an equation with 5 predictors may be written as

$$(13.10) \qquad \tilde{Y}_{12345} = A_{y.12345} + b_{y1.2345}X_1 + b_{y2.1345}X_2 + b_{y3.1245}X_3 + b_{y4.1235}X_4 + b_{y5.1234}X_5$$

$$(13.11) \text{ when } A_{y.12345} = \overline{Y} - b_{y1.2345}\overline{X}_1 - b_{y2.1345}\overline{X}_2 - b_{y3.1245}\overline{X}_3 - b_{y4.1235}\overline{X}_4 - b_{y5.1234}\overline{X}_5$$

The pattern of subscripts is clear and can be easily adapted to any number of variables. As before, A and all the b's are unknown and must be computed from the group data, while all the X's are known but vary from individual to individual. The criterion for obtaining the b's is that the sum of the squares of the errors of estimate, that is $\Sigma(Y - \tilde{Y})^2$, shall be made as small as possible. If values of the b's are chosen so as to make this residual sum of squares a minimum those same b's will make the correlation between observed Y and estimated $\tilde{Y}$ a maximum. Students familiar with the calculus will know the customary mathematical procedure for making the sum of squares a minimum. Others must take the end product for granted. That end product is a set of simultaneous linear equations which are called *normal equations*. (The term "normal" here has no reference whatever to the normal curve.) There are as many such equations in one problem as there are unknown b's. For a 5-predictor problem the set of normal equations is

(13.12)

$$\begin{aligned}
b^*_{y1.2345} + r_{12}b^*_{y2.1345} + r_{13}b^*_{y3.1245} + r_{14}b^*_{y4.1235} + r_{15}b^*_{y5.1234} &= r_{y1} \\
r_{12}b^*_{y1.2345} + b^*_{y2.1345} + r_{23}b^*_{y3.1245} + r_{24}b^*_{y4.1235} + r_{25}b^*_{y5.1234} &= r_{y2} \\
r_{13}b^*_{y1.2345} + r_{23}b^*_{y2.1345} + b^*_{y3.1245} + r_{34}b^*_{y4.1235} + r_{35}b^*_{y5.1234} &= r_{y3} \\
r_{14}b^*_{y1.2345} + r_{24}b^*_{y2.1345} + r_{34}b^*_{y3.1245} + b^*_{y4.1235} + r_{45}b^*_{y5.1234} &= r_{y4} \\
r_{15}b^*_{y1.2345} + r_{25}b^*_{y2.1345} + r_{35}b^*_{y3.1245} + r_{45}b^*_{y4.1235} + b^*_{y5.1234} &= r_{y5}
\end{aligned}$$

It should be noted that the unknowns in these equations are b^*'s but the b's can be obtained from them by multiplying by the ratio of standard deviations,

(13.13) $$b_{y4.1235} = b^*_{y4.1235} \frac{s_y}{s_4}$$

and similarly for the other b's. All r's are known, having been computed from the observed data. The correlation of every variable with every other variable is required.

Numerical values for the b^*'s can be obtained either by solving the normal equations symbolically and substituting the known values of the r's in the symbolic solutions or by substituting the numerical values of the r's directly in the normal equations and solving the resulting equations for the b^*'s. The former method produces a set of formulas for the b^*'s, and when there are only two or three predictor variables it is the simpler method to use. It has already been illustrated for the data of Table 13.2. When there are many predictor variables the formulas for the b^*'s become complicated and substitution in them involves a large number of steps. The solution can then be obtained much more economically by substituting the r's in the normal equations and employing an efficient routine for solution of the resulting numerical equations. Such a routine will be developed in later sections of this chapter.

No matter which method is employed for obtaining the numerical values of the b^*'s, the multiple correlation can be found by the formula

(13.14)

$$R_{y.12345} = \sqrt{r_{y1}b^*_{y1.2345} + r_{y2}b^*_{y2.1345} + r_{y3}b^*_{y3.1245} + r_{y4}b^*_{y4.1235} + r_{y5}b^*_{y5.1234}}$$

This formula is readily generalized to any number of variables.

EXERCISE 13.1

1. For the cases in Table 13.1 the data of Table 13.3 were obtained. By substitution in Formulas (13.1), (13.2), and (13.3) obtain the regression equation to estimate midterm test scores from scores on the two prognostic tests. Compare it with the equation obtained from the 10 cases of Table 13.2.

2. By substitution in Formula (13.6) obtain the multiple correlation $R_{y.12}$ and compare it with the value obtained from the 10 cases of Table 13.2.

3. Test the hypothesis that $\rho_{y.12} = 0$. Why is that hypothesis so much less credible in the light of the data from all 98 cases than in the light of the data from 10 cases?

4. Suppose a criterion variable Y is to be estimated from three predictor variables named X_2, X_6 and X_7. (a) Write a regression equation similar to equation (13.10) with subscripts properly placed. Note that the order in which the three predictors are arranged is unimportant and that therefore the order of secondary subscripts is unimportant. (b) Write the three normal equations similar to those in Formula (13.12). (c) Write a formula for $R_{y.267}$ similar to Formula (13.14)

5. If a criterion trait Y is to be estimated from two other traits X_4 and X_6, write out with appropriate subscripts the formulas for

(a) $b^*_{y4.6}$
(b) $b^*_{y6.4}$
(c) $b_{y4.6}$
(d) $b_{y6.4}$
(e) A = constant term in the regression equation
(f) $R_{y.46}$
(g) The normal equations

6. If a criterion trait X_1 is to be estimated from traits X_3 and X_7, write out with appropriate subscripts the formulas for

(a) $b^*_{13.7}$
(b) $b^*_{17.3}$
(c) $b_{13.7}$
(d) $b_{17.3}$
(e) A
(f) $R_{1.37}$
(g) The 3 normal equations

The Doolittle Method of Solving the Normal Equations by Successive Elimination. If there are more than two predictors in the regression equation, it is a laborious process to compute the regression coefficients by substituting the numerical values of the r's in formulas obtained by solving the normal equations symbolically, as was done in the preceding section for the case of two predictors. With more than two predictors it is easier to substitute the numerical values of the r's in the normal equations themselves, and then to solve the resulting equations. There are several commonly used methods for solving first degree equations, and the normal equations are of first degree. One of the most economical of such methods, is named for M. H. Doolittle. He improved on the method first used by Gauss and published his method in the Report for 1878 of the U.S. Coast and Geodetic Survey[1].

This method simplifies computation by taking advantage of certain symmetry relations among the correlations namely that

$$r_{12} = r_{21},\ r_{13} = r_{31},\ \text{etc.}$$

The Doolittle Method will be developed in some detail for the case in which there are only three predictors in order that the student may understand its rationale. For this purpose we may use the three prognostic tests of Table 13.1 as a basis for predicting midterm test scores. The pertinent data for all 98 cases are presented in Table 13.3. The three normal equations are

$$\begin{aligned} b^*_{y1.23} + r_{12}b^*_{y2.13} + r_{13}b^*_{y3.12} &= r_{y1} \\ r_{12}b^*_{y1.23} + b^*_{y2.13} + r_{23}b^*_{y3.12} &= r_{y2} \\ r_{13}b^*_{y1.23} + r_{23}b^*_{y2.13} + b^*_{y3.12} &= r_{y3} \end{aligned} \tag{13.15}$$

TABLE 13.3 Correlations of Midterm Marks and Scores on Three Prognostic Tests for Students in a First Course in Statistical Method.

	Test	Mean	s	Correlation X_1	X_2	X_3	Y
X_1	Difficult reading	35.69	7.68		.321	.477	.357
X_2	Artificial language	46.43	11.03	.321		.539	.620
X_3	Arithmetic-Algebra	31.38	7.28	.477	.539		.518
Y	Midterm	52.46	9.33	.357	.620	.518	

When the computed values of the r's are substituted in Equations (13.15) and the results are simplified by writing $-u_1 = b^*_{y1.23}$, $-u_2 = b^*_{y2.13}$ and $-u_3 = b^*_{y3.12}$, and both sides of the resulting equations are multiplied by -1, we have the new set of equations

$$\begin{aligned} &(1)\quad u_1 + .321u_2 + .477u_3 = -.357 \\ &(2)\quad .321u_1 + u_2 + .539u_3 = -.620 \\ &(3)\quad .477u_1 + .539u_2 + u_3 = -.518\,. \end{aligned} \tag{13.16}$$

The methods of solution of simultaneous equations studied in high school algebra are applicable, but unless steps are set down in an orderly routine there will be much waste effort. The student should study carefully the routine set forth in Table 13.4 until

TABLE 13.4 Detailed Solution of Equations (13.16)

Line	Step	
	THE FORWARD SOLUTION	
[1.1]	Write equation 1	$u_1 + .321\,u_2 + .477\,u_3 = -.357$
[1.2]	[1.1]·(− 1)	$-u_1 - .321\,u_2 - .477\,u_3 = .357$
[2.1]	Write equation 2	$.321\,u_1 + u_2 + .539\,u_3 = -.620$
[2.2]	[1.1]·(−.321)	$-.321\,u_1 - .103\,u_2 - .153\,u_3 = .115$
[2.3]	[2.1] + [2.2]	$0 + .897\,u_2 + .386\,u_3 = -.505$
[2.4]	[2.3] ÷ (− .897)	$0 - u_2 - .430\,u_3 = .563$
[3.1]	Write equation 3	$.477\,u_1 + .539\,u_2 + u_3 = -.518$
[3.2]	[1.1]·(− .477)	$-.477\,u_1 - .153\,u_2 - .228\,u_3 = .170$
[3.3]	[2.3]·(− .430)	$0 - .386\,u_2 - .166\,u_3 = .217$
[3.4]	[3.1] + [3.2] + [3.3]	$0 + 0 + .606\,u_3 = -.131$
[3.5]	[3.4] ÷ (− .606)	$0 + 0 - u_3 = .216$
	THE BACK SOLUTION	
[1.1*B*]	Enter [3.5]	$-u_3 = .216$
[2.1*B*]	Enter [2.4]	$-u_2 - .430\,u_3 = .563$
[2.2*B*]	[1.1*B*]·(− .430)	$.430\,u_3 = -.093$
[2.3*B*]	[2.1*B*] + [2.2*B*]	$-u_2 + 0 = .470$
[3.1*B*]	Enter [1.2]	$-u_1 - .321\,u_2 - .477\,u_3 = .357$
[3.2*B*]	[1.1*B*]·(− .477)	$.477\,u_3 = -.102$
[3.3*B*]	[2.3*B*]·(−.321)	$.321\,u_2 + 0 = -.152$
[3.4*B*]	[3.1*B*] + [3.2*B*] + [3.3*B*]	$-u_1 + 0 + 0 = .102$

he understands it fully and then should compare it with Table 13.5 so that he may understand how to generalize that abbreviated solution to a pattern accommodating any number of predictor variables. In Table 13.5 letters representing variables u_1, u_2 and u_3 have been omitted and only their coefficients printed. Certain unnecessary terms have also been omitted as well as signs of operation and equality.

The solution proceeds in cycles, there being as many cycles as there are unknowns, and one unknown being eliminated in each cycle. The lines have been numbered in such a way as to indicate both the cycle and the row within the cycle. Thus [3.2] indicates the 2d row in cycle 3.

The forward solution proceeds by successive elimination of one unknown after another until a value is found for one of the unknowns. Then the back solution consists of taking the values

TABLE 13.5 Abbreviated Solution of Equations (13.16)

THE FORWARD SOLUTION

Line	Step	X_1	X_2	X_3	Y	Check
[1.1]	Insert r_{1j}'s	1	.321	.477	−.357	1.441
[1.2]	1.1·(−1)	−1	−.321	−.477	.357	−1.441
[2.1]	Insert r_{2j}'s	.321	1.000	.539	−.620	1.240
[2.2]	[1.1]·(−.321)		−.103	−.153	.115	−.463
[2.3]	[2.1]+[2.2]		.897	.386	−.505	.777
[2.4]	[2.3]÷(−.897)		−1.000	−.430	.563	−.866
[3.1]	Insert r_{3j}'s	.477	.539	1.000	−.518	1.498
[3.2]	[1.1]·(−.477)			−.228	.170	−.687
[3.3]	[2.3]·(−.430)			−.166	.217	−.334
[3.4]	[3.1]+[3.2]+[3.3]			.606	−.131	.477
[3.5]	[3.4]÷(−.606)			−1.000	.216	−.787

THE BACK SOLUTION

Line	Step	X_1	X_2	X_3	Y	Check
[1.1*B*]	Enter [3.5]			−1.000	.216	−.787
[2.1*B*]	Enter [2.4]		−1.000	−.430	.563	−.866
[2.2*B*]	[1.1*B*]·(−.430)			.430	−.093	.338
[2.3*B*]	[2.1*B*]+2.2*B*		−1.000		.470	−.528
[3.1*B*]	Enter [1.2]	−1.000	−.321	−.477	.357	−1.441
[3.2*B*]	[1.1*B*]·(−.477)			.477	−.103	.375
[3.3*B*]	[2.3*B*]·(−.321)		.321		−.152	.169
[3.4*B*]	[3.1*B*]+[3.2*B*]+[3.3*B*]	−1.000			.102	−.897

$$b^*_{y3.12} = .216, \quad b^*_{y2.13} = .470, \quad b^*_{y1.23} = .102$$

$$R_{y.123} = \sqrt{r_{y1}b^*_{y1.23} + r_{y2}b^*_{y2.13} + r_{y3}b^*_{y3.12}} = .663$$

of those unknowns which have already been found and substituting them in equations to obtain values of the remaining unknowns.

Each cycle may be thought of as having a first line, a last line, a next-to-the-last line, and a set of "other" lines. (The first cycle is an exception, having only 2 lines.) The first step in each cycle of the forward solution is to record the values of the appropriate r's. In the third cycle these are the correlations of X_3 with the other variables, and similarly in a problem involving many predictors the correlations with X_k are recorded on the first line of cycle k. The column headed X_2 receives the correlations of X_2 with other variables and in general in a problem in which there are many predictors the column headed X_k receives correlations of X_k with other variables. The criterion variable is placed at the right of the predictors. This step is equivalent to recording the original equations in the detailed solution.

Following the line on which r's are entered, each cycle has one line obtained from each of the preceding cycles, as worked out in detail in Table 13.6 for cycle 5. Thus in a problem with many

TABLE 13.6 Detailed Steps for Cycle 5 in Forward Solution

[5.1]	Enter the correlation of X_5 with each of the other variables, placing r_{52} in column X_2, r_{57} in column X_7, etc. Enter the sum of all these correlations in the check column.
[5.2]	Multiply line [1.1] in cycle 1 by the entry in column X_5 and line [1.2]. Do not record any values to the left of column X_5. Multiply the entry in check column of [1.1] by same multiplier from line [1.2] and enter result in check column of [5.2].
[5.3]	Multiply line [2.3] in cycle 2 (including the entry in check column) by the entry in column X_5 and line [2.4], but do not record any values to the left of column X_5.
[5.4]	Multiply line [3.4] in cycle 3 (including the entry in check column) by the entry in column X_5 and line [3.5].
[5.5]	Multiply line [4.5] in cycle 4 (including the entry in check column) by the entry in column X_5 and line [4.6].
[5.6]	Add lines [5.1] to [5.5].
[5.7]	Divide line [5.6] by the first entry in that line, that is, the entry in column X_5, after having first changed the sign of the divisor. The first entry in [5.7] should be − 1.000. The entry now standing in the check column should be equal to the sum of the other entries in line [5.7].

predictors, cycle k would have $k - 1$ such lines. Each of these lines is obtained by multiplying the entries in the next-to-the-last line in one of the preceding cycles by an entry in the last line of that cycle. Thus line [1.1] is multiplied by an entry in [1.2] and line [2.3] by an entry in [2.4]. In a problem with many predictors this would be continued until all the preceding cycles had been covered. Each of the multiplying numbers is taken from column X_k when one is working in cycle k and entries to the left of column X_k are not recorded. This is the equivalent of multiplying the coefficients of the unknowns in a particular equation by a pertinent or helpful constant so that when equations are added one unknown will disappear.

The next-to-the-last line in each cycle is the sum of all the preceding lines in that cycle. Examination of the detailed solution will show that at this step one unknown is eliminated from the equations.

The last line in each cycle is obtained by multiplying each entry in the preceding line by the negative reciprocal of the first entry. This step makes the coefficient of the leading term −1, as it is in the detailed solution.

In the back solution the first line of each cycle is the last line of a cycle in the forward solution, the cycles being taken in reverse order.

Checks. Substitution of the computed values of the standard regression coefficients, the b^*'s, in the normal equations provides check on all b^*'s at once. For the data under consideration substitution in the equations

$$\begin{aligned} b^*_{y1.23} + r_{12}b^*_{y2.13} + r_{13}b^*_{y3.12} &= r_{y1} \\ r_{12}b^*_{y1.23} + b^*_{y2.13} + r_{23}b^*_{y3.12} &= r_{y2} \\ r_{13}b^*_{y1.23} + r_{23}b^*_{y2.13} + b^*_{y3.12} &= r_{y3} \end{aligned}$$

would yield the following check:

$$\begin{aligned} .102 + (.321)(.470) + (.477)(.216) &= .3559 \text{ while } r_{y1} = .357 \\ (.321)(.102) + (.470) + (.539)(.216) &= .6192 \text{ while } r_{y2} = .620 \\ (.477)(.102) + (.539)(.470) + (.216) &= .5180 \text{ while } r_{y3} = .518 \end{aligned}$$

Most experienced computers like to check their work step by step, so that if a mistake is made it may be caught immediately. For this purpose a check column is added at the right of the worksheet. For the first line in each cycle, the entry in this column is the sum of the r's entered on that line. All other entries in the column are obtained by the same set of directions which apply to the other columns. The check consists of ascertaining that the entry in the check column is equal to the sum of the other entries for the last line and for the next-to-the-last line in each cycle. In general, that relation will not hold for the other lines in the forward solution because of the omission of certain terms. It holds for all lines in the back solution. Even if the check column indicates no error, the check by substitution in the normal equations should be made because the entries in the check column do not provide an infallible check.

Fisher Modification of the Doolittle Method. The procedures described in the preceding section serve to obtain a multiple regression equation, and a multiple correlation coefficient and to test the significance of that correlation coefficient. To test the significance of the b^*'s in the regression equation another approach is necessary. The method to be described in this section will provide the standard error of a coefficient of partial regression and will thus make it possible (1) to test hypotheses about such coefficients, (2) to make an interval estimate of the population regression coefficient, and (3) to predict several different criterion variables from the same set of predictors.

The discussion will be carried out for the case of three predictors and illustrated by the data already used to predict midterm test scores from three prognostic tests. Here we shall (1) test hypotheses concerning the regression coefficients in the population, (2) make interval estimates concerning them, and (3) obtain two regression equations from the same predictors, one with midterm test scores as criterion and one with final examination grades as criterion. For these purposes certain supplementary values are needed.

Two explanations will now be offered. Explanation A should be helpful for persons who have studied matrix algebra and incomprehensible to most others. The latter need not look at it but may go on at once to explanation B. Persons who can read explanation A will not need explanation B. Those who cannot read explanation A will probably have to take the routine more or less on faith and need not strain to understand the underlying rationale.

A. Explanation in terms of matrices. The normal Equations (13.15) may be written in matrix notation as

$$\text{(13.17)} \quad \begin{Bmatrix} 1 & r_{12} & r_{13} \\ r_{12} & 1 & r_{23} \\ r_{13} & r_{23} & 1 \end{Bmatrix} \begin{Bmatrix} b^*_{y1.23} \\ b^*_{y2.13} \\ b^*_{y3.12} \end{Bmatrix} = \begin{Bmatrix} r_{y1} \\ r_{y2} \\ r_{y3} \end{Bmatrix}$$

When expanded, this becomes Equations (13.21) of explanation B. If both sides are premultiplied by the inverse of the matrix of r's, we have

(13.18)

$$\begin{Bmatrix} 1 & r_{12} & r_{13} \\ r_{12} & 1 & r_{23} \\ r_{13} & r_{23} & 1 \end{Bmatrix}^{-1} \begin{Bmatrix} 1 & r_{12} & r_{13} \\ r_{12} & 1 & r_{23} \\ r_{13} & r_{23} & 1 \end{Bmatrix} \begin{Bmatrix} b^*_{y1.23} \\ b^*_{y2.13} \\ b^*_{y3.12} \end{Bmatrix} = \begin{Bmatrix} 1 & r_{12} & r_{13} \\ r_{12} & 1 & r_{23} \\ r_{13} & r_{23} & 1 \end{Bmatrix}^{-1} \begin{Bmatrix} r_{y1} \\ r_{y2} \\ r_{y3} \end{Bmatrix}$$

Hence

$$\text{(13.19)} \quad \begin{Bmatrix} 1 & 0 & 0 \\ 0 & 1 & 0 \\ 0 & 0 & 1 \end{Bmatrix} \begin{Bmatrix} b^*_{y1.23} \\ b^*_{y2.13} \\ b^*_{y3.12} \end{Bmatrix} = \begin{Bmatrix} C_{11} & C_{12} & C_{13} \\ C_{21} & C_{22} & C_{23} \\ C_{31} & C_{32} & C_{33} \end{Bmatrix} \begin{Bmatrix} r_{y1} \\ r_{y2} \\ r_{y3} \end{Bmatrix}$$

When expanded (13.19) becomes Equations (13.22) of explanation *B*. The goal now is to obtain the values of the C's which are the elements of the inverse matrix. The product of the matrix of r's by its inverse, the matrix of C's is the identity matrix

$$(13.20) \qquad \begin{Bmatrix} 1 & r_{12} & r_{13} \\ r_{12} & 1 & r_{23} \\ r_{13} & r_{23} & 1 \end{Bmatrix} \begin{Bmatrix} C_{11} & C_{12} & C_{13} \\ C_{21} & C_{22} & C_{23} \\ C_{31} & C_{32} & C_{33} \end{Bmatrix} = \begin{Bmatrix} 1 & 0 & 0 \\ 0 & 1 & 0 \\ 0 & 0 & 1 \end{Bmatrix}$$

When expanded (13.20) becomes Equation (13.23) of explanation *B*. There are nine equations in (13.20) and 9 unknown C's to be computed. However, because of the symmetrical nature of the matrix of r's, the matrix of C's is also symmetrical and $C_{12} = C_{21}$, $C_{13} = C_{31}$, $C_{23} = C_{32}$. The C's which are elements of the inverse matrix are sometimes called *elements of the inverse solution*, or from relations (13.19), *multipliers* or *inverse multipliers*. They will be called *multipliers* in this book.

In section *C* a routine for obtaining these C's will be developed.

B. Explanation without matrices. The normal equations

$$(13.21) \qquad \begin{cases} 1 \cdot b^*_{y1.23} + r_{12}b^*_{y2.13} + r_{13}b^*_{y3.12} = r_{y1} \\ r_{12}b^*_{y1.23} + 1 \cdot b^*_{y2.13} + r_{23}b^*_{y3.12} = r_{y2} \\ r_{13}b^*_{y1.23} + r_{23}b^*_{y2.13} + 1 \cdot b^*_{y3.12} = r_{y3} \end{cases}$$

might be thought of as equations to obtain the values r_{y1}, r_{y2}, r_{y3} from the b^*'s. However what is usually needed are the inverse expressions for the b^*'s in terms of the correlations r_{y1}, r_{y2}, r_{y3} and the correlations among the predictors r_{12}, r_{13}, r_{23}. Equations (13.21) may be solved for the b^*'s but when there are more than two predictors the symbolic solutions are complicated. These solutions may be indicated by the set of inverse equations

$$(13.22) \qquad \begin{aligned} b^*_{y1.23} &= C_{11}r_{y1} + C_{12}r_{y2} + C_{13}r_{y3} \\ b^*_{y2.13} &= C_{21}r_{y1} + C_{22}r_{y2} + C_{23}r_{y3} \\ b^*_{y3.12} &= C_{31}r_{y1} + C_{32}r_{y2} + C_{33}r_{y3} \end{aligned}$$

where each C represents an expression involving the correlations r_{12}, r_{13}, r_{23}. These expressions for the C's become more and more complex as the number of predictor variables increases. Certain convenient relations among the C's and r's can be readily established by matrix algebra but will probably have to be taken on faith by the person who does not understand that subject. These relations are

$$\begin{aligned} 1 \cdot C_{11} + r_{12}C_{21} + r_{13}C_{31} &= 1 \\ r_{12}C_{11} + 1 \cdot C_{21} + r_{23}C_{31} &= 0 \\ r_{13}C_{11} + r_{23}C_{21} + 1 \cdot C_{31} &= 0 \end{aligned}$$

$$(13.23)\quad \begin{aligned} 1\cdot C_{12} + r_{12}C_{22} + r_{13}C_{32} &= 0 \\ r_{12}C_{12} + 1\cdot C_{22} + r_{23}C_{32} &= 1 \\ r_{13}C_{12} + r_{23}C_{22} + 1\cdot C_{32} &= 0 \\ \\ 1\cdot C_{13} + r_{12}C_{23} + r_{13}C_{33} &= 0 \\ r_{12}C_{13} + 1\cdot C_{23} + r_{23}C_{33} &= 0 \\ r_{13}C_{13} + r_{23}C_{23} + 1\cdot C_{33} &= 1 \end{aligned}$$

The nine Equations (13.23) can be compactly written as

$$(13.24)\quad \begin{aligned} 1\cdot C_{i1} + r_{12}C_{i2} + r_{13}C_{i3} &= 1, 0, 0 \\ r_{12}C_{i1} + 1\cdot C_{i2} + r_{23}C_{i3} &= 0, 1, 0 \\ r_{13}C_{i1} + r_{23}C_{i2} + 1\cdot C_{i3} &= 0, 0, 1 \end{aligned}$$

The C's may be called *elements of the inverse solution* or from the relations (13.23) *multipliers*, or *inverse multipliers*. They will be called *multipliers* in this book.

C. Routine for computing the multipliers. The goal is to obtain values of the C's which may be substituted in Equations (13.22) to obtain the b^*'s. The computational form is set up in the manner already used for the abbreviated solution on page 329 except that the column for criterion Y is omitted and in its place are several columns labeled C_{j1}, C_{j2}, C_{j3}. In a problem having m predictor variables there would be m such columns. For a 3-predictor problem the column labeled C_{j1} will eventually lead to the values C_{31}, C_{21}, and C_{11}, the column labeled C_{j2} will lead to the values C_{32}, C_{22} and C_{12}, and the column labeled C_{j3} will lead to C_{33}, C_{23} and C_{13}.

The numbers to be entered on the first lines of the forward solution are, for m predictors, as follows:

Line	X_1	X_2	$X_3 \ldots X_m$	C_{j1}	C_{j2}	$C_{j3} \ldots C_{jm}$
[1.1]	1	r_{12}	$r_{13} \ldots r_{1m}$	1	0	0 . . . 0
[2.1]	r_{12}	1	$r_{23} \ldots r_{2m}$	0	1	0 . . . 0
[3.1]	r_{13}	r_{23}	$1 \ldots r_{3m}$	0	0	1 . . . 0
.	.	.	. . . . .	.	.	. . . . .
[m.1]	r_{1m}	r_{2m}	$r_{3m} \ldots 1$	0	0	0 . . . 1

The succeeding steps are exactly like those of the previous solution. Values of the C's will appear on the last lines of various cycles in the columns headed C_{j1}, C_{j2}, C_{j3}. These have been taken out and set down in a separate tabulation where their symmetry can be noted. That symmetry provides one check on the computations. The b^*'s are now obtained by substituting the C's in

TABLE 13.7 Fisher-Doolittle Procedure for Computing the Multipliers

Line	Step	X_1	X_2	X_3	C_{j1}	C_{j2}	C_{j3}	Check
	FORWARD SOLUTION							
[1.1]	Enter data	1	.321	.477	−1.000	0	0	.798
[1.2]	[1.1]·(−1)	−1	−.321	−.477	1.000	0	0	−.798
[2.1]	Enter data	.321	1.000	.539	0	−1.000	0	.860
[2.2]	[1.1]·(−.321)		−.103	−.153	+.321	0	0	−.256
[2.3]	[2.1] + [2.2]		.897	.386	+.321	−1.000	0	.604
[2.4]	[2.3]·$(-\frac{1}{.897})$		−1.000	−.430	−.358	1.115	0	−.673
[3.1]	Enter data	.477	.539	1.000	0	0	−1.000	1.016
[3.2]	[1.1]·(−.477)			−.228	.477	0	0	−.381
[3.3]	[2.3]·(−.430)			−.166	−.138	.430	0	−.260
[3.4]	[3.1] + [3.2] + [3.3]			.606	.339	.430	−1.000	.375
[3.5]	[3.4]·$(-\frac{1}{.606})$			−1.000	−.559	−.710	1.650	−.619
	BACK SOLUTION							
[1.1B]	Enter [3.5]			−1.000	−.559	−.710	1.650	−.619
[2.1B]	Enter [2.4]		−1.000	−.430	−.358	1.115	0	−.673
[2.2B]	[1.1B]·(− .430)			.430	.240	.305	−.710	.266
[2.3B]	[2.1B] + 2.2B		−1.000	0	−.118	1.420	−.710	−.407
[3.1B]	Enter 1.2	−1.000	−.321	−.477	1.000	0	0	−.798
[3.2B]	[1.1B] (− .477)			.477	.267	.339	−.787	.295
[3.3B]	[2.3B] (− .321)		.321	0	.038	−.456	.228	.131
[3.4B]	[3.1B] + [3.2B] + [3.3B]	−1.000	0	0	1.305	−.117	−.559	−.371

Values of the C's Obtained from Fisher-Doolittle Solution

Line	C_{j1}	C_{j2}	C_{j3}
[1.1B]	$C_{31} = -.559$	$C_{32} = -.710$	$C_{33} = 1.650$
[2.3B]	$C_{21} = -.118$	$C_{22} = 1.420$	$C_{23} = -.710$
[3.4B]	$C_{11} = 1.305$	$C_{12} = -.117$	$C_{13} = -.559$

Equations (13.22). These are seen to agree with the previously computed values of the b^*'s except for small differences in the last digit due to rounding errors. The complete solution appears on page 335.

Values of b^*'s to Predict Midterm Test Scores

	Obtained by substituting C's in (13.22)	Previously obtained
$b^*_{y1.23} =$	$1.305(.357) - .117(.620) - .559(.518) = .104$	.102
$b^*_{y2.13} =$	$-.117(.357) + 1.420(.620) - .710(.518) = .471$	.470
$b^*_{y3.12} =$	$-.559(.357) - .710(.620) + 1.650(.518) = .215$	.216

$$b_{y1.23} = b^*_{y1.23}\frac{s_y}{s_1} = .124; \quad b_{y2.13} = .398; \quad b_{y3.12} = .277;$$

$$A = \overline{Y} - b_{y1.23}\overline{X}_1 - b_{y2.13}\overline{X}_2 - b_{y3.12}\overline{X}_3 = 20.86$$

Then $$\tilde{Y} = 20.86 + .124X_1 + .398X_2 + .277X_3$$

Regression Equation for a Different Criterion and the Same Predictors. The same set of C's can now be used to obtain the regression equation to predict a different criterion variable, if the correlations of that criterion with the predictors are available. From the data of Table 13.1, the correlations of the final examination with each of the three predictors can be found. Let final examination scores be designated Z. Then

$$r_{z1} = .325 \qquad r_{z2} = .508 \qquad r_{z3} = .502$$
$$s_z = 9.47 \qquad \overline{Z} = 49.15$$

$$b^*_{z1.23} = 1.305(.325) - .117(.508) - .559(.502) = .084$$
$$b^*_{z2.13} = -.117(.325) + 1.420(.508) - .710(.502) = .327$$
$$b^*_{z3.12} = -.559(.325) - .710(.508) + 1.650(.502) = .286$$

Check: $b^*_{z1.23} + r_{12}b^*_{z2.13} + r_{13}b^*_{z3.12} = .3254$ and $r_{z1} = .325$

$r_{12}b^*_{z1.23} + b^*_{z2.13} + r_{23}b^*_{z3.12} = .5081$ and $r_{z2} = .508$

$r_{13}b^*_{z1.23} + r_{23}b^*_{z2.13} + b^*_{z3.12} = .5023$ and $r_{z3} = .502$

Then $$R^2_{z.123} = r_{z1}b^*_{z1.23} + r_{z2}b^*_{z2.13} + r_{z3}b^*_{z3.12} = .3370$$
$$R_{z.123} = \sqrt{.3370} = .58$$

To obtain the regression equation we need

$$b_{z1.23} = b^*_{z1.23}\frac{s_z}{s_1} = .084\ \frac{9.47}{7.68} = .104$$

$$b_{z2.13} = b^*_{z2.13}\frac{s_z}{s_2} = .327\ \frac{9.47}{11.03} = .281$$

$$b_{z3.12} = b^*_{z3.12}\frac{s_z}{s_3} = .286\ \frac{9.47}{7.28} = .372$$

$$A = \overline{Z} - b_{z1.23}\overline{X}_1 - b_{z2.13}\overline{X}_2 - b_{z3.12}\overline{X}_3 = 20.77$$
$$\tilde{Z} = 20.77 + .104X_1 + .281X_2 + .373X_3$$

Tests of Significance for Partial Regression Coefficients. For this purpose we shall use a statistical model analogous to the one used in Chapter 10 for testing hypotheses about regression coefficients in problems with only a single predictor variable. Generalization will be made to a subset of samples in which the values of the predictors are exactly the same as in the observed sample. It will be assumed that values of the criterion variable Y vary from sample to sample with mean depending on the predictors and described for three predictors by the equation

$$E(Y) = \alpha + \beta_{y1.23}X_1 + \beta_{y2.13}X_2 + \beta_{y3.12}X_3 \tag{13.25}$$

The values of Y fluctuate around their expected value, there being a normal distribution of Y's for each different combination of X_1, X_2 and X_3, and all such Y distributions having the same variance.

The β's appearing in Formula (13.25) are the population parameters for which the b's are sample estimates. In testing hypotheses it is better to use the b^*'s rather than the b's since the latter are influenced by sampling errors in the sample standard deviations as well as by sampling errors in regression. We shall use the symbol β^* as the population parameter corresponding to the sample b^*. Then

(13.26)

$$\beta^*_{y1.23} = E(b^*_{y1.23}), \quad \beta^*_{y2.13} = E(b^*_{y2.13}), \quad \text{and} \quad \beta^*_{y3.12} = E(b^*_{y3.12})$$

Then the statistics

(13.27)

$$\frac{b^*_{y1.23} - \beta^*_{y1.23}}{\sqrt{\dfrac{(1 - R^2_{y.123})C_{11}}{N-4}}}, \quad \frac{b^*_{y2.13} - \beta^*_{y2.13}}{\sqrt{\dfrac{(1 - R^2_{y.123})C_{22}}{N-4}}}, \quad \text{and} \quad \frac{b^*_{y3.12} - \beta^*_{y3.12}}{\sqrt{\dfrac{(1 - R^2_{y.123})C_{33}}{N-4}}}$$

all have "Student's" Distribution with $N - 4$ degrees of freedom. If m predictors were used in the equation, $N - 4$ would be replaced by $N - m - 1$ and the statistic would have $N - m - 1$ degrees of freedom.

Returning now to the problem of predicting midterm score from the three prognostic tests, it will be of interest to test (for each of the three regression coefficients separately) the hypothesis that it is zero in a hypothetical population of students of which these 98 students may be considered a random sample. The regression equation has already been obtained in the two forms

$$\frac{\tilde{Y} - \overline{Y}}{s_y} = .102\,\frac{X_1 - \overline{X}_1}{s_1} + .470\,\frac{(X_2 - \overline{X}_2)}{s_2} + .216\,\frac{(X_3 - \overline{X}_3)}{s_3}$$

and $\tilde{Y} = .124X_1 + .398X_2 + .277X_3 + 20.86$

The multiple correlation coefficient related to these equations has been found to be $R_{y.123} = .663$ and this has been shown to be significantly different from zero. The multipliers

$$C_{11} = 1.305, \quad C_{22} = 1.420, \quad C_{33} = 1.650$$

have been found.

To test the three null hypotheses the following statistics are computed, each distributed as t with $N - m - 1 = 98 - 3 - 1 = 94$ degrees of freedom:

$$\frac{b^*_{y1.23} - 0}{\sqrt{\dfrac{(1 - R^2)C_{11}}{N - 4}}} = \frac{.102}{\sqrt{\dfrac{(.5604)(1.305)}{94}}} = 1.17$$

$$\frac{b^*_{y2.13} - 0}{\sqrt{\dfrac{(1 - R^2)C_{22}}{N - 4}}} = \frac{.470}{\sqrt{\dfrac{(.5604)(1.420)}{94}}} = 5.11$$

$$\frac{b^*_{y3.12} - 0}{\sqrt{\dfrac{(1 - R^2)C_{33}}{N - 4}}} = \frac{.216}{\sqrt{\dfrac{(.5604)(1.650)}{94}}} = 2.18$$

Interval estimates for these regression coefficients may be made by the method previously used in making an interval estimate for the mean and for other variables having a normal distribution. The standard error of $b^*_{y1.23}$ is

$$s_{b^*y1.23} = \sqrt{\frac{(1 - R^2_{y.123})C_{11}}{N - 4}} \tag{13.28}$$

To state the formula in more general terms we may for convenience drop the secondary subscripts and merely use R for the coefficient of multiple correlation and b^*_{yk} for the partial regression coefficient of Y on X_k. If there are m predictor variables, the standard error of b^*_{yk} is

$$s_{b^*_{yk}} = \sqrt{\frac{(1 - R^2)C_{kk}}{N - m - 1}} \tag{13.29}$$

Then the inequality

$$t_{\frac{1}{2}\alpha} < \frac{b^*_{yk} - \beta^*_{yk}}{s_{b^*}} < t_{1-\frac{1}{2}\alpha}$$

will produce an interval estimate for β^*_{yk} with confidence coefficient $1 - \alpha$:

(13.30)

$$b^*_{yk} + t_{\frac{1}{2}\alpha}\sqrt{\frac{(1 - R^2)C_{kk}}{N - m - 1}} < \beta^*_{yk} < b^*_{yk} + t_{1-\frac{1}{2}\alpha}\sqrt{\frac{(1 - R^2)C_{kk}}{N - m - 1}}$$

Now let us apply this procedure to obtain a confidence interval for each of the three β's in the data under consideration. If a 95% confidence interval is decided upon, $\alpha = .05$ and $t_{.975} = 1.96$ may be read from a table of normal probability as there are 94 degrees of freedom. The interval estimates are:

$$-.07 < \beta^*_{y1.23} < .27$$
$$.29 < \beta^*_{y2.13} < .65$$
$$.02 < \beta^*_{y3.12} < .41$$

Elimination of One Predictor from the Regression Equation. Either the test of the null hypothesis or the interval estimate for the population values of the regression coefficients would produce a lively suspicion that X_1, the reading test, may not be making any real contribution to the prediction of success in first term statistics since the observed $b^* = .102$ might quite possibly be a chance departure from $\beta^* = 0$. The other two measures must be considered to be making a significant contribution to the predicttion. Therefore it would be wise to make a search for a more useful substitute or, if testing time is at a premium, to consider omitting it altogether. (A passing comment might be in order, however, to the effect that while the reading test has made very little contribution to the general prediction of marks in the statistics course, individual students have often expressed appreciation of the opportunity to discover a weakness by its aid. Some students who have acquired the habit of reading very rapidly need to learn that in this subject one must read more deliberately, must weigh and compare and reread and reflect.)

How much would the predictive value of the regression equation for these 98 students be reduced by dropping variable X_1? For three predictors, the error sum of squares is

$$(1 - R^2_{y.123})\Sigma(Y - \overline{Y})^2$$

and for two predictors it will be $(1 - R^2_{y.23})\Sigma(Y - \overline{Y})^2$. The relation between these is

(13.31) $$1 - R^2_{y.23} = 1 - R^2_{y.123} + \frac{(b^*_{y1.23})^2}{C_{11}}$$

or, in general, if there are m predictors and predictor X_k is dropped from the equation, the sum of squares for residual errors is increased by

$$\frac{1}{C_{kk}}(b^*_{yk.12\ldots m})^2\Sigma(Y - \overline{Y})^2$$

For X_1 of this problem

$$\frac{1}{C_{11}}(b^*_{y1.23})^2 = \frac{1}{1.305}(.102)^2 = .008$$

A relative increase of only $.008\Sigma(Y - \overline{Y})$ in the error sum of squares appears negligible.

Then $$1 - R^2_{y.23} = 1 - (.663)^2 + .008 = .568$$

and $$R_{y.23} = \sqrt{.432} = .657$$

Some reasons have already been suggested as to why prediction of achievement by means of prognostic tests can never be perfect. In these data 43% of the variance of midterm scores is related to variation in the two tests X_2 and X_3, 57% to variation in other traits. This may seem inconsequential to persons who have not worked with such data, but few persons who have tried to predict achievement scores would consider the gain in knowledge a small one. In interpreting the multiple correlation it should be understood that the classes were conducted in a manner designed to destroy the validity of the prediction. The students with the best prognosis were in a larger class and one which studied topics not covered by the other sections and not included in the class tests. Some of the students for whom prognosis was poor were in a very small class where they had more opportunity for individual attention, others were in a section which met four hours a week whereas those with better prognosis were in a large class which met three hours a week.

Partial Correlation. Sometimes the computed coefficient of correlation between two variables is misleading because there is little or no intrinsic correlation between them beyond what is induced by their common dependence upon a third variable (or upon several others). One might make a very long list of traits which increase with age between 12 and 18 years of age, such as height, weight, strength of grip, vocabulary, interest in public affairs, money spent on wearing apparel, size of shoe, knowledge of public affairs, interest in the opposite sex, ability to understand abstract material, etc. Any two of these would almost certainly show positive correlation, but the correlation between money spent on wearing apparel and ability to understand abstract material would probably disappear if the effect of variation in age could be eliminated. In his *Statistical Method,* S. Florence remarks:

The contention that most people die in their beds and that therefore, a bed is the most unhealthy of places is a familiar example of failure to apply partial association. Going to bed is a usual consequence of being ill and dying occurs after a period of illness. Both phenomena are normal results of illness and to obtain a scientific proof it would be necessary to select only cases of illness and within the universe of illnesses to see whether those going to bed really die in greater proportion than those not going to bed.[5]

The data on the prediction of success in first term statistics do not display the striking contrasts which sometimes appear between zero order correlations and partial correlations. However they may be utilized to demonstrate what the formula for partial correlation means.

For the 98 cases of Table 13.1 the correlation between scores on the midterm test Y and scores on the arithmetic-algebra placement test was $r_{y3} = .52$. Is there a relation between these two traits which cannot be explained in terms of their common relationship to scores on the artificial language test?

Table 13.8 shows the scores on these three tests for a random sample of 10 cases out of Table 13.1. It also shows the predictions which would be made for Y and for X_3 by the regression equations

$$\tilde{Y} = b_{y2}X_2 + (\overline{Y} - b_{y2}\overline{X}_2)$$
$$\tilde{X}_3 = b_{32}X_2 + (\overline{X}_3 - b_{32}\overline{X}_2)$$

and shows the errors of estimate $Y - \tilde{Y}$ and $X_3 - \tilde{X}_3$. The correlation between these errors of estimate is

$$r_{Y-\tilde{Y},\ X_3-\tilde{X}_3} = \frac{\Sigma(Y - \tilde{Y})(X_3 - \tilde{X}_3)}{\sqrt{\Sigma(Y - \tilde{Y})^2\Sigma(X_3 - \tilde{X}_3)^2}} = \frac{116.29}{381.65} = .30$$

This correlation, which has sometimes been called a *net* correlation, is the partial correlation denoted by the symbol $r_{y3.2}$.

If both X_1 and X_2 has been used in the regression equation, the correlation between

$$Y - \tilde{Y} = Y - \overline{Y} - b_{y1.2}(X_1 - \overline{X}_1) - b_{y2.1}(X_2 - \overline{X}_2)$$

and $$X_3 - \tilde{X}_3 = X_3 - \overline{X}_3 - b_{31.2}(X_1 - \overline{X}_1) - b_{32.1}(X_2 - \overline{X}_2)$$

could have been found to be $r_{y3.12} = .08$

$$r_{y3} = .47 \left\langle \begin{matrix} r_{y3.1} = .26 \\ r_{y3.2} = .30 \end{matrix} \right\rangle r_{y3.12} = .08$$

TABLE 13.8 Correlation among Residual Errors for Ten Cases Chosen at Random from Table 13.1

Case	X_2	X_3	Y	$\tilde{X}_3$	$\tilde{Y}$	$X_3-\tilde{X}_3$	$Y-\tilde{Y}$	$(X_3-\tilde{X}_3)(Y-\tilde{Y})$
11	53	28	62	35.8	56.8	−7.8	5.2	−40.56
75	41	30	62	31.6	50.3	−1.6	11.7	−18.72
32	58	32	49	37.6	59.5	−5.6	−10.5	58.80
13	55	38	50	36.5	57.9	1.5	−7.9	−11.85
7	57	42	64	37.2	59.0	4.8	5.0	24.00
88	58	42	59	37.6	59.5	4.4	−.5	−2.20
47	53	37	62	35.8	56.8	1.2	5.2	6.24
78	60	43	71	38.3	60.6	4.7	10.4	48.88
97	34	33	41	29.2	46.5	3.8	−5.5	−20.90
25	52	30	43	35.5	56.2	−5.5	−13.2	72.60
Sum	521	355	563	355.1	563.1	−0.1	−0.1	116.3
Mean	52.1	35.5	56.3	35.51	56.31	−.01	−.01	
$\Sigma(\text{dev})^2$	616.9	284.5	884.1	75.6	181.4	207.6	701.5	

$$r_{y3.2} = \frac{\Sigma(X_3 - \tilde{X}_3)(Y - \tilde{Y})}{\sqrt{\Sigma(X_3 - \tilde{X}_3)^2}\sqrt{\Sigma(Y - \tilde{Y})^2}} = \frac{116.3}{\sqrt{(207.6)(701.5)}} = .30$$

$$r_{y3.2} = \frac{r_{y3} - r_{y2}r_{32}}{\sqrt{1 - r^2_{y2}}\sqrt{1 - r^2_{32}}} = \frac{.47 - (.45)(.52)}{(.893)(.854)} = .30$$

From these figures we note that variation in reading score and variation in artificial language score both have a considerable effect on the relation between algebra-arithmetic score and mid-term test. For corresponding data for the 98 cases, see Exercise 13.2, question 6.

The subscripts preceding the point are called primary subscripts; those following the point, secondary subscripts. The number of secondary subscripts is the *order*. Thus $r_{y3.12}$ is a second-order partial; $r_{y3.1}$ and $r_{y3.2}$ are first-order partials; r_{y3} is a zero-order coefficient.

Any partial correlation coefficient can be obtained from coefficients of the next lower order. Thus

(13.32)

$$r_{y3.1} = \frac{r_{y3} - r_{y1}r_{31}}{\sqrt{1-r^2_{y1}}\sqrt{1-r^2_{31}}} \quad \text{and} \quad r_{y3.2} = \frac{r_{y3} - r_{y2}r_{32}}{\sqrt{1-r^2_{y2}}\sqrt{1-r^2_{32}}}$$

If additional secondary subscripts are annexed to every r in Formula (13.32), the result is the formula for a partial of higher order. Thus

$$(13.33)\quad \begin{cases} r_{y3.12} = \dfrac{r_{y3.2} - r_{y1.2}r_{31.2}}{\sqrt{1 - r^2_{y1.2}}\sqrt{1 - r^2_{31.2}}} \\ \\ r_{y3.21} = \dfrac{r_{y3.1} - r_{y2.1}r_{32.1}}{\sqrt{1 - r^2_{y2.1}}\sqrt{1 - r^2_{32.1}}} \end{cases}$$

Since the arrangement of secondary subscripts is immaterial, $r_{y3.12} = r_{y3.21}$. The two Formulas (13.33) are algebraically identical but seldom give identical results in computation because rounding errors take a heavy toll. To obtain a partial correlation with a large number of secondary subscripts it is possible to work up step by step from zero-order coefficients to first order, to second order, etc. but the amount of labor involved increases rapidly as the order increases. If the secondary subscripts are numerous it is usually easier to use the Formula

$$(13.34)\qquad r^2_{12.3456} = b^*_{12.3456}b^*_{21.3456} = b_{12.3456}b_{21.3456}$$

obtaining each of the b^*'s by a Doolittle solution.

The study of partial correlation suggests one reason why correlation coefficients are difficult to interpret. There is no rule which the research worker can follow to tell him whether he needs a zero-order correlation or a partial. He is obliged to answer that question by intense and critical thinking about his data. Sometimes the zero-order r is really spurious, sometimes the partial, depending on the use to be made of it. The zero-order correlation of intelligence quotient with reading ability for all the children in a school system will be positive and is likely to be fairly high. However, if computed for children in the fourth grade only the correlation between intelligence quotient and reading ability is likely to be negative because within the single grade the brighter children are the younger and in the fourth grade the older children have a certain advantage in reading. Here the variable of "grade in school" has been literally *held constant.* The effect on the correlation coefficient is similar to, but not identical with, the effect of taking a partial in which a secondary subscript denotes "grade in school."

Test of Significance for a Partial Correlation. All the tests of significance for a zero-order correlation described in Chapter 10 may be applied to a partial if the number of degrees of freedom is decreased by 1 for each secondary subscript.

Relation of Partial and Multiple Correlation Coefficients. Using a 4-predictor problem as illustration, the multiple R may be written in terms of partial r's and a zero-order r as follows:

$$\begin{aligned} 1 - R^2_{y.1234} &= (1 - r^2_{y1})(1 - r^2_{y2.1})(1 - r^2_{y3.12})(1 - r^2_{y4.123}) \\ &= (1 - r^2_{y2})(1 - r^2_{y3.2})(1 - r^2_{y4.23})(1 - r^2_{y1.234}) \qquad (13.35) \\ &= (1 - r^2_{y3})(1 - r^2_{y4.3})(1 - r^2_{y1.34})(1 - r^2_{y2.134}) \end{aligned}$$

etc.

This formula does not provide a very economical computing routine but it furnishes some interesting comparisons which enable us to set a lower bound for a multiple R without computing it. Each of the parentheses on the right of Formula (13.35) contains a quantity which is smaller than 1 (except in the unusual case of $r = 0$). The product of several such quantities is smaller than any one of them. Therefore

$$1 - R^2_{y.1234} < 1 - r^2_{y4.123}$$

and

$$R^2_{y.1234} > r^2_{y4.123}$$

The right-hand member of (13.35) could be written in $4! = 24$ different ways, all algebraically identical, if the various partials are expressed in terms of zero-order r's. These 24 ways of writing the formula would involve every r having y as one of its primary subscripts, and each of these r's would be smaller than $R_{y.1234}$. However, there is no necessary relation between $R_{y.1234}$ and other r's for which y is not a primary subscript, as for example, $r_{23.14}$, or $r_{32.y4}$.

Consistency Among Coefficients. The relations between zero-order and partial coefficients are less definite than that which provides a lower bound for the multiple correlation. Occasionally a research worker encounters a partial coefficient which is larger than the zero-order coefficient with the same primary subscripts. For example $r_{12} = .30$, $r_{13} = .10$ and $r_{23} = .80$ would yield $r_{12.3} = .37$. More often in the data with which social scientists deal the partial coefficients are smaller than the related zero-order coefficients. Occasionally r_{12} and $r_{12.3}$ have opposite signs. For example for the r's just quoted $r_{13} = .10$ and $r_{13.2} = -.245$. The three coefficients r_{12}, r_{13} and r_{23} are always related in such a way that none of the partials is numerically larger than 1. This is called the consistency relation and it amounts to the requirement that

$$1 - r^2_{12} - r^2_{13} - r^2_{23} + 2r_{12}r_{13}r_{23} > 0 \qquad (13.36)$$

Thus $r_{12} = .80$, $r_{13} = .60$, $r_{23} = -.20$ are inconsistent because they would lead to partials larger than 1, and

$$1 - r^2_{12} - r^2_{13} - r^2_{23} + 2r_{12}r_{13}r_{23} = -.232$$

EXERCISE 13.2

1. Write the formula for each of the following partial-correlation coefficients in terms of zero-order coefficients: (a) $r_{63.2}$; (b) $r_{y3.7}$; (c) $r_{21.y}$.

2. Write the formula for $r_{24.56}$ in terms of first-order partials having 5 as secondary subscript.

3. Write the formula for $r_{43.2567}$ in terms of third-order partials having 2, 5, and 6 as secondary subscripts.

4. Write the formula for $r_{43.2567}$ in terms of the related regression coefficients.

5. Write the formula for $R_{3.126}$ in the manner of Formula (13.35).

6. For the data for the 98 cases of Table 13.1, using the zero-order correlation coefficients in Table 13.3, verify the following partial coefficients:

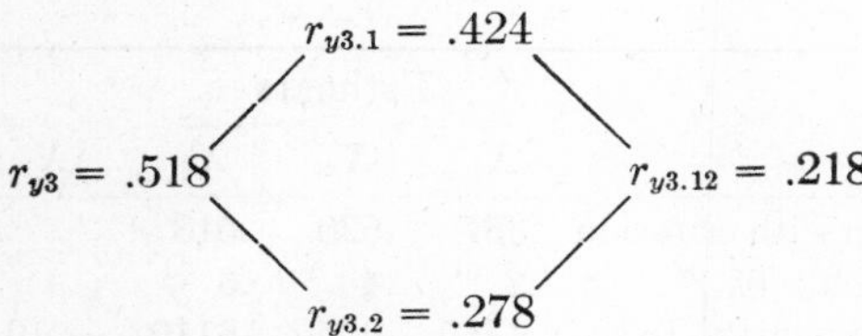

Iterative Method of Obtaining Regression Weights. An iterative method of obtaining the b^*'s for a multiple regression equation — usually called the Kelley-Salisbury Method [7,8,9] — will be described. It is useful only when some small errors in the b^*'s can be tolerated. When the number of predictor variables is small it does not save labor. Those who like to use iterative methods consider that when the predictor variables are numerous, this method is quicker than the Doolittle method. However it does not provide any method of testing the significance of the b^*'s individually. It will be illustrated here from the data already used for the Doolittle solution.

The Kelley-Salisbury method is based on the normal equations. For the present data these are

$$\begin{aligned} b^*_{y1.23} + .321b^*_{y2.13} + .477b^*_{y3.12} &= .357 \\ .321b^*_{y1.23} + b^*_{y2.13} + .539b^*_{y3.12} &= .620 \\ .477b^*_{y1.23} + .539b^*_{y2.13} + b^*_{y3.12} &= .518 \end{aligned}$$

The procedure is to make a rough estimate of the values of the b^*'s (called W_1 on line 2 on page 346), substitute those estimates in the normal equations and obtain a first approximation to the correlations with the criterion (called r_1 on line 3). Now, comparing the first approximations r_1 with the actual correlations we see that the approximation is close for r_{y2} but is considerably too large for r_{y1} and r_{y3}. We shall try reducing the estimate for one or the other of the corresponding b^*'s. Since r_{y1} shows the largest discrepancy we will reduce the entry for column 1. It is not necessary at this stage to seek for great precision, so we will reduce the estimate from .2 to .1 and will record $.1 - .2 = - .1$ as the amount of the change in column 1. It is now possible to substitute the new weights .1, .4 and .3 in the normal equations or merely to note that the estimate of r_{y1} will be changed by $- .1$, the estimate or r_{y2} by $- .1(.321)$ and the estimate of r_{y3} by $- .1(.477)$, producing the second estimates r_2 recorded in row 4. The iterative process may be carried on until agreement between estimated r's and observed is close enough to satisfy the computer.

Step	Estimate			Change		
	X_1	X_2	X_3	X_1	X_2	X_3
1. r_{yj} = correlation with criterion	.357	.620	.518			
2. W_1 = first estimate of b^*	.2	.4	.3			
3. r_1 = first approximation to r_{yj}	.4715	.6259	.6110	−.10		
4. r_2	.3715	.5938	.5633			−.05
5. r_3	.3476	.5669	.5133		+.05	
6. r_4	.3637	.6169	.5403			
7. W_2 = revised estimate of b^*	.10	.45	.25			
8. r_4 (check)	.3637	.6169	.5403			−.022
9. r_5	.3532	.6050	.5183		+.015	
10. r_6	.3580	.6200	.5264			−.008
11. r_7	.3542	.6157	.5184	.003		
12. r_8	.3572	.6167	.5197			
13. W_3 = revised estimate of b^*	.103	.465	.220			
14. r_8 (check)	.3572	.6167	.5197		.005	
15. r_9	.3588	.6217	.5224			−.004
16. r_{10}	.3569	.6195	.5184			
17. W_4 = final estimate of b^*	.103	.470	.216			
18. b^*_{yj} = value obtained from Doolittle solution presented here for comparison	.102	.470	.216			

REFERENCES

1. Doolittle, M. H., "Method Employed in the Solution of Normal Equations and the Adjustment of a Triangulation," *U.S. Coast and Geodetic Survey Report*, 1878, 115–120.

2. Dwyer, P. S., "The Doolittle Technique," *Annals of Mathematical Statistics*, 12 (1941), 449–458.
3. Dwyer, P. S., "The Solution of Simultaneous Equations," *Psychometrika* 6 (1941), 101–129.
4. Dwyer, P. S., *Linear Computations*, New York, John Wiley and Sons, 1951.
5. Florence, P. S., *The Statistical Method in Economics and Political Science*, New York, Harcourt Brace, 1929.
6. Kelley, T. L., *Fundamentals of Statistics*, Cambridge, Mass., Harvard University Press, 1947, Chapter 12.
7. Kelley, T. L. and McNemar, Quinn, "Doolittle versus the Kelley-Salisbury Iteration Method for Computing Multiple Regression Coefficients," *Journal of the American Statistical Association*, 24 (1929), 164–169.
8. Kelley, T. L. and Salisbury, F. S., "An Iteration Method for Determining Multiple Correlation Coefficients," *Journal of the American Statistical Association*, 21 (1926), 282–292.
9. Tolley, H. R. and Ezekiel, M., "The Doolittle Method for Solving Multiple Correlation Equations versus the Kelley-Salisbury Iteration Method," *Journal of the American Statistical Association*, 22 (1927), 497–500.
10. Walker, H. M. and Durost, W. N., "A Model to Aid in Teaching Partial Correlation," *The American Statistician*, 4 (October, 1950), 5–7.

14 Analysis of Variance with Two or More Variables of Classification

Some of the simpler applications of analysis of variance were considered in Chapter 9. This type of analysis may be applied to a great variety of complex experiments, some of which provide a method of studying the effects of two or more factors in the same experiment. As was the case in Chapters 7 and 9 it will be necessary to distinguish between situations in which only one observation is made on each individual and situations in which several observations are made on each individual.

Two Bases of Classification with *n* Individuals in Each Cell. An experiment on the teaching of reading to backward readers is described by Burt and Lewis[4]. A group of 48 backward readers was given instruction in reading by four methods called A. Alphabetic, B. Kinesthetic, C. Phonic, and D. Visual. In the following table, the improvement achieved by each of the pupils is recorded as 100 times the ratio of his final to his original reading score. Each ratio is classified both by the method used in remedial instruction and by the method previously used in the school which the pupil attended regularly. These ratios multiplied by 100 will now, for the sake of simplicity, be called scores. Note that the scores appear in 16 groups, three scores in a group. One of the groups corresponds to each possible pairing of method of instruction used in school and the method used in remedial teaching. The sixteen groups are customarily called *subclasses*. Since the subclasses are arranged in rows and columns it is convenient to speak of the groups of subclasses as *rows* and *columns*.

The advantage of this arrangement or *experimental design* is that each remedial method is applied equally often to students who have been taught previously by each of the four methods. Thus the outcomes of remedial instruction are unaffected by peculiarities of prior instruction. It is important that the 12 pupils in each column be assigned randomly to the four remedial methods to assure that variation in individual abilities does not bias the results of the experiment.

Before writing the necessary formulas it will be helpful to review the notation previously used in similar situations. A score in the subclass in the ith row and jth column will be denoted by the symbol $X_{ij\alpha}$ so that the three scores in the first row and second column are $X_{121} = 114.2$, $X_{122} = 101.6$ and $X_{123} = 113.0$. The mean of the scores in a subclass will be denoted by the symbol $\overline{X}_{ij}$, the mean of a row by $\overline{X}_{i.}$, the mean of a column by $\overline{X}_{.j}$ and the mean of all scores by $\overline{X}$. The corresponding population means are μ_{ij}, $\mu_{i.}$, $\mu_{.j}$ and μ.

The usual assumptions of normality and equality of standard deviation are made. All possible observations which may appear in a subclass are assumed to be independently and normally distributed about the mean, μ_{ij}, of the subclass, and each of these populations of observations is assumed to have the same standard deviation σ. Thus each group of three observations in a subclass of Table 14.1 is a sample from a normal population with the mean and standard deviation indicated above.

By use of the parameters three hypotheses can be formulated:

1. *The hypothesis that the row means are equal.* This hypothesis may be denoted by the symbol H_r. For the data in Table 14.1 the hypothesis is

$$H_r : \mu_{1.} = \mu_{2.} = \mu_{3.} = \mu_{4.} = \mu.$$

In terms of these data the hypothesis implies that in the population the four remedial methods are equally effective.

2. *The hypothesis that the column means are equal.* This hypothesis may be written

$$H_c : \mu_{.1} = \mu_{.2} = \mu_{.3} = \mu_{.4} = \mu.$$

In terms of the data in Table 14.1 this hypothesis implies that students improve equally well under remedial instruction regardless of the method of teaching originally used in their schools.

3. *The hypothesis that the interaction is zero.* In terms of the parameters this hypothesis may be written

$$H_{rc} : \mu_{ij} = (\mu_{i.} - \mu) + (\mu_{.j} - \mu) + \mu$$

or

$$\mu_{ij} - \mu_{i.} - \mu_{.j} + \mu = 0.$$

The interpretation of this hypothesis is that each subclass mean (μ_{ij}) can be found from the general mean by adding to the latter

TABLE 14.1 Improvement Scores of Pupils Given Remedial Instruction in Reading Classified According to Method of Original Instruction and Method of Remedial Instruction*

Method of remedial instruction	Improvement scores of pupils receiving original instruction by a given method				Sum	Mean
	A	B	C	D		
A. Alphabetic	98.7	114.2	102.8	103.2		
	109.4	101.6	96.1	111.5		
	100.2	113.0	110.2	106.4		
Sum	308.3	328.8	309.1	321.1	1267.3	105.61
Mean	102.77	109.6	103.03	107.03		
B. Kinesthetic	118.6	102.5	113.5	103.9		
	106.0	106.7	117.4	119.1		
	116.1	110.4	116.8	116.2		
Sum	340.7	319.6	347.7	339.2	1347.2	112.27
Mean	113.57	106.53	115.9	113.07		
C. Phonic	107.5	106.4	111.2	101.6		
	112.6	98.4	100.8	105.5		
	105.3	93.6	109.6	94.7		
Sum	325.4	298.4	321.6	301.8	1247.2	103.93
Mean	108.47	99.47	107.2	100.6		
D. Visual	128.1	113.4	119.8	101.2		
	119.0	119.2	106.6	108.0		
	126.5	111.3	107.9	107.6		
Sum	373.6	343.9	334.3	316.8	1368.6	114.05
Mean	124.53	114.63	111.43	105.6		
Grand Total	1348.0	1290.7	1312.7	1278.9	5230.3	
Grand Mean	112.33	107.56	109.39	106.58		108.96

* From Burt and Lewis[4].

the amount by which the row mean deviates from the general mean ($\mu_{i.} - \mu$) and the amount by which the column mean deviates from the general mean ($\mu_{.j} - \mu$), row and column being those in which the subclass is located. In terms of the data in Table 14.1 the hypothesis means that the variation from subgroup to subgroup may be explained by the addition of components due to the method of school instruction and method of remedial instruction; that the effectiveness of a method of remedial instruction is the same regardless of what method preceded it.

If the hypothesis H_{rc} is true, then we say that there is no *interaction* between the row and column components or that each exercises an influence apart from the other. If this hypothesis is not true we say that the interaction of the components produces effects which cannot be explained merely by adding the row and column components. The reader will notice that the hypothesis H_{rc} was also formulated in Chapter 9. In that chapter there was only one case in each subclass and it was, therefore, impossible to test for interaction. In this chapter we shall be concerned with situations where there are several cases in each subclass and a test for H_{rc} will be made.

To test the three hypotheses just formulated we shall subdivide into components the total sum of squares of deviations of the individual scores from the mean of all the scores. In Table 14.2

TABLE 14.2 Symbolic Description of Analysis of Variance in a Two-way Layout With Equal Numbers of Cases in the Subclasses

Source of variation	Degrees of freedom	Sum of squares	Computational formula for sum of squares
Total	$nrc - 1$	$\sum_i \sum_j \sum_\alpha (X_{ij\alpha} - \bar{X})^2$	$\sum_i \sum_j \sum_\alpha X^2_{ij\alpha} - \frac{T^2}{nrc}$
Rows	$r - 1$	$nc \sum_i (\bar{X}_{i.} - \bar{X})^2$	$\frac{1}{nc} \sum_i T^2_{i.} - \frac{T^2}{nrc}$
Columns	$c - 1$	$nr \sum_j (\bar{X}_{.j} - \bar{X})^2$	$\frac{1}{nr} \sum_j T^2_{.j} - \frac{T^2}{nrc}$
Interaction	$(r-1)(c-1)$	$n \sum_i \sum (\bar{X}_{ij} - \bar{X}_{i.} - \bar{X}_{.j} + \bar{X})^2$	$\frac{1}{n} \sum_i \sum_j T^2_{ij} - \frac{1}{nc} \sum_i T^2_{i.} - \frac{1}{nr} \sum_j T^2_{.j} + \frac{T^2}{nrc}$
Within classes	$rc(n - 1)$	$\sum_i \sum_j \sum_\alpha (X_{ij\alpha} - \bar{X}_{ij})^2$	$\sum_i \sum_j \sum_\alpha X^2_{ij\alpha} - \frac{1}{n} \sum_i \sum_j T^2_{ij}$

this subdivision will be shown, together with the degrees of freedom appropriate to each component and a further subdivision of the component sums of squares to simplify computations. We shall suppose in the table that there are r rows, c columns and n cases in each subclass. Hence the total number of cases is $nrc = N$.

It will be convenient to use the notation: T_{ij} = the sum of the scores in the subsample which is located in the ith row and jth column. $T_{i.}$ is the sum of all the scores in the ith row and $T_{.j}$ the sum in the jth column. T is the sum of all the scores.

The computational formulas in Table 14.2 will now be applied to the data in Table 14.1. The calculations will be set out in a number of steps.

(14.1) Correction term:

$$\frac{T^2}{nrc} = \frac{(5230.3)^2}{(4)(4)(3)} = 569{,}917.5$$

(14.2) Total sum of squares:

$$\sum_i \sum_j \sum_\alpha X^2_{ij\alpha} - \frac{T^2}{nrc} = (98.7)^2 + (109.4)^2 + \cdots + (107.6)^2 - 569{,}917.5$$
$$= 2883.2$$

(14.3) Sum of squares for rows (remedial methods)

$$\frac{1}{nc}\sum_i T^2_{i.} - \frac{1}{nrc}T^2$$
$$= \tfrac{1}{12}[(1267.3)^2 + (1347.2)^2 + (1247.2)^2 + (1368.6)^2] - 569{,}917.5$$
$$= 570{,}797.6 - 569{,}917.5 = 880.1$$

(14.4) Sum of squares for columns (methods used in school)

$$\frac{1}{nr}\sum_j T^2_{.j} - \frac{1}{nrc}T^2$$
$$= \tfrac{1}{12}[(1348.0)^2 + (1290.7)^2 + (1312.7)^2 + (1278.9)^2] - 569{,}917.5$$
$$= 570{,}148.1 - 569{,}917.5 = 230.6$$

(14.5) Sum of squares for interaction:

$$\frac{1}{n}\sum_i \sum_j T^2_{ij} - \frac{1}{nc}\sum_i T^2_{i.} - \frac{1}{nr}\sum_j T^2_{.j} + \frac{1}{nrc}T^2$$
$$= 571{,}793.1 - 570{,}797.6 - 570{,}148.1 + 569{,}917.5 = 764.9$$

(14.6) Sum of squares for variation within subclasses

$$\sum_i \sum_j \sum_\alpha X^2_{ij\alpha} - \frac{1}{n}\sum_i \sum_j T^2_{ij} = (98.7)^2 + (109.4)^2 + \cdots + (107.6)^2$$
$$- \tfrac{1}{3}[(308.3)^2 + (328.8)^2 + \cdots + (316.8)^2]$$
$$= 572{,}800.7 - 571.793.1 = 1007.6$$

As in Chapter 9, the F distribution will be used to test each of the three hypotheses. First, each of the three sums of squares must be divided by the appropriate number of degrees of freedom to produce a mean square. These mean squares are listed in Table 14.3 where the results of the preceding computations have been summarized. The values shown in the column headed F in that table were obtained by dividing each of the other mean squares by the subclass mean square 31.5. Values of $F_{.95}$ and $F_{.99}$ read from the probability tables with the appropriate degrees of freedom have been entered in the columns at the right of Table 14.3.

TABLE 14.3 Analysis of Variance of Improvement Scores Shown in Table 14.1

Source of variation	Sum of squares	Degrees of freedom	Mean square	F	$F_{.95}$	$F_{.99}$
Methods of remedial instruction	880.1	3	293.4	9.31	2.90	4.46
Methods of original teaching	230.6	3	76.9	2.44	2.90	4.46
Interaction	764.9	9	85.0	2.70	2.19	3.01
Individuals within subclasses	1007.6	32	31.5			

To test the hypothesis that remedial methods give equal results $F = 9.31$ is compared with $F_{.99} = 4.46$. It is evident that the null hypothesis can be rejected at the .01 level. (In fact, it can even be rejected at the .001 level, for $F_{.999}$ is only 6.94, but that value is not recorded in the F tables provided in this text.) It must therefore be assumed that remedial methods do differ in their effectiveness.

To test the second hypothesis $F = 2.44$ may be compared with $F_{.95} = 2.90$. It must be concluded that there is no justification for asserting that the methods originally used in teaching reading differentiate the groups after they have received remedial instruction.

To test the third hypothesis, $F = 2.70$ may be compared with $F_{.95} = 2.19$ and $F_{.99} = 3.01$. At the .05 level of significance the null hypothesis would be rejected. A very cautious person, preferring to work at the .01 level might retain the null hypothesis. That hypothesis is that the final results after remedial work can be explained by the additive effects of the methods originally used in school and the methods used in remedial teaching. As most people will probably use the .05 level of significance, they will conclude that some combinations of the two methods produce better results than others.

Having discovered a significant interaction, the research worker naturally wants to discover its source. If he is an experienced research worker he will have foreseen this possibility and will have tried to think ahead of time of meaningful comparisons which might be made among groups of subclasses. The person planning this experiment would know something about learning theory, would probably therefore decide that if interaction should prove significant he will make a comparison of the gain of the 12 pupils for whom the remedial method was the same as the original method and the gain of the 36 pupils for whom the method was changed. Even if he did not think of this idea before he saw the data, he might notice — while poring over Table 14.1 — that in each column the mean in the diagonal cell, that is the mean under repetition of method, is smaller than the grand mean for the column. If the explanation concerning the source of the interaction occurred to him before he saw the data, he could test the null hypothesis in standard manner. If the explanation was suggested by inspection of the data he would probably present it as intelligent speculation not verified by a statistical test. The good research worker habitually speculates about matters which go beyond his data, but he is at great pains to make clear when he is speculating and when he is reporting.

4. *The hypothesis that the mean of the 4 diagonal cells is equal to the mean of the 12 non-diagonal cells.* The data in Table 14.1 show the following:

$$\text{Mean of 12 scores in diagonal cells} = 105.5$$
$$\text{Mean of 36 scores in non-diagonal cells} = 110.1$$

These means suggest that greater gain is achieved when the remedial method differs from the original method of instruction than when the two methods are the same.

To test the significance of this difference between the means we can apply "Student's ratio" as in Chapter 7. The standard error of the difference is

$$\sigma\sqrt{\tfrac{1}{12} + \tfrac{1}{36}}$$

As an estimate of σ we use the error mean square from Table 14.3, so that

$$s = \sqrt{31.5}$$

Then "Student's ratio" is

$$t = \frac{110.1 - 105.5}{\sqrt{31.5}\sqrt{\tfrac{1}{12} + \tfrac{1}{36}}} = 2.45$$

The chance is less than .02 that a difference as great as the one indicated shall occur by chance as a result of random sampling from populations in which the means are equal. The difference may, therefore, be regarded as significant from the point of view of random sampling.

Subdivision of Sum of Squares. The comparison just completed can be made in another way which leads to the conclusion reached above and which provides additional information.

Call T_1 the sum of the scores in the diagonal cells and T_2 the sum in the remaining cells. The comparison can be made by using T_1 and T_2 directly if the difference in the number of cases is taken into account. Since T_1 is based on 12 cases and T_2 on 36, the comparison of totals can be made if we equalize the number of cases by writing $3T_1 - T_2$

We can now form the sum of squares due to this comparison by the expression

$$\frac{(3T_1 - T_2)^2}{12(3)^2 + 36(-1)^2}$$

Since $T_1 = 1266.3$ and $T_2 = 3964.0$ this sum of squares is 189.3.

If this sum of squares is subtracted from the total sum of squares for interaction the difference provides an independent component of sum of squares with value $764.9 - 189.3 = 575.6$. Each of these sums of squares can be tested for significance by using as error variance the mean square for variation among individuals within subclasses which appears in Table 14.3. The analysis of variance appears in Table 14.4.

TABLE 14.4 Subdivision of Interaction in Experiment on Reading

Source of variation	Sum of squares	*d.f.*	Mean square	F	$F_{.95}$
Between diagonal cells and all others	189.3	1	189.3	6.01	4.15
Other sources of variation among cells	575.6	8	72.0	2.29	2.25
Individuals within cells	1007.6	32	31.5		

Both F ratios are significant at the 5% level. It appears that there are significant elements of interaction other than the difference between diagonal and non-diagonal sums.

It is interesting to compare the result of this section with that of the previous section. In the previous section a t ratio of 2.45

was found, but $(2.45)^2 = 6.00$ and this differs from the F ratio of 6.01 only because of rounding errors. It is evident that the computing procedures of the two sections lead to the same conclusion, but the procedure of this section provides a means of subdividing a sum of squares. Such subdivision will be discussed more fully in the next section.

Orthogonal Comparisons. We have just seen that a combination of totals can be made up which reflects some interesting aspect of a statistical problem. The combination which was considered provided a comparison of elements of the problem, and was distributed with one degree of freedom. Theoretically every degree of freedom in a statistical problem can be used to provide information of some statistical interest. From this point of view each of the nine degrees of freedom for interaction in the reading problem should provide information of interest. It is usually difficult, however, to determine an element of interest that can be drawn from each of the degrees of freedom in a statistical problem.

In the following paragraphs we shall develop procedures for subdivision of a sum of squares into components each of which has one degree of freedom. The general formulas will be applied to a subdivision of the sum of squares of remedial reading methods.

Some definitions will be needed. Suppose that there are k totals $T_1, T_2, \ldots, T_k$ based on $N_1, N_2, \ldots, N_k$ cases respectively. Then a combination

$$l_1T_1 + l_2T_2 + \cdots + l_kT_k$$

is called a comparison if

$$N_1l_1 + N_2l_2 + \cdots + N_kl_k = 0 \tag{14.7}$$

As an illustration recall that in the previous section we had

$$k = 2,\ l_1 = 3,\ l_2 = -1,\ N_1 = 12,\ N_2 = 36,$$

so that

$$N_1l_1 + N_2l_2 = 0$$

The sum of squares due to this comparison is

$$\frac{(l_1T_1 + l_2T_2 + \cdots + l_kT_k)^2}{N_1l_1^2 + N_2l_2^2 + \cdots + N_kl_k^2} \tag{14.8}$$

The sums of squares due to a set of comparisons will be independent if the comparisons are *orthogonal*. Two comparisons among the same totals

$$l_1T_1 + l_2T_2 + \cdots + l_kT_k$$

and

$$m_1T_1 + m_2T_2 + \cdots + m_kT_k$$

are orthogonal if

$$N_1 l_1 m_1 + N_2 l_2 m_2 + \cdots + N_k l_k m_k = 0 \tag{14.9}$$

If the number of cases is the same for all totals, that is

$$N_1 = N_2 = \cdots = N_k$$

then a combination is a comparison if

$$l_1 + l_2 + \cdots + l_k = 0$$

and two comparisons are orthogonal if

$$l_1 m_1 + l_2 m_2 + \cdots + l_k m_k = 0$$

If as many comparisons are formed as there are degrees of freedom then the sums of squares of a set of orthogonal comparisons constitute a complete subdivision of the total sum of squares. It should be noted that orthogonal sets of comparisons can be made up in an endless number of ways.

Let us apply the formulas to obtaining a set of orthogonal comparisons among the methods of remedial reading. From Table 14.1 we have

Method of Instruction	*Total*
Alphabetic	$T_1 = 1267.3$
Kinesthetic	$T_2 = 1347.2$
Phonic	$T_3 = 1247.2$
Visual	$T_4 = 1368.6$

The following comparisons suggest themselves as being of interest:

The alphabetic and phonic methods jointly in contrast with kinesthetic and visual jointly. This comparison has the form

$$T_1 + T_3 - T_2 - T_4$$

The alphabetic in contrast with the phonic method, with the form $T_1 - T_3$

The kinesthetic in contrast with the visual $T_2 - T_4$

The multipliers of T_1, T_2, T_3, T_4 which describe these comparisons are then as follows:

T_1	T_2	T_3	T_4
1	−1	1	−1
1	0	−1	0
0	1	0	−1

For any row the sum of the multipliers is zero. For any two rows the sum of products of corresponding multipliers is zero. Hence the conditions for orthogonality are satisfied.

The sums of squares for the three comparisons are

$$\frac{(T_1 + T_3 - T_2 - T_4)^2}{12 + 12 + 12 + 12} = 844.20$$

$$\frac{(T_1 - T_3)^2}{12 + 12} = 16.83$$

$$\frac{(T_2 - T_4)^2}{12 + 12} = 19.08$$

$$\text{Total} \quad 880.11$$

The reader should compare 880.11 which is the total of the three sums of squares with the entry 880.1 which is the sum of squares for methods of remedial instruction in Table 14.3. The two are the same except for rounding errors.

The sum of squares for each of the three comparisons has one degree of freedom and can be tested for significance using the sum of squares of individuals within subclasses from Table 14.3 as the error sum of squares. The first comparison is highly significant, for $F = \dfrac{844.20}{31.5} = 26.8$ and $F_{.99} = 7.50$. Neither of the other comparisons is significant.

The Estimation of Error. The denominator used in setting up the F ratio is called the "error mean square," the "error variance," or briefly the "error." The problem of choosing the appropriate sum of squares for error requires careful consideration. The choice differs from situation to situation.

Mathematically the numerator mean square and denominator mean square in F must be estimates of the same population variance in order that the F distribution shall apply. Let us see how this consideration applies to the problem of remedial reading. In this problem the entire population of children sampled in the experiment may be considered as stratified into 16 cells or subclasses. *Under each of the three null hypotheses* considered above the means which appear in the numerator mean square are affected only by variations among individuals *within* the subclasses. Consequently if the null hypothesis is true each numerator mean square is an estimate of the same population variance as is estimated by the variation within subclasses.

The situation was different in the problem of Chapter 9 when the performance of individuals at archery when shooting at the 50-yard range in first, second and third order was considered. There each individual was measured on each of the three orders.

For eleven individuals there were 33 cells or subclasses with one score in each. If that one score were really the mean of all possible scores made by the given individual shooting at the 50-yard range in the given order, then the residual variance of Table 9.9 would be an interaction variance. Here the interaction would be between individual and order and would be due to the differential response of individuals to such factors as warming up, practice, and fatigue.

However the one score shown in a cell is not the mean but is merely one score out of an infinite population of scores corresponding to that cell. As representative of the cell it involves an error of measurement, and thus variation within cells is also present in the residual variance of Table 9.9.

When there is only one score in a cell, the only error variance available is the residual variance which includes both the variance among subclass means and the variance among individuals within subclasses. These are confounded and cannot be disentangled. There is no possibility of testing interaction against variance within cells.

Now let us consider the numerator mean square, that is the mean square among means of orders. These means are subject to sampling variation of two kinds. If new individuals are observed, the total level of performance of those individuals (their row means) will not affect the comparison among the order means but their differential response to order may.

As new individuals are observed, new subclasses arise and if there is interaction among the subclass means such interaction is properly a part of the error variance for testing order difference. The variation among the order means is also affected by the variation within subclasses, for each score involves a measurement error. Thus the numerator mean square among order means (that is column means in Table 9.9) is an estimate of the same population variance as is the residual variance which represents the discrepance of the subclass observations from the estimate provided by row and column means, this residual variance being a value which includes both interaction and variation within subclasses. When there is only one case in each subclass the discrepance is the only measure of error available and no problem of choice arises.

To illustrate a situation in which a choice of error variance must be made we may consider a problem structurally similar to that of the 11 archers except that several scores are available in each subclass. Four methods of instruction are carried on in each of five schools, with several persons in each school taught by the same method. Here there are four times five or twenty subclasses. However, these subclasses are *not* a stratification of the population since the schools are themselves a sample out of all possible schools just as the 11 archers were a sample out of all possible archers. The variation among means of methods is due in part to variation within each of the observed twenty subclasses but also in part to variation of subclass means from the values they would have if they were completely dependent upon their row and column means. The latter variation is measured by the interaction mean square.

Hence in a situation like the one just described a test is first made for significance of interaction by using the variation within subclasses as error. If the interaction mean square is significantly greater than the mean square within subclasses that interaction mean square is used as the error variance for testing significance of row and column effects. If the interaction mean square is not significantly greater than the variance within subclasses then this interaction may be considered an estimate of the same population variance as the mean square within subclasses. In such case the sum of squares for interaction and for variation within subclasses can be advantageously combined to form a new error variance for testing row and column effects. These procedures will be discussed.

Mathematical Models for the Two-way Layout. The discussion of the previous section will now be amplified by a symbolic analysis based on mathematical models used in analysis of variance. The mathematical model which is used to describe the population plays an important part in determining how the analysis of variance is to be carried out.

The effect of the mathematical model on the analysis of variance is due to the logic of the F distribution. It has been stated previously that the mean squares in the numerator of F and in its denominator must be estimates of the same variance in order that the F test may be made. For accurate use of the F test it is necessary to determine in each case whether this condition is satisfied.

Consider first the mathematical model used in the experiment on remedial reading. In this model the mean of each cell is assumed to be the constant μ_{ij}.

TABLE 14.5 Population Values Estimated by Mean Squares in an Experiment with *r* Rows, *c* Columns and *n* Individuals in each Cell

Source of variation	Mean square	Population value estimated
Rows	$\frac{cn}{r-1}\Sigma(\overline{X}_{i.} - \overline{X})^2$	$\sigma^2 + \frac{cn}{r-1}\Sigma(\mu_{i.} - \mu)^2$
Columns	$\frac{rn}{c-1}\Sigma(\overline{X}_{.j} - X)^2$	$\sigma^2 + \frac{rn}{c-1}\Sigma(\mu_{.j} - \mu)^2$
Interaction	$\frac{n\Sigma\Sigma(\overline{X}_{ij} - \overline{X}_{i.} - \overline{X}_{.j} + \overline{X})^2}{(r-1)(c-1)}$	$\sigma^2 + \frac{n\Sigma\Sigma(\mu_{ij} - \mu_{i.} - \mu_{.j} + \mu)^2}{(r-1)(c-1)}$
Individuals within subclasses	$\frac{\Sigma\Sigma\Sigma(X_{ij\alpha} - \overline{X}_{ij})^2}{rc(n-1)}$	σ^2

Population values estimated in Table 14.5 are determined only on this assumption. Each of the hypotheses H_r, H_c and H_{rc} modifies these values so that if the hypothesis is true the estimated value becomes σ^2 in each case. Consider for example the hypothesis H_r which states that $\mu_{1.} = \mu_{2.} \cdots = \mu_{k.} = \mu$. If this hypothesis is true each difference $\mu_{i.} - \mu$ is zero. Hence the expression $\frac{cn\Sigma(\mu_{i.} - \mu)^2}{r-1}$ is zero, and the estimated population value for rows is σ^2. It follows that under the appropriate hypothesis each F ratio formed in Table 14.3 satisfies the condition that the numerator and denominator are estimates of the same variance.

Consider now the model for an experiment in which four remedial reading methods are tried in each of several school systems, the school systems being chosen at random from a population of school systems. Suppose that the teaching methods are set up in rows and the school systems in columns. The mean of a row can be regarded as the same for all individuals in the row but the mean of a column is a variable which depends on the particular school system chosen for that column. The mean of a cell must take into account these components and their interaction.

The discussion will be clarified if the following symbols are introduced.

$\mu_{i.}$ is the mean of a method of instruction. This is the same (constant) for all samples. The mean of the $\mu_{i.}$ is μ.

a_j is a component due to the school system. This will vary as different school systems are introduced. We shall consider it a normally distributed variable with mean zero and variance σ_a^2.

b_{ij} is a component due to the interaction of method of instruction and school system. As different school systems are chosen, b_{ij} will vary. We shall consider b_{ij} as distributed normally and independently of a_j with mean zero and variance σ_b^2.

With this symbolism the mean of a cell in the ith row and jth column is

$$\mu_{i.} + a_{.j} + b_{ij}.$$

In Table 14.6 are shown sources of variation and related estimates of population values for the statistics in Table 14.2 under the model just described.

TABLE 14.6 Population Values Estimated in a Two-way Layout When the Column Means are Variables

Source of variation	Population value estimated by mean square
Rows	$\sigma^2 + n\sigma_b^2 + \frac{cn}{r-1}\Sigma(\mu_{i.} - \mu)^2$
Columns	$\sigma^2 + n\sigma_b^2 + nr\sigma_a^2$
Interaction	$\sigma^2 + n\sigma_b^2$
Individuals within subclasses	σ^2

Table 14.6 indicates that the F ratio cannot always have the mean square within subclasses as a denominator. Under the hypothesis that $\mu_{i.} = \mu$ for all row means, the estimated mean square for rows is $\sigma^2 + n\sigma_b^2$ while the mean square within subclasses is σ^2.

The tests of significance are carried out as follows. First, test for interaction using the mean square for interaction as numerator and the mean square within subclasses as denominator. Under the hypothesis that interaction is zero ($\sigma_b^2 = 0$) both mean squares are estimates of σ^2.

The tests for rows and columns depend on the outcome of the test for interaction. If the hypothesis that $\sigma_b^2 = 0$ is rejected, then under the hypothesis that $\mu_i = \mu$, the estimated mean square for rows is the same as for interaction. For columns, the hypothesis that there is no column effect is given by $\sigma_a^2 = 0$. Under this hypothesis, too, the F test is made by using the mean square for interaction in the denominator.

If the hypothesis that interaction is zero is accepted then either the mean square for interaction or the mean square within subclasses may be used. However, it is preferable to combine the sum of squares for interaction with the sum of squares within subclasses, and similarly to combine the degrees of freedom. Then from this combination a mean square is found to use in the denominator as estimate of the error variance. In this way more degrees of freedom are available in the denominator.

The experiment described under the second model is often referred to as a *randomized block experiment,* in analogy with agricultural experiments in which the same experiment is repeated on several blocks of land. Here the block is the school system. After the groups have been selected within each block, the methods of instruction are assigned randomly to the groups.

Experimental Procedure Replicated on Each of Several Individuals. In some experiments it is possible to carry out the entire experimental procedure on each individual in the study. A great advantage of carrying out an experiment in this way, when conditions permit it, is that differences between persons are eliminated from the comparisons among elements of the experiment. Another advantage is that fewer cases are needed, because several measures are obtained from each case. When several measures are obtained from the same individual, these measures are correlated and the calculations must take the correlations into account. Calculation appropriate for this kind of problem will be considered.

As an example of an experiment replicated on each of several individuals, we shall consider once more the experiment on archery discussed in Chapter 9. Each subject in that study shot daily for six days at ranges of 50, 40 and 30 yards. The order of shooting at these ranges varied from day to day so that each subject shot each range twice in the first position, twice in second, and twice in third. In Chapter 9 only part of these data were utilized. In Table 14.7 are given all the scores for the entire period for each of 11 subjects classified by range and by order of shooting that range. Each entry in the table is the sum of two scores. Thus, if on one day the ranges were shot 50–30–40 and on another day were shot 40–30–50, the two scores at range 30 would be combined to make the score for range 30 in the second order.

Note that each score in the Table 14.7 can be classified in three ways as belonging to a range, an order and a subject. It

TABLE 14.7 Scores of Eleven Archers Shooting at Three Ranges and in Three Orders at each Range*

Archer	Score at given range and order†									Total
	50 yards			40 yards			30 yards			
	1	2	3	1	2	3	1	2	3	
A	114	182	123	248	241	157	305	255	286	1911
B	99	121	119	101	160	153	203	188	225	1369
C	51	100	35	153	149	148	201	184	238	1259
D	78	144	72	114	142	132	163	167	219	1231
E	134	125	201	246	214	237	267	182	259	1865
F	71	38	49	105	117	84	146	120	157	887
G	66	67	107	122	125	133	195	235	181	1231
H	33	89	51	141	164	113	162	166	213	1132
I	146	159	157	181	222	187	275	240	227	1794
J	80	101	83	109	120	106	170	110	126	1005
K	105	113	113	186	185	188	232	166	221	1509
Total	977	1239	1110	1706	1839	1638	2319	2013	2352	15,193

* Data from Schroeder [11].

† The number 1 indicates that the given range was the first of the three ranges to be shot, and the numbers 2 and 3 are to have similar interpretations.

is convenient to think of each score as belonging to a cell in a rectangular solid, one score to a cell. The solid may be pictured as in Figure 14–1. Each of the 99 scores is represented as located

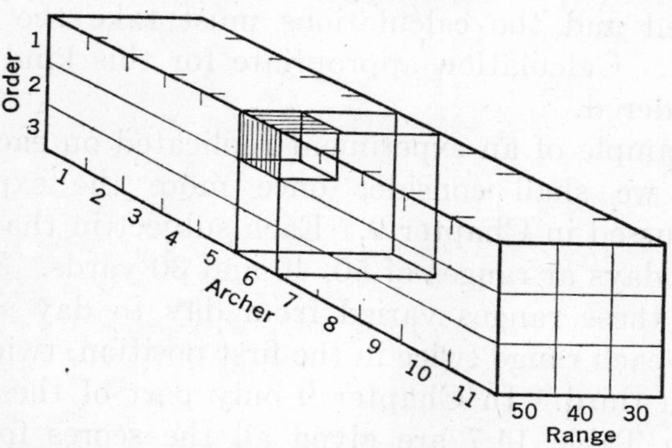

FIG. 14–1. Three dimensional solid representing scores made by 11 archers shooting in 3 orders at 3 ranges.

in one of the 99 cells of which this solid is composed. The 9 cells containing the scores of the sixth archer have been indicated by a cross section in which a shaded portion represents the cell containing the score made by archer 6 shooting at 50-yard range in first order.

In the same manner in which marginal totals are obtained in a flat or two-way layout, marginal totals are obtained for this three-way layout. The marginal totals are represented as two-way layouts, one set of marginal totals for each pair of variables. The sets of marginal totals will be presented in Tables 14.8, 14.9, and 14.10.

TABLE 14.8 Sum of Scores for All 11 Archers Classified by Order and Range

Order	Sum of scores at given range			Total
	50 yards	40 yards	30 yards	
1	977	1706	2319	5002
2	1239	1839	2013	5091
3	1110	1638	2352	5100
Total	3326	5183	6684	15,193

The reader may check that the nine entries giving sums for all subjects in Table 14.8 are the 9 entries in the lowest line of Table 14.7. He may verify the entries in Tables 14.9 and 14.10 by adding appropriate entries in Table 14.7. For example the first entry in Table 14.9 is 419 and equals 114 + 182 + 123 in 14.7.

From the data in Table 14.7 and its subtables the various component sums of squares can be calculated. There are seven of these components. Three are the main effects, the effects

TABLE 14.9 Sum of Scores for All 3 Orders Classified by Archer and Range

Archer	Sum of scores at given range			Total
	50 yards	40 yards	30 yards	
A	419	646	846	1911
B	339	414	616	1369
C	186	450	623	1259
D	294	388	549	1231
E	460	697	708	1865
F	158	306	423	887
G	240	380	611	1231
H	173	418	541	1132
I	462	590	742	1794
J	264	335	406	1005
K	331	559	619	1509
Total	3326	5183	6684	15,193

TABLE 14.10 Sum of Scores for All 3 Ranges
Classified by Archer and Order

Archer	Sum of scores at given order			Total
	1	2	3	
A	667	678	566	1911
B	403	469	497	1369
C	405	433	421	1259
D	355	453	423	1231
E	647	521	697	1865
F	322	275	290	887
G	383	427	421	1231
H	336	419	377	1132
I	602	621	571	1794
J	359	331	315	1005
K	523	464	522	1509
Total	5002	5091	5100	15,193

of range, order and subject. Three more are the interactions between pairs of factors, called first order interactions. The remaining one is the joint interaction between all three variables, called the second order interaction.

As usual the calculations begin with the correction term which is

$$\frac{(15{,}193)^2}{99} = 2{,}331{,}588$$

Then the sums of squares for main effects are as follows:

Archers:
$\frac{1}{9}[(1911)^2 + (1369)^2 + \cdots + (1005)^2 + (1509)^2] - 2{,}331{,}588 = 134{,}395$
Range: $\frac{1}{33}[(3326)^2 + (5183)^2 + (6684)^2] - 2{,}331{,}588 = 171{,}491$
Order: $\frac{1}{33}[(5002)^2 + (5091)^2 + (5100)^2] - 2{,}331{,}588 = 178$

Note that in these calculations the number by which each sum of squares is divided is the number of cases which enter into that sum.

The interactions can be computed from Tables 14.8, 14.9, and 14.10.

Range × Order interaction from Table 14.8:

$$\frac{1}{11}[(977)^2 + (1706)^2 + \cdots + (1638)^2 + (2352)^2]$$
$$- \frac{1}{33}[(3326)^2 + (5183)^2 + (6684)^2]$$
$$- \frac{1}{33}[(5002)^2 + (5091)^2 + (5100)^2] + (15{,}193)^2/99$$
$$= 2{,}514{,}453 - 2{,}503{,}079 - 2{,}331{,}766 + 2{,}331{,}588 = 11{,}196$$

Range × Archer interaction from Table 14.9:

$$\tfrac{1}{3}[(419)^2 + (646)^2 + \cdots + (559)^2 + (619)^2] - \tfrac{1}{33}[(3326)^2 + (5183)^2 + (6684)^2] - \tfrac{1}{9}[(1911)^2 + (1369)^2 + \cdots + (1005)^2 + (1509)^2] + (15{,}193)^2/99$$
$$= 2{,}656{,}966 - 2{,}503{,}079 - 2{,}465{,}983 + 2{,}331{,}588 = 19{,}492$$

Order × Archer interaction from Table 14.10:

$$\tfrac{1}{3}[(667)^2 + (678)^2 + \cdots + (464)^2 + (522)^2] - \tfrac{1}{33}[(5002)^2 + (5091)^2 + (5100)^2] - \tfrac{1}{9}[(1911)^2 + (1369)^2 + \cdots + (1509)^2] + (15{,}193)^2/99$$
$$= 2{,}480{,}800 - 2{,}331{,}766 - 2{,}465{,}983 + 2{,}331{,}588 = 14{,}639$$

Order × range × Archer interaction:

Perhaps the simplest way to calculate the second order interaction is to calculate it as a residual, subtracting from the total sum of squares the component sums of squares which have just been computed. The total sum of squares is obtained from Table 14.7 as the sum of the squares of the 99 scores minus the correction term.

$$(114)^2 + (182)^2 + \cdots + (166)^2 + (221)^2 - \frac{(15{,}193)^2}{99}$$
$$= 2{,}703{,}221 - 2{,}331{,}588 = 371{,}633$$

Then the second order interaction sum of squares is

$$371{,}633 - 134{,}395 - 171{,}491 - 178 - 11{,}196 - 19{,}492 - 14{,}639 = 20{,}242$$

The sums of squares together with their degrees of freedom and the derived mean squares are presented in Table 14.11. In this table are also presented the F ratios for interactions. A justification for using these ratios to furnish tests of significance is given below.

TABLE 14.11 Analysis of Variance of Data of Table 14.7 and Test for First Order Interaction

Source of variation	d.f.	Sum of squares	Mean square	F	$F_{.95}$	$F_{.99}$
Range	2	171,491	85,746			
Order	2	178	89			
Archers	10	134,395	13,440			
Order × range	4	11,196	2,799	5.53	2.61	3.83
Order × archer	20	14,639	732	1.45	1.84	2.37
Range × archer	20	19,492	975	1.93	1.84	2.37
Second order interaction	40	20,242	506			

The number of degrees of freedom for each main effect in the analysis of variance table is one less than the number of classes for that trait. For a first order interaction the number of degrees of freedom is the product of the degrees of freedom for the two main effects which enter into the interaction. For the second order interaction the number of degrees of freedom is the product of the degrees of freedom for the three main effects in the interaction. The sum of all degrees of freedom is one less than the number of cases in the study.

Sources of Variation. Before proceeding with tests of significance a discussion of the sources of variation which enter into the analysis of variance is desirable. The discussion will deal with the variables themselves, or the main effects, and with the interactions among the variables.

1. *The range.* This will be considered as having the same fixed values, 30, 40 and 50 yards, for all samples.

2. *The order of shooting.* This will be considered as having the same fixed values 1, 2 and 3, for all samples.

3. *The skill of the individual.* The individuals will be considered as a sample of all possible similar individuals. Skill, as represented by mean score of an individual in repeated trials, will vary from individual to individual, and, thus, mean skill will vary from sample to sample. To consider the mean skills of individuals as fixed from sample to sample would restrict the generalization to the individuals in the study and would make the study of little interest. Consequently the more general view will be adopted here.

4. *Interaction of range with order.* Since both range and order are fixed for all samples their interaction is also fixed.

5. *Interaction of range with skill of individuals.* Since the individuals vary from sample to sample, this interaction is a variable.

6. *Interaction of order with skill of individuals.* For the same reason this interaction is also a variable.

To show how this view of the sources of variation influences the analysis of variance we shall introduce symbolism with which to describe the mathematical model.

The following subscripts will be used: i indicating any one of the r ranges; j indicating any one of the s orders; α indicating any one of the t individuals.

The symbol μ_{ij} will be used for the population mean at the

ith range and jth order. The Greek letter μ indicates that this mean is the same for all samples and thus is really a character of the population from which the samples are drawn.

To describe the score $X_{ij\alpha}$ made by the αth individual shooting at range i in order j, symbols will be needed for three additional variables, and for these the Latin letters, a, b, and c, with appropriate subscripts will be used.

Symbol	*Component*	*Expectation*	*Variance*
a_α	Extent to which the αth individual differs from the population mean μ $a_\alpha = \mu_\alpha - \mu$	0	σ_a^2
$b_{i\alpha}$	Extent to which the αth individual shooting at range i differs from what is expected in terms of his own mean and the range mean $b_i = \mu_{i\alpha} - \mu_i - \mu_\alpha + \mu$	0	σ_b^2
$c_{j\alpha}$	Extent to which the αth individual shooting in order j differs from what is expected in terms of his own ability and the order mean $c_{j\alpha} = \mu_{j\alpha} - \mu_j - \mu_\alpha + \mu$	0	σ_c^2

These three components are assumed to vary from individual to individual, independently of each other and to be normally distributed. Then the score made by the αth individual shooting at range i in order j will differ from

$$\mu_{ij\alpha} = \mu_{ij} + a_\alpha + b_{i\alpha} + c_{j\alpha}$$

only through an error of measurement. All the possible scores which can be made by a particular individual shooting at fixed range and in fixed order may be considered as a normal population with mean $\mu_{ij\alpha}$ and variance σ^2. Each cell of the table has such a normal population, all populations having the same variance but quite possibly differing as to mean. In the data under consideration, however, we have only one observation from any one such population. Under the assumption that the second order interaction is zero in the population, the second order interaction of the sample provides an estimate of σ^2.

On the basis of this mathematical model the mean squares in Table 14.11 are estimates of the population values named in Table 14.12.

TABLE 14.12 Population Values Estimated by the Mean Squares of Table 14.11

Source of variation	Population values estimated
Range	$\sigma^2 + s\sigma_b^2 + \frac{st}{r-1}\Sigma(\mu_{i.} - \mu)^2$
Order	$\sigma^2 + r\sigma_c^2 + \frac{rt}{s-1}\Sigma(\mu_{.j} - \mu)^2$
Archers	$\sigma^2 + s\sigma_b^2 + r\sigma_c^2 + rs\sigma_a^2$
Range × Order	$\sigma^2 + \frac{t}{(r-1)(s-1)}\Sigma\Sigma(\mu_{ij} - \mu_{i.} - \mu_{.j} + \mu)^2$
Order × Archer	$\sigma^2 + r\sigma_c^2$
Range × Archer	$\sigma^2 + s\sigma_b^2$
Order × Range × Archer	σ^2

Tests of Significance for Interactions. By study of Table 14.12 the appropriate tests of significance can be ascertained. Consider first the tests of significance for interaction.

1. *Interaction of range with order.* The hypothesis that this interaction is zero is given by the expression

$$\mu_{ij} - \mu_{i.} - \mu_{.j} + \mu = 0$$

for each range and each order. Under this hypothesis the ratio of mean square for range × order interaction and the mean square for the order × range × archer interaction are independent estimates of σ^2. Consequently the F ratio using these mean squares is an appropriate test for the hypothesis that no interaction exists between order and range.

The entry in Table 14.11 shows that this F has the value 5.53, so that the effect of order appears to depend on range.

2. *Interaction of archer with range.* The hypothesis that this interaction is zero is given by the expression

$$\sigma_b^2 = 0$$

Hence the mean squares for interaction of range × archer and the second order interaction are both estimates of σ^2 and the F test applies. The value of F to test this interaction, as found in Table 14.11, is 1.93 which is significant at the 5% level and the hypothesis of no interaction may be rejected.

3. *Interaction of archer with order.* By an argument like the preceding the appropriate F test for this hypothesis is the ratio of mean square for order × archer to the mean square for the second order interaction. The F value is not significant at the 5% level.

Choice of Error Variance for the Main Effects. This choice must be made in the light of a preliminary examination of the first order interactions, such as is shown in Table 14.11. When the null hypothesis can be accepted for *all* of the first order interactions, then each of the four mean squares for interaction is an estimate of σ^2. The appropriate procedure then is to pool all the four sums of squares for interaction forming a new sum of squares for error, to pool the corresponding degrees of freedom, and to obtain a new estimate of σ^2 by dividing this sum of squares for error by the sum of the degrees of freedom for the various interactions. This estimate of the error variance forms the denominator in the F ratio used to test each of the main effects.

In the archery problem, however, the preliminary analysis indicates that one first order interaction may be treated as zero and the other two may not be. It will therefore be necessary to consider separately the estimate of error for each of the main effects.

Since the purpose of the experiment was to determine the effect of order only, the tests of range and of archers are of no practical import and are introduced here only to illustrate the appropriate procedures.

1. *Test that range means are equal.* Applying this hypothesis to the quantity named in Table 14.12 in the line headed range, we have $\frac{st}{r-1}\Sigma(\mu_{i.} - \mu)^2 = 0$, so the mean square for range under the null hypothesis for range is an estimate of $\sigma^2 + s\sigma_b{}^2$ if archer $\times$ range interaction exists and is σ^2 if archer $\times$ range interaction is zero ($\sigma_b{}^2 = 0$). In Table 14.11 this interaction has been tested and found significant. Therefore the mean square for range and the range $\times$ archer interaction are both estimates of $\sigma^2 + s\sigma_b{}^2$ and the latter is the appropriate denominator to use in the F ratio. Table 14.13 presents the final analysis for range.

2. *Test that order means are equal.* Applying this hypothesis to the quantity named in Table 14.12 in the line headed order, we have $\frac{rt}{s-1}\Sigma(\mu_{.j} - \mu)^2 = 0$, so the mean square for order is an estimate of $\sigma^2 + r\sigma_c{}^2$ under the null hypothesis for order. Since the preliminary analysis of Table 14.11 shows the archer $\times$ order interaction non-significant, we pool its sum of squares with that of the second order interaction and complete the analysis as in Table 14.14.

TABLE 14.13 Analysis of Variance for Testing the Significance of Range and of Archer in the Data from Table 14.11

Source of variation	d.f.	Sum of squares	Mean square	F	$F_{.95}$	$F_{.99}$
Range	2	171,491	85,746	87.944	3.49	5.85
Archers	10	134,395	13,440	13.785	2.35	3.37
Error	20	19,492	975			

TABLE 14.14 Analysis of Variance for Testing the Significance of Order in the Data from Table 14.11

Source of variation	d.f.	Sum of squares	Mean square	F	$F_{.95}$	$F_{.99}$
Order	2	178	89	.153	3.15	4.98
Error	60	34,881	581			

3. *Test that archer means are equal.* This test presents a more complex problem since the quantity named on the line headed archer in Table 14.12 contains two first order interactions. For our data the preliminary analysis has indicated that we may treat σ_c^2 as zero but may not so treat σ_b^2. Under the null hypothesis for archers, $\sigma_a^2 = 0$. Hence under that hypothesis the mean square for archers is an estimate of $\sigma^2 + s\sigma_b^2$. As this same quantity is also estimated by the archer × range interaction, the latter is the appropriate estimate of error, and the analysis proceeds as in Table 14.13.

If both of the first order interactions with archers had been found significant, we could not have treated either σ_b^2 or σ_c^2 as zero. Then no single interaction would provide a proper test for the difference among archers, which is the test that $\sigma_a^2 = 0$. The mean squares must now be combined to form a proper estimate of error, and we shall use the following key:

Symbol	*Mean square*
k_0	Archers
k_1	Archer × order interaction
k_2	Archer × range interaction
k_3	Archer × order × range interaction

Then

$$F = \frac{k_0}{k_1 + k_2 - k_3} \tag{14.10}$$

with $(t-1)$ degrees of freedom for the numerator and

$$(14.11)\quad n = \frac{(k_1 + k_2 - k_3)^2}{\dfrac{k_1^2}{(s-1)(t-1)} + \dfrac{k_2^2}{(t-1)(r-1)} + \dfrac{k_3^2}{(r-1)(s-1)(t-1)}}$$

degrees of freedom for the denominator.[8] (The reader may wish to be reminded that t has been used to indicate the number of archers, r the number of ranges and s the number of orders.)

Latin Square and Graeco-Latin Square. In problems which involve classification into several categories on each of several variables, it is often desirable to take observations for all combinations of the values of the different variables. By arranging the observations in one of the forms known as the Latin Square or the Graeco-Latin Square a large amount of information can be extracted from a relatively small number of observations. In the analysis of the data so obtained it is necessary to make the assumption that interactions are zero, and the investigator should recognize that he is making this assumption.

Suppose, for example, that the director of a statistical laboratory is about to buy new machines and has several models under consideration. He wants to study the speed with which a skilled computer can complete a given amount of work on each machine. Obviously, if one person should perform the same computations on each of several machines there would probably be a practice effect. Consequently he must perform different computations, and there is a risk that those computations may not be equally difficult. The solution therefore requires that there be as many computers as machines and as many problems as machines, and that each computer use each machine once and solve each problem once, and that each problem be computed once on each machine. In the following scheme, each row represents a machine, each column represents a problem, and the letters A, B, C, D and E represent computers.

	Problem				
	1	2	3	4	5
Machine I	A	B	C	D	E
Machine II	B	C	D	E	A
Machine III	C	D	E	A	B
Machine IV	D	E	A	B	C
Machine V	E	A	B	C	D

Latin Square

The 24 degrees of freedom among the 25 observations may be assigned as follows:

Machines	4
Problems	4
Computers	4
Residual error	12
Total	24

Now suppose it appears that the speed of a computer may be affected by the order in which he uses the machines. Then the experimental design must provide that each machine shall be used first by one computer, second by another, third by another, fourth by another, and last by the remaining computer. If now the small Greek letters, α (alpha), β (beta), γ (gamma), δ (delta), and ϵ (epsilon), be used to represent the order in which a machine is used, the design may be called a Graeco-Latin Square. (The same name, Graeco-Latin, is customarily applied even if the second factor is indicated by numerals or by small Latin letters instead of Greek letters.)

The 24 degrees of freedom now are assigned as follows:

Machines	4
Problems	4
Computers	4
Orders	4
Residual error	8
Total	24

	1	2	3	4	5
I	A α	B γ	C ϵ	D β	E δ
II	B β	C δ	D α	E γ	A ϵ
III	C γ	D ϵ	E β	A δ	B α
IV	D δ	E α	A γ	B ϵ	C β
V	E ϵ	A β	B δ	C α	D γ

Graeco-Latin Square

There are 4 variables (machines, operators, problems, orders). The data are classified into 5 categories on each of these variables. In the 25 observations recorded every category of one variable occurs once and only once in combination with every category of every other variable. Thus each row of the pattern displays every category of every variable except the row variable, and each column displays every category of every variable except the column variable.

Application of Graeco-Latin Square to Study on Memorizing Music. In the standard Latin Square or Graeco-Latin Square, there is one observation in each cell. We now shall consider an arrangement of that sort obtained by Rubin-Rabson [10] from an experiment in the memorizing of piano music and subsequently shall consider an adaptation of the arrangement in which there are several scores in each cell. Each subject came to the studio on four successive days. On each day he memorized one composition and exactly three weeks later he returned to the studio and relearned the same composition. The time in minutes required for the first learning of a composition, the time for its relearning and the reduction in that time (that is, the amount by which the time for the first learning exceeded the time for relearning) are the basic data of the study. Each of the four compositions was studied by a different method, and the comparison of the four methods is the chief goal of the study. The effect upon method difference caused by difference in difficulty of compositions and in order of presentation of the compositions has been controlled by the experimental design. Therefore, the variation in compositions and in order of presentation must not be allowed to contribute to the error variance in the statistical analysis.

The four methods to be compared will now be briefly described. The reader who is interested in more exact details should consult the original study.

A: Seated at a table the subject studied the musical score and its analysis for 20 minutes. Then he carried the score to the piano and practiced until he had memorized it. When he could play it through twice without errors and without stopping he was admonished not to practice it further and to think of it as little as possible.

B: This was the same as A except while the subject studied the score he was told to write down any relationship concerning voice movement, chords, etc., which he thought might help him in memorizing the composition, and was allowed 25 minutes for the pre-study.

C: There was no preliminary study period. Subject went directly to the piano but was warned to play the composition for the first time at a speed slow enough to avoid errors.

D: Subject was seated before a phonograph and given the musical score. He listened to four successive repetitions of the composition while he followed the score.

In each method, time was clocked from the beginning of the first playing of the composition until it was played through twice without errors. Three weeks later the subject returned to relearn the compositions in the same order as before but without any preliminary study.

Thirty-six subjects were tested in 4 groups according to the following scheme, where P, Q, R and S represent the 4 compositions and A, B, C and D the 4 methods:

Group	First day	Second day	Third day	Fourth day
1	AP	BQ	CR	DS
2	DR	CS	BP	AQ
3	BS	AR	DQ	CP
4	CQ	DP	AS	BR

From the description of the original study it is not clear whether the four groups should be considered as a classification variable or not. If individuals were not assigned to the groups at random, but groups were selected on the basis of some principle of convenience or existing class structure, then the variation from group to group might be large in relation to variation among individuals within groups and also large in relation to residual error. In that case the variation among group means should be taken out as a principal component. On the other hand, if individuals were assigned to groups by some purely random procedure the variation among groups is due to sampling error and should be a part of the error variance. It is true that no two groups were exposed to the same combination of method and composition on the same days, but that is of no importance if the assumption of zero interaction is justified. The interaction cannot be tested in this arrangement but is explicitly assumed to be zero. Inasmuch as the printed study does not state how persons were assigned to groups, it is not possible to be sure how groups should be treated in the analysis.

As a first analysis we shall ignore the variation among persons and shall consider as basic data the sum, for the nine individuals in one group, of the number of minutes by which the time for the original learning of a composition exceeded the time for relearning it. These data are presented in Table 14.15.

There are 16 observations yielding 15 degrees of freedom. If we consider group as a variable there are 4 variables — method, composition, day and group — each of which has 3 degrees of freedom. There remain $15 - (3 + 3 + 3 + 3) = 3$ degrees of freedom for error. Each F ratio obtained will thus have 3 degrees of freedom for the numerator variance and 3 for the denominator variance, and so must exceed $F_{.95} = 9.28$ to be significant at the .05 level. It is evident that this design cannot detect small differences among the methods.

TABLE 14.15 Reduction in Learning Time in Minutes for Compositions *P, Q, R,* and *S* When Studied by Methods *A, B,* C and *D.* (Each entry is the sum for 9 subjects. Numerals 1, 2, 3, and 4 indicate group.)

Method	First day		Second day		Third day		Fourth day		Total
A	P1	80	R3	28	S4	59	Q2	40	207
B	S3	128	Q1	70.5	P2	96	R4	41.5	336
C	Q4	50	S2	57	R1	8	P3	62	177
D	R2	50.5	P4	94	Q3	92	S1	33.5	270
Total		308.5		249.5		255.0		177.0	

The computation of the various sums of squares is shown in Table 14.16 and the resultant analysis of variance in Table 14.17.

Latin-Square Pattern with Several Observations in Each Cell. The previous analysis of the time required for memorizing piano music under different methods of study did not make use of all the data available. The raw data of the study which may be seen in Table 14.18, indicate that there were 9 observations in each

TABLE 14.16 Computation of the Relevant Sums of Squares for the Data of Table 14.15

	Methods		Compositions		Days		Groups	
	A	207	P	332	1	308.5	I	192
	B	336	Q	252.5	2	249.5	II	243.5
	C	177	R	128	3	255	III	310
	D	270	S	277.5	4	177	IV	244.5
$\sum_1^4\sum_1^4 X$		990		990		990		990
$\Sigma\left(\sum_1^4 X\right)^2$		259974		267370.5		253776.5		252036.5
$\frac{1}{4}\Sigma\left(\sum_1^4 X\right)^2$		64993.5		66842.6		63444.125		63009.125
$990^2/16$		61256.25		61256.25		61256.25		61256.25
Sum of squares		3737.25		5586.375		2187.875		1752.875

Total sum of squares: $\sum_{j=1}^{4}\sum_{i=1}^{4} X^2_{ij} - \frac{(\Sigma\Sigma X_{ij})^2}{16}$

$$= (80^2 + 128^2 + \cdots + 33.5^2) - \frac{990^2}{16}$$

$$= 75187 - \frac{980100}{16} = 75187 - 61256.25 = 13930.75$$

$$13930.75 - (3737.25 + 5586.375 + 2187.875 + 1752.875) = 666.375$$

TABLE 14.17 Analysis of Variance of Reduction in Learning Time for 4 Compositions Studied by 4 Groups Using 4 Methods on 4 Days

Source of variation	Sum of squares	d.f.	Mean square	F	$F_{.95}$
Total	13930.75				
Methods	3737.25	3	1245.75	5.61	9.28
Compositions	5586.375	3	1862.125	8.38	9.28
Days	2187.875	3	729.29	3.28	9.28
Groups	1752.875	3	584.29	2.63	9.28
Error	666.375	3	222.125		

group and that the variability among these was disregarded in the analysis of Table 14.17. As in the previous analysis, we shall work only with the *difference* in time required for initial learning and for relearning. There are 4 scores for each of 36 students or 144 scores in all.

For all 144 scores we have $\sum_{1}^{36}\sum_{1}^{4} X^2 = 15920.5$

and $$\sum_{1}^{36}\sum_{1}^{4} X = 990$$

Then the total sum of squares is

$$15920.5 - (990)^2/144 = 15920.5 - 6806.25 = 9114.25$$

To find the sum of squares among the 36 individuals we first compute

$$\sum_{1}^{36}\left(\sum_{1}^{4} X\right)^2 = 33^2 + 55.5^2 + (-13)^2 + \cdots + 33^2 + 12.5^2 = 41962$$

Then the sum of squares is

$$\tfrac{1}{4}\sum_{1}^{36}\left(\sum_{1}^{4} X\right)^2 - \tfrac{1}{144}\left(\sum_{1}^{36}\sum_{1}^{4} X\right)^2 = 10490.5 - 6806.25 = 3684.25$$

To find the sum of squares among groups we first compute

$$\sum_{1}^{4}\left(\sum_{1}^{9}\sum_{1}^{4} X\right)^2 = 192^2 + 243^2 + 310^2 + 244.5^2 = 461036$$

Then the sum of squares is

$$\frac{1}{36}(252036.5) - \frac{990^2}{144} = 194.76$$

and the mean square is $$\frac{194.76}{3} = 64.92$$

TABLE 14.18 Basic Data on Memorizing Piano Music*

Subject	Difference in Learning Time in Minutes					Subject	Difference in Learning Time in Minutes				
	A	B	C	D	Total		A	B	C	D	Total
1	12	12	1	8	33	19	7	16	11	21	55
2	33	18.5	− 1	5	55.5	20	− 2	3.5	18	− .5	19
3	− 11	6	− 6	− 2	− 13	21	1	29.5	13	32	75.5
4	− 8	8.5	5	6	11.5	22	10	18.5	− 5	11	34.5
5	11	12.5	− 1	2	24.5	23	2	8	1	− 3	8
6	14	6.5	2	4	26.5	24	4	34	16	19	73
7	12	9.5	11	9.5	42	25	6	10.5	1	11	28.5
8	2	− 7	1	4	0	26	0	5.5	2	.5	8
9	15	4	− 4	− 3	12	27	0	2.5	5	1	8.5
Sum	80	70.5	8	33.5	192	Sum	28	128	62	92	310
10	6	12	13	5	36	28	− 2	0	− 1	7	4
11	15	.5	10	20	45.5	29	7	8	11	8.5	34.5
12	7	17.5	16	10	50.5	30	4	1.5	8	12	25.5
13	0	3.5	− 8	0	− 4.5	31	9	6	17	16.5	48.5
14	9	27.5	− 3	2.5	36	32	9	5	0	12.5	26.5
15	0	3	− 2	− .5	.5	33	13	8	2	16.5	39.5
16	− 6	10	17	7.5	28.5	34	3	.5	7	10	20.5
17	10	13.5	7	4.5	35	35	5	9.5	7	11.5	33
18	− 1	8.5	7	1.5	16	36	11	3	− 1	− .5	12.5
Sum	40	96	57	50.5	243.5	Sum	59	41.5	50	94	244.5

* Data provided by Dr. Rubin-Rabson.

It will be observed that this is exactly $\frac{1}{9}$ of the value previously found, because now we are treating the group mean as the mean of 36 observations and previously we treated it as the mean of 4.

The sum of squares of individuals within groups is

$$3684.25 - 194.76 = 3489.49$$

and the mean square is $\dfrac{3489.49}{32} = 109.05$. The 32 degrees of freedom may be arrived at by noting that from the 35 degrees of freedom among 36 individuals there must be subtracted the 3 degrees of freedom among the 4 groups, or by noting that there are 8 degrees of freedom for the 9 individuals in each of the 4 groups.

The test of the differences among group means is therefore $F = \dfrac{64.92}{109.05} = .6$. The group means are not significantly different in respect to the variation among individuals.

In the analysis in Table 14.17, if group differences are not isolated they will form part of the estimate of error. In Table 14.19, if group differences are not isolated they will form part of the estimate of variation among individuals, which has here been separated from the error variance. Therefore, in the analysis of Table 14.17 if group differences are large it might be important to isolate them, while in the analysis of Table 14.19, no matter how large the differences among groups they cannot affect the error variance. Since we are not particularly interested in obtaining a correct estimate of the variation among individuals, there is no particular reason for investigating group differences.

In passing it should be noted that it was necessary to have the same number of individuals in each cell, otherwise no solution could have been reached.

The sum of squares among methods is

$$\frac{207^2 + 336^2 + 177^2 + 270^2}{36} - \frac{990^2}{144} = 7221.5 - 6806.25 = 415.25$$

which is exactly $\frac{1}{9}$ of the value previously found. In the same manner, the sum of squares among compositions and among days will be exactly $\frac{1}{9}$ of their former value.

The sum of squares among compositions is

$$\frac{332^2 + 252.5^2 + 128^2 + 277.5^2}{36} - \frac{990^2}{144} = 620.708$$

The sum of squares among days is

$$\frac{308.5^2 + 249.5^2 + 255^2 + 177^2}{36} - \frac{990^2}{144} = 243.097$$

Table 14.19 indicates a significant difference among methods, among compositions, and among individuals, but not among days.

TABLE 14.19 Analysis of Variance of Reduction in Learning Time for 4 Musical Compositions When Variations Among Individuals Is Used as Error Variance

Source of variation	Sum of squares	d.f.	Mean square	F	$F_{.95}$	$F_{.99}$
Total	9114.25	143				
Methods	415.25	3	138.4	3.30	2.70	3.98
Compositions	620.71	3	206.9	4.94	2.70	3.98
Days	243.10	3	81.0	1.93	2.70	3.98
Individuals	3684.25	35	105.3	1.54	1.54	1.83
Error	4150.94	99	41.9			

Unequal Frequencies in the Subclasses. When the frequencies in the subclasses are unequal, the computation of sums of squares becomes very complex, if an exact solution is sought. A simple approximate method will be described.

The method will be illustrated in relation to data in Table 13.1 on page 316. The data are based on scores of 96 students in a final examination in elementary statistics. The three sections were taught by different instructors. Students have been classified by section and by sex. Each cell of Table 14.20 contains an entry which shows the number of students in the subclass and the mean score of these students.

TABLE 14.20 Number of Male and Female Students in Each of Three Sections in a Course in Statistics and Mean Score on Final Examination for Each Subgroup

Section	Item	Male	Female
	N	28	13
I	ΣX	1432	706
	$\overline{X}$	51.142	54.308
	N	24	3
II	ΣX	1240	134
	$\overline{X}$	51.667	44.667
	N	18	10
III	ΣX	791	416
	$\overline{X}$	43.944	41.600

The sum of squares of deviations from subclass means is

$$240{,}579 - \left(\frac{1432^2}{28} + \frac{1240^2}{24} + \frac{791^2}{18} + \frac{706^2}{13} + \frac{134^2}{3} + \frac{416^2}{10}\right) = 6883.6$$

The number of degrees of freedom for variation within subclasses is $96 - 6 = 90$. Hence the mean square for variation within subclasses is $6883.6/90 = 76.48$.

To obtain the mean square for error, the mean square within subclasses is multiplied by the constant

$$\tfrac{1}{6}\left(\tfrac{1}{28} + \tfrac{1}{24} + \tfrac{1}{18} + \tfrac{1}{13} + \tfrac{1}{3} + \tfrac{1}{10}\right) = .10720$$

In this expression $\frac{1}{6}$ is the reciprocal of the number of subclasses and the quantity within parentheses is the sum of the reciprocals of subclass frequencies. The mean square for error is now

$$(76.48)(.10720) = 8.20$$

The sums of squares for rows, columns and interaction are now computed by treating each mean in Table 14.20 as a single observation. The computing procedure described in Table 9.13 on page 225 yields the analysis of variance in Table 14.21.

TABLE 14.21 Analysis of Variance of Data in Table 14.20

Source of variation	Sum of squares	Degrees of freedom	Mean square	F	$F_{.95}$	$F_{.99}$
Sex	6.4	1	6.4	.78	3.95	6.93
Section	99.3	2	49.6	6.05	3.10	4.85
Interaction	25.9	2	12.9	1.57	3.10	4.85
Error		90	8.20			

The analysis indicates a significant difference between sections but not between sexes. The non-significant interaction indicates that sex differences have not been found to vary from section to section.

Two Samples Matched in Subgroups on a Related Trait. Very often the comparison of the means of two samples on a particular trait which we may call X is confused by the fact that the groups have a noticeably different distribution on some other trait, which we may call Y. If X and Y are independent, the difference between the groups on Y may be disregarded, but if X and Y are related, some method must be found of compensating for that difference. For example, suppose a research worker is interested in exploring possible effects upon the emotional adjustment of young children of living in an orphanage as compared with living in foster homes.

If there should be a considerable difference in the age distribution of the two samples studied, a difference in measure of emotional adjustment between the groups which was in whole or part due to difference in age might be erroneously interpreted as due to difference in home life. A similar effect might arise if the two groups were unlike in distribution of intelligence quotients, or as to the proportion of children who had been diagnosed as problem cases before admission to the institution. However a difference in the proportion who were color-blind or left-handed, or who disliked spinach might reasonably be disregarded.

A very common method of eliminating the effect of such a difference in extraneous background traits which may be presumed to be related to the trait under scrutiny is that of matching individual for individual on the background traits. In a study of the sort referred to in the preceding paragraph, for example, a research worker might attempt to find pairs of children such that the members of each pair were of the same sex, of the same age within a specified limit, and of the same intelligence quotient within a specified limit. The prevalence of defects or of problem cases might be eliminated from consideration by limiting the study to children not known to be defective or maladjusted before admission. Each pair thus obtained is treated as one individual for whom there are two measures. The difference between those two measures is found, and analysis proceeds as in the problem on page 152.

There are several serious objections to this procedure. (1) It is usually very laborious. The search for closely matched cases often takes a very long time and the research worker quite properly feels that his energy could be better spent on something else. (2) Some of the cases, sometimes an alarmingly large number, have to be eliminated because no mates can be found. Thus sample size is reduced and reliability sacrificed. (3) Very often the cases finally retained at the conclusion of the matching process are not representative of either of the original populations. Therefore generalization from the sample of matched pairs can be made only to a universe of matched pairs and not to the two universes as originally defined.

Sometimes, instead of matching case for case, the two samples are made to have approximately the same mean and standard deviation on the background traits. In this procedure it is not necessary to have the two samples of the same size and fewer cases are sacrificed. However the work of matching is still tedious and the samples obtained are usually not representative of the original populations. A method proposed by Johnson and Neyman[7] avoiding all three of the principal disadvantages of case by case matching will now be described.

The usefulness of this method may be illustrated by application to a set of data obtained by W. W. Biddle[2]. He had an experimental and a control group in each of six different schools, so that in effect his research was carried out six times. These groups varied in size. Certain environmental factors varied from school to school, but were constant for the two groups in the same school. Each group was given a gullibility test designed to measure the ability to detect propaganda, the subject matter of this test being the Pacific relations of the United States. This test was given twice to all subjects, once, a week or more before any experimental material was presented to the experimental classes and once, a week or more after the close of the experimental teaching. The gain in score made by each student is the individual trait studied. Between the two administrations of the test, the experimental classes studied specially prepared lessons entitled *Manipulating the Public*, in which both subject matter and illustrations of propaganda were taken largely from the period of World War I. The control groups did not use this material. The data presented in Table 14.22 differ somewhat from those in the appendix of Biddle's study, being based on original data furnished by him.

The data of Table 14.22 form a two-way layout of k rows (6 schools) and 2 columns (2 methods) with disproportionate

TABLE 14.22 Gain in Measurement of Nationalist Gullibility for an Experimental Group and a Control Group in Each of Six Schools.*

School	Experimental group Frequency N_{i1}	Mean $\overline{X}_{i1}$	Control group Frequency N_{i2}	Mean $\overline{X}_{i2}$	Both groups Frequency N_i	Variance s_i^2
1	51	.496	26	.074	77	1.024
2	26	.202	35	.045	61	.856
3	8	.466	29	.315	37	.470
4	25	.246	12	− .123	37	.472
5	66	.241	16	− .245	82	.810
6	33	.450	29	.423	62	.817
Total	209		147		356	

* Data from Biddle[2].

frequencies in the $2k = 12$ cells. The two groups from one school may be considered as samples from a pair of populations matched with respect to school and environmental influences but differing with respect to the experimental variable method. Such data are likely to show significant variation among the school means. However the focus of interest is not on school differences but on method differences. Examination of the means in Table 14.22 shows that in each school the experimental group gained more than the control, so the difference $\overline{X}_{i1} - \overline{X}_{i2}$ was positive. Do these differences jointly indicate that the true population difference is not zero?

The Johnson-Neyman method is based on three assumptions:

(1) Within each of the $2k$ cells the observations are from a normal population;

(2) The population variance is the same for all cells;

(3) For the two matched populations from one school the mean difference is the same as for any other school, so $\mu_{i1} - \mu_{i2} = d$. This assumption is equivalent to the assumption that interaction of school and method is zero.

Since there are two columns, the column difference has only one degree of freedom and the test for column difference can be made by use of "Student's" distribution. We compute

$$D = \frac{\sum_{i=1}^{k} \frac{N_{i1}N_{i2}}{N_i}(\overline{X}_{i1} - \overline{X}_{i2})}{\sum_{i=1}^{k} \frac{N_{i1}N_{i2}}{N_i}} \tag{14.12}$$

$$s_D^2 = \frac{\sum_{i=1}^{k}(N_i - 1)s_i^2 - \frac{\left[\sum_{i=1}^{k} \frac{N_{i1}N_{i2}}{N_i}(\overline{X}_{i1} - \overline{X}_{i2})\right]^2}{\sum_{i=1}^{k} \frac{N_{i1}N_{i2}}{N_i}}}{(N - k - 1)\sum_{i=1}^{k} \frac{N_{i1}N_{i2}}{N_i}} \tag{14.13}$$

The statistic $\frac{D}{s_D}$ has "Student's" distribution with $N - k - 1$ degrees of freedom where N is the sum of all the cell frequencies.

For the data in Table 14.22

$$D = .2707 \quad \text{and} \quad s_D^2 = .01435$$

$$t = \frac{D}{s_D} = 2.26 \qquad t_{.975} = 1.96$$

The null hypothesis that there is no method difference may, therefore, be rejected.

An interval estimate for the population difference $\mu_1 - \mu_2$ made by the methods described in Chapter 7 is

$$C(.035 < \mu_1 - \mu_2 < .506) = .95$$

REFERENCES

1. Anderson, R. L. and Bancroft, T. A., *Statistical Theory in Research,* New York, 1952, McGraw-Hill Book Co., Inc., Chapters 18, 19, and 20.
2. Biddle, W. W., *Propaganda and Education,* New York, 1932, Teachers College, Columbia University, Bureau of Publications.
3. Bliss, C. I., *The Statistics of Bioassay,* New York, 1952, Academic Press, Inc., Chapter 3.
4. Burt, Cyril and Lewis, R. B., "Teaching Backward Readers," *British Journal of Educational Psychology,* 16 (1946), 116–132.
5. Edwards, Allen L., *Experimental Design in Psychological Research,* New York, 1950, Rinehart and Co., Inc., Chapters 12 to 16.
6. Fisher, R. A., *The Design of Experiments,* Edinburgh and London, 4th ed., 1945, Oliver and Boyd, Ltd.
7. Johnson, P. O. and Neyman, J., "Tests of Certain Linear Hypotheses and their Application to Some Educational Problems," *Statistical Research Memoirs,* 1 (1936), 57–93.
8. Mood, A. M., *Introduction to the Theory of Statistics,* New York, 1950, McGraw-Hill Book Co., Inc., 334–348.
9. Rao, C. R., *Advanced Statistical Methods in Biometric Research,* New York, 1952, John Wiley and Sons, Inc.
10. Rubin-Rabson, Grace, *The Influence of Analytical Pre-Study in Memorizing Piano Music,* Archives of Psychology, No. 220, 1937, page 503.
11. Schroeder, Elinor M., *On Measurement of Motor Skills,* New York, 1945, King's Crown Press.

15 Analysis of Covariance

The analysis of covariance is employed in the comparison of groups on one variable when information is available on another variable correlated with it, or on several such variables.

The variable on which the comparisons are made will be denoted by the letter Y. The related variables, which will be called *predictor* variables, will be denoted by the letters X and Z. The analysis will use regression equations by which the Y values are estimated from known values of the predictor variables. The mathematical model will be that of regression analysis described in Chapter 10, so that the values of the predictor variables are the same for all samples in the population, but the Y values differ from sample to sample.

The methods to be described involve a subdivision of the sum of cross-products into components similar to the subdivision of sums of squares in the analysis of variance. Because the sums of cross-products are related to covariance as sums of squares are related to variance, methods involving subdivisions of cross-products are classified under the general title of *analysis of covariance*.

Symbolism in the Analysis of Covariance. To facilitate computation we shall introduce a set of symbols formed by the letter C with subscripts to be described. Generally we write

$$C_{xx} = \Sigma(X - \overline{X})^2 = \Sigma X^2 - (\Sigma X)^2/N \tag{15.1}$$

$$C_{yy} = \Sigma(Y - \overline{Y})^2 = \Sigma Y^2 - (\Sigma Y)^2/N \tag{15.2}$$

$$C_{xy} = \Sigma(X - \overline{X})(Y - \overline{Y}) = \Sigma XY - (\Sigma X)(\Sigma Y)/N \tag{15.3}$$

Additional subscripts are used to distinguish total variation, variation within groups and variation between groups. The following equations relate the usual partition of the total sum of squares into portions within and between groups, to the C notation:

$$\sum_{i=1}^{k} \sum_{\alpha=1}^{N_i} (X_{i\alpha} - \overline{X})^2 = \sum_{i=1}^{k} \sum_{\alpha=1}^{N_i} (X_{i\alpha} - \overline{X}_i)^2 + \sum_{i=1}^{k} N_i(\overline{X}_i - \overline{X})^2 \tag{15.4}$$

$$C_{xxT} = C_{xxw} + C_{xxb} \tag{15.5}$$

A similar relationship holds for the sum of cross products

$$(15.6)\quad \sum_{i=1}^{k}\sum_{\alpha=1}^{N_i}(X_{i\alpha}-\overline{X})(Y_{i\alpha}-\overline{Y}) = \sum_{i=1}^{k}\sum_{\alpha=1}^{N_i}(X_{i\alpha}-\overline{X}_i)(Y_{i\alpha}-\overline{Y}_i) + \sum_{i=1}^{k} N_i(\overline{X}_i-\overline{X})(\overline{Y}_i-\overline{Y})$$

$$(15.7)\quad C_{xyT} = C_{xyw} + C_{xyb}$$

SEVERAL POPULATIONS WITH ONE PREDICTOR VARIABLE

In this situation, comparisons are made among means of a variable Y in several populations. Information is also available on a variable X. To make the problem concrete, consider the data in Table 15.1. These are artificial data so contrived as to exhibit vividly the various relationships involved. Three groups, each consisting of 5 subjects have been given a prognostic test (X) before the beginning of a learning experiment, and an achievement test (Y) after the experiment. Each group is taught by a different method and is considered as a sample from a population identified by that method. We wish to test the hypothesis that the three methods are equally effective.

TABLE 15.1 Prognostic Test Score (X) and Achievement Score (Y) for each of Fifteen Subjects in a Learning Experiment Employing Three Methods (I, II, and III)

I			II			III			Sum
Subject	X	Y	Subject	X	Y	Subject	X	Y	
1	2	5	6	14	7	11	20	20	
2	4	8	7	16	8	12	18	22	
3	5	7	8	15	10	13	23	26	
4	8	9	9	19	13	14	25	28	
5	6	11	10	11	12	15	24	24	
$T_x = \Sigma X$	25			75			110		210
ΣX^2	145			1159			2454		3758
$T_y = \Sigma Y$		40			50			120	210
ΣY^2		340			526			2920	3786
ΣXY	215			755			2670		3640
$\overline{X}$	5			15			22		
$\overline{Y}$		8			10			24	

The three samples have widely disparate means on the achievement test ($\overline{Y}_1 = 8$, $\overline{Y}_2 = 10$, $\overline{Y}_3 = 24$), and a simple analysis of variance solution applied to the Y scores yields $F = 53.0$, whereas $F_{.99}$ is only 3.88. We note, however, that the groups have widely disparate means on X also ($\overline{X}_1 = 5$, $\overline{X}_2 = 15$, $\overline{X}_3 = 22$). We may ask whether the differences among the Y means can be explained by the differences among X means. If such an explanation is valid, then the methods of instruction must be considered equally effective. The analysis related to this problem will be discussed in some detail.

Numerical Computation of *C* Values. The computations to be described will require all the C values listed in Table 15.2. Computing these from the data of Table 15.1 and setting them down in systematic fashion will facilitate the work. The computation of several of these will be carried out explicitly as in the illustration. The student should verify the others.

TABLE 15.2 Sums of Squares and Sums of Products Obtained from the Data of Table 15.1

Item	Group I	Group II	Group III	Within groups	Between groups	Total
Σx^2	$C_{xx1} = 20$	$C_{xx2} = 34$	$C_{xx3} = 34$	$C_{xxw} = 88$	$C_{xxb} = 730$	$C_{xxT} = 818$
Σxy	$C_{xy1} = 15$	$C_{xy2} = 5$	$C_{xy3} = 30$	$C_{xyw} = 50$	$C_{xyb} = 650$	$C_{xyT} = 700$
Σy^2	$C_{yy1} = 20$	$C_{yy2} = 26$	$C_{yy3} = 40$	$C_{yyw} = 86$	$C_{yyb} = 760$	$C_{yyT} = 846$

For the data in Table 15.1,

$$C_{xx1} = 145 - \frac{(25)^2}{5} = 145 - 125 = 20$$

$$C_{xxT} = 3758 - \frac{(210)^2}{5} = 3758 - 2940 = 818$$

$$C_{xxw} = \sum_{i=1}^{3} C_{xxi} = 20 + 34 + 34 = 88$$

$$C_{xxb} = C_{xxT} - C_{xxw} = 818 - 88 = 730$$

also
$$C_{xxb} = \frac{T^2_{x1} + T^2_{x2} + T^2_{x3}}{5} - \frac{T^2_{xT}}{15}$$

$$= \frac{(25)^2 + (75)^2 + (110)^2}{5} - \frac{(210)^2}{15} = 3670 - 2940 = 730$$

$$C_{xy1} = 215 - \frac{(25)(40)}{5} = 215 - 200 = 15$$

$$C_{xyT} = 3640 - \frac{(210)(210)}{15} = 3640 - 2940 = 700$$

$$C_{xyw} = \sum_{i=1}^{3} C_{xyi} = 15 + 5 + 30 = 50$$

$$C_{xyb} = C_{xyT} - C_{xyw} = 650$$

Comparison of Regression within the Groups with Regression for the Combined Group. If the regressions based on the separate groups are the same as that based on the total group, except for sampling variability, then the effects of different methods of instruction can be disregarded. Conversely, differences between those regressions not attributable to sampling error may be regarded as due to the methods of instruction.

The regression based on the total group is

$$\tilde{Y}_\alpha = \overline{Y} + b_T(X_\alpha - \overline{X}) \tag{15.8}$$

where

$$b_T = \frac{C_{xyT}}{C_{xxT}} \tag{15.9}$$

The regression for the ith group is

$$\tilde{Y}_{i\alpha} = \overline{Y}_i + b_i(X_{i\alpha} - \overline{X}_i) \tag{15.10}$$

where

$$b_i = \frac{C_{xyi}}{C_{xxi}} \tag{15.11}$$

For the data in Table 15.1 we have, using the computations in that Table and in Table 15.2, for the regression based on the entire group

$$\tilde{Y}_\alpha = 14 + .856(X_\alpha - 14)$$

and for the regressions based on the separate groups

$$\tilde{Y}_{1\alpha} = 8 + .75(X_{1\alpha} - 5)$$
$$\tilde{Y}_{2\alpha} = 10 + .147(X_{2\alpha} - 15)$$
$$\tilde{Y}_{3\alpha} = 24 + .882(X_{3\alpha} - 22)$$

A test of significance is called for to determine whether the differences between the regression equations may be ascribed to errors of sampling. Before proceeding with such a test we notice that the regression lines in the populations may differ for two reasons. (1) Their slopes may be different. (2) They may have the same slope, but they may be parallel rather than actually identical.

Test of Hypothesis of Common Slope. We shall now describe a test for the hypothesis that the slope of the regression line is the same for all populations, that is

$$H_1: \ \beta_1 = \beta_2 = \beta_3 = \beta_w$$

The best sample estimate of that common within-groups slope

β_w is provided by

$$b_w = \frac{C_{xyw}}{C_{xxw}} \tag{15.12}$$

For the data of Table 15.1,

$$b_w = .566.$$

If H_1 is true, the sample values b_1, b_2 and b_3 differ only because of sampling error. Then substituting b_w for each of these in (15.9) would produce a regression estimate $\overline{Y}_i + b_w(X_{i\alpha} - \overline{X}_i)$ differing from $\overline{Y}_i + b_i(X_{i\alpha} - \overline{X}_i)$ only because of sampling variability. If these differences

$$[\overline{Y}_i + b_w(X_{i\alpha} - \overline{X}_i)] - [\overline{Y}_i + b_i(X_{i\alpha} - \overline{X}_i)]$$

are squared and summed for all individuals in all groups the result is, after simplification

$$S_1 = \sum_{i=1}^{k} \frac{C^2_{xyi}}{C_{xxi}} - \frac{C^2_{xyw}}{C_{xxw}} \tag{15.13}$$

To make a test of significance this sum of squares can be compared with the sum of squares of deviations of individual scores from the separate regression estimates. This is found as the sum of squares of differences

$$Y_{i\alpha} - [\overline{Y}_i + b_i(X_{i\alpha} - \overline{X}_i)]$$

Calling this sum of squares S_2 we have, after simplification,

$$S_2 = C_{yyw} - \sum_{i=1}^{k} \frac{C^2_{xyi}}{C_{xxi}} \tag{15.14}$$

S_1/σ^2 and S_2/σ^2 are independently distributed as χ^2 with $k - 1$ and $N - 2k$ degrees of freedom respectively. Hence the ratio

$$F = \frac{S_1}{S_2} \cdot \frac{N - 2k}{k - 1} \tag{15.15}$$

has the F distribution with $n_1 = k - 1$ and $n_2 = N - 2k$.

For the illustrative data

$$S_1 = \left\{\frac{15^2}{20} + \frac{5^2}{34} + \frac{30^2}{34} - \frac{50^2}{88}\right\} = 10.0$$

$$S_2 = 86 - \left\{\frac{15^2}{20} + \frac{5^2}{24} + \frac{30^2}{34}\right\} = 47.6$$

$$N - 2k = 9, \quad k - 1 = 2$$

Then

$$F = \frac{10.0}{47.6} \cdot \frac{9}{2} = .95 \text{ with } n_1 = 2 \quad \text{and} \quad n_2 = 9,$$

so that F is not significant. The regression lines in the three populations may be assumed to have the same slope, of which b_w is the best estimate.

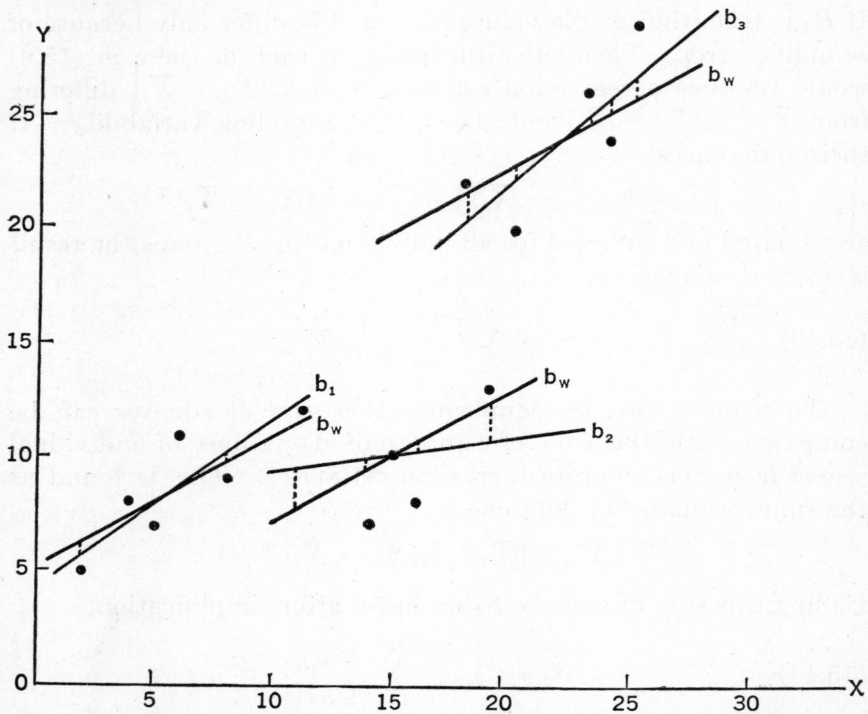

FIG. 15–1. Paired scores for data of Table 15.1; the regression line for each group; regression lines with common slope b_w through group means; and the differences in regression estimates resulting from use of b_w instead of b_i.

At this point some readers will be trying to visualize S_1 and S_2. On Figure 15–1 the paired scores of Table 15.1 have been indicated by heavy dots. The three regression lines with slopes b_1, b_2 and b_3 have been drawn through the means of their respective groups. Three lines with common slope b_w have been drawn through those same means. For each individual the difference in regression values obtained by using b_w or b_i is a line segment shown on the graph as a dotted line. The sum of the squares of all these lines is S_1. To obtain a picture of the line segments whose squares constitute S_2, you should draw for each individual his residual from the line with slope b_i. These residuals are drawn parallel to the vertical axis extending from the dot which represents the paired scores of an individual to the regression line for his group. Some of them will overlap the dotted lines already drawn.

Test of the Hypothesis $\beta_w = 0$. It has been established that all β's may be treated as equal, but there remains the possibility that they are all equal to 0. The test for the hypothesis that $\beta_w = 0$ is provided by the variance ratio

$$(15.16) \qquad F = \frac{C^2_{xyw}}{C_{xxw}C_{yyw} - C^2_{xyw}} \cdot \frac{N - 2k}{1}$$

which has the F distribution with $n_1 = 1$ and $n_2 = N - 2k$.

For our data $$F = \frac{50^2}{(88)(86) - 50^2} \cdot \frac{9}{1} = 4.44$$

Inasmuch as $F_{.95} = 5.12$ we might decide to ignore the X scores and to make our analysis on the Y scores alone. However, even if such a course could be defended, with so few cases and F so near the .05 value there is considerable risk of making a type-II error and accepting the null hypothesis when it is false. Hence, it is wiser to retain the X's in the analysis.

Measure of Sampling Variability. The sum of the squares of residuals from group regression lines divided by its degrees of freedom is an unbiased estimate of the error variance. This value is

$$(15.17) \qquad \frac{S_2}{N - 2k} = \frac{1}{N - 2k}\left\{C_{yyw} - \sum_1^k \frac{C^2_{xyi}}{C_{xxi}}\right\}$$

which was used as error variance in (15.15) to test the hypothesis $\beta_1 = \beta_2 = \cdots = \beta_k$. By accepting that hypothesis we established that $\frac{S_1}{k - 1}$ may also be considered an estimate of the error variance, and therefore that S_1 and S_2 may be pooled to obtain an estimate with greater number of degrees of freedom:

$$(15.18) \qquad S_w = S_1 + S_2 = C_{yyw} - \frac{C^2_{xyw}}{C_{xxw}}$$

and S_w/σ^2 is distributed as χ^2 with $N - k - 1$ degrees of freedom. In subsequent tests $S_w/(N - k - 1)$ will be used as estimate of error variance. See Figure 15–2 for a graphic interpretation of S_w.

Test of Hypothesis that a Single Regression Line Fits All Populations. If it is true that a single common line fits all of the populations, the regression estimates based on deviations within groups from a line with slope b_w [that is, $\overline{Y}_i + b_w(X_{i\alpha} - \overline{X}_i)$]

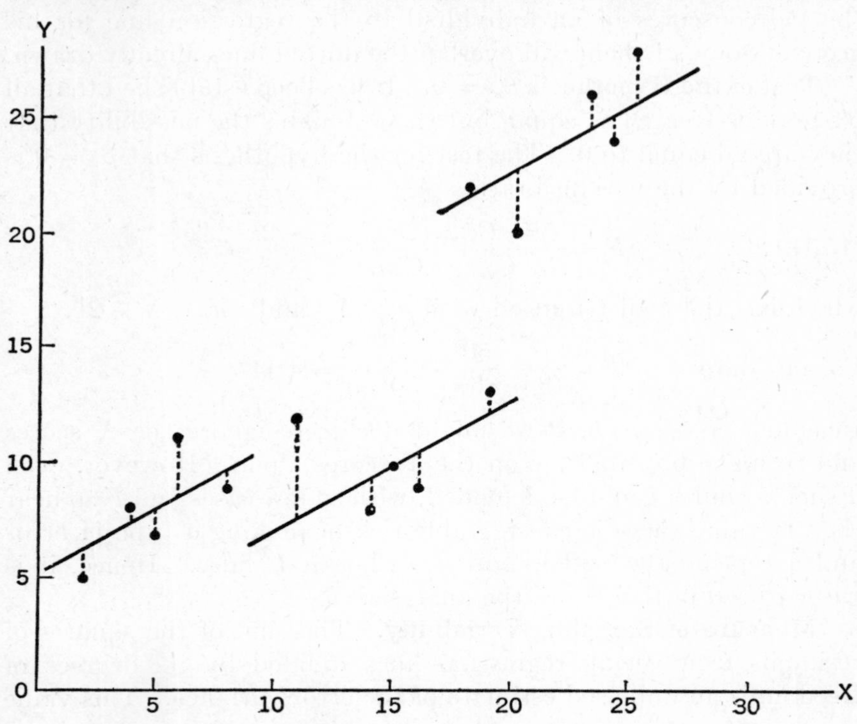

FIG. 15–2. Paired scores for data of Table 15.1; regression lines with common slope b_w through group means; and residuals from those regression lines.

should be very similar to the regression estimates based on deviations from the common mean and the regression line with slope b_T [that is, $\overline{Y} + b_T(X_\alpha - \overline{X})$]. The differences between these two

$$[\overline{Y}_i + b_w(X_{i\alpha} - \overline{X}_i)] - [\overline{Y} + b_T(X_\alpha - \overline{X})]$$

would then be due to sampling error. The sum of the squares of these differences may be reduced to

$$S_b = C_{yyb} + \frac{C^2_{xyw}}{C_{xxw}} - \frac{C^2_{xyT}}{C_{xxT}} \tag{15.19}$$

and S_b/σ^2 is distributed as χ^2 with $k - 1$ degrees of freedom. If the hypothesis of a single regression line is true, $S_b/(k - 1)$ is another estimate of sampling variance and will not be very different in size from $S_w/(N - k - 1)$. If the hypothesis is not true, $S_b/(k - 1)$ is expected to be larger than $S_w/(N - k - 1)$, which is a proper estimate of error regardless of whether the hypothesis is true or not. Then the quotient

$$F = \frac{S_b}{S_w} \cdot \frac{N - k - 1}{k - 1} \tag{15.20}$$

has the F distribution with $n_1 = k - 1$ and $n_2 = N - k - 1$. It may be used to test the hypothesis of a single regression line for all populations. For the illustrative data

$$S_b = 760 + \frac{50^2}{88} - \frac{700^2}{818} = 189.4$$

$$S_w = 86 - \frac{50^2}{88} = 57.6$$

$$F = \frac{189.4}{57.6} \cdot \frac{11}{2} = 18.1$$

For $n_1 = 2$ and $n_2 = 11$, $F_{.99}$ is only 7.20. The F ratio indicates strongly that the hypothesis of a common regression line should be rejected. In other words, the differences in achievement cannot be wholly explained by differences in original ability but must be at least partly ascribed to differences in the effectiveness of teaching method.

Total Sum of Squares. An interesting sidelight on the sums of squares S_w and S_b is that their sum is equal to the sum of squares of deviations of individual Y values from the regression estimates for Y if all groups are combined and the regression line has slope $b_T = \frac{C_{xyT}}{C_{xxT}}$. Hence the relationship

$$S_T = S_w + S_b \tag{15.21}$$

corresponds to a subdivision of the total sum of squares into portions as has been described in the analysis of variance. S_T can be computed independently of S_w and S_b by the formula

$$S_T = C_{yyT} - \frac{C^2_{xyT}}{C_{xxT}} \tag{15.22}$$

For the illustrative data S_T is $846 - \frac{(700)^2}{818} = 246.98$

while $S_w + S_b = 57.6 + 189.4 = 247.0$

The sums of squares which are components of S_T are listed with their formulas in Table 15.3.

TABLE 15.3 Summary of Components of Sum of Squares of Y about Regression Line $\tilde{Y}_\alpha = \overline{Y} + b_T(X_\alpha - \overline{X})$ with the Formula and the Number of Degrees of Freedom for Each

Nature of variation	Symbol	Formula	Degrees of freedom
Group regression coefficients about common coefficient	S_1	$\sum_{j=1}^{k} \frac{C^2_{xyi}}{C_{xxi}} - \frac{C^2_{xyw}}{C_{xxw}}$	$k - 1$
Scores about regression line for their own group	S_2	$C_{yyw} - \sum_{i=1}^{k} \frac{C^2_{xyi}}{C_{xxi}}$	$N - 2k$
Group means $\overline{Y}_i$ about regression line based on means	S_3	$C_{yyb} - \frac{C^2_{xyb}}{C_{xxb}}$	$k - 2$
Difference between regression coefficient based on means and common regression coefficient within groups	S_4	$\frac{C^2_{xyw}}{C_{xxw}} + \frac{C^2_{xyb}}{C_{xxb}} - \frac{C^2_{xyT}}{C_{xxT}}$	1
Scores about regression lines with common slope b_w	$S_w = S_1 + S_2$	$C_{yyw} - \frac{C^2_{xyw}}{C_{xxw}}$	$N - k - 1$
Group means about regression line with slope b_w	$S_b = S_3 + S_4$	$C_{yyb} + \frac{C^2_{xyw}}{C_{xxw}} - \frac{C^2_{xyT}}{C_{xxT}}$	$k - 1$
Scores about regression line for total group	S_T	$C_{yyT} - \frac{C^2_{xyT}}{C_{xxT}}$	$N - 2$

Regression among the Means. If there is a common regression line for all populations, then the pair of means for each population must lie on that line. These means are $\overline{X}_i$ and μ_i, where $\mu_i = E(Y_i)$ is the mean of Y for the ith population. However, even if there is no common regression line for all populations the means may still lie on a regression line determined by those means as in the adjacent sketch. Here the three solid lines have slope b_w and the dotted line is the regression line for means. This line would be estimated by formula

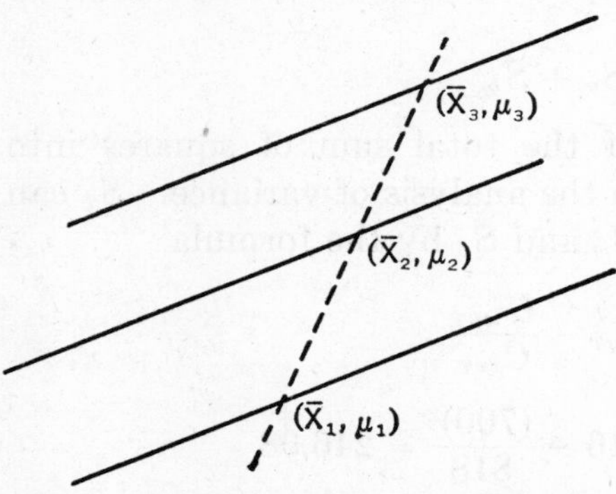

$$\tilde{Y}_i = \overline{Y} + b_b(\overline{X}_i - \overline{X}) \tag{15.23}$$

(15.24) where $$b_b = \frac{C_{xy\,b}}{C_{xx\,b}}$$

The sum of the squares of the deviations of these means from their estimate by (15.23) reduces to

(15.25) $$S_3 = C_{yy\,b} - \frac{C^2_{xy\,b}}{C_{xx\,b}}$$

and S_3/σ^2 has a χ^2 distribution with $k - 2$ degrees of freedom. The more closely the means cluster around a straight line, the smaller S_3 will be.

A test of the hypothesis that regression among the means is linear is provided by the ratio

(15.26) $$F = \frac{S_3}{S_w} \cdot \frac{N - k - 1}{k - 2}$$

which has the F distribution with $n_1 = k - 2$ and $n_2 = N - k - 1$. For the illustrative data,

$$S_3 = 760 - \frac{650^2}{730} = 181.2$$

and $$F = \frac{181.2}{57.6} \cdot \frac{11}{1} = 34.6$$

This value is much greater than $F_{.99} = 9.65$. It must be concluded that regression among means is not linear (see Figure 15–3).

Comparison of the Adjusted Means. In the illustrative data the differences among the means of $Y(\overline{Y}_1, \overline{Y}_2, \overline{Y}_3)$ are in part due to differences among teaching methods and in part to differences in the X means. To ascertain what the differences among Y means are because of differences among teaching methods alone, the effects of differences among X means should be eliminated. This elimination is achieved by adjusting all the means to a common X value, which, for convenience, may be taken as the mean of all X values, $\overline{X}$.

The adjustment is accomplished numerically by subtracting from each mean the amount it gains through being associated with an X mean which is above $\overline{X}$, or the loss through being associated with an X mean below $\overline{X}$. The adjustment is $b_w(\overline{X}_i - \overline{X})$. The adjustments are shown in Table 15.4.

The adjusted mean is least for Group II and greatest for Group III when all X means are adjusted to $\overline{X}$. The tests of significance have indicated that this difference cannot be explained by sampling variability.

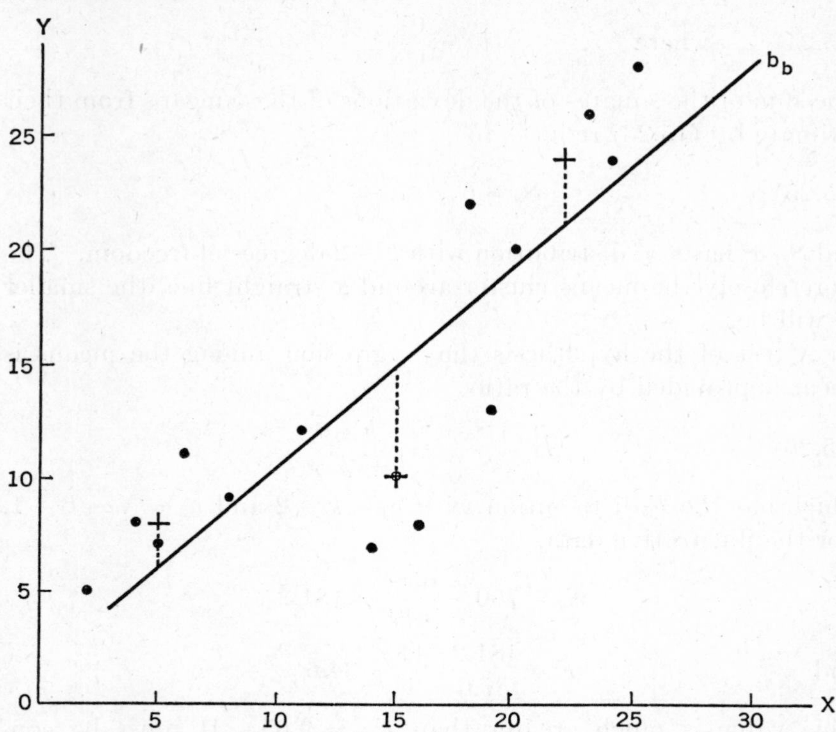

FIG. 15–3. Means of groups indicated by crosses; regression line determined by those means; and residuals of means from regression line. $S_3 = 5$ (sum of squares of dotted lines).

TABLE 15.4 Adjustment of Y Means for the Three Groups in Table 15.1

Group	Observed mean $\overline{Y}_i$	$\overline{X}_i$	Adjustment $.57(\overline{X}_i - \overline{X})$	Adjusted Y mean $\overline{Y}_i - .57(\overline{X}_i - \overline{X})$
I	8	5	− 5.13	13.13
II	10	15	.57	9.43
III	24	22	4.56	19.44
Combined	14	14		

MATCHED REGRESSION ESTIMATES. TWO POPULATIONS WITH ONE PREDICTOR VARIABLE

If the categorical trait is dichotomous, a method of analysis is available which is related to the foregoing but which has two great advantages over it. (1) This procedure does not depend upon the assumption that $\beta_1 = \beta_2$, and therefore it can be used in situations where the former would not apply. (2) By this procedure it is possible not only to explore the question of whether one of the two populations (or methods, or treatments) exceeds the other on the average but also to ask *for what values of the predictor variable* it does so.

In the situation considered here, there is one predictor variable X, and two populations; the regression of Y on X is assumed to be linear but not necessarily the same for the two populations; and Y is assumed to be normally distributed with constant variance for each value of X. On page 406 we shall consider a similar problem with two predictor variables.

Significance of the Difference $\tilde{Y}_1 - \tilde{Y}_2$ for a Particular Value of X. From the data, separate regression estimates for Y can be obtained from each group. These are

(15.27) $$\tilde{Y}_{1\alpha} = a_1 + b_1X_\alpha \quad \text{and} \quad \tilde{Y}_{2\alpha} = a_2 + b_2X_\alpha$$

where $$b_i = \frac{C_{xyi}}{C_{xxi}} \quad \text{and} \quad a_i = \overline{Y}_i - b_i\overline{X}_i$$

Now consider a specific value of X which may for convenience be called X'. For this value the difference in regression estimates for the two groups is

(15.28) $$D = \tilde{Y}_1 - \tilde{Y}_2 = (a_1 - a_2) + (b_1 - b_2)X'$$

The adjacent sketch illustrates the two regression lines and the value D for a selected X'. Obviously D is a variable which depends upon X. At the point X' the two groups may be said to be matched with respect to X, so that a comparison between $\tilde{Y}_1$ and $\tilde{Y}_2$ for X' is legitimate. If D should be zero for the entire range of X, then clearly the two regression lines coincide and the groups are indistinguishable with respect to Y.

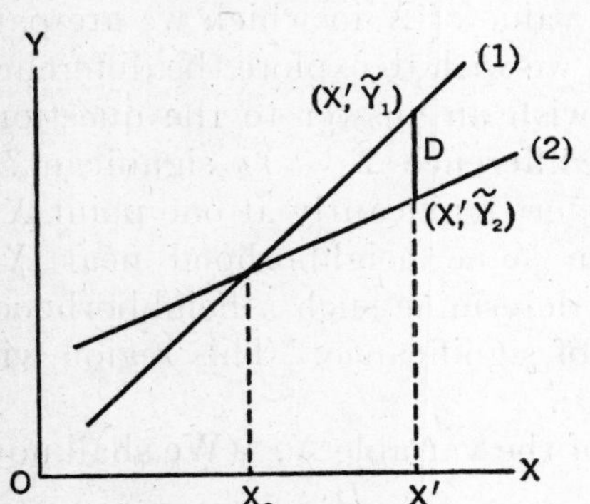

If the lines cross, the value X_0 corresponding to the point where they cross is the point at which $D = 0$ for the sample. This point will be called the *point of nonsignificance.* The purpose of this analysis is to define a *region* on the scale of X in which the value of D is non-significant. This region will have X_0 somewhere within it, probably near its center. On one side of this region of nonsignificance there may be a region of significance in which $\tilde{Y}_1 > \tilde{Y}_2$ and on the other side a region of significance in which $\tilde{Y}_2 > \tilde{Y}_1$. Whether there are two, one, or no region of significance depends upon the size and distribution of the sample as well as upon the position of the regression lines. If cases are few and the lines close together the region of non-significance may extend over all the observed values of X.

The variance of D depends upon the variability of the groups, the size of N_1 and N_2, the relation between X and Y, and the distance of X' from $\overline{X}_1$ and from $\overline{X}_2$. That variance is given by the formula

$$(15.29)\qquad s_D{}^2 = \frac{\left[\sum_{i=1}^{2}\left(C_{yyi} - \frac{C^2{}_{xyi}}{C_{xxi}}\right)\right]\left(\frac{N}{N_1N_2} + \sum_{i=1}^{2}\frac{(X' - \overline{X}_i)^2}{C_{xxi}}\right)}{N_1 + N_2 - 4}$$

For a fixed value of X' the ratio

$$t = \frac{D}{s_D}$$

can be calculated and its significance determined by reference to "Student's" distribution with $N_1 + N_2 - 4 = N - 4$ degrees of freedom.

Region of Significance. The procedure outlined thus far necessitates calculation of significance separately for each value of X'. Sometimes there is such a single value of X in which we are particularly interested and for which we wish to explore the difference in $\tilde{Y}_1$ and $\tilde{Y}_2$. More often we wish an answer to the question, "For what values of X is the difference $\tilde{Y}_1 - \tilde{Y}_2$ significant?" Clearly, if two regression lines differ significantly at one point X', they must differ significantly in some neighborhood near X'. It is interesting and valuable to determine such a neighborhood, which may be called the region of significance. This region will now be determined.

Both D and s_D are functions of the variable X. (We shall now drop the prime for convenience.) The ratio $\frac{D}{s_D}$ has the t distribution for each fixed value of X. Hence those values of X for which

$$\frac{D}{s_D} > t_{1-\alpha}$$

provide a one-tailed region of significance α with positive values of $\tilde{Y}_1 - \tilde{Y}_2$ critical; those values for which

$$\frac{D}{s_D} < t_\alpha$$

provide a one-tailed region of significance α with negative values of $\tilde{Y}_1 - \tilde{Y}_2$ critical.

A two-sided region with significance level α is determined by values of X for which $\dfrac{D^2}{s_D{}^2} > t^2{}_{1-\frac{1}{2}\alpha}$. We shall now work out the two-sided region, but all that is needed to obtain the one-sided region is to substitute α for $\frac{1}{2}\alpha$ and to allocate critical values to the appropriate end of the scale.

The two-sided region of significance consists of those values of X which satisfy the inequality

$$D^2 - s_D{}^2 t^2{}_{\frac{1}{2}\alpha} > 0 \tag{15.30}$$

This is an inequality in X since $D = a_1 - a_2 + (b_1 - b_2)X$ and it may be written

$$AX^2 + 2BX + C > 0 \tag{15.31}$$

where

$$A = \frac{-t^2{}_{\frac{1}{2}\alpha}}{N-4}\left[\sum_{i=1}^{2}\left(C_{yyi} - \frac{C^2{}_{xyi}}{C_{xxi}}\right)\right]\left(\frac{1}{C_{xx1}} + \frac{1}{C_{xx2}}\right) + (b_1 - b_2)^2 \tag{15.32}$$

$$B = \frac{t^2{}_{\frac{1}{2}\alpha}}{N-4}\left[\sum_{i=1}^{2}\left(C_{yyi} - \frac{C^2{}_{xyi}}{C_{xxi}}\right)\right]\left(\frac{\overline{X}_1}{C_{xx1}} + \frac{\overline{X}_2}{C_{xx2}}\right) + (a_1 - a_2)(b_1 - b_2) \tag{15.33}$$

$$C = \frac{-t^2{}_{\frac{1}{2}\alpha}}{N-4}\left[\sum_{i=1}^{2}\left(C_{yyi} - \frac{C^2{}_{xyi}}{C_{xxi}}\right)\right]\left(\frac{N}{N_1N_2} + \frac{\overline{X}_1{}^2}{C_{xx1}} + \frac{\overline{X}_2{}^2}{C_{xx2}}\right) + (a_1 - a_2)^2 \tag{15.34}$$

The value of X for which $D = 0$ is

$$X_0 = \frac{a_2 - a_1}{b_1 - b_2} \tag{15.35}$$

Bounding values for the region of significance may be obtained by solving the equation $AX^2 + 2BX + C = 0$ where the numerical values of A, B, and C are obtained from formulas (15.32) to (15.34). The solution is

$$X = \frac{-B \pm \sqrt{B^2 - AC}}{A} \tag{15.36}$$

If $B^2 - AC > 0$, the equation has two solutions and those solutions are bounding values such that the region of non-significance lies between them, the region of significance outside them. If $B^2 - AC < 0$, there is no region of significance. It is highly unlikely that $B^2 - AC$ will be exactly zero.

Warning. Because formula (15.31) has been written with $2B$ instead of B as the coefficient of X, the solution given in (15.36) differs slightly from the form which may be familiar to the reader.

Data reported by Bills [2] may be used to clarify the procedure. Eighteen slow readers in the third grade were studied for three periods of 30 days each. The first period was a control period, the second was the therapy period, the third was a period for studying cumulative effects of therapy. All the children were given reading tests at the beginning and end of the first period, and intelligence tests during the period, but received no other experimental treatment. During the therapy period, 8 of the children received play therapy, the other 10 did not. Reading tests were given at the end of the therapy period. Nothing was done with the children during the third period but they were again tested at the end. The variable we shall use as criterion will be the gain in reading score during the therapy period. Several predictor variables are available such as chronological age, mental age, initial reading score, but we shall at this time use only one, the gain in reading score during the control period. The raw data for the analysis are shown in Table 15.5 and the derived data in

TABLE 15.5 Gain on Reading Test for Each Child during Control and Therapy Periods*

I. Therapy group			II. Non-therapy group		
Child	Gain during control period	Gain during therapy period	Child	Gain during control period	Gain during therapy period
1	.00	.80	1	.00	.20
2	.10	1.35	2	− .30	− .05
3	.10	.90	3	.00	.45
4	− .45	.45	4	.33	.15
5	− .20	.65	5	− .33	.28
6	.25	2.05	6	.00	.20
7	.25	1.45	7	− .60	.45
8	.20	.45	8	− .45	.15
			9	− .20	.15
			10	− .35	.25

* Data taken from Bills, R. E.[2]

Table 15.6. Here X is used to represent gain during control period and Y to represent gain during therapy period.

TABLE 15.6 Statistics Computed from the Data of Table 15.5 for Problem Using Method of Matched Regression Estimates

Statistic	I Therapy group	II Non-therapy group
N_i	8	10
$T_y = \Sigma Y$	8.10	2.23
$\overline{Y}_i$	1.0125	.223
$T_x = \Sigma X$	.25	− 1.90
$\overline{X}_i$	.03125	− .19
C_{xxi}	.4197	.6718
C_{yyi}	2.2038	.1986
C_{xyi}	.6044	− .0592
b_{yxi}	1.4400	− .0881
a_i	.9675	.2063

On Figure 15–4 the 8 small circles represent the paired scores for the 8 children in the Therapy group. The regression equation for this group

$$\tilde{Y}_1 = .97 + 1.44X_1$$

is also drawn. The 10 small crosses on the same figure represent the paired scores for the 10 children in the Non-therapy group. The regression line for this group

$$\tilde{Y}_2 = .24 - .088X_2$$

appears to the eye strikingly different from the first one. The point of non-significance is

$$X_0 = \frac{.2063 - .9675}{1.440 + .088} = -.50$$

and on Figure 15–4 the two regression lines are seen to cross at a point for which $X = -.50$ and $Y = .25$.

Substitution of the statistics (Table 15.6) in Formulas (15.32) to (15.34) with $\alpha = .05$, yields

$$A = .71,\ B = 1.02,\ C = .41,\ X_1 = -2.7,\ X_2 = -.14.$$

There is a region of significance for $X > -.14$, and in that region $\tilde{Y}_1 > \tilde{Y}_2$. The other region of significance, for which $X < -2.7$ is of no practical interest because it is entirely outside the range of the observed data. It may be concluded that children who gained during the initial period or lost not more than .14 will make higher gains in a subsequent period if they have therapy. For other children, the evidence does not indicate whether they will do better under therapy or not.

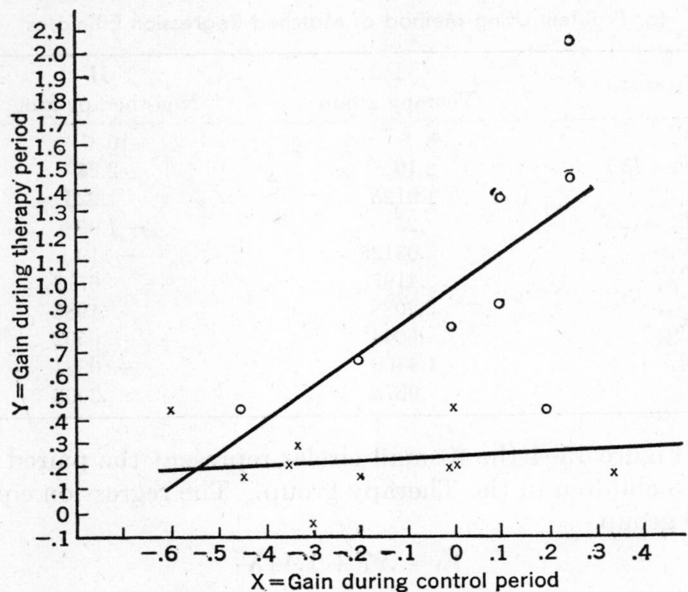

FIG. 15–4. Regression of gain during therapy period on gain during control period for two groups of children. (Data from Bills.[2])

o = child in therapy group
x = child in non-therapy group
X_0 = −.50 point of non-significance
$X > -.27$ is region of significance favoring therapy group

SEVERAL POPULATIONS WITH TWO PREDICTOR VARIABLES

This situation is a natural extension of that described on page 388 in which there was a single scaled predictor. However, because the regression equation now involves two predictor variables, changes must be made in the computational pattern and in the degrees of freedom.

The *total sum of squares* S_T which is to be analyzed is the sum of the squares of the residuals $Y_\alpha - \tilde{Y}_\alpha$ where

$$\tilde{Y}_\alpha = \overline{Y} + b_{xT}(X_\alpha - \overline{X}) + b_{zT}(Z_\alpha - \overline{Z})$$

This is the equation of a regression plane as discussed in Chapter 13. The three means $\overline{Y}$, $\overline{X}$ and $\overline{Z}$ are the means of the total group. The two regression coefficients are also computed for the total group. (Here b_x and b_z have been used as abbreviations for $b_{yx.z}$

and $b_{yz.x}$.) In a problem in analysis of covariance it is not usually necessary to compute the regression equation but only to obtain S_T. If it were desirable to compute the regression coefficients, that could be easily done by the Formulas

$$(15.37)\quad b_{xT} = \frac{C_{yxT}C_{zzT} - C_{yzT}C_{xzT}}{C_{xxT}C_{zzT} - C^2_{xzT}} \quad \text{and} \quad b_{zT} = \frac{C_{yzT}C_{xxT} - C_{yxT}C_{xzT}}{C_{xxT}C_{zzT} - C^2_{xzT}}$$

which are algebraically equivalent to Formulas (13.2) on page 319. The total sum of squares computed as

$$(15.38)\quad S_T = C_{yyT} - \frac{C^2_{xyT}C_{zzT} + C^2_{yzT}C_{xxT} - 2C_{yxT}C_{yzT}C_{xzT}}{C_{xxT}C_{zzT} - C^2_{xzT}}$$

has $N - 3$ degrees of freedom.

As on page 395, the total sum of squares may be separated into two components S_w and S_b and each of these separated into two others:

$$S_w = S_1 + S_2$$
$$S_b = S_3 + S_4$$
$$S_T = S_w + S_b = S_1 + S_2 + S_3 + S_4$$

Under the null hypothesis, each of these component sums divided by its respective degrees of freedom is an unbiased estimate of the common variance. The formulas for computing the various sums and the degrees of freedom associated with each are shown in Table 15.7.

TABLE 15.7 Summary of Components of Sum of Squares of Y about Regression Plane $\tilde{Y}_\alpha = \bar{Y} + b_{xT}(X_\alpha - \bar{X}) + b_{zT}(Z_\alpha - \bar{Z})$ with the Formula and Degrees of Freedom for Each

Symbol	Formula	Degrees of freedom
S_T	$C_{yyT} - \dfrac{C^2_{xyT}C_{zzT} + C^2_{yzT}C_{xxT} - 2C_{xyT}C_{xzT}C_{yzT}}{C_{xxT}C_{zzT} - C^2_{xzT}}$	$N - 3$
S_w	$C_{yyw} - \dfrac{C^2_{xyw}C_{zzw} + C^2_{yzw}C_{xxw} - 2C_{xyw}C_{xzw}C_{yzw}}{C_{xxw}C_{zzw} - C^2_{xzw}}$	$N - k - 2$
S_b	$S_T - S_w$	$k - 1$
S_2	$C_{yyw} - \sum_{i=1}^{k} \dfrac{C^2_{xyi}C_{zzi} + C^2_{yzi}C_{xxi} - 2C_{xyi}C_{xzi}C_{yzi}}{C_{xxi}C_{zzi} - C^2_{xzi}}$	$N - 3k$
S_1	$S_w - S_2$	$2(k - 1)$
S_3	$C_{yyb} - \dfrac{C^2_{xyb}C_{zzb} + C^2_{yzb}C_{xxb} - 2C_{xyb}C_{xzb}C_{yzb}}{C_{xxb}C_{zzb} - C^2_{xzb}}$	$k - 3$
S_4	$S_b - S_3$	2

The sums of squares listed in Table 15.7 are analogous in meaning to those in Table 15.3 except that the phrase "regression plane" is to be substituted for "regression line." The tests of hypotheses are also analogous.

MATCHED REGRESSION ESTIMATES. TWO POPULATIONS WITH TWO PREDICTOR VARIABLES

The procedures and the rationale employed in this situation are analogous to those described on page 399 except that (1) the computing formulas are somewhat more involved, (2) the figure is three dimensional, and (3) the region of significance is not a line segment but a portion of a plane.

Regression estimates can be calculated for each group:

$$\tilde{Y}_{1\alpha} = a_1 + b_{x1}X_\alpha + b_{z1}Z_\alpha \quad \text{and} \quad \tilde{Y}_{2\alpha} = a_2 + b_{x2}X_\alpha + b_{z2}Z_\alpha$$

where

$$b_{xi} = \frac{C_{xyi}C_{zzi} - C_{xzi}C_{zyi}}{C_{xxi}C_{zzi} - C^2_{xzi}} \tag{15.39}$$

$$b_{zi} = \frac{C_{yzi}C_{xxi} - C_{xzi}C_{xyi}}{C_{xxi}C_{zzi} - C^2_{xzi}} \tag{15.40}$$

$$a_i = \overline{Y}_i - b_{xi}\overline{X}_i - b_{zi}\overline{Z}_i \tag{15.41}$$

For each pair of fixed variables, X', Z', the significance of the difference

$$D = (a_1 - a_2) + (b_{x1} - b_{x2})X' + (b_{z1} - b_{z2})Z' \tag{15.42}$$

may be tested.

The variance of D is

$$s_D{}^2 = \frac{PQ}{N - 6} \tag{15.43}$$

where

$$P = \sum_{i=1}^{2} (C_{yyi} - C_{xyi}b_{xi} - C_{yzi}b_{zi}) \tag{15.44}$$

and

$$Q = \frac{N_1 + N_2}{N_1N_2} + \sum_{i=1}^{2} \frac{C_{xxi}C_{zzi}}{C_{xxi}C_{zzi} - C^2_{xzi}} \left\{ \frac{(X' - \overline{X}_i)^2}{C_{xxi}} - \frac{2C_{xzi}(X' - \overline{X}_i)(Z' - \overline{Z}_i)}{C_{xxi}C_{zzi}} + \frac{(Z' - \overline{Z}_i)^2}{C_{zzi}} \right\} \tag{15.45}$$

The ratio $t = \dfrac{D}{s_D}$ has "Student's" distribution with $N - 6$ degrees of freedom.

Region of Significance. From the inequality $D^2 - s_D{}^2t^2{}_{\frac{1}{2}\alpha} \geqq 0$, a region of significance α may be obtained by a procedure analogous to that on page 400, except that the region which, in that discussion, lay on the X-axis, now lies in the XZ plane. From this inequality, the limits of the region of significance may be found by drawing the curve which is given by the second degree equation

$$(15.46) \qquad AX^2 + 2BXZ + CZ^2 + 2EX + 2GZ + H = 0,$$

where

$$(15.47) \quad A = (b_{x1} - b_{x2})^2 - \frac{t^2{}_{\frac{1}{2}\alpha}P}{N-6}\sum_{i=1}^{2}\frac{C_{zzi}}{C_{xxi}C_{zzi} - C^2{}_{xzi}}$$

$$(15.48) \quad B = (b_{x1} - b_{x2})(b_{z1} - b_{z2}) + \frac{t^2{}_{\frac{1}{2}\alpha}P}{N-6}\sum_{i=1}^{2}\frac{C_{xzi}}{C_{xxi}C_{zzi} - C^2{}_{xzi}}$$

$$(15.49) \quad C = (b_{z1} - b_{z2})^2 - \frac{t^2{}_{\frac{1}{2}\alpha}P}{N-6}\sum_{i=1}^{2}\frac{C_{xxi}}{C_{xxi}C_{zzi} - C^2{}_{xzi}}$$

$$(15.50) \quad E = (a_1 - a_2)(b_{x1} - b_{x2}) + \frac{t^2{}_{\frac{1}{2}\alpha}P}{N-6}\sum_{i=1}^{2}\frac{\overline{X}_iC_{zzi} - \overline{Z}_iC_{xzi}}{C_{xxi}C_{zzi} - C^2{}_{xzi}}$$

$$(15.51) \quad G = (a_1 - a_2)(b_{z1} - b_{z2}) + \frac{t^2{}_{\frac{1}{2}\alpha}P}{N-6}\sum_{i=1}^{2}\frac{\overline{Z}_iC_{xxi} - \overline{X}_iC_{xzi}}{C_{xxi}C_{zzi} - C^2{}_{xzi}}$$

$$(15.52) \quad H = (a_1 - a_2)^2 - \frac{t^2{}_{\frac{1}{2}\alpha}P}{N-6}\left[\sum_{i=1}^{2}\frac{C_{xxi}C_{zzi}}{C_{xxi}C_{zzi} - C^2{}_{xzi}}\left(\frac{\overline{X}_i{}^2}{C_{xxi}} - \frac{2\overline{X}_i\overline{Z}_iC_{xzi}}{C_{xxi}C_{zzi}} + \frac{\overline{Z}_i{}^2}{C_{zzi}}\right) \cdot \frac{N}{N_1N_2}\right]$$

When the coefficients A to H have been calculated the curve which is represented by equation (15.46) may be plotted on the X, Z plane. The curve is a conic. The determination of conic sections from a second degree equation is discussed in textbooks on plane analytic geometry.

In order to assist the reader a brief discussion of the procedure in plotting the conic will be given. The discussion will not be complete, but will cover situations which are likely to arise in practice.

The conic, if it exists at all, will be an ellipse or hyperbola, and in general will be centered at a point other than the intersection of the XZ axes and will be oblique to these axes. Plotting such a conic is fairly laborious but the work can be considerably simplified by locating new axes X', Z' in relation to which the conic is a central conic and determining the equation of the conic in terms of X', Z' coordinates.

We shall assume that $AC - B^2 \neq 0$.

The new axes intersect at the point (X_0, Z_0) with coordinates

$$X_0 = \frac{GB - CE}{AC - B^2} \tag{15.53}$$

and

$$Z_0 = \frac{BE - AG}{AC - B^2} \tag{15.54}$$

This point is to be marked on the diagram. The new X' axis is a line passing through the point X_0, Z_0 with slope

$$m = \frac{C - A \pm \sqrt{4B^2 + (A - C)^2}}{2B} \tag{15.55}$$

The sign of the radical in m is to be taken as the same as that of B. The X' axis is given by the equation $Z = Z_0 + m(X - X_0)$. This line should be drawn on the chart and a line drawn perpendicular to it at X_0Z_0.

In terms of the new X', Z' axes, the conic has the form

$$A'(X')^2 + C'(Z')^2 + H' = 0 \tag{15.56}$$

where

$$A' = \tfrac{1}{2}\{A + C + (\pm\sqrt{(A - C)^2 + 4B^2})\} \tag{15.57}$$

$$C' = \tfrac{1}{2}\{A + C - (\pm\sqrt{(A - C)^2 + 4B^2})\} \tag{15.58}$$

the sign before the radical being the same as that of B, and

$$H' = AX_0^2 + 2BX_0Z_0 + CZ_0^2 + 2EX_0 + 2GZ_0 + H \tag{15.59}$$

It does not seem at all likely that in practice H' will be equal to zero, hence we shall assume that it is not zero.

The type of curve represented by Equation (15.56) can be determined by examination of the coefficients A', C', and H' as follows:

(1) If A', C', and H' all have the same sign, there is no conic and no region of significance;

(2) If A' and C' have the same sign, but H' has the opposite sign, there is a region of significance bounded by an ellipse;

(3) If A' and C' have different signs, there is a region of significance bounded by a hyperbola.

If the conic exists, it can best be plotted when Equation (15.56) is put into the form

$$\frac{(X')^2}{\frac{-H'}{A'}} + \frac{(Z')^2}{\frac{-H'}{C'}} = 1 \tag{15.60}$$

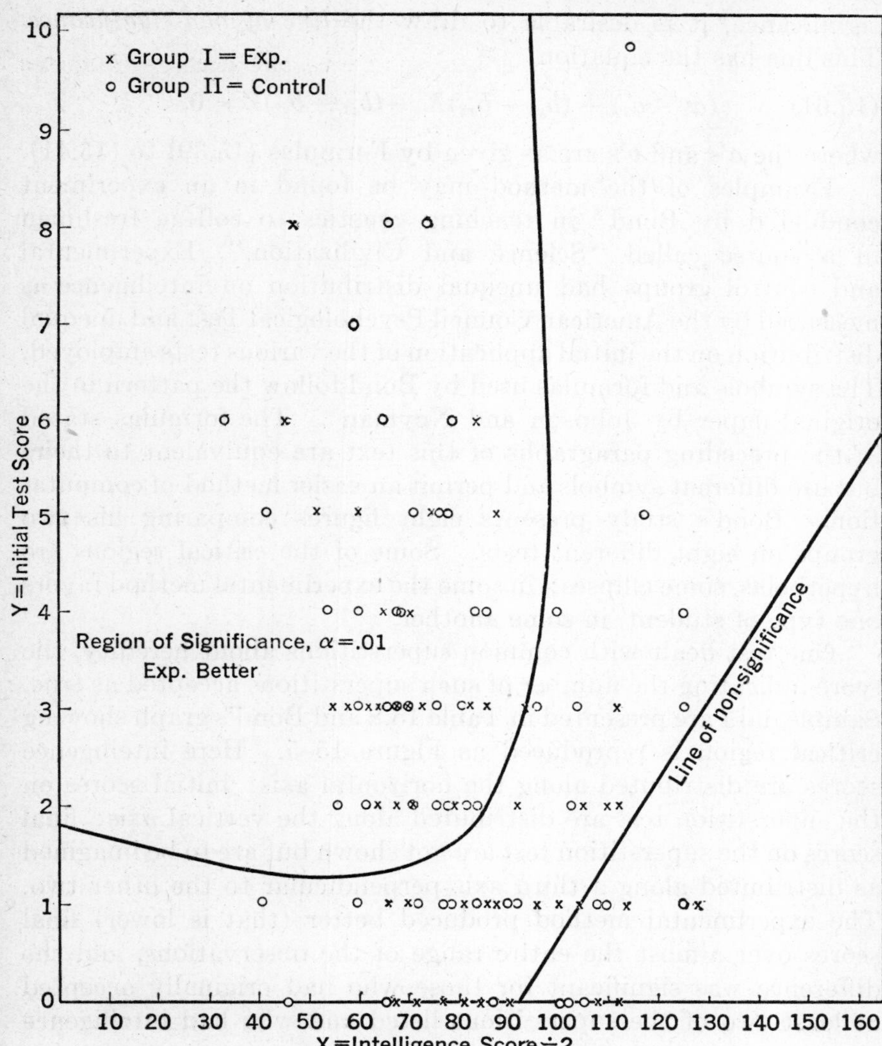

FIG. 15–5. Comparison of two groups on a test of superstitions. From Austin Bond.[3]

Plotting this equation on the original XZ chart would be difficult because the new axes are oblique to the lines of the grid. However the graph of Equation (15.60) may be plotted on another grid; then the axes of this grid may be aligned with the X', Z' axes as drawn on the original grid, and the graph traced on the original grid with tracing paper.

In addition to plotting the conic which outlines the region of significance, it is desirable to draw the *line of non-significance.* This line has the equation

$$(15.61) \qquad (a_1 - a_2) + (b_{x1} - b_{x2})X + (b_{z1} - b_{z2})Z = 0,$$

where the a's and b's are as given by Formulas (15.39) to (15.41).

Examples of the method may be found in an experiment conducted by Bond [3] in teaching genetics to college freshmen in a course called "Science and Civilization." Experimental and control groups had unequal distribution on intelligence as measured by the American Council Psychological Test and unequal distribution on the initial application of the various tests employed. The symbols and formulas used by Bond follow the pattern in the original paper by Johnson and Neyman [5]. The formulas stated in the preceding paragraphs of this text are equivalent to theirs but use different symbols and permit an easier method of computation. Bond's study presents eight figures comparing his two groups on eight different tests. Some of the critical regions are hyperbolas, some ellipses; in some the experimental method favors one type of student, in some another.

One test dealt with common superstitions about heredity, the score indicating the number of such superstitions accepted as true. Sample data are presented in Table 15.8 and Bond's graph showing critical region is reproduced as Figure 15–5. Here intelligence scores are distributed along the horizontal axis; initial scores on the superstition test are distributed along the vertical axis; final scores on the superstition test are not shown but are to be imagined as distributed along a third axis perpendicular to the other two. The experimental method produced better (that is lower) final scores over almost the entire range of the observations, and the difference was significant for those who had originally accepted at least two of the superstitions listed and who had intelligence average to low.

Sample data from a test on opinions on imperialism shown graphically in Figure 15–6 present a somewhat different picture. Looking at the line of non-significance we note that regardless of the intelligence level the experimental method produced better results on the final test for students whose initial test score was low while the method used with the control group produced better results for students whose initial test score was high. However such differences are significant only for students in approximately the lower third of the distribution of scores and these derive significant advantage from the experimental method.

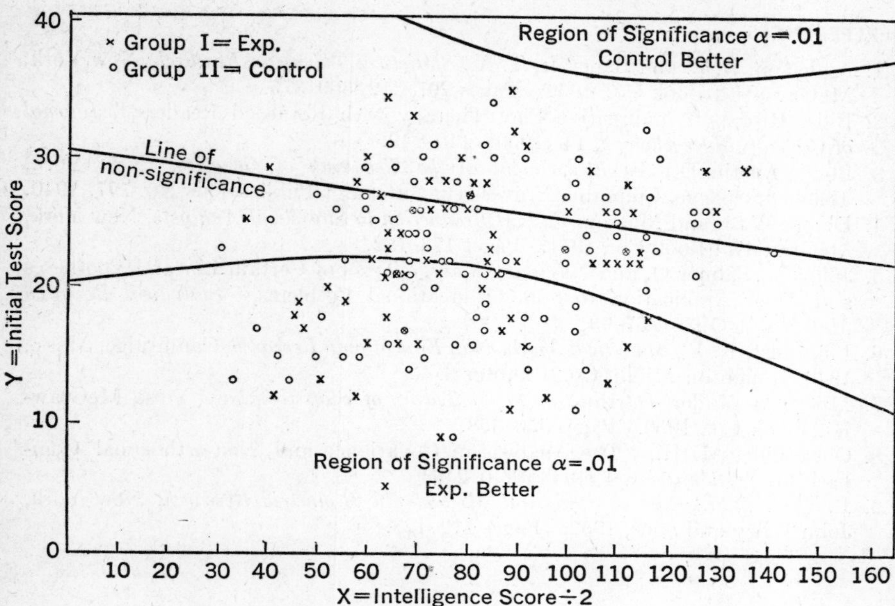

FIG. 15–6. Comparison of two groups on a test of opinions on imperialism. From Austin Bond.[3]

TABLE 15.8 Sample Data for Comparison of Two Groups in Regard to Superstitions Concerning the Laws of Heredity*

Datum	Experimental group	Control group
Number of cases	$N_1 = 54$	$N_2 = 57$
Sum of scores on final superstitions test	$\Sigma Y = 90$	$\Sigma Y = 176$
Sum of scores on initial superstitions test	$\Sigma Z = 119$	$\Sigma Z = 173$
Sum of scores on intelligence	$\Sigma X = 446$	$\Sigma X = 455$
Mean final test score	$\overline{Y}_1 = 1.667$	$\overline{Y}_2 = 3.088$
Mean initial test score	$\overline{Z}_1 = 2.204$	$\overline{Z}_2 = 3.035$
Mean intelligence score	$\overline{X}_1 = 82.59$	$\overline{X}_2 = 79.82$
$\Sigma(Y_{i\alpha} - \overline{Y}_i)^2$	$C_{yy1} = 101.9$	$C_{yy2} = 280.4$
$\Sigma(Z_{i\alpha} - \overline{Z}_i)^2$	$C_{zz1} = 172.6$	$C_{zz2} = 306.0$
$\Sigma(X_{i\alpha} - \overline{X}_i)^2$	$C_{xx1} = 26806$	$C_{xx2} = 26250$
$\Sigma(Y_{i\alpha} - \overline{Y}_i)(Z_i - \overline{Z}_i)$	$C_{yz1} = 74.56$	$C_{yz2} = 217.94$
$\Sigma(Y_{i\alpha} - \overline{Y}_i)(X_i - \overline{X}_i)$	$C_{yx1} = -416.6$	$C_{yx2} = -813.9$
$\Sigma(Z_{i\alpha} - \overline{Z}_i)(X_i - \overline{X}_i)$	$C_{xz1} = -888.4$	$C_{xz2} = -300.4$

Y = Final score on superstitions test
Z = Initial score on superstitions test
X = Score on American Council Psychological Examination
Large value of Y or Z indicates acceptance of superstitions

* From Bond.[3]

REFERENCES

1. Anderson, R. L. and Bancroft, T. A., *Statistical Theory in Research*, New York, McGraw-Hill Book Co., 1952. Pages 297–312, 369–375.
2. Bills, R. E., "Nondirective Play Therapy with Retarded Readers," *Journal of Consulting Psychology*, 14 (1950), 140–149.
3. Bond, Austin D., *An Experiment in the Teaching of Genetics*. New York, Teachers College, Columbia University, Bureau of Publications No. 797, 1940.
4. Dixon, W. J. and Massey, F. J., *Introduction to Statistical Analysis*, New York, McGraw-Hill Book Co., 1951. Pages 173–182.
5. Johnson, Palmer O. and Neyman, Jerzy, "Tests of Certain Linear Hypotheses and Their Application to Some Educational Problems," *Statistical Research Memoirs*, 1 (1936), 57–93.
6. Lindquist, E. F., *Statistical Analysis in Educational Research*, Cambridge, Mass., 1940, Houghton Mifflin Co., Chapter 6.
7. Mood, Alexander, *Introduction to the Theory of Statistics*, New York, McGraw-Hill Book Co., 1950. Pages 350–358.
8. Quenouille, M. H., "The Analysis of Covariance and Non-orthogonal Comparisons," *Biometrics*, 4 (1948), 240–246.
9. Rao, C. R., *Advanced Statistical Methods in Biometric Research*, New York, John Wiley and Sons, 1952. Pages 119–128.

16 Percentiles

In the preceding chapters we have considered inferences based on sample moments such as the mean, variance and covariance, and on functions of these moments. In this chapter inferences based on percentiles will be discussed.

The computation of percentiles is desirable in two classes of situations:

1. When percentiles are actually more satisfactory statistics for estimation of population characteristics. For some populations the moments do not satisfy the conditions of consistency and efficiency as these are described in Chapters 3 and 7, but percentiles, or functions of percentiles, do satisfy the condition of consistency and at least approximate the condition of efficiency.

2. When percentiles are less satisfactory statistics than the moments but serve to simplify computations.

These situations and the related computations will presently be discussed in detail.

Notation for Percentiles. In agreement with the notation used in previous chapters, percentiles will be indicated by a symbol based on the variable, and a subscript which is the decimal equivalent of the percentile. Thus $X_{.20}$ is to be the notation for the twentieth sample percentile of the variable X, $X_{.50}$ is to be the median, etc. The corresponding population percentiles will be denoted as $\xi_{.20}$, $\xi_{.50}$, etc. (ξ is the Greek letter xi). The symbols X_p and ξ_p will indicate the $(100p)$th percentile, because p is the decimal equivalent of the percent $100p$. We shall need to refer to the population ordinate at the $(100p)$th percentile. This will be denoted as y_p.

Quantiles. The term quantile is often used in place of percentile. It differs from the percentile only in the fact that it is referred directly to the proportion instead of to the percent equivalent of the proportion. Thus $X_{.25}$, in the present notation, is the 25th percentile or the quantile of order .25. The terms decile, quartile, and percentile are all subsumed under the term quantile. Because the term percentile is in more common use that term will be employed here.

Distribution of Percentiles in Large Samples. In large samples X_p has an approximately normal distribution with mean ξ_p and standard error

$$\frac{1}{y_p}\sqrt{\frac{p(1-p)}{N}} \tag{16.1}$$

In particular, the median has an approximately normal distribution with mean $\xi_{.50}$ and standard error

$$\frac{1}{2y_{.50}\sqrt{N}} \tag{16.2}$$

If sampling is from a normal population the ordinate at the population median is $1/(\sigma\sqrt{2\pi})$. Therefore, for samples from a normal population, the standard error of the median is

$$\frac{1}{2y_{.50}\sqrt{N}} = \sigma\sqrt{\frac{\pi}{2N}} = 1.57\,\frac{\sigma}{\sqrt{N}} \tag{16.3}$$

Consistency of Estimate. From Formula (16.1) it is clear that the standard error of a percentile approaches zero as N becomes increasingly great. Hence, for large values of N there is little likelihood that the sample percentile will differ greatly from the population percentile, and the sample percentile is, therefore, a *consistent estimate* of the population percentile.

In sampling from a normal population the mean and median are both consistent estimates of μ. However there exist populations such that the sample mean is not a consistent estimate of the central parameter but the median is. These populations are characterized by the fact that extreme cases are likely to occur frequently in samples.

Efficiency of Estimate. It has been stated that, for samples from a normal population, both the sample mean and sample median are consistent estimates of μ. However, for such samples the standard error of the mean is $\frac{\sigma}{\sqrt{N}}$ but the standard error of the median is $1.57\,\frac{\sigma}{\sqrt{N}}$. Since the mean has the smaller standard error it is preferred to the median as an estimate of μ.

Similarly in samples from a normal population a consistent estimate of σ is given by

$$s = \sqrt{\frac{\Sigma(X-\overline{X})^2}{N-1}},$$

and also by $.74(X_{.75} - X_{.25})$. However, s is the preferred estimate because its standard error is smaller.

In general there may be many consistent estimates of a population characteristic. The estimate which has the least standard error is called *efficient.* Other estimates, called *inefficient,* may, nevertheless, be used because of computational convenience. When inefficient estimates are used it is desirable to have a measure of their efficiency. For this purpose the following measure of the efficiency of a statistic has been adopted:

$$\text{(16.4)} \quad \text{Efficiency of a given statistic} = \frac{\text{variance of efficient statistic}}{\text{variance of given statistic}}$$

It is evident from the formula that an efficient statistic has efficiency one, but an inefficient statistic has efficiency less than one. When this formula is applied to the median of a sample from a normal population the efficiency of this statistic is

$$\text{(16.5)} \qquad \text{Efficiency of median} = \frac{\sigma^2/N}{1.57(\sigma^2/N)} = .64$$

An important interpretation of this concept of efficiency is that it is a measure of a loss in number of cases. An efficiency of .80 is equivalent to sampling reliability based on 80% of the cases in the sample.

Classes of Efficient Statistics. Certain classes of statistics are known to be efficient. Among the best known of these are the *maximum likelihood statistics.* These are statistics which, when substituted for the parameter in expressions for the probability density, make the likelihood of the sample a maximum. Under the usual assumptions, that samples are drawn from a normal or binomial population, most of the statistics which have been studied in this text, as the percent, mean, variance, correlation coefficient and regression coefficient are maximum likelihood statistics. These statistics not only have minimum standard error but are distributed normally for large samples.

The maximum likelihood statistics are a subclass of a class of statistics known as BAN estimates, which have the common property of being normally distributed with minimum variance and with the true parameter value as mean. BAN stands for *best asymptotically normal.* For a fuller treatment of these classes of estimates the reader must consult the mathematical literature of statistics.

Estimation of the Mean and Standard Deviation by Percentiles. It has been stated that the median has efficiency .64 as an estimate of the mean of a normal population. More efficient estimates can be obtained by computing averages of several percentiles symmetrically placed about the median.[5] Several such estimates together with their efficiencies are listed in Table XVII, in the Appendix. This table shows that very high efficiency can be achieved by use of several percentiles. While even five percentiles provide an efficiency which is less than unity there may be an advantage in estimating a mean by these methods because of great saving of time. Such a saving will occur when a frequency distribution has data grouped in unequal class intervals. The method is particularly important when the ends of a distribution are open so that the mean cannot be computed at all by usual methods.

Another occasion when the use of percentiles provides a saving of time is when data are punched on IBM cards. The cards can be sorted in order and the percentiles can be located by a simple count.

When percentiles are used to estimate the standard deviation of a normal population the statistics listed in Table XVIII have high efficiency.

The decision as to whether to use an efficient statistic or to choose one of lesser efficiency depends upon circumstances. If speed is important, estimates based on two percentiles may be used. If the number of cases is great, a saving in labor can be achieved without too great loss in efficiency by using estimates based on four or six percentiles instead of just two. When data are scarce or are expensive to obtain and labor of computation is less important than labor of obtaining original data, then efficient statistics should always be used in order to obtain the maximum information from the minimum number of cases. When data are cheap and readily available and when computation must be done by inexperienced persons — as is often the case in industry — or when the results of computation are needed very quickly, then it may be advisable to use inefficient statistics and to compensate for the loss of information by taking a larger sample.

EXERCISE 16.1

The frequency distribution below is based on scores of 160 persons in a mental test of 30 multiple-choice items. Table 16.1 contains estimates of the mean and standard deviation based on $\overline{X}$, s and on percentiles. The reader may verify the indicated values and may compute estimates based on other statistics. The reader should check the accuracy of computations based on percentiles with that based on statistics which have efficiency one.

TABLE 16.1 Frequency Distribution of Scores of 160 Persons on 30 Items

X	f	Estimates of the mean: Formula	Value
28	2		
27	2	$\overline{X} = \Sigma fX/N$	21.012
26	4	$X_{.50}$	21.115
25	7	$\frac{1}{2}(X_{.75} + X_{.25})$	21.020
24	11	$\frac{1}{3}(X_{.83} + X_{.50} + X_{.17})$	20.993
23	21	$\frac{1}{4}(X_{.875} + X_{.625} + X_{.375} + X_{.125})$	20.992
22	23		
21	26	**Estimates of the standard deviation: Formula**	**Value**
20	19		
19	17		
18	10		
17	9	$s = \sqrt{\dfrac{\Sigma fX^2 - \dfrac{(\Sigma fX)^2}{N}}{N-1}}$	2.76
16	6		
15	1	$.339(X_{.93} - X_{.07})$	2.81
14	1	$.171(X_{.95} + X_{.90} - X_{.10} - X_{.05})$	2.79
13	1	$.120(X_{.98} + X_{.90} + X_{.80} - X_{.20} - X_{.10} - X_{.02})$	2.76

Estimation of the Mean and Standard Deviation from Item Analysis Data. Concepts analogous to those used in estimating the mean and standard deviation of a population from percentiles may be used in estimating these population characteristics from item analysis data. Answers to each item are classified as correct with score 1 or as incorrect with score 0. The item analysis which is considered here is based on high and low groups of test scores, a test score being the number of items answered correctly. The high and low groups are placed symmetrically about the median of test scores, as the high and low 50%, or high and low 27%. Data are assumed available for all items in the test.

The discussion will be facilitated by the introduction of an appropriate notation:

N = the number of persons for whom test scores are available.
k = the number of test items.
p = the proportion in one of the extreme groups, $p \leqq .50$. Hence the number of persons in one of the groups is pN.

R_{Hi} = the number of correct responses to the ith item in the high group.
R_{Li} = the corresponding number for the low group.
$X_{H\alpha}$ = } the score of the αth individual in the
$X_{L\alpha}$ = } high group and low group, respectively.
y_p = ordinate of unit normal curve below which the area is equal to p.

In the type of item analysis described above, R_{Hi} and R_{Li} are known for each item. Consider now the sum $\sum_{i=1}^{k} R_{Hi}$ over all items. This is the total number of correct responses in the high group. Now the total number of correct responses in the high group can also be obtained as the sum of all scores of individuals in the high group, namely $\sum_{\alpha=1}^{pN} X_{H\alpha}$. Since these two sums are equal to the same thing

$$\sum_{i=1}^{k} R_{Hi} = \sum_{\alpha=1}^{pN} X_{H\alpha} \quad \text{and also} \quad \sum_{i=1}^{k} R_{Li} = \sum_{\alpha=1}^{pN} X_{L\alpha}$$

The mean scores of the two subgroups are

$$\frac{\Sigma X_{H\alpha}}{pN} \quad \text{and} \quad \frac{\Sigma X_{L\alpha}}{pN}$$

On the assumption that the scores are distributed normally these means are approximations of the corresponding population means in large samples, or

$$\frac{\Sigma X_{H\alpha}}{pN} \cong \mu + \frac{y_p}{p}\sigma \tag{16.6}$$

and

$$\frac{\Sigma X_{L\alpha}}{pN} \cong \mu - \frac{y_p}{p}\sigma \tag{16.7}$$

The symbol $\cong$ means approximately equal.

If in (16.6) and (16.7) we substitute for $\Sigma X_{H\alpha}$ and $\Sigma X_{L\alpha}$ their equals ΣR_{Hi} and ΣR_{Li} and the two formulas are combined we have

$$\frac{1}{2}\left(\frac{\Sigma R_{Hi}}{pN} + \frac{\Sigma R_{Li}}{pN}\right) \cong \mu$$

Hence an appropriate estimate of the mean for large samples is

$$\text{Estimate of } \mu = \frac{\Sigma R_{Hi} + \Sigma R_{Li}}{2pN} \tag{16.8}$$

Similarly

$$(16.9)\quad \text{Estimate of } \sigma = \frac{1}{2Ny_p}\left[\Sigma R_{Hi} - \Sigma R_{Li}\right]$$

When upper and lower halves are used Formulas (16.8) and (16.9) yield

$$(16.10)\quad \text{Estimate of } \mu = \frac{\Sigma R_{Hi} + \Sigma R_{Li}}{N}$$

$$(16.11)\quad \text{Estimate of } \sigma = 1.254\,\frac{\Sigma R_{Hi} - \Sigma R_{Li}}{N}$$

When upper and lower 27% are used the estimates are

$$(16.12)\quad \text{Estimate of } \mu = 1.851\,\frac{\Sigma R_{Hi} + \Sigma R_{Li}}{N}$$

$$(16.13)\quad \text{Estimate of } \sigma = 1.512\,\frac{\Sigma R_{Hi} - \Sigma R_{Li}}{N}$$

The estimates based on items give results which are quite accurate if all the items making up the test used as criterion are available. If some of the items have been eliminated after a review of the item analysis, the remaining item data may still be useful for estimation of μ and σ. The important consideration in determining usefulness of the estimates is whether the elimination of items has changed the order of test scores to any great extent. If many test scores have been shifted from their original grouping, high, low or middle, then the estimates will not be satisfactory.

It is interesting to remark that the estimate of standard deviation based on high-low 50% as shown in Formula (16.11) is identical with the mean deviation of test scores when data are available for all items. The mean deviation is assumed based on deviations from the median.

$$1.254\,\frac{\Sigma R_{Hi} - \Sigma R_{Li}}{N} = 1.254\,\frac{\Sigma X_{H\alpha} - \Sigma X_{L\alpha}}{N}$$

Now subtract the median test score from each score on the right. This does not affect the value of the estimate since

$$\sum_{\alpha=1}^{N/2} X_{H\alpha} - \sum_{\alpha=1}^{N/2} X_{L\alpha} = \sum_{\alpha=1}^{N/2} (X_{H\alpha} - X_{.50}) - \sum_{\alpha=1}^{N/2} (X_{L\alpha} - X_{.50})$$

Also $\qquad (X_{H\alpha} - X_{.50}) = |\, X_{H\alpha} - X_{.50} \,|$

and $\qquad -(X_{L\alpha} - X_{.50}) = |\, X_{L\alpha} - X_{.50} \,|$

$$\text{Hence} \qquad 1.254\,\frac{\Sigma R_{Hi} - \Sigma R_{Li}}{N} = 1.254\,\frac{\sum_{\alpha=1}^{N} | X_\alpha - X_{.50} |}{N}$$

The expression on the right is an estimate of σ based on the mean deviation. This estimate is known to have efficiency .88. Hence .88 is also the efficiency of the estimate of σ in (16.11). The estimate of the mean in (16.10) has efficiency one. The efficiency of estimates when groups are not upper and lower 50% is not known to the authors.

This discussion suggests that the quantity

$$(16.14) \qquad \frac{R_{Hi} - R_{Li}}{2Ny_p}$$

may be called an *index of reliability* of the *i*th item corresponding to the index of reliability suggested by Gulliksen[2]. Like that index, it has the property that when summed over all items it provides an estimate of σ. The corresponding index of item difficulty is

$$(16.15) \qquad \frac{R_{Hi} + R_{Li}}{2pN}$$

Estimation of the Correlation Coefficient. If the correlation coefficient ρ of a bivariate normal population is to be estimated, the Pearson product moment r is an efficient estimate. Inefficient estimates of ρ will be described in this section.[5]

The following procedure provides an estimate of ρ which has efficiency of .52 when $\rho = 0$:

1. Arrange the cases in order of size on one of the variables, say X. Select the 27% of the cases for which X is greatest and the 27% for which X is least. Discard the 46% remaining cases.

2. Find the median Y score of the 54% of cases selected in step 1. This median may not be the same as the Y median of the entire sample.

3. Count the cases in each of the four groups and designate the number in each group as follows:

n_1 above Y median of selected cases and in upper 27% of X scores
n_2 above Y median of selected cases and in lower 27% of X scores
n_3 below Y median of selected cases and in lower 27% of X scores
n_4 below Y median of selected cases and in upper 27% of X scores

These four numbers are shown diagrammatically on page 421.

	Low 27% on X	46%	High 27% on X	Total
Above Y median of selected cases	n_2		n_1	$n_1 + n_2 = .27N$
Below Y median of selected cases	n_3		n_4	$n_3 + n_4 = .27N$
Total	$n_2 + n_3 = .27N$		$n_1 + n_4 = .27N$	$n_1 + n_2 + n_3 + n_4 = .54N$

The estimate of the correlation coefficient is read from Chart XV. As a first step in the use of this figure compute X_0. If $n_1 + n_3 > n_2 + n_4$

$$X_0 = \frac{n_1 + n_3}{n_1 + n_2 + n_3 + n_4}$$

Locate X_0 on the horizontal scale of Chart XV and draw a vertical line through X_0 to intersect the curve $A = 27$. Draw a horizontal line from this intersection over to the vertical scale. The point where this horizontal cuts the vertical scale indicates the required estimate of ρ. Of course one does not actually *draw* these vertical and horizontal lines on the diagram but notes their position by using a ruler or the edge of a card.

If $n_1 + n_3 < n_2 + n_4$ evaluate the ratio

$$X_0 = \frac{n_2 + n_4}{n_1 + n_2 + n_3 + n_4}$$

and proceed as before, but the estimate is now negative.

Actually, not only 27% but any percentage will serve the purpose. However, the estimate is more efficient when 27% is used.[3] Chart XV provides a means of estimating ρ by several high-low proportions. In particular, the use of high-low 50% on X provides an estimate equivalent to that available from the tetrachoric coefficient for the special case when each variable is split at the median of the sample.

The actual procedure can be carried out conveniently by use of cards or by a scatter diagram. If cards are available, the procedure can be carried out in the manner described above. If a scatter diagram is used, the cases are partitioned as in Figure 16–1.

From this figure

$$X_0 = \frac{19 + 19}{19 + 8 + 19 + 8} = .70$$

On Chart XV a vertical line through the point $X = .70$ on the horizontal axis intersects the line marked .27 in the point with vertical coordinate $\rho = .40$. $X_0 = 38/54 = .70$ and, therefore, ρ is read from Chart XV as .40.

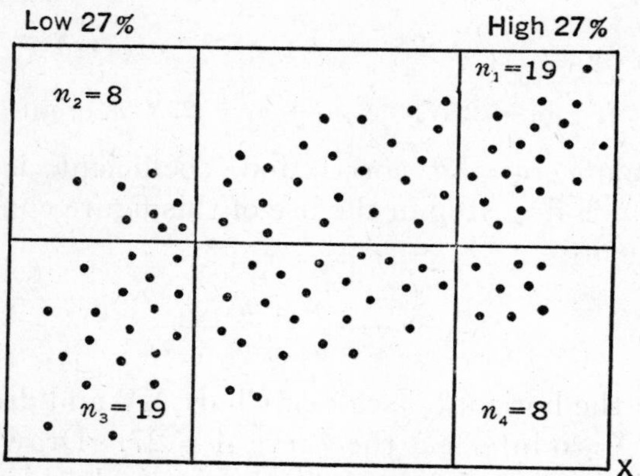

Fig. 16–1. Scatter diagram of 100 cases partitioned for estimation of ρ.

REFERENCES

1. Dixon, W. J., and Massey, F. J. Jr., *Introduction to Statistical Analysis,* New York, 1951, McGraw-Hill Book Co., Inc., Chapter 16.
2. Gulliksen, Harold, *Theory of Mental Tests,* New York, 1950, John Wiley & Sons.
3. Kelley, Truman L., "The Selection of Upper and Lower Groups for the Validation of Test Items," *Journal of Educational Psychology,* 30 (1939), 17.
4. Kelley, Truman L., *Fundamentals of Statistics,* Cambridge, Mass., 1947, Harvard University Press.
5. Mosteller, Frederick, "On Some Useful 'Inefficient' Statistics," *Annals of Mathematical Statistics,* 17 (1946), 377–408.

17 Transformation of Scales

A great deal of the theory presented in previous chapters was based on the assumption that the variable under consideration has a normal distribution. When this assumption appears dubious, the variable, or scale, may often be transformed into another variable with a distribution approximating the normal. The formulas for the variance of certain statistics involve the unknown parameters of which those statistics are estimates. Examples are $\sigma_p^2 = \frac{PQ}{N}$ and $\sigma_r^2 = \frac{1 - \rho^2}{N - 1}$. In such a case, it is a great advantage if a related statistic can be found with variance dependent only on sample size and not on any unknown parameter. Several transformations which serve one or both of these purposes will be briefly presented in this chapter.

The transformation of the correlation coefficient r into

$$z_r = \frac{1}{2} \log \frac{1 + r}{1 - r},$$

discussed in Chapter 10 and tabulated in Table XII, is an example of a transformation which achieves both purposes.

Transformation of Proportions into Angles. Because of the unknown parameter in $\sigma_p^2 = PQ/N$ it is often useful to transform proportions into angles by the formula

$$\phi = 2 \arcsin \sqrt{p} \tag{17.1}$$

This formula may also be written as

$$\phi = 2 \sin^{-1} \sqrt{p} \tag{17.2}$$

Both formulas may be read "ϕ is twice the angle whose sine is $\sqrt{p}$." Arcsin and $\sin^{-1}$ are discussed in trigonometry texts.

If ϕ is expressed in radians its variance is approximately

$$\sigma_\phi^2 = 1/N \tag{17.3}$$

This formula is valid with only slight inaccuracy when

$$.05 < P < .95 \quad \text{and} \quad N \geqq 20.$$

For large samples the acceptable range of P is even greater.

The value of ϕ in radians corresponding to a given p other than 0 or 1 can be read from Appendix Table XIXA. Bartlett [1,4] has given the formulas

$$\phi_0 = \arcsin \sqrt{\frac{1}{4N}} \text{ for } p = 0 \quad (17.4)$$

and

$$\phi_1 = 3.1416 - 2 \arcsin \sqrt{\frac{1}{4N}} \text{ for } p = 1 \quad (17.5)$$

The values of ϕ_0 and ϕ_1 can be read from Table XIXB. In testing the hypothesis $P = P_H$ the statistic

$$z = \sqrt{N}\,(2 \arcsin \sqrt{p} - 2 \arcsin \sqrt{P_H}) \quad (17.6)$$

is useful because its distribution is approximately normal with unit variance. A test using this statistic is preferable to the test described in Chapter 3 because the distribution of ϕ is more nearly normal than that of p. When the observations in an analysis of variance problem are proportions, homogeneity of variance cannot be assumed because the σ_p^2 varies with P and with N. If all proportions are based on the same N and if each is transformed to an angle homogeneity of variance is secured because each angle has the same variance, $1/N$, even though the proportions differ.

The Square Root Transformation. A very skewed distribution known as the Poisson Distribution which often arises in connection with the frequency of occurrence of a very rare event has $\sigma^2 = \mu$. To make tests of significance concerning the means of such distributions the variable (that is the number of occurrences) should be replaced by its square root.

The Logarithmic Transformation. If the scores in an analysis of variance layout are so distributed that the mean of each subgroup is approximately equal to its standard deviation, then each score should be replaced by its logarithm before the analysis of variance is carried out. For example, if the entries are sample variances this situation would occur.

Transformation of Ranks to Normal Deviates. The use of ranks in computing a correlation coefficient was described in Chapter 11. It often seems reasonable to assume that the underlying variable represented by the ranks is normally distributed. Appendix Table XX may be used to transform a set of ranks into a set of scores from a normal distribution in which $\mu = 50$ and $\sigma = 10$, for samples in which $5 \leqq N \leqq 30$. To find the normal equivalent of a rank R when $N > 30$, first find the proportion

$$p = 1 - \frac{R - 0.5}{N} \quad (17.7)$$

then read in Table II the normal deviate z_p in a unit normal curve corresponding to the proportion p. The corresponding normal deviate when $\mu = 50$ and $\sigma = 10$ is

$$Z_p = 10z_p + 50$$

Normalization of the *F* Distribution. The F distribution has so far been tabulated for only a few significance levels.* When a statistician needs to know the significance of a value of F lying between these tabulated values, he may take the cube root of the observed F and substitute it in a formula given by Paulson [6]

$$u = \frac{\left(1 + \frac{2}{9n_2}\right)F^{\frac{1}{3}} - \left(1 - \frac{2}{9n_1}\right)}{\sqrt{\frac{2}{9n_2}F^{\frac{2}{3}} + \frac{2}{9n_1}}} \tag{17.8}$$

The statistic u has a distribution which is nearly unit normal when the error variance has at least 3 degrees of freedom. Therefore, a good approximation to the significance level for F can be obtained by computing u and taking α as the area in the two tails of the normal distribution.

Uniformization. When the form of distribution of a variable is not known or is presumed to be not normal, the ordinary tests of significance are not justified. Then the scores may be transformed to ranks and a non-parametric test based on rank order may be performed.

REFERENCES

1. Bartlett, M. S., "Some Examples of Statistical Methods of Research in Agriculture and Applied Biology," *Supplement to the Journal of the Royal Statistical Society*, 4 (1937), 137–183.
2. Bartlett, M. S., "The Use of Transformations," *Biometrics*, 3 (1947), 39–52.
3. Edwards, Allen, *Experimental Design in Psychological Research*, New York, 1950, Rinehart and Co., Inc., pages 198–204.
4. Eisenhart, C., Hastay, M. W. and Wallis, W. A., *Selected Techniques of Statistical Analysis*, New York, McGraw-Hill Book Co., Inc., 1947. Chapters 7 and 16.
5. Hotelling H. and Frankel, L. R., "The Transformation of Statistics to Simplify their Distribution," *Annals of Mathematical Statistics*, 9 (1938), 87–96.
6. Paulson, Edward, "An Approximate Normalization of the Analysis of Variance Distribution," *Annals of Mathematical Statistics*, 13 (1942), 233–235.
7. Rao, C. R., *Advanced Statistical Methods in Biometric Research*, New York, 1952, John Wiley and Sons, Inc., pp. 207–214.

* The forthcoming edition of Pearson's *Statistical Tables* (Cambridge University Press), will contain the table of percentage points of the F distribution by Merrington and Thompson. This tabulation, most of which appeared in *Biometrika* 33 (1943), is the most extensive yet made.

8 Non-Parametric Methods *

Most of the methods presented in previous chapters depend upon the assumption that samples have been drawn from a normal population. In many problems, this assumption looks quite unreasonable. In this chapter several methods will be described for making inferences without any assumption as to the form of distribution in the population. Such statistical methods are called *non-parametric* or *distribution-free*. Examples of non-parametric methods which have already been studied are the χ^2 test, the percentiles, and the rank-correlation coefficient.

Since the methods to be presented are valid for *any* parent population (or, in some cases, for any parent population on a continuous variable), they could be validly applied to samples from normal populations. Almost always this would be unwise because of the loss of efficiency, as this concept was discussed on page 414. The tests based on normality assumptions are in general *best possible* tests for samples from a normal population and the use of other tests is disadvantageous.

If the samples are not from a normal population and we use a non-parametric test with level of significance α, then for any parent population whatever the probability of an error of the first kind is actually equal to α or less than α because of discreteness. On the other hand, using a normal theory test with level of significance α under the same circumstances does *not* assure that the probability of an error of the first kind is controlled at level α. That probability may be greater or less than α, depending upon the form of the parent population; generally we have no way of knowing the direction or degree of departure from α.

A. Tests for Comparison of Two Samples

Kolmogorov-Smirnov Test. A two-sample test [12] which is sensitive to *any* kind of difference in the distributions from which

* This chapter was written by Professor Lincoln Moses of Stanford University. Because of limitations of space, the manuscript was slightly changed after it left his hands. For any errors which may have been caused by such abridgment the authors take full responsibility.

the samples are drawn, is one based on the sample cumulative percentage polygons. If two samples have, in fact, been drawn from populations with the same continuous distribution, then both cumulative percentage distributions should resemble the parent distribution, and should resemble each other. If the distributions are too far apart at any point it is cause for rejecting the null hypothesis. The test statistic is D = the maximum vertical difference between the two polygons.

TABLE 18.1 Significance Points for Maximum Difference between Two Sample Cumulative Distribution Functions ($N_1 = N_2 \leqq 40$) *

$D = k/N$

N	Values of k for		
	$\alpha \leqq .05$	$\alpha \leqq .03$	$\alpha \leqq .01$
10 or 11		6	7
12	6		7
13	6	7	8
14 or 15		7	8
16 or 17	7	8	9
18 or 19		8	9
20 – 22	8	9	10
23		9	10
24		9	11
25 – 27	9	10	11
28 or 29		10	12
30 – 32	10		12
33 or 34		11	
35 – 39	11	12	
40		12	

* Adapted from Massey [12]

For $N_1 = N_2 \leqq 40$ values of ND calling for rejection at various significance levels are given in Table 18.1. For larger values of N_1 and N_2, whether or not they are equal, rejection values can be calculated from the formulas in Table 18.2.

It is important to note that the scale on which the observations are made need not have a zero point or even have equal intervals in order for this test procedure to be valid; it is only necessary that the order of size of observations be reflected in the scale of measurement. The reader can see that this statement is reasonable by observing that if the horizontal scale along which the scores are measured be stretched in some parts, and compressed in others

TABLE 18.2 Significance Points for Maximum Difference Between Two Sample Cumulative Distribution Functions (N_1, $N_2 > 40$) *

α	Value of D so large as to call for rejection at level α
.1	$1.22\sqrt{\frac{N_1+N_2}{N_1N_2}}$
.05	$1.36\sqrt{\frac{N_1+N_2}{N_1N_2}}$
.025	$1.48\sqrt{\frac{N_1+N_2}{N_1N_2}}$
.01	$1.63\sqrt{\frac{N_1+N_2}{N_1N_2}}$
.005	$1.73\sqrt{\frac{N_1+N_2}{N_1N_2}}$
.001	$1.95\sqrt{\frac{N_1+N_2}{N_1N_2}}$

* From Smirnov [21]

the maximum *vertical* distances between the polygons will remain unchanged.

Run Test.[24] Suppose we have a sample of N_1 observations which may be called X and a sample of N_2 observations which may be called Y, and wish to test the null hypothesis that the populations from which these samples come have the same distribution. The run test has the property that if the hypothesis tested at level α is true, then the probability of rejecting that hypothesis is α no matter what the form of the common population may be. If on the other hand, the two population distributions differ in *any way whatever*, then the probability of rejection tends to one as the two sample sizes are increased without limit.

The $N_1 + N_2$ observations should be arranged in order of increasing size. A run in the observations so ordered is defined as a sequence of letters of the same kind which cannot be extended by incorporating an adjacent observation. Thus in the 21 observations below (arranged in increasing order) there are 10 runs:

$$\underline{X_1X_2X_3}\ \overline{Y_1}\ \underline{X_4}\ \overline{Y_2Y_3Y_4Y_5}\ \underline{X_5X_6}\ \overline{Y_6}\ \underline{X_7X_8X_9}\ \overline{Y_7}\ \underline{X_{10}X_{11}}\ \overline{Y_8Y_9Y_{10}}$$

The X runs are underlined; the Y runs are overscored. If the two samples are from a common population the X's and Y's will generally be well mixed and the number of runs will be large. If the X population has a much higher median than the Y population, a long run of Y's is to be expected at the left end, a long run of X's at the right end, and consequently, a reduced total number of runs. If the X's come from a population with much greater dispersion, there should be a long run of X's at each end, and consequently a reduced total number of runs. Generally, then, rejection of the null hypothesis will be indicated if the runs are too few in number. Let v represent the number of runs in the sample. If $N_1 > 10$ and $N_2 > 10$, the test of significance is obtained by taking v to be normally distributed with mean

(18.1) $$\mu_v = \frac{2N_1N_2}{N_1 + N_2} + 1, \quad \text{and variance}$$

(18.2) $$\sigma^2_v = \frac{2N_1N_2(2N_1N_2 - N_1 - N_2)}{(N_1 + N_2)^2(N_1 + N_2 - 1)}$$

In the example given, $v = 10$ with $N_1 = 11$ and $N_2 = 10$.

$$\mu_v = 1 + \frac{2(11)(10)}{21} = 11.48$$

$$\sigma_v = \sqrt{\frac{2(11)(10)\{2(11)(10) - 11 - 10\}}{(11 + 10)^2(11 + 10 - 1)}} = \sqrt{4.96} = 2.23$$

and $$z = \frac{v - \mu_v}{\sigma_v} = \frac{10 - 11.48}{2.23} = -.66$$

The null hypothesis is not rejected and the two samples may be regarded as coming from a common population.

Since the test is to be used for continuous variables no ties should appear; if there are a few ties they should be broken at random. Suppose for example that three X's and two Y's are tied at a common value. To determine where the two values of Y are to be placed in this list, enter a table of random numbers, and read down a column until you reach one of the digits 1, 2, 3, 4, or 5. Suppose the digit 3 is reached first and then the digit 1. Then one Y will take position 3 and the other take position 1. The X values will take the remaining positions. Then the set of 5 tied observations is rewritten as $Y\ X\ Y\ X\ X$. If any tied set consists only of X's or only of Y's there is no need to break the tie. An alternative procedure is to break the ties in all possible ways and for each such way to calculate the number of runs and the associated probability, and then to take the average of these probabilities for the probability associated with the sample.

The run test may be used either where the original data are ranks or where the original data have been recorded as measurements and reduced to ranks in order to perform the test.

It is important to note that the run test, being sensitive to *any* kind of difference in the two populations is not a very powerful test of difference in location, that is, a situation in which one population tends to have higher scores or higher ranks than the other. If the investigator wishes to test against a particular kind of alternative (such as difference of means) he should usually use a test designed for this alternative rather than the run test. Several such tests will now be presented.

The Sign Test. The sign test is one of the easiest and most widely applicable of statistical tests. It was used in Chapter 1 of this text. An even number of subjects, say $2N$, is divided into N pairs, the two members of each pair being as similar as possible to each other with respect to certain extraneous variables which are not the subject of investigation, but which may affect the observations. In each pair of subjects, the choice of which member receives experimental condition A is determined by some random device.

If it seems reasonable to assume that differences are normally and independently distributed with common variance and that differences are measured on a scale in which intervals are equal, the mean and standard deviation of the N differences should be computed and a t-test used to test the hypothesis that the mean difference is zero (as was done on page 152). When the investigator cannot make, or prefers to avoid, these assumptions, he may employ the sign test. It tests the hypothesis that the median of the population of differences is zero and makes no assumption about the form of distribution of these differences.

The appropriate statistic is the number of differences which are positive (or the number negative). If the null hypothesis is true, a sample will usually show about $\frac{1}{2}N$ positive and about $\frac{1}{2}N$ negative differences. Clearly the sampling distribution of the statistic $m = Np$ is the binomial distribution $(Q + P)^N$ with $Q = P = .5$.

For samples of $N \leqq 25$ the required probability can be read directly from Table IVB. Suppose d is the number of differences of one sign and $d < \frac{1}{2}N$. For instance suppose there are 5 negative and 14 positive differences in a sample of 19 pairs. In row $N = 19$ and column $m = 5$ of Table IVB the entry is .032. For a two-tailed test, the result would be significant at $\alpha = 2(.032) = .064$.

For larger samples, an approximation to the exact probabilities can be obtained by computing χ^2 with one degree of freedom (corrected for continuity). Both theoretical frequencies are $F_i = \frac{1}{2}N$. The values of f_i are the sample frequencies shifted by .5 toward $\frac{1}{2}N$. If this method had been used for the problem of the preceding paragraph we should have shifted the observed frequencies from 5 and 14 to 5.5 and 13.5; computed $\chi^2 = 3.368$ as indicated; and found $z = \sqrt{3.368} = 1.84$. Referring to a normal

f	F	$\frac{(f-F)^2}{F}$
5.5	9.5	1.684
13.5	9.5	1.684
		$3.368 = \chi^2$

probability table we find that for a two-sided test, this is significant at $\alpha = .066$ which is a good approximation to the exact value previously found. In the case of a one-sided hypothesis it is necessary to remember that rejection of the null hypothesis at level α is in order only when $\chi^2 > \chi^2_{1-\alpha}$ *and* the more frequent sign is opposite to the hypothesized direction. A procedure equivalent to computing χ^2 corrected for continuity is to compute

$$\frac{2m \pm 1}{\sqrt{N}} - \sqrt{N}$$

and to regard it as a normal deviate. The 1 is added or subtracted in such a way as to change $2m$ to a value nearer N. Thus for $m = 5$ and $N = 19$ we should have

$$\frac{2(5) + 1}{\sqrt{19}} - \sqrt{19} = 2.524 - 4.359 = -1.835$$

as before.

The assumptions underlying the test are that the differences are continuously distributed and independent. There is no assumption as to the form of the distribution. In particular nothing analogous to homogeneity of variance is assumed. The sign test is obviously well suited to data for which measurement is difficult but judgment between a pair of objects is possible.

Extension of the Sign Test. If the data are measurements on a scale of equal intervals, certain more general hypotheses may be tested. For example by subtracting a constant C from every difference, that is by taking $d'_i = X_{A_i} - X_{B_i} - C$ we can test the null hypothesis that the median difference $X_A - X_B$ in the population is at least C. The hypothesis is rejected for too many d'_i positive.

If the data are measurements on a scale of equal intervals and if a zero point exists, then by considering the differences

$$d''_i = X_{A_i} - kX_{B_i}$$

we can test the hypothesis

$$H : P(X_A > kX_B) \leqq .5$$

rejecting it for too many d''_i positive. This device can be used only where X is *necessarily* always positive.

As these tests are intended to be used with continuous variables, ties should occur only rarely as a result of approximation in measurement. If a few differences are zero, such pairs are omitted from the sample, since they can give no information for comparing the two experimental conditions.

Signed Rank Test for Paired Observations. Like the sign test, this test can be used when observations are obtained in matched pairs. The hypothesis tested is that the differences between observations are symmetrically distributed around a mean of zero. As before $2N$ subjects are divided into N pairs, the two members of each pair being matched as nearly as possible. In each pair the choice of which member receives experimental condition A is made at random.

The difference between the score under treatment A and the score under treatment B in the ith pair will be denoted

$$d_i = X_{A_i} - X_{B_i}$$

To perform the test rank the d_i in increasing order of absolute magnitude. (Thus in the example which follows the difference $5.4 - 5.3 = .1$ is given rank one because in absolute value it is smaller than any of the other differences). Each rank is then suffixed by the sign of the difference from which it arose. The sum of all the ranks with plus signs will for convenience be called the positive rank sum; the sum of all the ranks with negative signs will be called the negative rank sum. Under the null hypothesis these two rank sums should be about equal. If most of the differences d_i are positive, and the negative ones are small, then the negative rank sum will be small and rejection of the null hypothesis in favor of $E(d_i) > 0$ is invited. A two-sided test requires rejection if *either* rank sum is too small. Table 18.3 gives approximate two-sided significance points for $N \leqq 25$. If more

TABLE 18.3 Significance Points for the Absolute Value of the Smaller Sum of Signed Ranks (T) Obtained from Paired Observations *

N	$\alpha = .05$	$\alpha = .02$	$\alpha = .01$
6	0	–	–
7	2	0	–
8	4	2	0
9	6	3	2
10	8	5	3
11	11	7	5
12	14	10	7
13	17	13	10
14	21	16	13
15	25	20	16
16	30	24	20
17	35	28	23
18	40	33	28
19	46	38	32
20	52	43	38
21	59	49	43
22	66	56	49
23	73	62	55
24	81	69	61
25	89	77	68

* From Wilcoxon [26] by permission of the author and the American Cyanamid Company

than 25 pairs are involved, then T, the absolute value of the smaller rank sum is approximately normally distributed with

$$\mu_T = \frac{N(N+1)}{4} \tag{18.3}$$

(18.4) and
$$\sigma_T = \sqrt{\frac{(2N+1)(N)(N+1)}{24}}$$

The following example will serve to illustrate the computations for the signed rank test:

Pair	X_A	X_B	$d = X_A - X_B$	Rank of d	Signed rank
1	7.6	7.3	.3	3	3
2	6.3	5.7	.5	4	4
3	10.3	10.5	− .2	2	2 −
4	6.2	4.7	1.5	8	8
5	5.4	5.3	.1	1	1
6	9.3	8.9	1.1	6	6
7	10.0	9.1	.9	5	5
8	8.4	7.0	1.4	7	7

Positive rank sum = 34; Negative rank sum = 2; Smaller rank sum is $T = 2$.

e 18.3 we find that a T of 4 or less is significant at ; the two-sided hypothesis $E(d) = 0$. If our hypothesis $\leqq 0$ then a negative rank total of 4 or less is significant)25 (approximately).

ı **of Ranks.** The statistical procedure to be described can be used to test the hypothesis that the N_1 values of X he N_2 values of Y are samples from a common population. It is sometimes called a test of difference in location. It guards against the one-sided alternatives $P(X > Y) < \frac{1}{2}$ or $P(X > Y) > \frac{1}{2}$, or against the two-sided alternative $P(X > Y) \neq \frac{1}{2}$.

Consider the two samples shown here, with $N_1 = 9$ and $N_2 = 8$.

Group I		Group II	
Score X	Rank	Score Y	Rank
11.5	3	15.2	7
12.6	5	8.6	1
19.4	13	9.3	2
21.3	14	14.4	6
32.5	17	15.6	8
18.6	12	11.8	4
17.0	10	16.3	9
23.4	15	17.8	11
29.6	16		
	$R_1 = 105$		$R_2 = 48$

As a first step, ranks from least to greatest have been assigned to the entire $N = N_1 + N_2 = 17$ scores and the sum of the ranks obtained for each group separately. The sum of ranks for group i will be denoted R_i. As a check, it should be noted that $R_1 + R_2$ must equal $\frac{N(N+1)}{2}$. In this case

$$\frac{N(N+1)}{2} = \frac{17(18)}{2} = 153 \quad \text{and} \quad 105 + 48 = 153.$$

If N_1 and N_2 are each as large as 8, or larger, the statistic

$$\frac{2R_i - N_i(N+1)}{\sqrt{\frac{N_1N_2(N+1)}{3}}} \tag{18.5}$$

has a distribution which is approximately unit normal. If R_i is taken from the first sample we have

$$z = \frac{2(105) - 9(18)}{\sqrt{\frac{9(8)(18)}{3}}} = \frac{210 - 162}{\sqrt{432}} = \frac{48}{20.8} = 2.31.$$

If R_1 is taken from the second sample we have

$$z = \frac{2(48) - 8(18)}{\sqrt{\frac{8(9)(18)}{3}}} = \frac{96 - 144}{\sqrt{432}} = -\frac{48}{20.8} = -2.31.$$

For a two-sided test, this would be significant at

$$\alpha = 2(.0104) = .021,$$

and for a one-sided test, at level $\alpha = .0104$. If the null hypothesis states that the X-median is not greater than the Y-median we should reject only when R_2 is significantly large (that is, R_1 is small), and vice versa.

If the number in either sample is small, a table [24] may be used to obtain exact probabilities.

This test was proposed by Wilcoxon [25] in the situation in which $N_1 = N_2$ and exact probabilities given for small samples. It has since been derived by several other people and is usually known as the Mann-Whitney Test.[10]

Median Test for Two Samples. An even simpler test than that based on ranks is arrived at by merely classifying all scores as being above or not above the median of the combined samples. (When $N = N_1 + N_2$ is an odd number one of the scores is the median, and this median score will fall into the class of scores "not above the median.") A contingency table is now set up and χ^2 computed, or if the number of cases is small the exact probability may be computed by the method described on page 102.

	Group I	Group II	Total
Above median	7	1	8
Not above median	2	7	9
	9	8	17

The data of the preceding paragraph with 16.3 as median of the combined sample produce the contingency table shown here. For samples as small as this, Fisher's exact method described on page 103 must be used. For large enough frequencies χ^2 corrected for continuity is the test statistic.

B. Comparison of k Samples

Median Test for k Samples. This test is a natural extension of the two-sample test described in the preceding paragraph.

Suppose that 28 subjects are divided at random into 5 groups A, B, C, D, and E, and each group is afforded a different motivating rationale for excelling in a maze test. They are then given the same maze test and the time required for completion is recorded. Let the time in seconds be:

A	B	C	D	E
18.1	16.7	24.7	18.2	12.4
24.0	17.4	36.5	25.9	18.8
31.7	22.4	42.1	27.0	19.3
32.3	27.1	43.2	36.6	22.5
35.5	35.8	48.7	37.6	35.1
46.2		50.4	39.8	

The grand median is found to lie between 27.1 and 31.7, therefore 4 observations in group A are greater than this median, which we call $X_{.50}$. In group B only one observation is greater than $X_{.50}$. Continuing in this way we arrive at the following summary:

	A	B	C	D	E	
Above $X_{.50}$	4	1	5	3	1	14
Below $X_{.50}$	2	4	1	3	4	14
N_i	6	5	6	6	5	

The data exhibit some discrepancy from what might be expected under the null hypothesis. To assess whether the discrepancy is significant we may treat the data as a contingency table and compute χ^2 from the frequencies (which are large enough in this example to justify that procedure). The value of χ^2 with 4 degrees of freedom is 6.93 which is not large enough to be significant even at level $\alpha = .10$; so the null hypothesis is not rejected.

If N, the number of observations in all k samples taken together, is odd then one of the observations will be $X_{.50}$. Consider that observation as being below the median.

This test is based upon the assumption that all populations have the same form of distribution. It is believed, however, that the test is not sensitive to differences in population form.

Sum of Ranks for Comparing *k* Samples. This extension of the two sample comparison by ranks to problems in which there are k samples is due to Kruskal and Wallis.[9] The samples are merged and a rank of 1 assigned to the lowest score, 2 to the next lowest, and so on. Then the sum of the ranks is found for each of the k samples. Let N_i be the number of observations in the

ith sample; R_i the sum of the ranks assigned to the observations in that sample; and $N = \sum_{1}^{k} N_i$. The test statistic to be computed if there are no ties is

$$(18.6) \qquad H = \frac{12}{N(N+1)} \sum_{1}^{k} \frac{R^2_i}{N_i} - 3(N+1)$$

If there are ties in rank because two or more observations are equal, each observation is given the mean of the ranks which those observations would have received had there been no ties, and H is divided by

$$(18.7) \qquad 1 - \frac{\Sigma T}{N(N^2-1)}$$

If t is the number of observations in one tied set, $T = (t-1)t(t+1)$ for that set. ΣT is taken over all groups of ties.

If the k samples come from identical populations, and the N's are not very small, H is distributed approximately as χ^2 with

TABLE 18.4 Computation of Analysis of Variance by Ranks (One Criterion of Classification)

	Rank of Individual									
	A		B		C		D		E	
	Score	Rank	Score	Rank	Score	Rank	Score	Rank	Score	Rank
	18.1	4	16.7	2	24.7	11	18.2	5	12.4	1
	24.0	10	17.4	3	36.5	20	25.9	12	18.8	6
	31.7	15	22.4	8	42.1	24	27.0	13	19.3	7
	32.3	16	27.1	14	43.2	25	36.6	21	22.5	9
	35.5	18	35.8	19	48.7	27	37.6	22	35.1	17
	46.2	26			50.4	28	39.8	23		
R_i		89		46		135		96		40
N_i		6		5		6		6		5

A check is provided by the relation $\sum_{1}^{k} R_i = \frac{N(N+1)}{2}$

$$89 + 46 + 135 + 96 + 40 = 406$$

$$\text{and } \frac{28(29)}{2} = 406$$

$$H = \frac{12}{28(29)} \left\{ \frac{89^2}{6} + \frac{46^2}{5} + \frac{135^2}{6} + \frac{96^2}{6} + \frac{40^2}{5} \right\} - 3(29) = 11.1$$

and for 4 degrees of freedom $\chi^2_{.975} = 11.1$

$k - 1$ degrees of freedom. The hypothesis is rejected for large values of H.

By way of illustration let ranks be assigned to the data of the preceding section for the times required for running a maze under the various motivations A, B, C, D, and E. The ranks and the sum of the ranks for the five groups would be as in Table 18.4.

This result differs from the non-significant result obtained with the median test. This is not particularly surprising. The present procedure employing ranks utilizes the magnitudes of the observations more fully and so may be expected to be somewhat more sensitive than a procedure which merely classifies observations as above or not above the median.

Analysis of Variance by Ranks. The analysis of variance by ranks is a very easy procedure and does not depend on assumptions of normality or of homogeneity of variance. It has the further advantage of enabling data which are inherently only ranks to be examined for significance. If the Wallis-Kruskal H test is parallel to the one-way analysis of variance, then a test due to Friedmann is parallel to randomized blocks.[4]

Suppose each of m subjects is measured under each of p situations (or p treatments); or each of m groups takes each of p tests. In such situations, it is often not reasonable to assume homogeneity of variance.

TABLE 18.5 Analysis of Variance with Ranked Data. Two-way Classification

Subject	Score under Treatment					Rank of Treatment				
	A	B	C	D	E	A	B	C	D	E
1	11	14	13	9	20	4	2	3	5	1
2	12	11	13	10	18	3	4	2	5	1
3	15	19	8	6	25	3	2	4	5	1
4	9	11	14	10	16	5	3	2	4	1
T_i = Total						15	11	11	19	4

The p treatments are ranked for each subject, and the ranks summed for all subjects as in Table 18.5. The correctness of the totals may be checked by noting that their sum must be $\dfrac{mp(p+1)}{2}$, which for Table 18.5 is $\dfrac{4(5)(5+1)}{2} = 60$. If the treatments are not very different, the rank totals may be expected to turn out about equal. In the present example there seems to be a marked disparity. To evaluate its significance we compute the statistic

$$\chi^2_r = \frac{12}{mp(p+1)} \Sigma T^2_r - 3m(p+1) \tag{18.8}$$

which has approximately the χ^2 distribution with $p - 1$ degrees of freedom. χ^2_r is identically equal to $m(p - 1)W$ where W is the coefficient of concordance discussed on page 284. For the data of Table 18.5, $m = 4$, $p = 5$ and

$$\chi^2_r = \frac{12}{4(5)(6)} (15^2 + 11^2 + 11^2 + 19^2 + 4^2) - 3(4)(6)$$

$$= 84.4 - 72 = 12.4$$

For 4 degrees of freedom this is significant at the .01 level.

Actually the values of m and p in this example are so small that the χ^2 distribution evaluates the significance somewhat roughly. In fact, the 1% point for the test statistic with $m = 4$, $p = 5$, is 10.93; thus the use of the χ^2 table here introduces a certain distortion. Generally, if $p > 7$ and $m \geqq 6$ the χ^2 approximation will be quite adequate. For values below this a set of data may be more significant than the test indicates. If the sample sizes are such that $3p + m \geqq 20$, whether or not they are large enough for the χ^2 approximation to serve, another approximation serves well to evaluate the significance of the statistic χ^2_r. We may take

$$F = \frac{(m-1)\chi^2_r}{m(p-1) - \chi^2_r} \tag{18.9}$$

to be distributed as F with

(18.10) $n_1 = p - 1 - \dfrac{2}{m}$ degrees of freedom for the numerator

(18.11) and

$n_2 = (m - 1)\left(p - 1 - \dfrac{2}{m}\right)$ degrees of freedom for the denominator

These degrees of freedom are not integers and interpolation in the F table may be necessary. In the foregoing example

$$F = \frac{3(12.4)}{4(4) - 12.4} = \frac{37.2}{3.6} = 10.3$$

$$n_1 = 5 - 1 - \tfrac{2}{4} = 3.5$$

$$n_2 = 3(3.5) = 10.5$$

In this example, as in many cases, interpolation is not necessary, since the obtained F is larger than $F_{.99}$ for $n_1 = 3$ and $n_2 = 10$, and is of necessity larger than $F_{.99}$ for $n_1 = 3.5$ and $n_2 = 10.5$.

C. Confidence Intervals

Confidence Interval for the Median. In Chapter 16 a formula for the standard error of the median was given. This standard error may be used to determine a confidence interval for the median when the form of population distribution can be assumed as known. We shall now describe a method for computing a confidence interval for the median when no assumption can be made about the form of parent population.

The confidence interval can be developed from the simple notion that a random observation is as likely to exceed the population median as to be less than that median. All observations in a continuous population may be considered as falling in one of two classes (smaller than median, not smaller) with a probability of .5 for each class. For a sample of observations from any population, the number of observations above (or below) the median will have the binomial distribution described in Chapter 2, with $P = .5$.

Suppose for simplicity that a sample of two observations is to be drawn, the smaller being denoted X_1, and the larger X_2. Then the probability that both X_1 and X_2 will be less than the population median is $(.5)(.5) = .25$. Also the probability that both observations will exceed the median is .25. The remaining alternative is that one observation will exceed and the other be less than the median, and this situation has probability .5. In other words, the probability that two random observations will include the population median between them is .50.

The corresponding computation for a larger number of cases will be described in relation to the 11 archery scores of Table 9.8, in the column headed First Order. Arranged in ascending order these scores are 33, 51, 66, 71, 78, 80, 99, 105, 114, 134, 146.

Let the observations in ascending order be denoted

$$X_1 < X_2 < X_3 \ldots X_9 < X_{10} < X_{11}$$

The probability that m observations in a sample of 11 cases will be smaller than the population median $\xi_{.50}$ is given by the appropriate entry in row $N = 11$ of Table IVB. In the column headed 1, the entry .006 is the probability that 0 or 1 observation but not more than 1 will be less than $\xi_{.50}$. Similarly in the column 9 the entry

.994 is the probability that 9 or fewer observations will be less than $\xi_{.50}$. Hence for any sample of 11 cases

$$P(X_2 < \xi_{.50} < X_{10}) = .994 - .006 = .988$$

Applied to the 11 observed archery scores, this probability becomes the confidence interval

$$C(51 < \xi_{.50} < 134) = .988$$

The reader may verify by similar methods that

$$P(X_3 < \xi_{.50} < X_9 \mid N = 11) = .934$$
$$P(X_4 < \xi_{.50} < X_8 \mid N = 11) = .774$$

and for the 11 archery scores

$$C(66 < \xi_{.50} < 114) = .934$$
$$C(71 < \xi_{.50} < 105) = .774$$

Table IVB is useful for samples of 25 or fewer. For larger samples we use the normal approximation to the binomial with mean $= NP = .5N$ and standard deviation $\sqrt{NPQ} = .5\sqrt{N}$. We take the integer next larger than $z_{1-\frac{1}{2}\alpha}\,(.5\sqrt{N})$ and count that many observations to the left and to the right from the sample median. The observations thus reached are the limits of a confidence interval with coefficient $1 - \alpha$ or larger. Thus if $\alpha = .05$ and $N = 36$ the sample median lies between X_{18} and X_{19}, and

$$z_{1-\frac{1}{2}\alpha}\,(.5\sqrt{N}) = 5.88$$

Counting off 6 observations each way from the median produces the interval $X_{12} < \xi_{.50} < X_{25}$.

Kolmogorov-Smirnov Confidence Band for Cumulative Frequency. From the cumulative percentage distribution of a sample this method enables one to draw a confidence band for the cumulative percentage distribution of the population.[1, 11] For example consider a sample of 10 observations:

9.1, 10.3, 11.6, 12.4, 12.5, 13.0, 13.6, 14.2, 16.1, and 18.7

The cumulative percentage distribution for these is shown by the solid line in Figure 18–1. In order to construct a band such that the cumulative population distribution can with confidence $1 - \alpha$ be asserted to lie within it, we enter Table 18.5 with N = number of cases in the sample and obtain a value of ND_α. In the row $N = 10$ and column $\alpha = .01$ we find $ND_\alpha = 5$ or $D_\alpha = .5$. Then one dotted line is drawn parallel to the sample line in Figure 18–1 and 0.5 above it; a second dotted line is drawn parallel to the sample

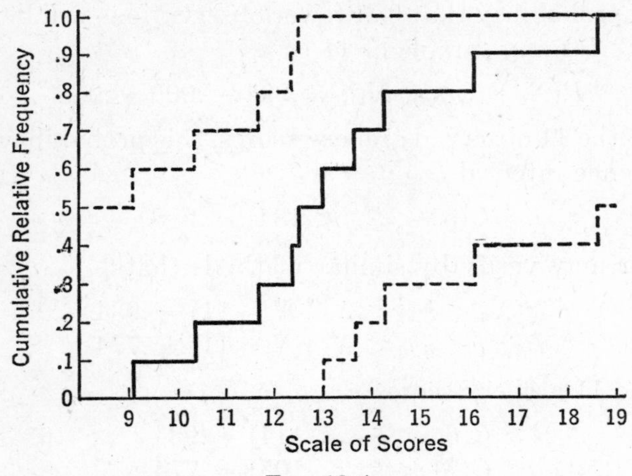

FIG. 18–1

line and 0.5 below it. We may now assert with confidence .99 that the cumulative percentage distribution for the population from which our sample was drawn lies inside the band bounded by these dotted lines.

TABLE 18.5 Values of ND_α.* D_α = Smallest absolute discrepancy between an observed and hypothetical frequency distribution which will cause rejection of hypothesis at significance level α

N	$\alpha \leqq .05$	$\alpha \leqq .03$	$\alpha \leqq .01$	N	$\alpha \leqq .05$	$\alpha \leqq .03$	$\alpha \leqq .01$
8		4	5	41	9	10	11
9	4		5	42–47		10	11
10			5	48		11	12
11–12		5	6	49		10	12
13–14	5		6	50–56	10	11	12
15–18		6	7	57–59		11	13
19	6		7	60–65	11	12	13
20–21	6	7	8	66–67	11	12	14
22–24		7	8	68–70		12	14
25	7		8	71–76	12	13	14
26–28	7	8	9	84–87	13	14	15
29–31		8	9	88–91	13	14	16
32	8		9	92–94	13	14	
33–36	8	9	10	95		14	
37–40		9	10	96–100	14	15	

* Abstracted from Birnbaum[1]

The same method affords a test of goodness of fit. If the cumulative distribution function specified by some hypothesis about the population lies entirely within the confidence band constructed with confidence coefficient $1 - \alpha$ around the sample distribution, then the hypothesis is not rejected. If at any point the hypothetical curve lies outside the band, the hypothesis is rejected at level α.

Comparison of Kolmogorov-Smirnov Method with χ^2. The χ^2 goodness of fit test, which is also non-parametric, is applicable to either continuous or discrete variables; the Kolmogorov-Smirnov test may be applied only to continuous variables. The χ^2 test can be applied where only the *form* of the distribution is hypothesized and some parameters remain to be estimated from the sample; the K–S test can be used only where the hypothesis specifies the hypothetical distribution *completely*, giving the form and the numerical values of all parameters of the distribution. The K–S test can be used as in the illustration, with samples too small to justify the χ^2 test. The K–S test requires less computation than the χ^2 test. Finally, where the Kolmogorov-Smirnov test is applicable, there are good reasons to believe it is a more sensitive test than the χ^2 test.

Confidence Interval for $\mu_x - \mu_y$. If the distributions of two populations can be assumed to have the same shape, differing only by translation, then a confidence interval for the amount of translation, that is $\mu_x - \mu_y$, can be constructed by graphical methods.

Let the scores in one sample be denoted $X_1, X_2, \ldots X_{N_1}$ and in the other $Y_1, Y_2 \ldots Y_{N_2}$. It is convenient though not necessary to have all scores positive with the smallest not much greater than zero. To make this transformation, add a constant (positive or negative as may be necessary) to each of the $N_1 + N_2$ scores. On graph paper, plot the new X-values along the horizontal and the new Y-values along the vertical axis. Place a dot at the point determined by each (X, Y) pair of values. There will be N_1N_2 such points.

If a 45° line were drawn through the origin, all points to the right of that line would have $X > Y$ and all points to the left have $Y > X$. Instead of a 45° line through the origin, two 45° lines will be drawn so that a predetermined number of points will lie outside them. The X-values of the intersections of these lines with the horizontal axis will provide the limits of the confidence interval. If N_1 and N_2 are both 8 or more and α is not small (e.g., .01 with $N_1, N_2 \geqq 8$ or .001 with $N_1, N_2 \geqq 15$) the number of points outside the pair of lines on each side is

$$(18.12)\qquad U = \frac{1}{2}\left\{N_1N_2 + z_{\frac{1}{2}\alpha}\sqrt{\frac{N_1N_2(N_1+N_2+1)}{3}}\right\}$$

After U has been computed, take a 45° drawing triangle and construct a line at an angle of 45° to the axes, having U of the (X,Y) points above it and passing through the $(U+1)$st point, counting from the left. Construct a second 45° line having U of the plotted points below it and passing through the $(U+1)$st point counting from the right. The intersections of these lines with the horizontal (or with the vertical) axis give the confidence interval.

As an example, consider the data previously used in the discussion of *sum of ranks* with $N_1 = 9$, and $N_2 = 8$.

X: 11.5, 12.6, 19.4, 21.3, 32.5, 18.6, 17.0, 23.4, and 29.6

Y: 15.2, 8.6, 9.3, 14.4, 15.6, 11.8, 16.3, 17.8

We shall find the 95% confidence interval and also for purposes of illustration the 99.9% interval for $\mu_x - \mu_y$.

The first step is to subtract 8 from each observation; to plot the resulting values of X on the horizontal axis and Y on the vertical and to mark the 72 (X,Y) points. The purpose of subtracting 8 is merely to produce a more compact chart, with plotted points nearer to the origin. The second step is to compute

$$U = \frac{1}{2}\left\{8(9) - 1.96\sqrt{\frac{8(9)(18)}{3}}\right\} = 15.6$$

On the diagram two lines are drawn each excluding 15 points and passing through the 16th. (The line at the right passes through both the 16th and 17th points.) These are the solid lines in Figure 18–2. They intersect the horizontal axis at 1.4 and 10.0, so we write

$$C\{1.4 \leqq \mu_x - \mu_y \leqq 10.0\} = .95$$

If α is very small Formula (18.12) is inadequate. Then we read from White's tables[24] the sum of ranks R which is significantly small at level α. From this value of R, the number of points to be excluded by each 45° line is computed as

$$(18.13)\qquad U = R - \frac{N_i(N_i+1)}{2}$$

where N_i is the number of cases in the smaller sample. For an interval with confidence coefficient .999, $\alpha = .001$ and White's table shows $R = 40$ if $N_1 = 9$ and $N_2 = 8$. Then $U = 40 - 36 = 4$.

The dashed lines in Figure 18–2 correspond to this value. The line at the left excludes four points and passes through the fifth and sixth. The lower line excludes four points and passes through the fifth. In this case the lower line intersects the x-axis at 14.7, and the upper line intersects the y-axis at 3.7; it is clear that this line if extended intersects the x-axis at $-$ 3.7. We therefore write:

$$.999 = C\{-3.9 \leqq \mu_x - \mu_y \leqq 14.7\}$$

The justification of this procedure rests on the Mann-Whitney test which is described on page 434.

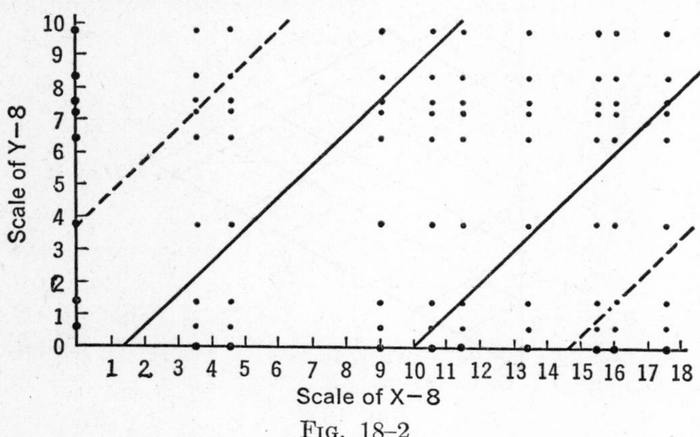

Fig. 18–2

Graphic Method of Obtaining Confidence Interval for $E(d)$. This convenient procedure devised by John Tukey (unpublished paper) is related to the signed rank test for paired comparisons described on page 432. The underlying assumption is that the distribution of X_{A_i} and of X_{B_i} differ only by translation.

The differences $d_i = X_{A_i} - X_{B_i}$ (taken *with regard to sign*) are denoted by heavy dots on a vertical scale as in Figure 18–3, the top point being here marked B and the bottom C. A point midway between B and C is found and marked A. On the horizontal line through A a point D is marked at some convenient distance. The line segments BD and CD form an isosceles triangle. Through each dot on the line BC one line is drawn parallel to CD and another parallel to BD. Each intersection (including those on the vertical scale) is marked with a heavy dot. The number of such dots is $N(N + 1)/2$.

This construction is simplified either by use of triangular coordinate paper or by choosing D with the aid of a draftsman's triangle in such a way as to facilitate constructing the parallel lines with the same triangle.

The confidence interval will be an interval on the vertical scale. To find it, read from Table 18.3, T_r, the largest significant value for T, which is the absolute value of the smaller rank sum. To this value add 1. In the example on page 433 which has been used for Figure 18–3, $T_r = 4$, and $T_r + 1 = 5$. Find the $(T_r + 1)$st dot (which in Figure 18–3 is the 5th) from the top and draw a horizontal line through it. Indicate the intersection of this horizontal line with the vertical scale as U.* Now find the $(T_r + 1)$st dot from the bottom, draw a horizontal line through it, and indicate the intersection of this line with the vertical as L. The points U and L are then the endpoints of the confidence interval. In Figure 18–3 these points have scale values 1.25 and .15. Therefore we can write

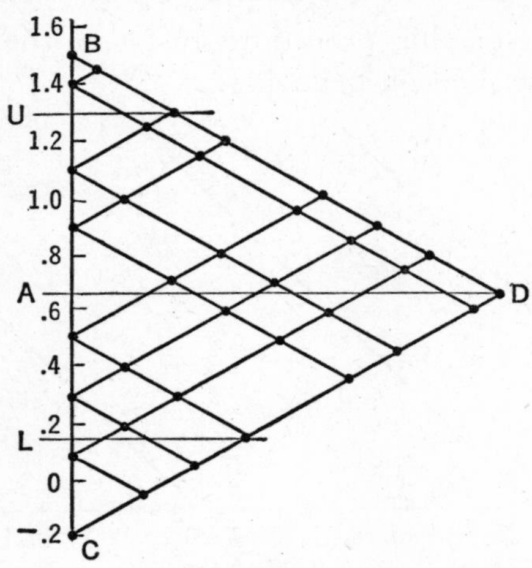

Fig. 18–3

$$C(.15 < E(d) < 1.25) = 1 - .05 = .95$$

D. Tests of Independence

Where each observation consists of a pair of values — say a measurement of intelligence and one of scholastic achievement, we may ask, "Are the two qualities interrelated, or independent of one another?" The student is well acquainted with numerous attacks on this problem. If the population of measurements on the two variables is bivariate normal then the product moment correlation coefficient, r, and the tests of significance discussed in Chapter 10 are appropriate.

* Upper horizontal line has been incorrectly drawn through 4th instead of 5th point.

If less is known about the form of the parent population, or if the population is known not to be bivariate normal, the scores may be replaced by their ranks and Spearman's rank correlation coefficient, R_s, or Kendall's τ (page 286) may be calculated and tested for significance. With fairly large samples confidence intervals may be obtained for τ. Finally, χ^2 provides a test of independence. This test may be readily applied to a bivariate distribution by dividing the scatter-diagram into 4 quadrants by lines drawn through the medians of the two variables. The χ^2 test is then applied to the numbers of scores in the quadrants. The data need not even be of the sort which permit ranking, but may be strictly categorical. For example, the characteristics "Favorite sport" and "Occupation" may or may not be related. Any statistical test of their independence will have to be one which does not rely on order. These three methods (R_s, τ, and χ^2) all provide well-known distribution-free tests of the null hypothesis of independence between two qualities or characteristics.

Corner Test of Association. There is another test of independence which is untuitively appealing and easy to perform, having as its chief drawback the necessity of drawing a scatter diagram.[17] It has the practical advantage that no tables are necessary for evaluating significance. The test essentially ignores the mass of data near the center of the scatter diagram and is based on those observations at the periphery. If association of one variable with another *in the extreme cases* is of central interest then there is probably no more suitable test known.

The application of the procedure is made clear by considering an example. Suppose that 18 subjects have the following scores on a scale of ethnocentrism (X) and of verbal intelligence (Y):

Y	32	36	32	37	41	18	43	27	49	47	28	32	46	32	22	45	40	29
X	−.1	1.2	1.9	.1	.8	−.1	1.4	1.2	−.4	2.5	−.3	1.1	.2	.6	.2	.9	−.4	.6

Ethnocentrism Score. The points are plotted in a scatter-diagram and then a horizontal line is drawn through the Y median ($Y_{.50} = 34$) and a vertical line through the X median ($X_{.50} = .4$). Then the line L_1 is obtained by placing a ruler horizontally at the top of the diagram and moving it down until a point is reached which lies on the opposite side of the X median from the topmost point. The number of points above the line L_1 is called r_1. If these points (there is one in the diagram) lie in the first quadrant, r_1 is recorded with a plus sign; if they lie in the second quadrant, with a minus sign. The line L_2 is then located by moving a vertically placed ruler in from the right hand edge until a point is reached on the opposite side of the Y median from the point farthest to the right. The number of points to the right of L_2 is called r_2. In the example $r_2 = 1$, and a plus sign is affixed because the point is in the first quadrant. The lines L_3 and L_4 are similarly constructed, and r_3 and r_4 are found by counting. Points in the first and third quadrants are counted positively; points in the

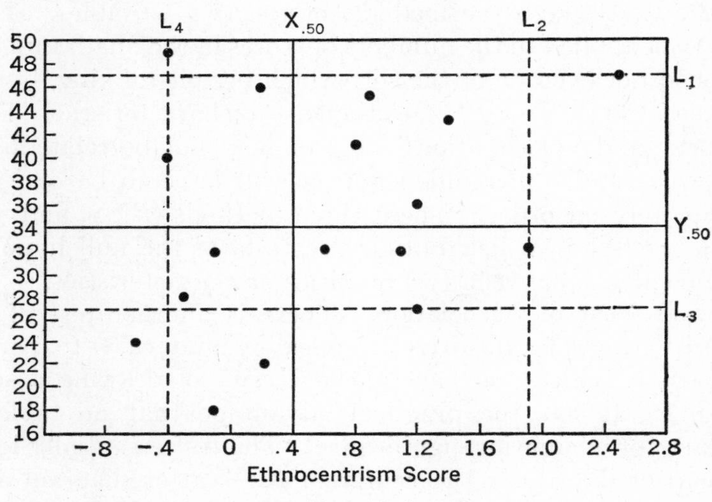

FIG. 18–4

second and fourth quadrants are counted negatively. The algebraic sum $r = r_1 + r_2 + r_3 + r_4$ is the test statistic. Provided $N \geqq 10$ the null hypothesis of independence is rejected at the 5% level if r exceeds 11 in absolute value, and at the 1% level if r exceeds 14 in absolute value. In the present case the null hypothesis is not rejected since $r = -1 + 1 + 3 + 1 = 4$ only.

If the number of cases is not an even number then each median line will pass through a point. If it is the same point it may be omitted. Otherwise the two points, one lying on the X median line and the other on the Y median line, are removed and one new point is added; it has the X coordinate of the point which lay on the Y median and the Y coordinate of the other. Then the test is carried out as before.

The test is designed for use with continuous populations so ties should not arise. If a small number of ties do appear, however, they will require special treatment. If two points (or four, or six, etc.) lie on, say, the X median line, then the first is displaced slightly to right or left (choose the direction at random) and the other is slightly displaced in the opposite direction. Similar instructions apply to pairs of points lying on the Y median line. If in constructing one of the L lines one encounters a set of tied observations, he draws the line through them all but takes for the contribution to r_1 a number (which may be a fraction):

$$\frac{n_s}{n_0 + 1}$$

where n_s is the number of the observations in the tied set which are on the *same* side of the median as the initial point, and n_0 the number of them on the *opposite* side.

It is clear that the test depends chiefly on the extreme observations and depends upon the degree to which the data are concentrated in diagonally opposite corners. A study of the diagram shows that a point (such as the one in the lower left-hand corner) which is an extreme deviate on both the X and Y scales is counted twice. This test does not depend on scaling of the values for X and Y; only the *relative order positions* of the X's and Y's are utilized. At the same time the procedure does not yield an index which measures degree of association in the way that the correlation coefficient does.

REFERENCES

1. Birnbaum, Z. W., "Numerical Tabulation of the Distribution of Kolmogorov's Statistic for Finite Sample Size," *Journal of the American Statistical Association* 47 (1952), 425–441.
2. Dixon, W. J. and Mood, A. M., "The Statistical Sign Test," *Journal of the American Statistical Association* 41 (1946), 557–566.
3. Dixon, W. J. and Massey, F. J., *An Introduction to Statistical Analysis*, New York, 1951, McGraw-Hill Book Co., Chapter 17.
4. Friedman, Milton, "The Use of Ranks to Avoid the Assumption of Normality," *Journal of the American Statistical Association* 32 (1937), 675–701.
5. Friedman, Milton, "A Comparison of Alternative Tests of Significance for the Problem of *m* Rankings," *Annals of Mathematical Statistics* 11 (1940), 86–92.
6. Kendall, M. G. and Smith, B. B., "The Problem of *m* Rankings," *Annals of Mathematical Statistics* 10 (1939), 275–287.
7. Kendall, M. G., *The Advanced Theory of Statistics*, I, London, 1945, 388–421.
8. Kendall, M. G., *Rank Correlation Methods*, London, 1948, Charles Griffin and Co., Ltd.
9. Kruskal, Wm. H. and Wallis, W. A., "Use of Ranks in One-Criterion Variance Analysis," *Journal of the American Statistical Association* 47 (1952), 583–621.
10. Mann, H. B. and Whitney, D. R., "On a Test of Whether One of Two Random Variables is Stochastically Larger than the Other," *Annals of Mathematical Statistics* 18 (1947), 50–60.

11. Massey, F. J., Jr., "The Kolmogorov-Smirnov Test for Goodness of Fit," *Journal of the American Statistical Association* 46 (1951), 68–78.
12. Massey, F. J., Jr., "The Distribution of the Maximum Deviation between Two Sample Cumulative Step Functions," *Annals of Mathematical Statistics* 22 (1951), 125–128.
13. Massey, F. J., Jr., "A Note on a Two-sample Test," *Annals of Mathematical Statistics* 22 (1951), 304–306.
14. Mood, A. M., *Introduction to the Theory of Statistics*, New York, 1950, McGraw-Hill Book Co., Chapter 16.
15. Moore, G. H. and Wallis, W. A., "Time Series Significance Tests Based on Signs of Differences," *Journal of the American Statistical Association* 38 (1943), 153–164.
16. Moses, Lincoln, "Non-Parametric Statistics for Psychological Research," *Psychological Bulletin* 49 (1952), 122–143.
17. Olmstead, P. S. and Tukey, J. W., "A Corner Test for Association," *Annals of Mathematical Statistics* 18 (1947), 495–513.
18. Pitman, E. J. G., "Significance Tests which may be Applied to Samples from any Population," *Supplement to the Journal of the Royal Statistical* 4 (1937), 117–130, 225–232.
19. Pitman, E. J. G., "Significance Tests which may be Applied to Samples from any Population, III. The Analysis of Variance Test," *Biometrika* 29 (1938), 322–335.
20. Scheffé, Henry, "Statistical Inference in the Non-Parametric Case," *Annals of Mathematical Statistics* 14 (1943), 305–332.
21. Smirnov, N., "Table for Estimating the Goodness of Fit of Empirical Distributions," *Annals of Mathematical Statistics* 19 (1948), 279–281.
22. Wald, A. and Wolfowitz, J., "Statistical Tests Based on Permutations of the Observations," *Annals of Mathematical Statistics* 15 (1944), 358–372.
23. Wallis, W. A., "Rough and Ready Statistical Tests," *Industrial Quality Control* 8 (1952), 35–40.
24. White, Colin, "The Use of Ranks in a Test of Significance for Comparing Two Treatments," *Biometrics* 8 (1952), 33–41.
25. Wilcoxon, Frank, "Individual Comparisons by Ranking Methods," *Biometrics Bulletin* 1 (1945), 80–82.
26. Wilcoxon, Frank, *Some Rapid Approximate Statistical Procedures*, Stamford, Conn., 1949, American Cyanimid Co.

Appendix

Tables and Charts in the Appendix

TABLE I Areas Under the Unit Normal Curve

z_α	$z_{1-\alpha}$	α	$1-\alpha$	2α	z_α	$z_{1-\alpha}$	α	$1-\alpha$	2α
0	0	.500	.500	1.000	− 2.1	2.1	.018	.982	.036
− .1	.1	.460	.540	.920	− 2.2	2.2	.014	.986	.028
− .2	.2	.421	.579	.841	− 2.3	2.3	.011	.989	.021
− .3	.3	.382	.618	.764	− 2.4	2.4	.008	.992	.016
− .4	.4	.345	.655	.689	− 2.5	2.5	.006	.994	.012
− .5	.5	.309	.691	.617	− 2.6	2.6	.005	.995	.009
− .6	.6	.274	.726	.549	− 2.7	2.7	.003	.997	.007
− .7	.7	.242	.758	.484	− 2.8	2.8	.003	.997	.005
− .8	.8	.212	.788	.424	− 2.9	2.9	.002	.998	.004
− .9	.9	.184	.816	.368	− 3.0	3.0	.00135	.99865	.00270
− 1.0	1.0	.159	.841	.317	− 3.1	3.1	.00097	.99903	.00194
− 1.1	1.1	.136	.864	.271	− 3.2	3.2	.00069	.99931	.00137
− 1.2	1.2	.115	.885	.230	− 3.3	3.3	.00048	.99952	.00097
− 1.3	1.3	.097	.903	.194	− 3.4	3.4	.00034	.99966	.00067
− 1.4	1.4	.081	.919	.162	− 3.5	3.5	.00023	.99977	.00047
− 1.5	1.5	.067	.933	.134	− 3.6	3.6	.00016	.99984	.00032
− 1.6	1.6	.055	.945	.110	− 3.7	3.7	.00011	.99989	.00022
− 1.7	1.7	.045	.955	.089	− 3.8	3.8	.00007	.99993	.00014
− 1.8	1.8	.036	.964	.072	− 3.9	3.9	.00005	.99995	.00010
− 1.9	1.9	.029	.971	.057	− 4.0	4.0	.00003	.99997	.00006
− 2.0	2.0	.023	.977	.046					

TABLE II Percentile Values of the Unit Normal Curve *

Area to the left of z	z	Area to the left of z	z	Area to the left of z	z	Area to the left of z	z	Area to the left of z	z
.0001	− 3.719	.045	− 1.695	.280	− .583	.700	.524	.950	1.645
.0002	− 3.540	.050	− 1.645	.300	− .524	.720	.583	.955	1.695
.0003	− 3.432	.055	− 1.598	.320	− .468	.740	.643	.960	1.751
.0004	− 3.353	.060	− 1.555	.340	− .412	.750	.6745	.965	1.812
.0005	− 3.291	.065	− 1.514	.360	− .358	.760	.706	.970	1.881
.001	− 3.090	.070	− 1.476	.380	− .305	.780	.772	.975	1.960
.002	− 2.878	.075	− 1.440	.400	− .253	.800	.842	.980	2.054
.003	− 2.748	.080	− 1.405	.420	− .202	.820	.915	.985	2.170
.004	− 2.652	.085	− 1.372	.440	− .151	.840	.994	.990	2.326
.005	− 2.576	.090	− 1.341	.460	− .100	.860	1.080	.991	2.366
.006	− 2.512	.095	− 1.311	.480	− .050	.880	1.175	.992	2.409
.007	− 2.457	.100	− 1.282	.500	.000	.900	1.282	.993	2.457
.008	− 2.409	.120	− 1.175	.520	.050	.905	1.311	.994	2.512
.009	− 2.366	.140	− 1.080	.540	.100	.910	1.341	.995	2.576
.010	− 2.326	.160	− .994	.560	.151	.915	1.372	.996	2.652
.015	− 2.170	.180	− .915	.580	.202	.920	1.405	.997	2.748
.020	− 2.054	.200	− .842	.600	.253	.925	1.440	.998	2.878
.025	− 1.960	.220	− .772	.620	.305	.930	1.476	.999	3.090
.030	− 1.881	.240	− .706	.640	.358	.935	1.514	.9995	3.291
.035	− 1.812	.250	− .6745	.660	.412	.940	1.555	.9996	3.353
.040	− 1.751	.260	− .643	.680	.468	.945	1.598	.9999	3.719

* Entries in this table are taken from *The Kelley Statistical Tables*, Harvard University Press, 1938, revised 1948, by permission of the author, Truman Lee Kelley.

z is the percentile value named by the area to the left of z. Thus $z_{.30} = -.524$ is the 30th percentile. Discussion of the reading of this table is found on page 34.

TABLE III Ordinates and Areas of the Normal Curve *
(In terms of σ units)

$\frac{x}{\sigma}$	Area	Ordinate	$\frac{x}{\sigma}$	Area	Ordinate	$\frac{x}{\sigma}$	Area	Ordinate
00	.0000	.3989	.50	.1915	.3521	1.00	.3413	.2420
.01	.0040	.3989	.51	.1950	.3503	1.01	.3438	.2396
.02	.0080	.3989	.52	.1985	.3485	1.02	.3461	.2371
.03	.0120	.3988	.53	.2019	.3467	1.03	.3485	.2347
.04	.0160	.3986	.54	.2054	.3448	1.04	.3508	.2323
.05	.0199	.3984	.55	.2088	.3429	1.05	.3531	.2299
.06	.0239	.3982	.56	.2123	.3410	1.06	.3554	.2275
.07	.0279	.3980	.57	.2157	.3391	1.07	.3577	.2251
.08	.0319	.3977	.58	.2190	.3372	1.08	.3599	.2227
.09	.0359	.3973	.59	.2224	.3352	1.09	.3621	.2203
.10	.0398	.3970	.60	.2257	.3332	1.10	.3643	.2179
.11	.0438	.3965	.61	.2291	.3312	1.11	.3665	.2155
.12	.0478	.3961	.62	.2324	.3292	1.12	.3686	.2131
.13	.0517	.3956	.63	.2357	.3271	1.13	.3708	.2107
.14	.0557	.3951	.64	.2389	.3251	1.14	.3729	.2083
.15	.0596	.3945	.65	.2422	.3230	1.15	.3749	.2059
.16	.0636	.3939	.66	.2454	.3209	1.16	.3770	.2036
.17	.0675	.3932	.67	.2486	.3187	1.17	.3790	.2012
.18	.0714	.3925	.68	.2517	.3166	1.18	.3810	.1989
.19	.0753	.3918	.69	.2549	.3144	1.19	.3830	.1965
.20	.0793	.3910	.70	.2580	.3123	1.20	.3849	.1942
.21	.0832	.3902	.71	.2611	.3101	1.21	.3869	.1919
.22	.0871	.3894	.72	.2642	.3079	1.22	.3888	.1895
.23	.0910	.3885	.73	.2673	.3056	1.23	.3907	.1872
.24	.0948	.3876	.74	.2703	.3034	1.24	.3925	.1849
.25	.0987	.3867	.75	.2734	.3011	1.25	.3944	.1826
.26	.1026	.3857	.76	.2764	.2989	1.26	.3962	.1804
.27	.1064	.3847	.77	.2794	.2966	1.27	.3980	.1781
.28	.1103	.3836	.78	.2823	.2943	1.28	.3997	.1758
.29	.1141	.3825	.79	.2852	.2920	1.29	.4015	.1736
.30	.1179	.3814	.80	.2881	.2897	1.30	.4032	.1714
.31	.1217	.3802	.81	.2910	.2874	1.31	.4049	.1691
.32	.1255	.3790	.82	.2939	.2850	1.32	.4066	.1669
.33	.1293	.3778	.83	.2967	.2827	1.33	.4082	.1647
.34	.1331	.3765	.84	.2995	.2803	1.34	.4099	.1626
.35	.1368	.3752	.85	.3023	.2780	1.35	.4115	.1604
.36	.1406	.3739	.86	.3051	.2756	1.36	.4131	.1582
.37	.1443	.3725	.87	.3078	.2732	1.37	.4147	.1561
.38	.1480	.3712	.88	.3106	.2709	1.38	.4162	.1539
.39	.1517	.3697	.89	.3133	.2685	1.39	.4177	.1518
.40	.1554	.3683	.90	.3159	.2661	1.40	.4192	.1497
.41	.1591	.3668	.91	.3186	.2637	1.41	.4207	.1476
.42	.1628	.3653	.92	.3212	.2613	1.42	.4222	.1456
.43	.1664	.3637	.93	.3238	.2589	1.43	.4236	.1435
.44	.1700	.3621	.94	.3264	.2565	1.44	.4251	.1415
.45	.1736	.3605	.95	.3289	.2541	1.45	.4265	.1394
.46	.1772	.3589	.96	.3315	.2516	1.46	.4279	.1374
.47	.1808	.3572	.97	.3340	.2492	1.47	.4292	.1354
.48	.1844	.3555	.98	.3365	.2468	1.48	.4306	.1334
.49	.1879	.3538	.99	.3389	.2444	1.49	.4319	.1315
.50	.1915	.3521	1.00	.3413	.2420	1.50	.4332	.1295

* This table is reproduced from J. E. Wert, *Educational Statistics*, by courtesy of McGraw-Hill Book Co.

Ordinates and Areas of the Normal Curve. — (*Concluded*)
(In terms of σ units)

$\frac{x}{\sigma}$	Area	Ordinate	$\frac{x}{\sigma}$	Area	Ordinate	$\frac{x}{\sigma}$	Area	Ordinate
1.50	.4332	.1295	2.00	.4772	.0540	2.50	.4938	.0175
1.51	.4345	.1276	2.01	.4778	.0529	2.51	.4940	.0171
1.52	.4357	.1257	2.02	.4783	.0519	2.52	.4941	.0167
1.53	.4370	.1238	2.03	.4788	.0508	2.53	.4943	.0163
1.54	.4382	.1219	2.04	.4793	.0498	2.54	.4945	.0158
1.55	.4394	.1200	2.05	.4798	.0488	2.55	.4946	.0154
1.56	.4406	.1182	2.06	.4803	.0478	2.56	.4948	.0151
1.57	.4418	.1163	2.07	.4808	.0468	2.57	.4949	.0147
1.58	.4429	.1145	2.08	.4812	.0459	2.58	.4951	.0143
1.59	.4441	.1127	2.09	.4817	.0449	2.59	.4952	.0139
1.60	.4452	.1109	2.10	.4821	.0440	2.60	.4953	.0136
1.61	.4463	.1092	2.11	.4826	.0431	2.61	.4955	.0132
1.62	.4474	.1074	2.12	.4830	.0422	2.62	.4956	.0129
1.63	.4484	.1057	2.13	.4834	.0413	2.63	.4957	.0126
1.64	.4495	.1040	2.14	.4838	.0404	2.64	.4959	.0122
1.65	.4505	.1023	2.15	.4842	.0395	2.65	.4960	.0119
1.66	.4515	.1006	2.16	.4846	.0387	2.66	.4961	.0116
1.67	.4525	.0989	2.17	.4850	.0379	2.67	.4962	.0113
1.68	.4535	.0973	2.18	.4854	.0371	2.68	.4963	.0110
1.69	.4545	.0957	2.19	.4857	.0363	2.69	.4964	.0107
1.70	.4554	.0940	2.20	.4861	.0355	2.70	.4965	.0104
1.71	.4564	.0925	2.21	.4864	.0347	2.71	.4966	.0101
1.72	.4573	.0909	2.22	.4868	.0339	2.72	.4967	.0099
1.73	.4582	.0893	2.23	.4871	.0332	2.73	.4968	.0096
1.74	.4591	.0878	2.24	.4875	.0325	2.74	.4969	.0093
1.75	.4599	.0863	2.25	.4878	.0317	2.75	.4970	.0091
1.76	.4608	.0848	2.26	.4881	.0310	2.76	.4971	.0088
1.77	.4616	.0833	2.27	.4884	.0303	2.77	.4972	.0086
1.78	.4625	.0818	2.28	.4887	.0297	2.78	.4973	.0084
1.79	.4633	.0804	2.29	.4890	.0290	2.79	.4974	.0081
1.80	.4641	.0790	2.30	.4893	.0283	2.80	.4974	.0079
1.81	.4649	.0775	2.31	.4896	.0277	2.81	.4975	.0077
1.82	.4656	.0761	2.32	.4898	.0270	2.82	.4976	.0075
1.83	.4664	.0748	2.33	.4901	.0264	2.83	.4977	.0073
1.84	.4671	.0734	2.34	.4904	.0258	2.84	.4977	.0071
1.85	.4678	.0721	2.35	.4906	.0252	2.85	.4978	.0069
1.86	.4686	.0707	2.36	.4909	.0246	2.86	.4979	.0067
1.87	.4693	.0694	2.37	.4911	.0241	2.87	.4979	.0065
1.88	.4699	.0681	2.38	.4913	.0235	2.88	.4980	.0063
1.89	.4706	.0669	2.39	.4916	.0229	2.89	.4981	.0061
1.90	.4713	.0656	2.40	.4918	.0224	2.90	.4981	.0060
1.91	.4719	.0644	2.41	.4920	.0219	2.91	.4982	.0058
1.92	.4726	.0632	2.42	.4922	.0213	2.92	.4982	.0056
1.93	.4732	.0620	2.43	.4925	.0208	2.93	.4983	.0055
1.94	.4738	.0608	2.44	.4927	.0203	2.94	.4984	.0053
1.95	.4744	.0596	2.45	.4929	.0198	2.95	.4984	.0051
1.96	.4750	.0584	2.46	.4931	.0194	2.96	.4985	.0050
1.97	.4756	.0573	2.47	.4932	.0189	2.97	.4985	.0048
1.98	.4761	.0562	2.48	.4934	.0184	2.98	.4986	.0047
1.99	.4767	.0551	2.49	.4936	.0180	2.99	.4986	.0046
2.00	.4772	.0540	2.50	.4938	.0175	3.00	.4987	.0044

TABLE IV † Cumulative Binomial Probabilities

Sum of First $(m + 1)$ Terms in Expansion of $(Q + P)^N$.
(Decimal points omitted to save space)

$$\sum_{r=0}^{m} \binom{N}{r} Q^{N-r} P^r$$

A. $Q = .25$ and $P = .75$

N \ m	0	1	2	3	4	5	6	7	8	9	10	11	12	13	14	15
5	001	016	104	367	763	*										
6		005	038	169	466	822	*									
7		001	013	071	244	555	867	*								
8			004	027	114	321	633	900	*							
9			001	010	049	166	399	700	925	*						
10				004	020	078	224	474	756	944	*					
11				001	008	034	115	287	545	803	958	*				
12					003	014	054	158	351	609	842	968	*			
13					001	006	024	080	206	416	667	873	976	*		
14						002	010	038	112	258	479	719	899	982	*	
15						001	004	017	057	148	314	539	764	920	987	*
16							002	007	027	080	190	370	595	803	937	990
17							001	003	012	040	107	235	426	647	836	950
18								001	005	019	057	139	283	481	694	865
19									002	009	029	077	175	332	535	737
20									001	004	014	041	102	214	383	585
21										002	006	021	056	130	256	433
22										001	003	010	030	075	162	301
23											001	005	015	041	096	196
24											001	002	007	021	055	121
25												001	003	011	030	071

B. $Q = P = .5$

N \ m	0	1	2	3	4	5	6	7	8	9	10	11	12	13	14	15
5	031	188	500	812	969	*										
6	016	109	344	656	891	984	*									
7	008	062	227	500	773	938	992	*								
8	004	035	145	363	637	855	965	996	*							
9	002	020	090	254	500	746	910	980	998	*						
10	001	011	055	172	377	623	828	945	989	999	*					
11		006	033	113	274	500	726	887	967	994	*	*				
12		003	019	073	194	387	613	806	927	981	997	*	*			
13		002	011	046	133	291	500	709	867	954	989	998	*	*		
14		001	006	029	090	212	395	605	788	910	971	994	999	*	*	
15			004	018	059	151	304	500	696	849	941	982	996	*	*	*
16			002	011	038	105	227	402	598	773	895	962	989	998	*	*
17			001	006	025	072	166	315	500	685	834	928	975	994	999	*
18			001	004	015	048	119	240	407	593	760	881	952	985	996	999
19				002	010	032	084	180	324	500	676	820	916	968	990	998
20				001	006	021	058	132	252	412	588	748	868	942	979	994
21				001	004	013	039	095	192	332	500	668	808	905	961	987
22					002	008	026	067	143	262	416	584	738	857	933	974
23					001	005	017	047	105	202	339	500	661	798	895	953
24					001	003	011	032	076	154	271	419	581	729	846	924
25						002	007	022	054	115	212	345	500	655	788	885

† Discussion of the reading of this table is found on page 57.

* 1.0 or approximately 1.0.

TABLE IV (*Continued*)

C. $Q = .75$ and $P = .25$

N \ m	0	1	2	3	4	5	6	7	8	9	10	11	12	13
5	237	633	896	984	999	*								
6	178	534	831	962	995	*	*							
7	133	445	756	929	987	999	*	*						
8	100	367	679	886	973	996	*	*	*					
9	075	300	601	834	951	990	999	*	*	*				
10	056	244	526	776	922	980	996	*	*	*	*			
11	042	197	455	713	885	966	992	999	*	*	*	*		
12	032	158	391	649	842	946	986	997	*	*	*	*	*	
13	024	127	333	584	794	920	976	994	999	*	*	*	*	*
14	018	101	281	521	742	888	962	990	998	*	*	*	*	*
15	013	080	236	461	686	852	943	983	996	999	*	*	*	*
16	010	063	197	405	630	810	920	973	993	998	*	*	*	*
17	008	050	164	353	574	765	893	960	988	997	999	*	*	*
18	006	039	135	306	519	717	861	943	981	995	999	*	*	*
19	004	031	111	263	465	668	825	923	971	991	998	*	*	*
20	003	024	091	225	415	617	786	898	959	986	996	999	*	*
21	002	019	075	192	367	567	744	870	944	979	994	998	*	*
22	002	015	061	162	323	517	699	838	925	970	990	997	999	*
23	001	012	049	137	283	468	654	804	904	959	985	995	999	*
24	001	009	040	115	247	422	607	766	879	945	979	993	998	999
25	001	007	032	096	214	378	561	727	851	929	970	989	997	999

TABLE V* Numerical Coefficients in the Expansion of $(Q + P)^N$

N	0	1	2	3	4	5	6	7	8	9	10	Sum of Coefficients
0	1											$2^{0} = 1$
1	1	1										$2^{1} = 2$
2	1	2	1									$2^{2} = 4$
3	1	3	3	1								$2^{3} = 8$
4	1	4	6	4	1							$2^{4} = 16$
5	1	5	10	10	5	1						$2^{5} = 32$
6	1	6	15	20	15	6	1					$2^{6} = 64$
7	1	7	21	35	35	21	7	1				$2^{7} = 128$
8	1	8	28	56	70	56	28	8	1			$2^{8} = 256$
9	1	9	36	84	126	126	84	36	9	1		$2^{9} = 512$
10	1	10	45	120	210	252	210	120	45	10	1	$2^{10} = 1024$
11	1	11	55	165	330	462	462	330	165	55	11	$2^{11} = 2048$
12	1	12	66	220	495	792	924	792	495	220	66	$2^{12} = 4096$
13	1	13	78	286	715	1287	1716	1716	1287	715	286	$2^{13} = 8192$
14	1	14	91	364	1001	2002	3003	3432	3003	2002	1001	$2^{14} = 16384$
15	1	15	105	455	1365	3003	5005	6435	6435	5005	3003	$2^{15} = 32768$
16	1	16	120	560	1820	4368	8008	11440	12870	11440	8008	$2^{16} = 65536$
17	1	17	136	680	2380	6188	12376	19448	24310	24310	19448	$2^{17} = 131072$
18	1	18	153	816	3060	8568	18564	31824	43758	48620	43758	$2^{18} = 262144$
19	1	19	171	969	3876	11628	27132	50388	75582	92378	92378	$2^{19} = 524288$
20	1	20	190	1140	4845	15504	38760	77520	125970	167960	184756	$2^{20} = 1048576$

Note: After 2^{10} part of the distribution is omitted, but the sum can be obtained thus:

$$2^{13} = 2(1 + 13 + 78 + 286 + 715 + 1287 + 1716)$$
$$2^{14} = 2(1 + 14 + 91 + 364 + 1001 + 2002 + 3003) + 3432$$

* Discussion of the reading of this table is found on page 59.

CHART VI Interval Estimate of Population Proportion P with Confidence Coefficient .95 for N = 10, 15, 20, 30, 50, 100, 250, and 1000.*

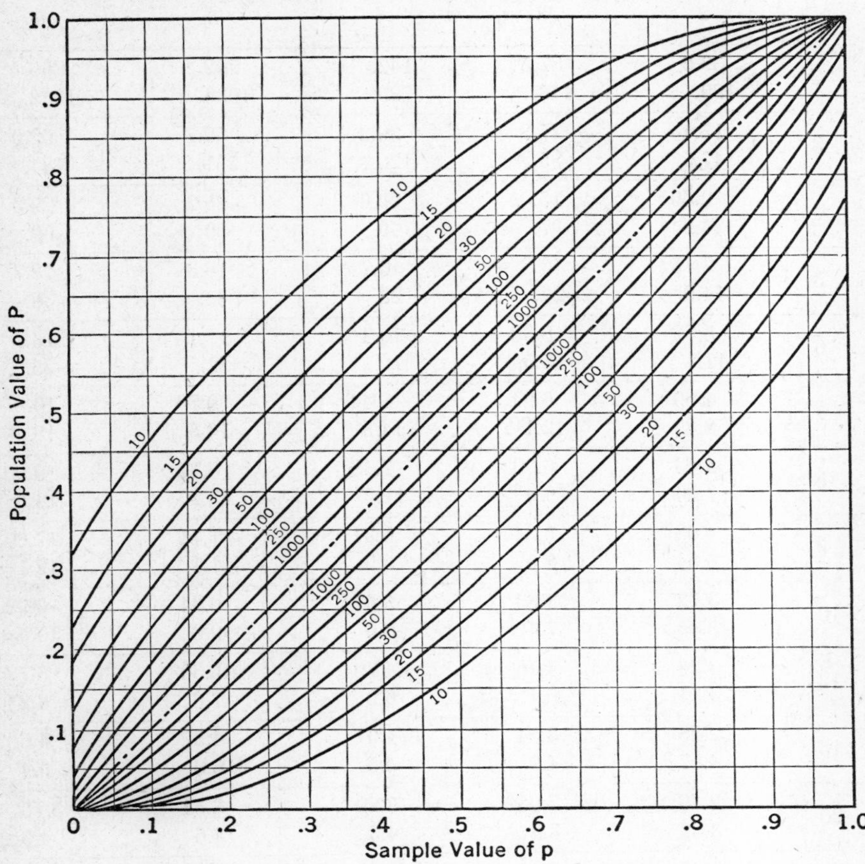

* Reproduced by permission of the authors and the editor from Clopper, C. J. and Pearson, E. S., "The Use of Confidence or Fiducial Limits Illustrated in the Case of the Binomial," *Biometrika,* 26 (1934), 404–413.

TABLE VII 95th and 99th Percentile Values of $F_{max} = s^2{}_{max}/s^2{}_{min}$ in a

n \ k	2	3	4	5	6
2	39.0 199.	87.5 448.	142. 729.	202. 1036.	266. 1362.
3	15.4 47.5	27.8 85.	39.2 120.	50.7 151.	62.0 184.
4	9.60 23.2	15.5 37.	20.6 49.	25.2 59.	29.5 69.
5	7.15 14.9	10.8 22.	13.7 28.	16.3 33.	18.7 38.
6	5.82 11.1	8.38 15.5	10.4 19.1	12.1 22.	13.7 25.
7	4.99 8.89	6.94 12.1	8.44 14.5	9.70 16.5	10.8 18.4
8	4.43 7.50	6.00 9.9	7.18 11.7	8.12 13.2	9.03 14.5
9	4.03 6.54	5.34 8.5	6.31 9.9	7.11 11.1	7.80 12.1
10	3.72 5.85	4.85 7.4	5.67 8.6	6.34 9.6	6.92 10.4
12	3.28 4.91	4.16 6.1	4.79 6.9	5.30 7.6	5.72 8.2
15	2.86 4.07	3.54 4.9	4.01 5.5	4.37 6.0	4.68 6.4
20	2.46 3.32	2.95 3.8	3.29 4.3	3.54 4.6	3.76 4.9
30	2.07 2.63	2.40 3.0	2.61 3.3	2.78 3.4	2.91 3.6
60	1.67 1.96	1.85 2.2	1.96 2.3	2.04 2.4	2.11 2.4
∞	1.00 1.00	1.00 1.00	1.00 1.00	1.00 1.00	1.00 1.00

† Reproduced by permission of the author H. A. David and the Editor of *Biometrika*. Values in the column $k = 2$ and in the rows $n = 2$ and ∞ are exact. Elsewhere the

Set of *k* Mean Squares each Based on *n* Degrees of Freedom †

7	8	9	10	11	12	n
333. 1705.	403. 2063.	475. 2432.	550. 2813.	626. 3204.	704. 3605.	2
72.9 216.*	83.5 249.*	93.9 281.*	104. 310.*	114. 337.*	124. 361.*	3
33.6 79.	37.5 89.	41.1 97.	44.6 106.	48.0 113.	51.4 120.	4
20.8 42.	22.9 46.	24.7 50.	26.5 54.	28.2 57.	29.9 60.	5
15.0 27.	16.3 30.	17.5 32.	18.6 34.	19.7 36.	20.7 37.	6
11.8 20.	12.7 22.	13.5 23.	14.3 24.	15.1 26.	15.8 27.	7
9.78 15.8	10.5 16.9	11.1 17.9	11.7 18.9	12.2 19.8	12.7 21.	8
8.41 13.1	8.95 13.9	9.45 14.7	9.91 15.3	10.3 16.0	10.7 16.6	9
7.42 11.1	7.87 11.8	8.28 12.4	8.66 12.9	9.01 13.4	9.34 13.9	10
6.09 8.7	6.42 9.1	6.72 9.5	7.00 9.9	7.25 10.2	7.48 10.6	12
4.95 6.7	5.19 7.1	5.40 7.3	5.59 7.5	5.77 7.8	5.93 8.0	15
3.94 5.1	4.10 5.3	4.24 5.5	4.37 5.6	4.49 5.8	4.59 5.9	20
3.02 3.7	3.12 3.8	3.21 3.9	3.29 4.0	3.36 4.1	3.39 4.2	30
2.17 2.5	2.22 2.5	2.26 2.6	2.30 2.6	2.33 2.7	2.36 2.7	60
1.00 1.00	1.00 1.00	1.00 1.00	1.00 1.00	1.00 1.00	1.00 1.00	∞

third digit may be in error by several units. Upper value in each cell is the 95th percentile, lower value is the 99th. * indicates that third digit is uncertain.

TABLE VIII Percentile Values of the Chi-square Distribution *

n	$\chi^2_{.005}$	$\chi^2_{.01}$	$\chi^2_{.02}$	$\chi^2_{.025}$	$\chi^2_{.05}$	$\chi^2_{.10}$	$\chi^2_{.25}$	$\chi^2_{.50}$	$\chi^2_{.75}$	$\chi^2_{.90}$	$\chi^2_{.95}$	$\chi^2_{.975}$	$\chi^2_{.98}$	$\chi^2_{.99}$	$\chi^2_{.995}$	$\chi^2_{.999}$	n
1	—	—	—	—	—	.02	.10	.46	1.3	2.7	3.8	5.0	5.4	6.6	7.9	10.8	1
2	.01	.02	.04	.05	.10	.21	.58	1.4	2.8	4.6	6.0	7.4	7.8	9.2	10.6	13.8	2
3	.07	.11	.18	.22	.35	.58	1.21	2.4	4.1	6.3	7.8	9.4	9.8	11.3	12.8	16.3	3
4	.21	.30	.43	.48	.71	1.1	1.92	3.4	5.4	7.8	9.5	11.1	11.7	13.3	14.9	18.5	4
5	.41	.55	.75	.83	1.1	1.6	2.7	4.4	6.6	9.2	11.1	12.8	13.4	15.1	16.7	20.5	5
6	.68	.87	1.13	1.2	1.6	2.2	3.5	5.4	7.8	10.6	12.6	14.4	15.0	16.8	18.5	22.5	6
7	.99	1.24	1.56	1.7	2.2	2.8	4.3	6.4	9.0	12.0	14.1	16.0	16.6	18.5	20.3	24.3	7
8	1.3	1.65	2.03	2.2	2.7	3.5	5.1	7.3	10.2	13.4	15.5	17.5	18.2	20.1	22.0	26.1	8
9	1.7	2.09	2.53	2.7	3.3	4.2	5.9	8.3	11.4	14.7	16.9	19.0	19.7	21.7	23.6	27.9	9
10	2.2	2.55	3.06	3.2	3.9	4.9	6.7	9.3	12.5	16.0	18.3	20.5	21.2	23.2	25.2	29.6	10
11	2.6	3.05	3.61	3.8	4.6	5.6	7.6	10.3	13.7	17.3	19.7	21.9	22.6	24.7	26.8	31.3	11
12	3.1	3.57	4.18	4.4	5.2	6.3	8.4	11.3	14.8	18.5	21.0	23.3	24.1	26.2	28.3	32.9	12
13	3.6	4.11	4.76	5.0	5.9	7.0	9.3	12.3	16.0	19.8	22.4	24.7	25.5	27.7	29.8	34.5	13
14	4.1	4.66	5.37	5.6	6.6	7.8	10.2	13.3	17.1	21.1	23.7	26.1	26.9	29.1	31.3	36.1	14
15	4.6	5.23	5.98	6.3	7.3	8.5	11.0	14.3	18.2	22.3	25.0	27.5	28.3	30.6	32.8	37.7	15
16	5.1	5.81	6.61	6.9	8.0	9.3	11.9	15.3	19.4	23.5	26.3	28.8	29.6	32.0	34.3	39.3	16
17	5.7	6.41	7.26	7.6	8.7	10.1	12.8	16.3	20.5	24.8	27.6	30.2	31.0	33.4	35.7	40.8	17
18	6.3	7.02	7.91	8.2	9.4	10.9	13.7	17.3	21.6	26.0	28.9	31.5	32.3	34.8	37.2	42.3	18
19	6.9	7.63	8.57	8.9	10.1	11.7	14.6	18.3	22.7	27.2	30.1	32.9	33.7	36.2	38.6	43.8	19
20	7.4	8.26	9.24	9.6	10.9	12.4	15.5	19.3	23.8	28.4	31.4	34.2	35.0	37.6	40.0	45.3	20
21	8.0	8.9	9.9	10.3	11.6	13.2	16.3	20.3	24.9	29.6	32.7	35.5	36.3	38.9	41.4	46.8	21
22	8.6	9.5	10.6	11.0	12.3	14.0	17.2	21.3	26.0	30.8	33.9	36.8	37.7	40.3	42.8	48.3	22
23	9.3	10.2	11.3	11.7	13.1	14.8	18.1	22.3	27.1	32.0	35.2	38.1	39.0	41.6	44.2	49.7	23
24	9.9	10.9	12.0	12.4	13.8	15.7	19.0	23.3	28.2	33.2	36.4	39.4	40.3	43.0	45.6	51.2	24
25	10.5	11.5	12.7	13.1	14.6	16.5	19.9	24.3	29.3	34.4	37.7	40.6	41.6	44.3	46.9	52.6	25
26	11.2	12.2	13.4	13.8	15.4	17.3	20.8	25.3	30.4	35.6	38.9	41.9	42.9	45.6	48.3	54.0	26
27	11.8	12.9	14.1	14.6	16.2	18.1	21.7	26.3	31.5	36.7	40.1	43.2	44.1	47.0	49.6	55.5	27
28	12.5	13.6	14.8	15.3	16.9	18.9	22.7	27.3	32.6	37.9	41.3	44.5	45.4	48.3	51.0	56.9	28
29	13.1	14.3	15.6	16.0	17.7	19.8	23.6	28.3	33.7	39.1	42.6	45.7	46.7	49.6	52.4	58.3	29
30	13.8	15.0	16.3	16.8	18.5	20.6	24.5	29.3	34.8	40.3	43.8	47.0	48.0	50.9	53.3	59.7	30
40	20.7	22.2	23.8	24.4	26.5	29.1	33.7	39.3	45.6	51.8	55.8	59.3	60.4	63.7	66.8	73.5	40
60	35.5	37.5	39.7	40.5	43.2	46.5	52.3	59.3	67.0	74.4	79.1	83.3	84.6	88.4	92.0	99.7	60
100	67.3	70.0	73.1	74.2	77.9	82.4	90.1	99.3	109.1	118.5	124.3	129.6	131.1	135.8	140.2	149.5	100

* Abridged from table in *Biometrika*, Vol. 32 (1941), and published with the permission of the author, Catherine M. Thompson, and the editor of *Biometrika*. Columns $\chi^2_{.02}$, $\chi^2_{.98}$, and $\chi^2_{.999}$ are reprinted abridged from R. A. Fisher and F. Yates, Statistical Tables, published by Oliver and Boyd Ltd. by permission of the authors and publishers.

TABLE IX Percentile Values of "Student's" Distribution *

(For instructions on reading table, see p. 145)

n	$t_{.75}$	$t_{.80}$	$t_{.90}$	$t_{.95}$	$t_{.975}$	$t_{.99}$	$t_{.995}$	$t_{.9995}$	n
1	1.00	1.38	3.08	6.31	12.71	31.82	63.66	636.62	1
2	.82	1.06	1.89	2.92	4.30	6.96	9.92	31.60	2
3	.76	.98	1.64	2.35	3.18	4.54	5.84	12.94	3
4	.74	.94	1.53	2.13	2.78	3.75	4.60	8.61	4
5	.73	.92	1.48	2.02	2.57	3.36	4.03	6.86	5
6	.72	.91	1.44	1.94	2.45	3.14	3.71	5.96	6
7	.71	.90	1.42	1.89	2.36	3.00	3.50	5.40	7
8	.71	.89	1.40	1.86	2.31	2.90	3.36	5.04	8
9	.70	.88	1.38	1.83	2.26	2.82	3.25	4.78	9
10	.70	.88	1.37	1.81	2.23	2.76	3.17	4.59	10
11	.70	.88	1.36	1.80	2.20	2.72	3.11	4.44	11
12	.70	.87	1.36	1.78	2.18	2.68	3.05	4.32	12
13	.69	.87	1.35	1.77	2.16	2.65	3.01	4.22	13
14	.69	.87	1.34	1.76	2.14	2.62	2.98	4.14	14
15	.69	.87	1.34	1.75	2.13	2.60	2.95	4.07	15
16	.69	.87	1.34	1.75	2.12	2.58	2.92	4.02	16
17	.69	.86	1.33	1.74	2.11	2.57	2.90	3.96	17
18	.69	.86	1.33	1.73	2.10	2.55	2.88	3.92	18
19	.69	.86	1.33	1.73	2.09	2.54	2.86	3.88	19
20	.69	.86	1.32	1.72	2.09	2.53	2.85	3.85	20
21	.69	.86	1.32	1.72	2.08	2.52	2.83	3.82	21
22	.69	.86	1.32	1.72	2.07	2.51	2.82	3.79	22
23	.69	.86	1.32	1.71	2.07	2.50	2.81	3.77	23
24	.68	.86	1.32	1.71	2.06	2.49	2.80	3.74	24
25	.68	.86	1.32	1.71	2.06	2.48	2.79	3.72	25
26	.68	.86	1.32	1.71	2.06	2.48	2.78	3.71	26
27	.68	.86	1.31	1.70	2.05	2.47	2.77	3.69	27
28	.68	.85	1.31	1.70	2.05	2.47	2.76	3.67	28
29	.68	.85	1.31	1.70	2.04	2.46	2.76	3.66	29
30	.68	.85	1.31	1.70	2.05	2.46	2.75	3.65	30
40	.68	.85	1.30	1.68	2.02	2.42	2.70	3.55	40
60	.68	.85	1.30	1.67	2.00	2.39	2.66	3.46	60
120	.68	.85	1.29	1.66	1.98	2.36	2.62	3.37	120
∞	.67	.84	1.282	1.645	1.960	2.326	2.576	3.291	∞
	$-t_{.25}$	$-t_{.20}$	$-t_{.10}$	$-t_{.05}$	$-t_{.025}$	$-t_{.01}$	$-t_{.005}$	$-t_{.0005}$	

* Reprinted abridged from R. A. Fisher and F. Yates, Statistical Tables, published by Oliver and Boyd Ltd. by permission of the authors and publishers.

TABLE X 95th and 99th Percentile

95TH PERCENTILE IN LIGHT-FACE TYPE,

n_1 = degrees of freedom

n_2 = degrees of freedom for denominator

n_2	1	2	3	4	5	6	7	8	9	10	11	12
1	161	200	216	225	230	234	237	239	241	242	243	244
	4,052	**4,999**	**5,403**	**5,625**	**5,764**	**5,859**	**5,928**	**5,981**	**6,022**	**6,056**	**6,082**	**6,106**
2	18.51	19.00	19.16	19.25	19.30	19.33	19.36	19.37	19.38	19.39	19.40	19.41
	98.49	**99.01**	**99.17**	**99.25**	**99.30**	**99.33**	**99.34**	**99.36**	**99.38**	**99.40**	**99.41**	**99.42**
3	10.13	9.55	9.28	9.12	9.01	8.94	8.88	8.84	8.81	8.78	8.76	8.74
	34.12	**30.81**	**29.46**	**28.71**	**28.24**	**27.91**	**27.67**	**27.49**	**27.34**	**27.23**	**27.13**	**27.05**
4	7.71	6.94	6.59	6.39	6.26	6.16	6.09	6.04	6.00	5.96	5.93	5.91
	21.20	**18.00**	**16.69**	**15.98**	**15.52**	**15.21**	**14.98**	**14.80**	**14.66**	**14.54**	**14.45**	**14.37**
5	6.61	5.79	5.41	5.19	5.05	4.95	4.88	4.82	4.78	4.74	4.70	4.68
	16.26	**13.27**	**12.06**	**11.39**	**10.97**	**10.67**	**10.45**	**10.27**	**10.15**	**10.05**	**9.96**	**9.89**
6	5.99	5.14	4.76	4.53	4.39	4.28	4.21	4.15	4.10	4.06	4.03	4.00
	13.74	**10.92**	**9.78**	**9.15**	**8.75**	**8.47**	**8.26**	**8.10**	**7.98**	**7.87**	**7.79**	**7.72**
7	5.59	4.74	4.35	4.12	3.97	3.87	3.79	3.73	3.68	3.63	3.60	3.57
	12.25	**9.55**	**8.45**	**7.85**	**7.46**	**7.19**	**7.00**	**6.84**	**6.71**	**6.62**	**6.54**	**6.47**
8	5.32	4.46	4.07	3.84	3.69	3.58	3.50	3.44	3.39	3.34	3.31	3.28
	11.26	**8.65**	**7.59**	**7.01**	**6.63**	**6.37**	**6.19**	**6.03**	**5.91**	**5.82**	**5.74**	**5.67**
9	5.12	4.26	3.86	3.63	3.48	3.37	3.29	3.23	3.18	3.13	3.10	3.07
	10.56	**8.02**	**6.99**	**6.42**	**6.06**	**5.80**	**5.62**	**5.47**	**5.35**	**5.26**	**5.18**	**5.11**
10	4.96	4.10	3.71	3.48	3.33	3.22	3.14	3.07	3.02	2.97	2.94	2.91
	10.04	**7.56**	**6.55**	**5.99**	**5.64**	**5.39**	**5.21**	**5.06**	**4.95**	**4.85**	**4.78**	**4.71**
11	4.84	3.98	3.59	3.36	3.20	3.09	3.01	2.95	2.90	2.86	2.82	2.79
	9.65	**7.20**	**6.22**	**5.67**	**5.32**	**5.07**	**4.88**	**4.74**	**4.63**	**4.54**	**4.46**	**4.40**
12	4.75	3.88	3.49	3.26	3.11	3.00	2.92	2.85	2.80	2.76	2.72	2.69
	9.33	**6.93**	**5.95**	**5.41**	**5.06**	**4.82**	**4.65**	**4.50**	**4.39**	**4.30**	**4.22**	**4.16**
13	4.67	3.80	3.41	3.18	3.02	2.92	2.84	2.77	2.72	2.67	2.63	2.60
	9.07	**6.70**	**5.74**	**5.20**	**4.86**	**4.62**	**4.44**	**4.30**	**4.19**	**4.10**	**4.02**	**3.96**
14	4.60	3.74	3.34	3.11	2.96	2.85	2.77	2.70	2.65	2.60	2.56	2.53
	8.86	**6.51**	**5.56**	**5.03**	**4.69**	**4.46**	**4.28**	**4.14**	**4.03**	**3.94**	**3.86**	**3.80**
15	4.54	3.68	3.29	3.06	2.90	2.79	2.70	2.64	2.59	2.55	2.51	2.48
	8.68	**6.36**	**5.42**	**4.89**	**4.56**	**4.32**	**4.14**	**4.00**	**3.89**	**3.80**	**3.73**	**3.67**
16	4.49	3.63	3.24	3.01	2.85	2.74	2.66	2.59	2.54	2.49	2.45	2.42
	8.53	**6.23**	**5.29**	**4.77**	**4.44**	**4.20**	**4.03**	**3.89**	**3.78**	**3.69**	**3.61**	**3.55**
17	4.45	3.59	3.20	2.96	2.81	2.70	2.62	2.55	2.50	2.45	2.41	2.38
	8.40	**6.11**	**5.18**	**4.67**	**4.34**	**4.10**	**3.93**	**3.79**	**3.68**	**3.59**	**3.52**	**3.45**
18	4.41	3.55	3.16	2.93	2.77	2.66	2.58	2.51	2.46	2.41	2.37	2.34
	8.28	**6.01**	**5.09**	**4.58**	**4.25**	**4.01**	**3.85**	**3.71**	**3.60**	**3.51**	**3.44**	**3.37**
19	4.38	3.52	3.13	2.90	2.74	2.63	2.55	2.48	2.43	2.38	2.34	2.31
	8.18	**5.93**	**5.01**	**4.50**	**4.17**	**3.94**	**3.77**	**3.63**	**3.52**	**3.43**	**3.36**	**3.30**
20	4.35	3.49	3.10	2.87	2.71	2.60	2.52	2.45	2.40	2.35	2.31	2.28
	8.10	**5.85**	**4.94**	**4.43**	**4.10**	**3.87**	**3.71**	**3.56**	**3.45**	**3.37**	**3.30**	**3.23**
21	4.32	3.47	3.07	2.84	2.68	2.57	2.49	2.42	2.37	2.32	2.28	2.25
	8.02	**5.78**	**4.87**	**4.37**	**4.04**	**3.81**	**3.65**	**3.51**	**3.40**	**3.31**	**3.24**	**3.17**
22	4.30	3.44	3.05	2.82	2.66	2.55	2.47	2.40	2.35	2.30	2.26	2.23
	7.94	**5.72**	**4.82**	**4.31**	**3.99**	**3.76**	**3.59**	**3.45**	**3.35**	**3.26**	**3.18**	**3.12**
23	4.28	3.42	3.03	2.80	2.64	2.53	2.45	2.38	2.32	2.28	2.24	2.20
	7.88	**5.66**	**4.76**	**4.26**	**3.94**	**3.71**	**3.54**	**3.41**	**3.30**	**3.21**	**3.14**	**3.07**
24	4.26	3.40	3.01	2.78	2.62	2.51	2.43	2.36	2.30	2.26	2.22	2.18
	7.82	**5.61**	**4.72**	**4.22**	**3.90**	**3.67**	**3.50**	**3.36**	**3.25**	**3.17**	**3.09**	**3.03**
25	4.24	3.38	2.99	2.76	2.60	2.49	2.41	2.34	2.28	2.24	2.20	2.16
	7.77	**5.57**	**4.68**	**4.18**	**3.86**	**3.63**	**3.46**	**3.32**	**3.21**	**3.13**	**3.05**	**2.99**
26	4.22	3.37	2.98	2.74	2.59	2.47	2.39	2.32	2.27	2.22	2.18	2.15
	7.72	**5.53**	**4.64**	**4.14**	**3.82**	**3.59**	**3.42**	**3.29**	**3.17**	**3.09**	**3.02**	**2.96**

Values of the F Distribution *

99th Percentile in Bold-Face Type

for numerator

14	16	20	24	30	40	50	75	100	200	500	∞	n_2
245	246	248	249	250	251	252	253	253	254	254	254	1
6,142	**6,169**	**6,208**	**6,234**	**6,258**	**6,286**	**6,302**	**6,323**	**6,334**	**6,352**	**6,361**	**6,366**	
19.42	19.43	19.44	19.45	19.46	19.47	19.47	19.48	19.49	19.49	19.50	19.50	2
99.43	**99.44**	**99.45**	**99.46**	**99.47**	**99.48**	**99.48**	**99.49**	**99.49**	**99.49**	**99.50**	**99.50**	
8.71	8.69	8.66	8.64	8.62	8.60	8.58	8.57	8.56	8.54	8.54	8.53	3
26.92	**26.83**	**26.69**	**26.60**	**26.50**	**26.41**	**26.35**	**26.27**	**26.23**	**26.18**	**26.14**	**26.12**	
5.87	5.84	5.80	5.77	5.74	5.71	5.70	5.68	5.66	5.65	5.64	5.63	4
14.24	**14.15**	**14.02**	**13.93**	**13.83**	**13.74**	**13.69**	**13.61**	**13.57**	**13.52**	**13.48**	**13.46**	
4.64	4.60	4.56	4.53	4.50	4.46	4.44	4.42	4.40	4.38	4.37	4.36	5
9.77	**9.68**	**9.55**	**9.47**	**9.38**	**9.29**	**9.24**	**9.17**	**9.13**	**9.07**	**9.04**	**9.02**	
3.96	3.92	3.87	3.84	3.81	3.77	3.75	3.72	3.71	3.69	3.68	3.67	6
7.60	**7.52**	**7.39**	**7.31**	**7.23**	**7.14**	**7.09**	**7.02**	**6.99**	**6.94**	**6.90**	**6.88**	
3.52	3.49	3.44	3.41	3.38	3.34	3.32	3.29	3.28	3.25	3.24	3.23	7
6.35	**6.27**	**6.15**	**6.07**	**5.98**	**5.90**	**5.85**	**5.78**	**5.75**	**5.70**	**5.67**	**5.65**	
3.23	3.20	3.15	3.12	3.08	3.05	3.03	3.00	2.98	2.96	2.94	2.93	8
5.56	**5.48**	**5.36**	**5.28**	**5.20**	**5.11**	**5.06**	**5.00**	**4.96**	**4.91**	**4.88**	**4.86**	
3.02	2.98	2.93	2.90	2.86	2.82	2.80	2.77	2.76	2.73	2.72	2.71	9
5.00	**4.92**	**4.80**	**4.73**	**4.64**	**4.56**	**4.51**	**4.45**	**4.41**	**4.36**	**4.33**	**4.31**	
2.86	2.82	2.77	2.74	2.70	2.67	2.64	2.61	2.59	2.56	2.55	2.54	10
4.60	**4.52**	**4.41**	**4.33**	**4.25**	**4.17**	**4.12**	**4.05**	**4.01**	**3.96**	**3.93**	**3.91**	
2.74	2.70	2.65	2.61	2.57	2.53	2.50	2.47	2.45	2.42	2.41	2.40	11
4.29	**4.21**	**4.10**	**4.02**	**3.94**	**3.86**	**3.80**	**3.74**	**3.70**	**3.66**	**3.62**	**3.60**	
2.64	2.60	2.54	2.50	2.46	2.42	2.40	2.36	2.35	2.32	2.31	2.30	12
4.05	**3.98**	**3.86**	**3.78**	**3.70**	**3.61**	**3.56**	**3.49**	**3.46**	**3.41**	**3.38**	**3.36**	
2.55	2.51	2.46	2.42	2.38	2.34	2.32	2.28	2.26	2.24	2.22	2.21	13
3.85	**3.78**	**3.67**	**3.59**	**3.51**	**3.42**	**3.37**	**3.30**	**3.27**	**3.21**	**3.18**	**3.16**	
2.48	2.44	2.39	2.35	2.31	2.27	2.24	2.21	2.19	2.16	2.14	2.13	14
3.70	**3.62**	**3.51**	**3.43**	**3.34**	**3.26**	**3.21**	**3.14**	**3.11**	**3.06**	**3.02**	**3.00**	
2.43	2.39	2.33	2.29	2.25	2.21	2.18	2.15	2.12	2.10	2.08	2.07	15
3.56	**3.48**	**3.36**	**3.29**	**3.20**	**3.12**	**3.07**	**3.00**	**2.97**	**2.92**	**2.89**	**2.87**	
2.37	2.33	2.28	2.24	2.20	2.16	2.13	2.09	2.07	2.04	2.02	2.01	16
3.45	**3.37**	**3.25**	**3.18**	**3.10**	**3.01**	**2.96**	**2.89**	**2.86**	**2.80**	**2.77**	**2.75**	
2.33	2.29	2.23	2.19	2.15	2.11	2.08	2.04	2.02	1.99	1.97	1.96	17
3.35	**3.27**	**3.16**	**3.08**	**3.00**	**2.92**	**2.86**	**2.79**	**2.76**	**2.70**	**2.67**	**2.65**	
2.29	2.25	2.19	2.15	2.11	2.07	2.04	2.00	1.98	1.95	1.93	1.92	18
3.27	**3.19**	**3.07**	**3.00**	**2.91**	**2.83**	**2.78**	**2.71**	**2.68**	**2.62**	**2.59**	**2.57**	
2.26	2.21	2.15	2.11	2.07	2.02	2.00	1.96	1.94	1.91	1.90	1.88	19
3.19	**3.12**	**3.00**	**2.92**	**2.84**	**2.76**	**2.70**	**2.63**	**2.60**	**2.54**	**2.51**	**2.49**	
2.23	2.18	2.12	2.08	2.04	1.99	1.96	1.92	1.90	1.87	1.85	1.84	20
3.13	**3.05**	**2.94**	**2.86**	**2.77**	**2.69**	**2.63**	**2.56**	**2.53**	**2.47**	**2.44**	**2.42**	
2.20	2.15	2.09	2.05	2.00	1.96	1.93	1.89	1.87	1.84	1.82	1.81	21
3.07	**2.99**	**2.88**	**2.80**	**2.72**	**2.63**	**2.58**	**2.51**	**2.47**	**2.42**	**2.38**	**2.36**	
2.18	2.13	2.07	2.03	1.98	1.93	1.91	1.87	1.84	1.81	1.80	1.78	22
3.02	**2.94**	**2.83**	**2.75**	**2.67**	**2.58**	**2.53**	**2.46**	**2.42**	**2.37**	**2.33**	**2.31**	
2.14	2.10	2.04	2.00	1.96	1.91	1.88	1.84	1.82	1.79	1.77	1.76	23
2.97	**2.89**	**2.78**	**2.70**	**2.62**	**2.53**	**2.48**	**2.41**	**2.37**	**2.32**	**2.28**	**2.26**	
2.13	2.09	2.02	1.98	1.94	1.89	1.86	1.82	1.80	1.76	1.74	1.73	24
2.93	**2.85**	**2.74**	**2.66**	**2.58**	**2.49**	**2.44**	**2.36**	**2.33**	**2.27**	**2.23**	**2.21**	
2.11	2.06	2.00	1.96	1.92	1.87	1.84	1.80	1.77	1.74	1.72	1.71	25
2.89	**2.81**	**2.70**	**2.62**	**2.54**	**2.45**	**2.40**	**2.32**	**2.29**	**2.23**	**2.19**	**2.17**	
2.10	2.05	1.99	1.95	1.90	1.85	1.82	1.78	1.76	1.72	1.70	1.69	26
2.86	**2.77**	**2.66**	**2.58**	**2.50**	**2.41**	**2.36**	**2.28**	**2.25**	**2.19**	**2.15**	**2.13**	

n_2 = degrees of freedom for denominator

* From Snedecor, G. W., *Statistical Methods*, Iowa State College Press, Inc., by permission of author and publisher.

TABLE X 95th and 99th Percentile

95th Percentile in Light-Face Type,

n_1 = degrees of freedom

n_2 = degrees of freedom for denominator

n_2	1	2	3	4	5	6	7	8	9	10	11	12
27	4.21 **7.68**	3.35 **5.49**	2.96 **4.60**	2.73 **4.11**	2.57 **3.79**	2.46 **3.56**	2.37 **3.39**	2.30 **3.26**	2.25 **3.14**	2.20 **3.06**	2.16 **2.98**	2.13 **2.93**
28	4.20 **7.64**	3.34 **5.45**	2.95 **4.57**	2.71 **4.07**	2.56 **3.76**	2.44 **3.53**	2.36 **3.36**	2.29 **3.23**	2.24 **3.11**	2.19 **3.03**	2.15 **2.95**	2.12 **2.90**
29	4.18 **7.60**	3.33 **5.42**	2.93 **4.54**	2.70 **4.04**	2.54 **3.73**	2.43 **3.50**	2.35 **3.33**	2.28 **3.20**	2.22 **3.08**	2.18 **3.00**	2.14 **2.92**	2.10 **2.87**
30	4.17 **7.56**	3.32 **5.39**	2.92 **4.51**	2.69 **4.02**	2.53 **3.70**	2.42 **3.47**	2.34 **3.30**	2.27 **3.17**	2.21 **3.06**	2.16 **2.98**	2.12 **2.90**	2.09 **2.84**
32	4.15 **7.50**	3.30 **5.34**	2.90 **4.46**	2.67 **3.97**	2.51 **3.66**	2.40 **3.42**	2.32 **3.25**	2.25 **3.12**	2.19 **3.01**	2.14 **2.94**	2.10 **2.86**	2.07 **2.80**
34	4.13 **7.44**	3.28 **5.29**	2.88 **4.42**	2.65 **3.93**	2.49 **3.61**	2.38 **3.38**	2.30 **3.21**	2.23 **3.08**	2.17 **2.97**	2.12 **2.89**	2.08 **2.82**	2.05 **2.76**
36	4.11 **7.39**	3.26 **5.25**	2.86 **4.38**	2.63 **3.89**	2.48 **3.58**	2.36 **3.35**	2.28 **3.18**	2.21 **3.04**	2.15 **2.94**	2.10 **2.86**	2.06 **2.78**	2.03 **2.72**
38	4.10 **7.35**	3.25 **5.21**	2.85 **4.34**	2.62 **3.86**	2.46 **3.54**	2.35 **3.32**	2.26 **3.15**	2.19 **3.02**	2.14 **2.91**	2.09 **2.82**	2.05 **2.75**	2.02 **2.69**
40	4.08 **7.31**	3.23 **5.18**	2.84 **4.31**	2.61 **3.83**	2.45 **3.51**	2.34 **3.29**	2.25 **3.12**	2.18 **2.99**	2.12 **2.88**	2.07 **2.80**	2.04 **2.73**	2.00 **2.66**
42	4.07 **7.27**	3.22 **5.15**	2.83 **4.29**	2.59 **3.80**	2.44 **3.49**	2.32 **3.26**	2.24 **3.10**	2.17 **2.96**	2.11 **2.86**	2.06 **2.77**	2.02 **2.70**	1.99 **2.64**
44	4.06 **7.24**	3.21 **5.12**	2.82 **4.26**	2.58 **3.78**	2.43 **3.46**	2.31 **3.24**	2.23 **3.07**	2.16 **2.94**	2.10 **2.84**	2.05 **2.75**	2.01 **2.68**	1.98 **2.62**
46	4.05 **7.21**	3.20 **5.10**	2.81 **4.24**	2.57 **3.76**	2.42 **3.44**	2.30 **3.22**	2.22 **3.05**	2.14 **2.92**	2.09 **2.82**	2.04 **2.73**	2.00 **2.66**	1.97 **2.60**
48	4.04 **7.19**	3.19 **5.08**	2.80 **4.22**	2.56 **3.74**	2.41 **3.42**	2.30 **3.20**	2.21 **3.04**	2.14 **2.90**	2.08 **2.80**	2.03 **2.71**	1.99 **2.64**	1.96 **2.58**
50	4.03 **7.17**	3.18 **5.06**	2.79 **4.20**	2.56 **3.72**	2.40 **3.41**	2.29 **3.18**	2.20 **3.02**	2.13 **2.88**	2.07 **2.78**	2.02 **2.70**	1.98 **2.62**	1.95 **2.56**
55	4.02 **7.12**	3.17 **5.01**	2.78 **4.16**	2.54 **3.68**	2.38 **3.37**	2.27 **3.15**	2.18 **2.98**	2.11 **2.85**	2.05 **2.75**	2.00 **2.66**	1.97 **2.59**	1.93 **2.53**
60	4.00 **7.08**	3.15 **4.98**	2.76 **4.13**	2.52 **3.65**	2.37 **3.34**	2.25 **3.12**	2.17 **2.95**	2.10 **2.82**	2.04 **2.72**	1.99 **2.63**	1.95 **2.56**	1.92 **2.50**
65	3.99 **7.04**	3.14 **4.95**	2.75 **4.10**	2.51 **3.62**	2.36 **3.31**	2.24 **3.09**	2.15 **2.93**	2.08 **2.79**	2.02 **2.70**	1.98 **2.61**	1.94 **2.54**	1.90 **2.47**
70	3.98 **7.01**	3.13 **4.92**	2.74 **4.08**	2.50 **3.60**	2.35 **3.29**	2.23 **3.07**	2.14 **2.91**	2.07 **2.77**	2.01 **2.67**	1.97 **2.59**	1.93 **2.51**	1.89 **2.45**
80	3.96 **6.96**	3.11 **4.88**	2.72 **4.04**	2.48 **3.56**	2.33 **3.25**	2.21 **3.04**	2.12 **2.87**	2.05 **2.74**	1.99 **2.64**	1.95 **2.55**	1.91 **2.48**	1.88 **2.41**
100	3.94 **6.90**	3.09 **4.82**	2.70 **3.98**	2.46 **3.51**	2.30 **3.20**	2.19 **2.99**	2.10 **2.82**	2.03 **2.69**	1.97 **2.59**	1.92 **2.51**	1.88 **2.43**	1.85 **2.36**
125	3.92 **6.84**	3.07 **4.78**	2.68 **3.94**	2.44 **3.47**	2.29 **3.17**	2.17 **2.95**	2.08 **2.79**	2.01 **2.65**	1.95 **2.56**	1.90 **2.47**	1.86 **2.40**	1.83 **2.33**
150	3.91 **6.81**	3.06 **4.75**	2.67 **3.91**	2.43 **3.44**	2.27 **3.14**	2.16 **2.92**	2.07 **2.76**	2.00 **2.62**	1.94 **2.53**	1.89 **2.44**	1.85 **2.37**	1.82 **2.30**
200	3.89 **6.76**	3.04 **4.71**	2.65 **3.88**	2.41 **3.41**	2.26 **3.11**	2.14 **2.90**	2.05 **2.73**	1.98 **2.60**	1.92 **2.50**	1.87 **2.41**	1.83 **2.34**	1.80 **2.28**
400	3.86 **6.70**	3.02 **4.66**	2.62 **3.83**	2.39 **3.36**	2.23 **3.06**	2.12 **2.85**	2.03 **2.69**	1.96 **2.55**	1.90 **2.46**	1.85 **2.37**	1.81 **2.29**	1.78 **2.23**
1,000	3.85 **6.66**	3.00 **4.62**	2.61 **3.80**	2.38 **3.34**	2.22 **3.04**	2.10 **2.82**	2.02 **2.66**	1.95 **2.53**	1.89 **2.43**	1.84 **2.34**	1.80 **2.26**	1.76 **2.20**
∞	3.84 **6.64**	2.99 **4.60**	2.60 **3.78**	2.37 **3.32**	2.21 **3.02**	2.09 **2.80**	2.01 **2.64**	1.94 **2.51**	1.88 **2.41**	1.83 **2.32**	1.79 **2.24**	1.75 **2.18**

Values of the F Distribution* *(Continued)*

99th Percentile in Bold-Face Type

for numerator

14	16	20	24	30	40	50	75	100	200	500	∞	n_2
2.08 **2.83**	2.03 **2.74**	1.97 **2.63**	1.93 **2.55**	1.88 **2.47**	1.84 **2.38**	1.80 **2.33**	1.76 **2.25**	1.74 **2.21**	1.71 **2.16**	1.68 **2.12**	1.67 **2.10**	27
2.06 **2.80**	2.02 **2.71**	1.96 **2.60**	1.91 **2.52**	1.87 **2.44**	1.81 **2.35**	1.78 **2.30**	1.75 **2.22**	1.72 **2.18**	1.69 **2.13**	1.67 **2.09**	1.65 **2.06**	28
2.05 **2.77**	2.00 **2.68**	1.94 **2.57**	1.90 **2.49**	1.85 **2.41**	1.80 **2.32**	1.77 **2.27**	1.73 **2.19**	1.71 **2.15**	1.68 **2.10**	1.65 **2.06**	1.64 **2.03**	29
2.04 **2.74**	1.99 **2.66**	1.93 **2.55**	1.89 **2.47**	1.84 **2.38**	1.79 **2.29**	1.76 **2.24**	1.72 **2.16**	1.69 **2.13**	1.66 **2.07**	1.64 **2.03**	1.62 **2.01**	30
2.02 **2.70**	1.97 **2.62**	1.91 **2.51**	1.86 **2.42**	1.82 **2.34**	1.76 **2.25**	1.74 **2.20**	1.69 **2.12**	1.67 **2.08**	1.64 **2.02**	1.61 **1.98**	1.59 **1.96**	32
2.00 **2.66**	1.95 **2.58**	1.89 **2.47**	1.84 **2.38**	1.80 **2.30**	1.74 **2.21**	1.71 **2.15**	1.67 **2.08**	1.64 **2.04**	1.61 **1.98**	1.59 **1.94**	1.57 **1.91**	34
1.98 **2.62**	1.93 **2.54**	1.87 **2.43**	1.82 **2.35**	1.78 **2.26**	1.72 **2.17**	1.69 **2.12**	1.65 **2.04**	1.62 **2.00**	1.59 **1.94**	1.56 **1.90**	1.55 **1.87**	36
1.96 **2.59**	1.92 **2.51**	1.85 **2.40**	1.80 **2.32**	1.76 **2.22**	1.71 **2.14**	1.67 **2.08**	1.63 **2.00**	1.60 **1.97**	1.57 **1.90**	1.54 **1.86**	1.53 **1.84**	38
1.95 **2.56**	1.90 **2.49**	1.84 **2.37**	1.79 **2.29**	1.74 **2.20**	1.69 **2.11**	1.66 **2.05**	1.61 **1.97**	1.59 **1.94**	1.55 **1.88**	1.53 **1.84**	1.51 **1.81**	40
1.94 **2.54**	1.89 **2.46**	1.82 **2.35**	1.78 **2.26**	1.73 **2.17**	1.68 **2.08**	1.64 **2.02**	1.60 **1.94**	1.57 **1.91**	1.54 **1.85**	1.51 **1.80**	1.49 **1.78**	42
1.92 **2.52**	1.88 **2.44**	1.81 **2.32**	1.76 **2.24**	1.72 **2.15**	1.66 **2.06**	1.63 **2.00**	1.58 **1.92**	1.56 **1.88**	1.52 **1.82**	1.50 **1.78**	1.48 **1.75**	44
1.91 **2.50**	1.87 **2.42**	1.80 **2.30**	1.75 **2.22**	1.71 **2.13**	1.65 **2.04**	1.62 **1.98**	1.57 **1.90**	1.54 **1.86**	1.51 **1.80**	1.48 **1.76**	1.46 **1.72**	46
1.90 **2.48**	1.86 **2.40**	1.79 **2.28**	1.74 **2.20**	1.70 **2.11**	1.64 **2.02**	1.61 **1.96**	1.56 **1.88**	1.53 **1.84**	1.50 **1.78**	1.47 **1.73**	1.45 **1.70**	48
1.90 **2.46**	1.85 **2.39**	1.78 **2.26**	1.74 **2.18**	1.69 **2.10**	1.63 **2.00**	1.60 **1.94**	1.55 **1.86**	1.52 **1.82**	1.48 **1.76**	1.46 **1.71**	1.44 **1.68**	50
1.88 **2.43**	1.83 **2.35**	1.76 **2.23**	1.72 **2.15**	1.67 **2.06**	1.61 **1.96**	1.58 **1.90**	1.52 **1.82**	1.50 **1.78**	1.46 **1.71**	1.43 **1.66**	1.41 **1.64**	55
1.86 **2.40**	1.81 **2.32**	1.75 **2.20**	1.70 **2.12**	1.65 **2.03**	1.59 **1.93**	1.56 **1.87**	1.50 **1.79**	1.48 **1.74**	1.44 **1.68**	1.41 **1.63**	1.39 **1.60**	60
1.85 **2.37**	1.80 **2.30**	1.73 **2.18**	1.68 **2.09**	1.63 **2.00**	1.57 **1.90**	1.54 **1.84**	1.49 **1.76**	1.46 **1.71**	1.42 **1.64**	1.39 **1.60**	1.37 **1.56**	65
1.84 **2.35**	1.79 **2.28**	1.72 **2.15**	1.67 **2.07**	1.62 **1.98**	1.56 **1.88**	1.53 **1.82**	1.47 **1.74**	1.45 **1.69**	1.40 **1.62**	1.37 **1.56**	1.35 **1.53**	70
1.82 **2.32**	1.77 **2.24**	1.70 **2.11**	1.65 **2.03**	1.60 **1.94**	1.54 **1.84**	1.51 **1.78**	1.45 **1.70**	1.42 **1.65**	1.38 **1.57**	1.35 **1.52**	1.32 **1.49**	80
1.79 **2.26**	1.75 **2.19**	1.68 **2.06**	1.63 **1.98**	1.57 **1.89**	1.51 **1.79**	1.48 **1.73**	1.42 **1.64**	1.39 **1.59**	1.34 **1.51**	1.30 **1.46**	1.28 **1.43**	100
1.77 **2.23**	1.72 **2.15**	1.65 **2.03**	1.60 **1.94**	1.55 **1.85**	1.49 **1.75**	1.45 **1.68**	1.39 **1.59**	1.36 **1.54**	1.31 **1.46**	1.27 **1.40**	1.25 **1.37**	125
1.76 **2.20**	1.71 **2.12**	1.64 **2.00**	1.59 **1.91**	1.54 **1.83**	1.47 **1.72**	1.44 **1.66**	1.37 **1.56**	1.34 **1.51**	1.29 **1.43**	1.25 **1.37**	1.22 **1.33**	150
1.74 **2.17**	1.69 **2.09**	1.62 **1.97**	1.57 **1.88**	1.52 **1.79**	1.45 **1.69**	1.42 **1.62**	1.35 **1.53**	1.32 **1.48**	1.26 **1.39**	1.22 **1.33**	1.19 **1.28**	200
1.72 **2.12**	1.67 **2.04**	1.60 **1.92**	1.54 **1.84**	1.49 **1.74**	1.42 **1.64**	1.38 **1.57**	1.32 **1.47**	1.28 **1.42**	1.22 **1.32**	1.16 **1.24**	1.13 **1.19**	400
1.70 **2.09**	1.65 **2.01**	1.58 **1.89**	1.53 **1.81**	1.47 **1.71**	1.41 **1.61**	1.36 **1.54**	1.30 **1.44**	1.26 **1.38**	1.19 **1.28**	1.13 **1.19**	1.08 **1.11**	1,000
1.69 **2.07**	1.64 **1.99**	1.57 **1.87**	1.52 **1.79**	1.46 **1.69**	1.40 **1.59**	1.35 **1.52**	1.28 **1.41**	1.24 **1.36**	1.17 **1.25**	1.11 **1.15**	1.00 **1.00**	∞

n_2 = degrees of freedom for denominator

* From Snedecor, G. W., *Statistical Methods*, Iowa State College Press, Inc., by permission of author and publisher.

TABLE XI * Percentile Values of r for n Degrees of Freedom when $\rho = 0$

n	$r_{.95}$	$r_{.975}$	$r_{.99}$	$r_{.995}$	$r_{.9995}$	n	$r_{.95}$	$r_{.975}$	$r_{.99}$	$r_{.995}$	$r_{.9995}$
1	.988	.997	.9995	.9999	1.000	30	.296	.349	.409	.449	.554
2	.900	.950	.980	.990	.999	35	.275	.325	.381	.418	.519
3	.805	.878	.934	.959	.991	40	.257	.304	.358	.393	.490
4	.729	.811	.882	.917	.974	45	.243	.288	.338	.372	.465
5	.669	.754	.833	.874	.951	50	.231	.273	.322	.354	.443
6	.622	.707	.789	.834	.925	55	.220	.261	.307	.338	.424
7	.582	.666	.750	.798	.898	60	.211	.250	.295	.325	.408
8	.550	.632	.716	.765	.872	65	.203	.240	.284	.312	.393
9	.521	.602	.685	.735	.847	70	.195	.232	.274	.302	.380
10	.497	.576	.658	.708	.823	75	.189	.224	.264	.292	.368
11	.476	.553	.634	.684	.801	80	.183	.217	.256	.283	.357
12	.458	.532	.612	.661	.780	85	.178	.211	.249	.275	.347
13	.441	.514	.592	.641	.760	90	.173	.205	.242	.267	.338
14	.426	.497	.574	.623	.742	95	.168	.200	.236	.260	329
15	.412	.482	.558	.606	.725	100	.164	.195	.230	.254	.321
16	.400	.468	.542	.590	.708	125	.147	.174	.206	.228	.288
17	.389	.456	.528	.575	.693	150	.134	.159	.189	.208	.264
18	.378	.444	.516	.561	.679	175	.124	.148	.174	.194	.248
19	.369	.433	.503	.549	.665	200	.116	.138	.164	.181	.235
20	.360	.423	.492	.537	.652	300	.095	.113	.134	.148	.188
22	.344	.404	.472	.515	.629	500	.074	.088	.104	.115	.148
24	.330	.388	.453	.496	.607	1000	.052	.062	.073	.081	.104
25	.323	.381	.445	.487	.597	2000	.037	.044	.016	.058	.074
	$r_{—.05}$	$—_{.025}$	$-r_{.01}$	$-r_{.095}$	$-r_{.0005}$		$-r_{.05}$	$-r_{.025}$	$-r_{.01}$	$-r_{.005}$	$-r_{.0005}$

* Reprinted abridged from R. A. Fisher and F. Yates, Statistical Tables, published by Oliver and Boyd Ltd. by permission of the authors and publishers.

TABLE XII* Values for Transforming r into $z = \frac{1}{2} \log_e \frac{1+r}{1-r}$.

	.00	.01	.02	.03	.04	.05	.06	.07	.08	.09
.0	.0000	.0100	.0200	.0300	.0400	.0500	.0599	.0699	.0798	.0898
.1	.0997	.1096	.1194	.1293	.1391	.1489	.1587	.1684	.1781	.1878
.2	.1974	.2070	.2165	.2260	.2355	.2449	.2543	.2636	.2729	.2821
.3	.2913	.3004	.3095	.3185	.3275	.3364	.3452	.3540	.3627	.3714
.4	.3800	.3885	.3969	.4053	.4136	.4219	.4301	.4382	.4462	.4542
.5	.4621	.4700	.4777	.4854	.4930	.5005	.5080	.5154	.5227	.5299
.6	.5370	.5441	.5511	.5581	.5649	.5717	.5784	.5850	.5915	.5980
.7	.6044	.6107	.6169	.6231	.6291	.6352	.6411	.6469	.6527	.6584
.8	.6640	.6696	.6751	.6805	.6858	.6911	.6963	.7014	.7064	.7114
.9	.7163	.7211	.7259	.7306	.7352	.7398	.7443	.7487	.7531	.7574
1.0	.7616	.7658	.7699	.7739	.7779	.7818	.7857	.7895	.7932	.7969
1.1	.8005	.8041	.8076	.8110	.8144	.8178	.8210	.8243	.8275	.8306
1.2	.8337	.8367	.8397	.8426	.8455	.8483	.8511	.8538	.8565	.8591
1.3	.8617	.8643	.8668	.8693	.8717	.8741	.8764	.8787	.8810	.8832
1.4	.8854	.8875	.8896	.8917	.8937	.8957	.8977	.8996	.9015	.9033
1.5	.9052	.9069	.9087	.9104	.9121	.9138	.9154	.9170	.9186	.9202
1.6	.9217	.9232	.9246	.9261	.9275	.9289	.9302	.9316	.9329	.9342
1.7	.9354	.9367	.9379	.9391	.9402	.9414	.9425	.9436	.9447	.9458
1.8	.9468	.9478	.9498	.9488	.9508	.9518	.9527	.9536	.9545	.9554
1.9	.9562	.9571	.9579	.9587	.9595	.9603	.9611	.9619	.9626	.9633
2.0	.9640	.9647	.9654	.9661	.9668	.9674	.9680	.9687	.9693	.9699
2.1	.9705	.9710	.9716	.9722	.9727	.9732	.9738	.9743	.9748	.9753
2.2	.9757	.9762	.9767	.9771	.9776	.9780	.9785	.9789	.9793	.9797
2.3	.9801	.9805	.9809	.9812	.9816	.9820	.9823	.9827	.9830	.9834
2.4	.9837	.9840	.9843	.9846	.9849	.9852	.9855	.9858	.9861	.9863
2.5	.9866	.9869	.9871	.9874	.9876	.9879	.9881	.9884	.9886	.9888
2.6	.9890	.9892	.9895	.9897	.9899	.9901	.9903	.9905	.9906	.9908
2.7	.9910	.9912	.9914	.9915	.9917	.9919	.9920	.9922	.9923	.9925
2.8	.9926	.9928	.9929	.9931	.9932	.9933	.9935	.9936	.9937	.9938
2.9	.9940	.9941	.9942	.9943	.9944	.9945	.9946	.9947	.9949	.9950
3.0	.9951									
4.0	.9993									
5.0	.9999									

* Reprinted abridged from R. A. Fisher and F. Yates, Statistical Tables, published by Oliver and Boyd Ltd. by permission of the authors and publishers. The figures in the body of the table are values of r corresponding to z-values read from the scales on the left and top of the table.

TABLE XIII * A Table of the Values of the Product-Moment Coefficient of Correlation in a Normal Bivariate Population Corresponding to Given Proportions of Success

Columns: Proportion of successes in the 27 per cent scoring highest on the continuous variable. Rows: Proportion of successes in the 27 per cent scoring lowest on the continuous variable.

	01	02	04	06	08	10	12	14	16	18	20	22	24	26	28	30	32	34	36	38	40	42	44	46	48	50
01	0	11	23	30	35	40	43	46	49	51	53	55	57	59	61	62	63	65	66	67	68	69	70	71	72	72
02	−11	0	12	19	25	30	34	37	40	43	46	48	50	51	53	55	56	58	59	61	62	63	64	66	67	68
04	−23	−12	0	08	14	19	23	26	30	33	36	38	40	42	44	46	48	49	51	53	54	56	57	58	60	61
06	−30	−19	−08	0	06	11	15	19	23	26	29	31	33	36	38	40	42	44	45	47	48	50	52	53	55	56
08	−35	−25	−14	−06	0	05	09	13	17	20	23	25	28	30	32	35	37	38	40	42	44	45	47	49	51	52
10	−40	−30	−19	−11	−05	0	04	08	12	15	18	21	23	26	28	30	32	34	36	38	40	41	43	45	47	48
12	−43	−34	−23	−15	−09	−04	0	04	07	11	13	16	19	21	24	26	28	30	32	34	36	38	39	41	43	45
14	−46	−37	−26	−19	−13	−08	−04	0	03	07	10	12	15	18	20	22	25	27	29	31	33	34	36	38	40	42
16	−49	−40	−30	−23	−17	−12	−07	−03	0	03	06	09	12	14	17	19	21	24	26	28	30	31	33	35	37	39
18	−51	−43	−33	−26	−20	−15	−11	−07	−03	0	03	06	08	11	13	16	18	20	23	25	27	28	30	32	34	36
20	−53	−46	−36	−29	−23	−18	−13	−10	−06	−03	0	03	06	08	11	13	15	17	19	22	24	26	27	29	31	33
22	−55	−48	−38	−31	−25	−21	−16	−12	−09	−06	−03	0	03	06	08	10	12	15	17	19	21	23	25	27	29	31
24	−57	−50	−40	−33	−28	−23	−19	−15	−12	−08	−06	−03	0	03	05	08	10	12	14	16	18	20	22	24	26	28
26	−59	−51	−42	−36	−30	−26	−21	−18	−14	−11	−08	−06	−03	0	02	05	07	09	12	14	16	18	20	22	24	26
28	−61	−53	−44	−38	−32	−28	−24	−20	−17	−13	−11	−08	−05	−02	0	02	04	07	09	11	13	15	17	19	21	23
30	−62	−55	−46	−40	−35	−30	−26	−22	−19	−16	−13	−10	−08	−05	−02	0	02	04	07	09	11	13	15	17	19	21
32	−63	−56	−48	−42	−37	−32	−28	−25	−21	−18	−15	−12	−10	−07	−04	−02	0	02	04	07	09	11	13	15	17	19
34	−65	−58	−49	−44	−38	−34	−30	−27	−24	−20	−17	−15	−12	−09	−07	−04	−02	0	02	04	06	09	11	13	15	17
36	−66	−59	−51	−45	−40	−36	−32	−29	−26	−23	−19	−17	−14	−12	−09	−07	−04	−02	0	02	04	06	08	11	13	15
38	−67	−61	−53	−47	−42	−38	−34	−31	−28	−25	−22	−19	−16	−14	−11	−09	−07	−04	−02	0	02	04	06	08	11	13
40	−68	−62	−54	−48	−44	−40	−36	−33	−30	−27	−24	−21	−18	−16	−13	−11	−09	−06	−04	−02	0	02	04	06	08	10

* Reproduced from Thorndike, R. L., *Personal Selection, Test and Measurement Techniques,* New York, 1949, by courtesy of John Wiley and Sons and by permission of John C. Flanagan who computed the table and distributed it privately.

Proportion of successes in the 27 per cent scoring lowest on the continuous variable																										
42	−69	−63	−56	−50	−45	−41	−38	−34	−31	−28	−26	−23	−20	−18	−15	−13	−11	−09	−06	−04	−02	0	02	04	06	08
44	−70	−64	−57	−52	−47	−43	−39	−36	−33	−30	−27	−25	−22	−20	−17	−15	−13	−11	−08	−06	−04	−02	0	02	04	06
46	−71	−66	−58	−53	−49	−45	−41	−38	−35	−32	−29	−27	−24	−22	−19	−17	−15	−13	−11	−08	−06	−04	−02	0	02	04
48	−72	−67	−60	−55	−51	−47	−43	−40	−37	−34	−31	−29	−26	−24	−21	−19	−17	−15	−13	−11	−08	−06	−04	−02	0	02
50	−72	−68	−61	−56	−52	−48	−45	−42	−39	−36	−33	−31	−28	−26	−23	−21	−19	−17	−15	−13	−10	−08	−06	−04	−02	0
52	−73	−69	−62	−57	−53	−50	−46	−43	−40	−38	−35	−33	−30	−28	−26	−23	−21	−19	−17	−15	−12	−10	−08	−06	−04	−02
54	−74	−70	−63	−59	−55	−51	−48	−45	−42	−39	−37	−34	−32	−30	−27	−25	−23	−21	−19	−16	−14	−12	−10	−08	−06	−04
56	−75	−71	−64	−60	−56	−53	−49	−47	−44	−41	−39	−36	−34	−32	−29	−27	−25	−23	−21	−18	−16	−14	−12	−10	−08	−06
58	−76	−72	−66	−61	−58	−54	−51	−48	−45	−43	−40	−38	−36	−33	−31	−29	−27	−25	−22	−20	−18	−16	−14	−12	−10	−08
60	−77	−73	−67	−62	−59	−56	−52	−50	−47	−45	−42	−40	−37	−35	−33	−31	−29	−27	−25	−22	−21	−18	−16	−14	−12	−10
62	−78	−73	−68	−64	−60	−57	−54	−51	−49	−47	−44	−42	−39	−37	−35	−33	−31	−29	−27	−25	−22	−20	−18	−16	−15	−13
64	−78	−74	−69	−65	−61	−58	−55	−53	−50	−48	−46	−43	−41	−39	−37	−35	−33	−31	−29	−27	−25	−22	−21	−19	−17	−15
66	−79	−75	−70	−66	−63	−60	−57	−54	−52	−49	−47	−45	−43	−41	−39	−37	−35	−33	−31	−29	−27	−25	−23	−21	−19	−17
68	−80	−76	−71	−67	−64	−61	−58	−56	−53	−51	−49	−47	−45	−42	−40	−38	−37	−35	−33	−31	−29	−27	−25	−23	−21	−19
70	−81	−77	−72	−68	−65	−63	−60	−57	−55	−53	−51	−49	−46	−44	−42	−40	−38	−37	−35	−33	−31	−29	−27	−25	−23	−21
72	−82	−78	−73	−70	−66	−64	−61	−59	−57	−54	−52	−50	−48	−46	−44	−42	−40	−39	−37	−35	−33	−31	−29	−27	−26	−23
74	−82	−79	−74	−71	−68	−65	−63	−60	−58	−56	−54	−52	−50	−48	−46	−44	−42	−41	−39	−37	−35	−33	−32	−30	−28	−26
76	−83	−80	−75	−72	−69	−67	−64	−62	−60	−58	−56	−54	−52	−50	−48	−46	−45	−43	−41	−39	−37	−36	−34	−32	−30	−28
78	−83	−80	−76	−73	−70	−68	−66	−63	−61	−60	−57	−56	−54	−52	−50	−49	−47	−45	−43	−42	−40	−38	−36	−34	−33	−31
80	−84	−81	−77	−74	−72	−70	−67	−65	−63	−61	−60	−57	−56	−54	−52	−51	−49	−47	−46	−44	−42	−40	−39	−37	−35	−33
82	−85	−82	−78	−76	−73	−71	−69	−67	−65	−63	−61	−60	−58	−56	−54	−53	−51	−49	−48	−47	−45	−43	−41	−39	−38	−36
84	−86	−83	−80	−77	−75	−72	−70	−68	−67	−65	−63	−61	−60	−58	−57	−55	−53	−52	−50	−49	−47	−45	−44	−42	−40	−39
86	−87	−84	−81	−78	−76	−74	−72	−70	−68	−67	−65	−63	−62	−60	−59	−57	−56	−54	−53	−51	−50	−48	−47	−45	−43	−42
88	−87	−85	−82	−80	−77	−76	−73	−72	−70	−69	−67	−66	−64	−63	−61	−60	−58	−57	−55	−54	−52	−51	−49	−48	−46	−45
90	−88	−86	−83	−81	−79	−77	−76	−74	−72	−71	−70	−68	−67	−65	−64	−63	−61	−60	−58	−57	−56	−54	−53	−51	−50	−48
92	−89	−87	−84	−82	−81	−79	−77	−76	−75	−73	−72	−70	−69	−68	−66	−65	−64	−63	−61	−60	−59	−58	−56	−55	−53	−52
94	−90	−88	−86	−84	−82	−81	−80	−78	−77	−76	−74	−73	−72	−71	−70	−68	−67	−66	−65	−64	−62	−61	−60	−59	−57	−56
96	−91	−90	−88	−86	−84	−83	−82	−81	−80	−78	−77	−76	−75	−74	−73	−72	−71	−70	−69	−68	−67	−66	−64	−63	−62	−61
98	−92	−91	−90	−88	−87	−86	−85	−84	−83	−82	−81	−80	−80	−79	−78	−77	−76	−75	−74	−73	−73	−72	−71	−70	−69	−68
99	−93	−92	−91	−90	−89	−88	−87	−87	−86	−85	−84	−83	−83	−82	−82	−81	−80	−79	−78	−78	−77	−76	−75	−74	−73	−72

TABLE XIII A Table of the Values of the Product-Moment Coefficient of Correlation in a Normal Bivariate Population Corresponding to Given Proportions of Success (*Continued*)

Proportion of successes in the 27 per cent scoring lowest on the continuous variable	Proportion of successes in the 27 per cent scoring highest on the continuous variable																								
	52	54	56	58	60	62	64	66	68	70	72	74	76	78	80	82	84	86	88	90	92	94	96	98	99
01	73	74	75	76	77	78	78	79	80	81	82	82	83	83	84	85	86	87	87	88	89	90	91	92	93
02	69	70	71	72	73	73	74	75	76	77	78	79	80	80	81	82	83	84	85	86	87	88	90	91	92
04	62	63	64	66	67	68	69	70	71	72	73	74	75	76	77	78	80	81	82	83	84	86	88	90	91
06	57	59	60	61	62	64	65	66	67	68	70	71	72	73	74	76	77	78	80	81	82	84	86	88	90
08	53	55	56	58	59	60	61	63	64	65	66	68	69	70	72	73	75	76	77	79	81	82	84	87	89
10	50	51	53	54	56	57	58	60	61	63	64	65	67	68	70	71	72	74	76	77	79	81	83	86	88
12	46	48	49	51	52	54	55	57	58	60	61	63	64	66	67	69	70	72	73	76	77	80	82	85	87
14	43	45	47	48	50	51	53	54	56	57	59	60	62	63	65	67	68	70	72	74	76	78	81	84	87
16	40	42	44	45	47	49	50	52	53	55	57	58	60	61	63	65	67	68	70	72	75	77	80	83	86
18	38	39	41	43	45	47	48	49	51	53	54	56	58	60	61	63	65	67	69	71	73	76	78	82	85
20	35	37	39	40	42	44	46	47	49	51	52	54	56	57	60	61	63	65	67	70	72	74	77	81	84
22	33	34	36	38	40	42	43	45	47	49	50	52	54	56	57	60	61	63	66	68	70	73	76	80	83
24	30	32	34	36	37	39	41	43	45	46	48	50	52	54	56	58	60	62	64	67	69	72	75	80	83
26	28	30	32	33	35	37	39	41	42	44	46	48	50	52	54	56	58	60	63	65	68	71	74	79	82
28	26	27	29	31	33	35	37	39	40	42	44	46	48	50	52	54	57	59	61	64	66	70	73	78	82
30	23	25	27	29	31	33	35	37	38	40	42	44	46	49	51	53	55	57	60	63	65	68	72	77	81
32	21	23	25	27	29	31	33	35	37	38	40	42	45	47	49	51	53	56	58	61	64	67	71	76	80
34	19	21	23	25	27	29	31	33	35	37	39	41	43	45	47	49	52	54	57	60	63	66	70	75	79
36	17	19	21	22	25	27	29	31	33	35	37	39	41	43	46	48	50	53	55	58	61	65	69	74	78
38	15	16	18	20	22	25	27	29	31	33	35	37	39	42	44	47	49	51	54	57	60	64	68	73	78
40	12	14	16	18	21	22	25	27	29	31	33	35	37	40	42	45	47	50	52	56	59	62	67	73	77

Proportion of successes in the 27 per cent scoring lowest on the continuous variable																									
42	10	12	14	16	18	20	22	25	27	29	31	33	36	38	40	43	45	48	51	54	58	61	66	72	76
44	08	10	12	14	16	18	21	23	25	27	29	32	34	36	39	41	44	47	49	53	56	60	64	71	75
46	06	08	10	12	14	16	19	21	23	25	27	30	32	34	37	39	42	45	48	51	55	59	63	70	74
48	04	06	08	10	12	15	17	19	21	23	26	28	30	33	35	38	40	43	46	50	53	57	62	69	73
50	02	04	06	08	10	13	15	17	19	21	23	26	28	31	33	36	39	42	45	48	52	56	61	68	72
52	0	02	04	06	08	11	13	15	17	19	21	24	26	29	31	34	37	40	43	47	51	55	60	67	72
54	−02	0	02	04	06	08	11	13	15	17	19	22	24	27	29	32	35	38	41	45	49	53	58	66	71
56	−04	−02	0	02	04	06	08	11	13	15	17	20	22	25	27	30	33	36	39	43	47	52	57	64	70
58	−06	−04	−02	0	02	04	06	09	11	13	15	18	20	23	26	28	31	34	38	41	45	50	56	63	69
60	−08	−06	−04	−02	0	02	04	06	09	11	13	16	18	21	24	27	30	33	36	40	44	48	54	62	68
62	−11	−08	−06	−04	−02	0	02	04	07	09	11	14	16	19	22	25	28	31	34	38	42	47	53	61	67
64	−13	−11	−08	−06	−04	−02	0	02	04	07	09	12	14	17	19	23	26	29	32	36	40	45	51	59	66
66	−15	−13	−11	−09	−06	−04	−02	0	02	04	07	09	12	15	17	20	24	27	30	34	38	44	49	58	65
68	−17	−15	−13	−11	−09	−07	−04	02	0	02	04	07	10	12	15	18	21	25	28	32	37	42	48	56	63
70	−19	−17	−15	−13	−11	−09	−07	−04	−02	0	02	05	08	10	13	16	19	22	26	30	35	40	46	55	62
72	−21	−19	−17	−15	−13	−11	−09	−07	−04	−02	0	02	05	08	11	13	17	20	24	28	32	38	44	53	61
74	−24	−22	−20	−18	−16	−14	−12	−09	−07	−05	−02	0	03	06	08	11	14	18	21	26	30	36	42	51	59
76	−26	−24	−22	−20	−18	−16	−14	−12	−10	−08	−05	−03	0	03	06	08	12	15	19	23	28	33	40	50	57
78	−29	−27	−25	−23	−21	−19	−17	−15	−12	−10	−08	−06	−03	0	03	06	09	12	16	21	25	31	38	48	55
80	−31	−29	−27	−26	−24	−22	−19	−17	−15	−13	−11	−08	−06	−03	0	03	06	10	13	18	23	29	36	46	53
82	−34	−32	−30	−28	−27	−25	−23	−20	−18	−16	−13	−11	−08	−06	−03	0	03	07	11	15	20	26	33	43	51
84	−37	−35	−33	−31	−30	−28	−26	−24	−21	−19	−17	−14	−12	−09	−06	−03	0	03	07	12	17	23	30	40	49
86	−40	−38	−36	−34	−33	−31	−29	−27	−25	−22	−20	−18	−15	−12	−10	−07	−03	0	04	08	13	19	26	37	46
88	−43	−41	−39	−38	−36	−34	−32	−30	−28	−26	−24	−21	−19	−16	−13	−11	−07	−04	0	04	09	15	23	34	43
90	−47	−45	−43	−41	−40	−38	−36	−34	−32	−30	−28	−26	−23	−21	−18	−15	−12	−08	−04	0	05	11	19	30	40
92	−51	−49	−47	−45	−44	−42	−40	−38	−37	−35	−32	−30	−28	−25	−23	−20	−17	−13	−09	−05	0	06	14	25	35
94	−55	−53	−52	−50	−48	−47	−45	−44	−42	−40	−38	−36	−33	−31	−29	−26	−23	−19	−15	−11	−06	0	08	19	30
96	−60	−58	−57	−56	−54	−53	−51	−49	−48	−46	−44	−42	−40	−38	−36	−33	−30	−26	−23	−19	−14	−08	0	12	23
98	−67	−66	−64	−63	−62	−61	−59	−58	−56	−55	−53	−51	−50	−48	−46	−43	−40	−37	−34	−30	−25	−19	−12	0	11
99	−72	−71	−70	−69	−68	−67	−66	−65	−63	−62	−61	−59	−57	−55	−53	−51	−49	−46	−43	−40	−35	−30	−23	−11	0

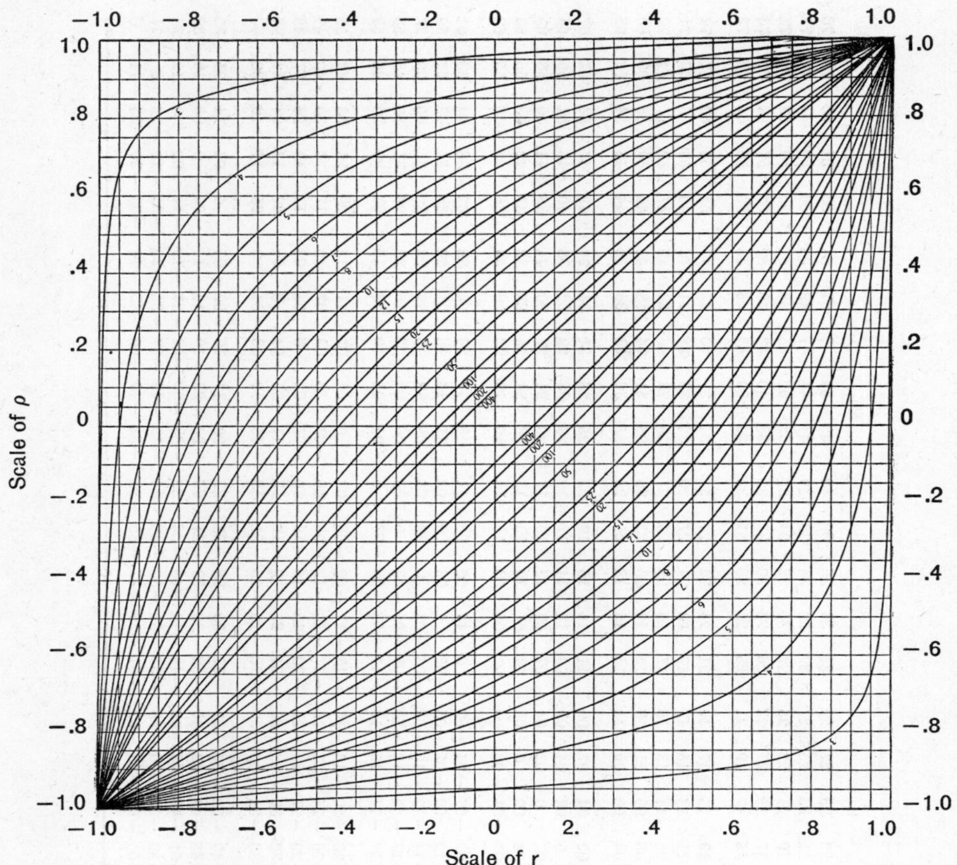

CHART XIV Confidence belt for the correlation coefficient $\alpha = .05$. Numbers on the curves indicate sample size. (Reproduced with the permission of E.S. Pearson from David, F.N., *Tables of the Correlation Coefficient*, The *Biometrika* Office, London.)

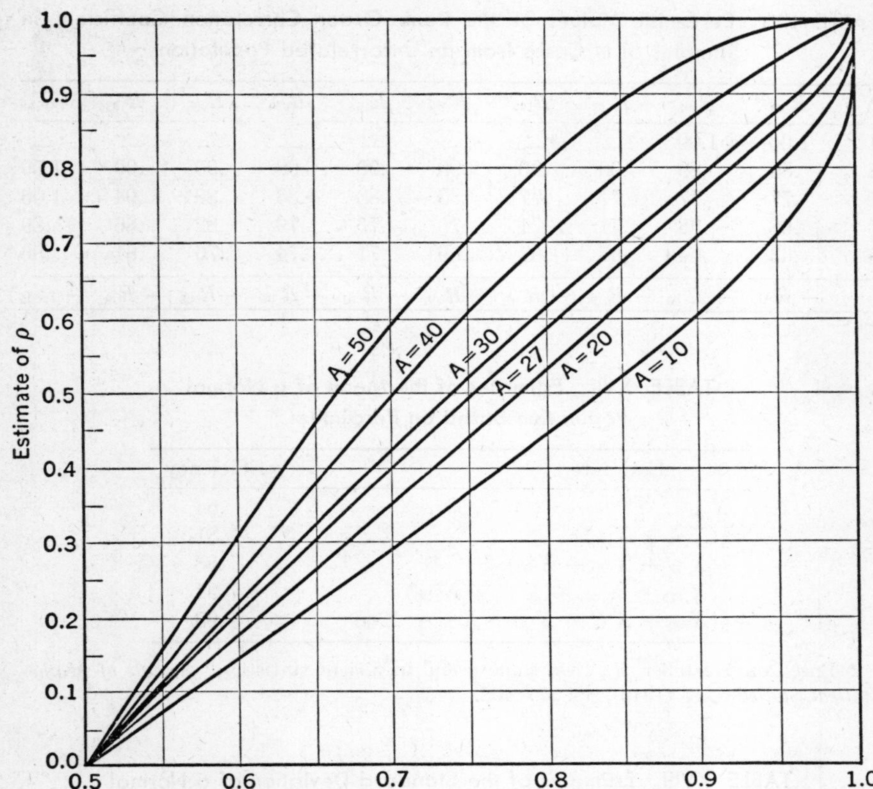

CHART XV Chart for estimating the correlation coefficient. (From Frederick Mosteller, "On Some Useful 'Inefficient' Statistics," *Annals of Mathematical Statistics,* 17 (1946), p. 405. Used with the permission of the author and the editor of *Annals.*) The use of this chart is discussed on page 420.

TABLE XVI Percentile Values of the Rank Order Correlation Coefficient in Samples of *N* Cases from an Uncorrelated Population

N	$R_{.90}$	$R_{.91}$	$R_{.92}$	$R_{.93}$	$R_{.94}$	$R_{.95}$	$R_{.96}$	$R_{.97}$	$R_{.98}$	$R_{.99}$
4	1.00	1.00	—	—	—	—	—	—	—	—
5	.80	.80	.90	.90	.90	.90	.90	.90	.90	1.00
6	.77	.77	.77	.77	.83	.83	.83	.89	.94	1.00
7	.68	.68	.71	.71	.75	.75	.79	.82	.86	.89
8	.63	.64	.67	.67	.69	.71	.74	.76	.81	.86
	$-R_{.10}$	$-R_{.09}$	$-R_{.08}$	$-R_{.07}$	$-R_{.06}$	$-R_{.05}$	$-R_{.04}$	$-R_{.03}$	$-R_{.02}$	$-R_{.01}$

TABLE XVII Estimates of the Mean of a Normal Population Based on Percentiles.*

Estimate	Efficiency
$X_{.50}$	.64
$\frac{1}{2}(X_{.75} + X_{.25})$	.81
$\frac{1}{3}(X_{.83} + X_{.50} + X_{.17})$	.88
$\frac{1}{4}(X_{.875} + X_{.625} + X_{.375} + X_{.125})$	.91
$\frac{1}{5}(X_{.90} + X_{.70} + X_{.50} + X_{.30} + X_{.10})$	.93

* Based on Mosteller, F., "On some useful inefficient statistics," *Annals of Mathematical Statistics*, 17 (1946), pp. 377–408.

TABLE XVIII Estimates of the Standard Deviation of a Normal Population Based on Percentiles.*

Estimate	Efficiency
$.339(X_{.93} - X_{.07})$	.65
$.171(X_{.95} + X_{.90} - X_{.10} - X_{.05})$	.76
$.120(X_{.98} + X_{.90} + X_{.80} - X_{.20} - X_{.10} - X_{.02})$	.87

* Based on Mosteller, F., "On some useful inefficient statistics," *Annals of Mathematical Statistics*, 17 (1946), pp. 377–408.

A. TABLE XIX * Transformation of a Proportion (p) to Radians (ϕ) [$\phi = 2 \arcsin \sqrt{p}$]

p	ϕ	p	ϕ	p	ϕ	p	ϕ	p	ϕ	p	ϕ
.001	.0633	.036	.3818	.26	1.0701	.61	1.7826	.951	2.6952	.986	2.9044
.002	.0895	.037	.3871	.27	1.0928	.62	1.8132	.952	2.6998	.987	2.9131
.003	.1096	.038	.3924	.28	1.1152	.63	1.8338	.953	2.7045	.988	2.9221
.004	.1266	.039	.3976	.29	1.1374	.64	1.8546	.954	2.7093	.989	2.9315
.005	.1415	.040	.4027	.30	1.1593	.65	1.8755	.955	2.7141	.990	2.9413
.006	.1551	.041	.4078	.31	1.1810	.66	1.8965	.956	2.7189	.991	2.9516
.007	.1675	.042	.4128	.32	1.2025	.67	1.9177	.957	2.7238	.992	2.9625
.008	.1791	.043	.4178	.33	1.2239	.68	1.9391	.958	2.7288	.993	2.9741
.009	.1900	.044	.4227	.34	1.2451	.69	1.9606	.959	2.7338	.994	2.9865
.010	.2003	.045	.4275	.35	1.2661	.70	1.9823	.960	2.7389	.995	3.0001
.011	.2101	.046	.4323	.36	1.2870	.71	2.0042	.961	2.7440	.996	3.0150
.012	.2195	.047	.4371	.37	1.3078	.72	2.0264	.962	2.7492	.997	3.0320
.013	.2285	.048	.4418	.38	1.3284	.73	2.0488	.963	2.7545	.998	3.0521
.014	.2372	.049	.4464	.39	1.3490	.74	2.0715	.964	2.7598	.999	3.0783
.015	.2456	.050	.4510	.40	1.3694	.75	2.0944	.965	2.7652		
.016	.2537	.06	.4949	.41	1.3898	.76	2.1177	.966	2.7707		
.017	.2615	.07	.5355	.42	1.4101	.77	2.1412	.967	2.7762		
.018	.2691	.08	.5735	.43	1.4303	.78	2.1652	.968	2.7819		
.019	.2766	.09	.6094	.44	1.4505	.79	2.1895	.969	2.7876		
.020	.2838	.10	.6435	.45	1.4706	.80	2.2143	.970	2.7934		
.021	.2909	.11	.6761	.46	1.4907	.81	2.2395	.971	2.7993		
.022	.2978	.12	.7075	.47	1.5108	.82	2.2653	.972	2.8053		
.023	.3045	.13	.7377	.48	1.5308	.83	2.2916	.973	2.8115		
.024	.3111	.14	.7670	.49	1.5508	.84	2.3186	.974	2.8177		
.025	.3176	.15	.7954	.50	1.5708	.85	2.3462	.975	2.8240		
.026	.3239	.16	.8230	.51	1.5908	.86	2.3746	.976	2.8305		
.027	.3301	.17	.8500	.52	1.6108	.87	2.4037	.977	2.8371		
.028	.3363	.18	.8763	.53	1.6308	.88	2.4341	.978	2.8438		
.029	.3423	.19	.9021	.54	1.6509	.89	2.4655	.979	2.8507		
.030	.3482	.20	.9273	.55	1.6710	.90	2.4981	.980	2.8578		
.031	.3540	.21	.9521	.56	1.6911	.91	2.5319	.981	2.8650		
.032	.3597	.22	.9764	.57	1.7113	.92	2.5681	.982	2.8725		
.033	.3654	.23	1.0004	.58	1.7315	.93	2.6062	.983	2.8801		
.034	.3709	.24	1.0239	.59	1.7518	.94	2.6467	.984	2.8879		
.035	.3764	.25	1.0472	.60	1.7722	.950	2.6906	.985	2.8960		

* Discussion of the use of this table is found on page 423

B. Values of ϕ_0 and ϕ_1 for Samples of 10 to 50 *

Sample size	ϕ_0	ϕ_1	Sample size	ϕ_0	ϕ_1
10	.3176	2.8240	30	.1828	2.9588
11	.3027	2.8389	31	.1798	2.9617
12	.2897	2.8519	32	.1770	2.9646
13	.2782	2.8633	33	.1743	2.9673
14	.2681	2.8735	34	.1717	2.9699
15	.2589	2.8827	35	.1692	2.9724
16	.2507	2.8909	36	.1669	2.9747
17	.2431	2.8985	37	.1646	2.9770
18	.2363	2.9053	38	.1624	2.9792
19	.2299	2.9117	39	.1603	2.9813
20	.2241	2.9175	40	.1583	2.9833
21	.2187	2.9229	41	.1563	2.9853
22	.2136	2.9280	42	.1545	2.9871
23	.2089	2.9327	43	.1526	2.9889
24	.2045	2.9371	44	.1509	2.9907
25	.2003	2.9413	45	.1492	2.9924
26	.1964	2.9452	46	.1476	2.9940
27	.1927	2.9488	47	.1460	2.9956
28	.1893	2.9523	48	.1445	2.9971
29	.1860	2.9556	49	.1430	2.9986
			50	.1415	3.0001

* From *Techniques of Statistical Analysis* by permission of the author of Chapter 16, Churchill Eisenhart, and the publisher, the McGraw-Hill Book Co.

TABLE XX Transformation of Ranks to Standard Scores

Rank	Number of Persons Ranked																										Rank
	5	6	7	8	9	10	11	12	13	14	15	16	17	18	19	20	21	22	23	24	25	26	27	28	29	30	
1	63	64	65	65	66	66	67	67	68	68	68	69	69	69	69	70	70	70	70	70	71	71	71	71	71	71	1
2	55	57	58	59	60	60	61	62	62	62	63	63	64	64	64	64	65	65	65	65	66	66	66	66	66	66	2
3	50	52	54	55	56	57	57	58	59	59	60	60	60	61	61	62	62	62	62	63	63	63	63	63	64	64	3
4	45	48	50	52	53	54	55	55	56	57	57	58	58	59	59	59	60	60	60	61	61	61	61	62	62	62	4
5	37	43	46	48	50	51	52	53	54	55	55	56	56	57	57	58	58	58	59	59	59	59	60	60	60	60	5
6		36	42	45	47	49	50	51	52	53	53	54	55	55	56	56	56	57	57	57	58	58	58	59	59	59	6
7			35	41	44	46	48	49	50	51	52	52	53	54	54	55	55	55	56	56	56	57	57	57	58	58	7
8				35	40	43	45	47	48	49	50	51	51	52	53	53	54	54	55	55	55	56	56	56	57	57	8
9					34	40	43	45	46	47	48	49	50	51	51	52	52	53	53	54	54	54	55	55	55	55	9
10						34	39	42	44	45	47	48	49	49	50	51	51	52	52	53	53	53	54	54	55	55	10
11							33	38	41	43	45	46	47	48	49	49	50	51	51	52	52	52	53	53	54	54	11
12								33	38	41	43	44	45	46	47	48	49	49	50	51	51	51	52	52	53	53	12
13									32	38	40	42	44	45	46	47	48	48	49	49	50	50	51	51	52	52	13
14										32	37	40	42	43	44	45	46	47	48	48	49	50	50	50	51	51	14
15											32	37	40	41	43	44	45	46	47	47	48	49	49	50	50	50	15
16												31	36	39	41	42	44	45	45	46	47	48	48	49	49	50	16
17													31	36	39	41	42	43	44	45	46	47	47	48	48	49	17
18														31	36	38	40	42	43	44	45	46	46	47	47	48	18
19															31	36	38	40	41	43	44	44	45	46	46	47	19
20																30	35	38	40	41	42	43	44	45	45	46	20
21																	30	35	38	39	41	42	43	44	45	45	21
22																		30	35	37	39	41	42	43	43	45	22
23																			30	35	37	39	40	41	42	43	23
24																				30	34	37	39	40	41	42	24
25																					29	34	37	38	40	41	25
26																						29	34	37	38	40	26
27																							29	34	36	38	27
28																								29	34	36	28
29																									29	34	29
30																										29	30

From *Improvement of Grading Practices for Air Training Command Schools,* ATRC Manual 50–900–9.

TABLE XXI Squares, Square Roots, and Reciprocals

n	n^2	$\sqrt{n}$	$\sqrt{10n}$	$1/n$	n	n^2	$\sqrt{n}$	$\sqrt{10n}$	$1/n$
1	1	1.000	3.162	1.00000	51	2601	7.141	22.583	.01961
2	4	1.414	4.472	.50000	52	2704	7.211	22.804	.01923
3	9	1.732	5.477	.33333	53	2809	7.280	23.022	.01887
4	16	2.000	6.325	.25000	54	2916	7.348	23.238	.01852
5	25	2.236	7.071	.20000	55	3025	7.416	23.452	.01818
6	36	2.449	7.746	.16667	56	3136	7.483	23.664	.01786
7	49	2.646	8.367	.14286	57	3249	7.550	23.875	.01754
8	64	2.828	8.944	.12500	58	3364	7.616	24.083	.01724
9	81	3.000	9.487	.11111	59	3481	7.681	24.290	.01695
10	100	3.162	10.000	.10000	60	3600	7.746	24.495	.01667
11	121	3.317	10.488	.09091	61	3721	7.810	24.698	.01639
12	144	3.464	10.954	.08333	62	3844	7.874	24.900	.01613
13	169	3.606	11.402	.07692	63	3969	7.937	25.100	.01587
14	196	3.742	11.832	.07143	64	4096	8.000	25.298	.01562
15	225	3.873	12.247	.06667	65	4225	8.062	25.495	.01538
16	256	4.000	12.649	.06250	66	4356	8.124	25.690	.01515
17	289	4.123	13.038	.05882	67	4489	8.185	25.884	.01493
18	324	4.243	13.416	.05556	68	4624	8.246	26.077	.01471
19	361	4.359	13.784	.05263	69	4761	8.307	26.268	.01449
20	400	4.472	14.142	.05000	70	4900	8.367	26.458	.01429
21	441	4.583	14.491	.04762	71	5041	8.426	26.646	.01408
22	484	4.690	14.832	.04545	72	5184	8.485	26.833	.01389
23	529	4.796	15.166	.04348	73	5329	8.544	27.019	.01370
24	576	4.899	15.492	.04167	74	5476	8.602	27.203	.01351
25	625	5.000	15.811	.04000	75	5625	8.660	27.386	.01333
26	676	5.099	16.125	.03846	76	5776	8.718	27.568	.01316
27	729	5.196	16.432	.03704	77	5929	8.775	27.749	.01299
28	784	5.292	16.733	.03571	78	6084	8.832	27.928	.01282
29	841	5.385	17.029	.03448	79	6241	8.888	28.107	.01266
30	900	5.477	17.321	.03333	80	6400	8.944	28.284	.01250
31	961	5.568	17.607	.03226	81	6561	9.000	28.460	.01235
32	1024	5.657	17.889	.03125	82	6724	9.055	28.636	.01220
33	1089	5.745	18.166	.03030	83	6889	9.110	28.810	.01205
34	1156	5.831	18.439	.02941	84	7056	9.165	28.983	.01190
35	1225	5.916	18.708	.02857	85	7225	9.220	29.155	.01176
36	1296	6.000	18.974	.02778	86	7396	9.274	29.326	.01163
37	1369	6.083	19.235	.02703	87	7569	9.327	29.496	.01149
38	1444	6.164	19.494	.02632	88	7744	9.381	29.665	.01136
39	1521	6.245	19.748	.02564	89	7921	9.434	29.833	.01124
40	1600	6.325	20.000	.02500	90	8100	9.487	30.000	.01111
41	1681	6.403	20.248	.02439	91	8281	9.539	30.166	.01099
42	1764	6.481	20.494	.02381	92	8464	9.592	30.332	.01087
43	1849	6.557	20.736	.02326	93	8649	9.644	30.496	.01075
44	1936	6.633	20.976	.02273	94	8836	9.695	30.659	.01064
45	2025	6.708	21.213	.02222	95	9025	9.747	30.822	.01053
46	2116	6.782	21.448	.02174	96	9216	9.798	30.984	.01042
47	2209	6.856	21.679	.02128	97	9409	9.849	31.145	.01031
48	2304	6.928	21.909	.02083	98	9604	9.899	31.305	.01020
49	2401	7.000	22.136	.02041	99	9801	9.950	31.464	.01010
50	2500	7.071	22.361	.02000	100	10000	10.000	31.623	.01000

TABLE XXII Four-Place Logarithms

n	0	1	2	3	4	5	6	7	8	9
10	0000	0043	0086	0128	0170	0212	0253	0294	0334	0374
11	0414	0453	0492	0531	0569	0607	0645	0682	0719	0755
12	0792	0828	0864	0899	0934	0969	1004	1038	1072	1106
13	1139	1173	1206	1239	1271	1303	1335	1367	1399	1430
14	1461	1492	1523	1553	1584	1614	1644	1673	1703	1732
15	1761	1790	1818	1847	1875	1903	1931	1959	1987	2014
16	2041	2068	2095	2122	2148	2175	2201	2227	2253	2279
17	2304	2330	2355	2380	2405	2430	2455	2480	2504	2529
18	2553	2577	2601	2625	2648	2672	2695	2718	2742	2765
19	2788	2810	2833	2856	2878	2900	2923	2945	2967	2989
20	3010	3032	3054	3075	3096	3118	3139	3160	3181	3201
21	3222	3243	3263	3284	3304	3324	3345	3365	3385	3404
22	3424	3444	3464	3483	3502	3522	3541	3560	3579	3598
23	3617	3636	3655	3674	3692	3711	3729	3747	3766	3784
24	3802	3820	3838	3856	3874	3892	3909	3927	3945	3962
25	3979	3997	4014	4031	4048	4065	4082	4099	4116	4133
26	4150	4166	4183	4200	4216	4232	4249	4265	4281	4298
27	4314	4330	4346	4362	4378	4393	4409	4425	4440	4456
28	4472	4487	4502	4518	4533	4548	4564	4579	4594	4609
29	4624	4639	4654	4669	4683	4698	4713	4728	4742	4757
30	4771	4786	4800	4814	4829	4843	4857	4871	4886	4900
31	4914	4928	4942	4955	4969	4983	4997	5011	5024	5038
32	5051	5065	5079	5092	5105	5119	5132	5145	5159	5172
33	5185	5198	5211	5224	5237	5250	5263	5276	5289	5302
34	5315	5328	5340	5353	5366	5378	5391	5403	5416	5428
35	5441	5453	5465	5478	5490	5502	5514	5527	5539	5551
36	5563	5575	5587	5599	5611	5623	5635	5647	5658	5670
37	5682	5694	5705	5717	5729	5740	5752	5763	5775	5786
38	5798	5809	5821	5832	5843	5855	5866	5877	5888	5899
39	5911	5922	5933	5944	5955	5966	5977	5988	5999	6010
40	6021	6031	6042	6053	6064	6075	6085	6096	6107	6117
41	6128	6138	6149	6160	6170	6180	6191	6201	6212	6222
42	6232	6243	6253	6263	6274	6284	6294	6304	6314	6325
43	6335	6345	6355	6365	6375	6385	6395	6405	6415	6425
44	6435	6444	6454	6464	6474	6484	6493	6503	6513	6522
45	6532	6542	6551	6561	6571	6580	6590	6599	6609	6618
46	6628	6637	6646	6656	6665	6675	6684	6693	6702	6712
47	6721	6730	6739	6749	6758	6767	6776	6785	6794	6803
48	6812	6821	6830	6839	6848	6857	6866	6875	6884	6893
49	6902	6911	6920	6928	6937	6946	6955	6964	6972	6981
50	6990	6998	7007	7016	7024	7033	7042	7050	7059	7067
51	7076	7084	7093	7101	7110	7118	7126	7135	7143	7152
52	7160	7168	7177	7185	7193	7202	7210	7218	7226	7235
53	7243	7251	7259	7267	7275	7284	7292	7300	7308	7316
54	7324	7332	7340	7348	7356	7364	7372	7380	7388	7396

TABLE XXII Four-Place Logarithms (*Continued*)

n	0	1	2	3	4	5	6	7	8	9
55	7404	7412	7419	7427	7435	7443	7451	7459	7466	7474
56	7482	7490	7497	7505	7513	7520	7528	7536	7543	7551
57	7559	7566	7574	7582	7589	7597	7604	7612	7619	7627
58	7634	7642	7649	7657	7664	7672	7679	7686	7694	7701
59	7709	7716	7723	7731	7738	7745	7752	7760	7767	7774
60	7782	7789	7796	7803	7810	7818	7825	7832	7839	7846
61	7853	7860	7868	7875	7882	7889	7896	7903	7910	7917
62	7924	7931	7938	7945	7952	7959	7966	7973	7980	7987
63	7993	8000	8007	8014	8021	8028	8035	8041	8048	8055
64	8062	8069	8075	8082	8089	8096	8102	8109	8116	8122
65	8129	8136	8142	8149	8156	8162	8169	8176	8182	8189
66	8195	8202	8209	8215	8222	8228	8235	8241	8248	8254
67	8261	8267	8274	8280	8287	8293	8299	8306	8312	8319
68	8325	8331	8338	8344	8351	8357	8363	8370	8376	8382
69	8388	8395	8401	8407	8414	8420	8426	8432	8439	8445
70	8451	8457	8463	8470	8476	8482	8488	8494	8500	8506
71	8513	8519	8525	8531	8537	8543	8549	8555	8561	8567
72	8573	8579	8585	8591	8597	8603	8609	8615	8621	8627
73	8633	8639	8645	8651	8657	8663	8669	8675	8681	8686
74	8692	8698	8704	8710	8716	8722	8727	8733	8739	8745
75	8751	8756	8762	8768	8774	8779	8785	8791	8797	8802
76	8808	8814	8820	8825	8831	8837	8842	8848	8854	8859
77	8865	8871	8876	8882	8887	8893	8899	8904	8910	8915
78	8921	8927	8932	8938	8943	8949	8954	8960	8965	8971
79	8976	8982	8987	8993	8998	9004	9009	9015	9020	9025
80	9031	9036	9042	9047	9053	9058	9063	9069	9074	9079
81	9085	9090	9096	9101	9106	9112	9117	9122	9128	9133
82	9138	9143	9149	9154	9159	9165	9170	9175	9180	9186
83	9191	9196	9201	9206	9212	9217	9222	9227	9232	9238
84	9243	9248	9253	9258	9263	9269	9274	9279	9284	9289
85	9294	9299	9304	9309	9315	9320	9325	9330	9335	9340
86	9345	9350	9355	9360	9365	9370	9375	9380	9385	9390
87	9395	9400	9405	9410	9415	9420	9425	9430	9435	9440
88	9445	9450	9455	9460	9465	9469	9474	9479	9484	9489
89	9494	9499	9504	9509	9513	9518	9523	9528	9533	9538
90	9542	9547	9552	9557	9562	9566	9571	9576	9581	9586
91	9590	9595	9600	9605	9609	9614	9619	9624	9628	9633
92	9638	9643	9647	9652	9657	9661	9666	9671	9675	9680
93	9685	9689	9694	9699	9703	9708	9713	9717	9722	9727
94	9731	9736	9741	9745	9750	9754	9759	9763	9768	9773
95	9777	9782	9786	9791	9795	9800	9805	9809	9814	9818
96	9823	9827	9832	9836	9841	9845	9850	9854	9859	9863
97	9868	9872	9877	9881	9886	9890	9894	9899	9903	9908
98	9912	9917	9921	9926	9930	9934	9939	9943	9948	9952
99	9956	9961	9965	9969	9974	9978	9983	9987	9991	9996

TABLE XXIII Random Numbers

Line \ Col.	(1)	(2)	(3)	(4)	(5)	(6)	(7)	(8)	(9)	(10)	(11)	(12)	(13)	(14)
1	10480	15011	01536	02011	81647	91646	69179	14194	62590	36207	20969	99570	91291	90700
2	22368	46573	25595	85393	30995	89198	27982	53402	93965	34095	52666	19174	39615	99505
3	24130	48360	22527	97265	76393	64809	15179	24830	49340	32081	30680	19655	63348	58629
4	42167	93093	06243	61680	07856	16376	39440	53537	71341	57004	00849	74917	97758	16379
5	37570	39975	81837	16656	06121	91782	60468	81305	49684	60672	14110	06927	01263	54613
6	77921	06907	11008	42751	27756	53498	18602	70659	90655	15053	21916	81825	44394	42880
7	99562	72905	56420	69994	98872	31016	71194	18738	44013	48840	63213	21069	10634	12952
8	96301	91977	05463	07972	18876	20922	94595	56869	69014	60045	18425	84903	42508	32307
9	89579	14342	63661	10281	17453	18103	57740	84378	25331	12566	58678	44947	05585	56941
10	85475	36857	53342	53988	53060	59533	38867	62300	08158	17983	16439	11458	18593	64952
11	28918	69578	88231	33276	70997	79936	56865	05859	90106	31595	01547	85590	91610	78188
12	63553	40961	48235	03427	49626	69445	18663	72695	52180	20847	12234	90511	33703	90322
13	09429	93969	52636	92737	88974	33488	36320	17617	30015	08272	84115	27156	30613	74952
14	10365	61129	87529	85689	48237	52267	67689	93394	01511	26358	85104	20285	29975	89868
15	07119	97336	71048	08178	77233	13916	47564	81056	97735	85977	29372	74461	28551	90707
16	51085	12765	51821	51259	77452	16308	60756	92144	49442	53900	70960	63990	75601	40719
17	02368	21382	52404	60268	89368	19885	55322	44819	01188	65255	64835	44919	05944	55157
18	01011	54092	33362	94904	31273	04146	18594	29852	71585	85030	51132	01915	92747	64951
19	52162	53916	46369	58586	23216	14513	83149	98736	23495	64350	94738	17752	35156	35749
20	07056	97628	33787	09998	42698	06691	76988	13602	51851	46104	88916	19509	25625	58104
21	48663	91245	85828	14346	09172	30168	90229	04734	59193	22178	30421	61666	99904	32812
22	54164	58492	22421	74103	47070	25306	76468	26384	58151	06646	21524	15227	96909	44592
23	32639	32363	05597	24200	13363	38005	94342	28728	35806	06912	17012	64161	18296	22851
24	29334	27001	87637	87308	58731	00256	45834	15398	46557	41135	10367	07684	36188	18510
25	02488	33062	28834	07351	19731	92420	60952	61280	50001	67658	32586	86679	50720	94953

Taken from the 30-page table of 105,000 random digits prepared by the Bureau of Transport Economics and Statistics of the Interstate Commerce Commission, Washington, D.C., Mr. W. H. S. Stevens, Director. It is used in this text with their permission.

Line \ Col.	(1)	(2)	(3)	(4)	(5)	(6)	(7)	(8)	(9)	(10)	(11)	(12)	(13)	(14)
26	81525	72295	04839	96423	24878	82651	66566	14778	76797	14780	13300	87074	79666	95725
27	29676	20591	68086	26432	46901	20849	89768	81536	86645	12659	92259	57102	80428	25280
28	00742	57392	39064	66432	84673	40027	32832	61362	98947	96067	64760	64584	96096	98253
29	05366	04213	25669	26422	44407	44048	37937	63904	45766	66134	75470	66520	34693	90449
30	91921	26418	64117	94305	26766	25940	39972	22209	71500	64568	91402	42416	07844	69618
31	00582	04711	87917	77341	42206	35126	74087	99547	81817	42607	43808	76655	62028	76630
32	00725	69884	62797	56170	86324	88072	76222	36086	84637	93161	76038	65855	77919	88006
33	69011	65795	95876	55293	18988	27354	26575	08625	40801	59920	29841	80150	12777	48501
34	25976	57948	29888	88604	67917	48708	18912	82271	65424	69774	33611	54262	85963	03547
35	09763	83473	73577	12908	30883	18317	28290	35797	05998	41688	34952	37888	38917	88050
36	91567	42595	27958	30134	04024	86385	29880	99730	55536	84855	29080	09250	79656	73211
37	17955	56349	90999	49127	20044	59931	06115	20542	18059	02008	73708	83517	36103	42791
38	46503	18584	18845	49618	02304	51038	20655	58727	28168	15475	56942	53389	20562	87338
39	92157	89634	94824	78171	84610	82834	09922	25417	44137	48413	25555	21246	35509	20468
40	14577	62765	35605	81263	39667	47358	56873	56307	61607	49518	89656	20103	77490	18062
41	98427	07523	33362	64270	01638	92477	66969	98420	04880	45585	46565	04102	46880	45709
42	34914	63976	88720	82765	34476	17032	87589	40836	32427	70002	70663	88863	77775	69348
43	70060	28277	39475	46473	23219	53416	94970	25832	69975	94884	19661	72828	00102	66794
44	53976	54914	06990	67245	68350	82948	11398	42878	80287	88267	47363	46634	06541	97809
45	76072	29515	40980	07391	58745	25774	22987	80059	39911	96189	41151	14222	60697	59583
46	90725	52210	83974	29992	65831	38857	50490	83765	55657	14361	31720	57375	56228	41546
47	64364	67412	33339	31926	14883	24413	59744	92351	97473	89286	35931	04110	23726	51900
48	08962	00358	31662	25388	61642	34072	81249	35648	56891	69352	48373	45578	78547	81788
49	95012	68379	93526	70765	10592	04542	76463	54328	02349	17247	28865	14777	62730	92277
50	15664	10493	20492	38391	91132	21999	59516	81652	27195	48223	46751	22923	32261	85653
51	16408	81899	04153	53381	79401	21438	83035	92350	36693	31238	59649	91754	72772	02338
52	18629	81953	05520	91962	04739	13092	97662	24822	94730	06496	35090	04822	86774	98289
53	73115	35101	47498	87637	99016	71060	88824	71013	18735	20286	23153	72924	35165	43040
54	57491	16703	23167	49323	45021	33132	12544	41035	80780	45393	44812	12515	98931	91202
55	30405	83946	23792	14422	15059	45799	22716	19792	09983	74353	68668	30429	70735	25499
56	16631	35006	85900	98275	32388	52390	16815	69298	82732	38480	73817	32523	41961	44437
57	96773	20206	42559	78985	05300	22164	24369	54224	35083	19687	11052	91491	60383	19746
58	38935	64202	14349	82674	66523	44133	00697	35552	35970	19124	63318	29686	03387	59846
59	31624	76384	17403	53363	44167	64486	64758	75366	76554	31601	12614	33072	60332	92325
60	78919	19474	23632	27889	47914	02584	37680	20801	72152	39339	34806	08930	85001	87820

TABLE XXIV Pre-registration Scores of 447 College Students on the Cooperative Test Service English Test (Data supplied by Dr. Irving Lorge)

Subject	Score	Subject	Score	Subject	Score	Subject	Score	Subject	Score
1	141	41	133	81	102	121	156	161	093
2	120	42	146	82	138	122	098	162	094
3	150	43	138	83	132	123	085	163	119
4	156	44	138	84	118	124	115	164	139
5	122	45	128	85	135	125	129	165	166
6	128	46	127	86	100	126	143	166	108
7	112	47	142	87	111	127	108	167	103
8	178	48	173	88	169	128	087	168	092
9	120	49	109	89	124	129	121	169	175
10	160	50	131	90	134	130	187	170	160
11	104	51	157	91	135	131	179	171	152
12	088	52	111	92	180	132	140	172	140
13	100	53	114	93	102	133	136	173	177
14	191	54	117	94	117	134	086	174	133
15	137	55	115	95	085	135	175	175	111
16	108	56	155	96	169	136	120	176	114
17	147	57	190	97	127	137	175	177	106
18	127	58	159	98	128	138	133	178	147
19	156	59	141	99	131	139	107	179	090
20	201	60	100	100	167	140	119	180	167
21	131	61	125	101	118	141	135	181	156
22	174	62	116	102	142	142	100	182	130
23	096	63	148	103	143	143	102	183	143
24	140	64	169	104	094	144	138	184	142
25	102	65	139	105	117	145	129	185	151
26	090	66	145	106	114	146	134	186	168
27	177	67	084	107	091	147	145	187	134
28	125	68	180	108	091	148	148	188	120
29	164	69	139	109	120	149	155	189	124
30	150	70	166	110	119	150	124	190	176
31	181	71	159	111	135	151	109	191	170
32	118	72	126	112	158	152	103	192	120
33	192	73	177	113	138	153	113	193	165
34	169	74	165	114	123	154	135	194	102
35	117	75	174	115	199	155	117	195	109
36	152	76	173	116	111	156	123	196	116
37	176	77	149	117	105	157	101	197	145
38	089	78	173	118	100	158	107	198	136
39	151	79	093	119	158	159	108	199	099
40	148	80	118	120	103	160	093	200	163

Subject	Score	Subject	Score	Subject	Score	Subject	Score	Subject	Score
201	108	251	098	301	130	351	095	401	068
202	144	252	104	302	140	352	185	402	078
203	117	253	128	303	113	353	095	403	063
204	166	254	131	304	189	354	160	404	077
205	115	255	099	305	152	355	133	405	032
206	089	256	178	306	105	356	120	406	058
207	128	257	119	307	111	357	149	407	063
208	165	258	114	308	109	358	137	408	070
209	176	259	090	309	139	359	137	409	058
210	148	260	129	310	110	360	115	410	053
211	127	261	148	311	156	361	087	411	080
212	143	262	096	312	156	362	097	412	072
213	143	263	108	313	103	363	124	413	052
214	183	264	162	314	165	364	128	414	078
215	151	265	121	315	121	365	158	415	069
216	144	266	154	316	105	366	157	416	083
217	139	267	178	317	153	367	149	417	066
218	146	268	168	318	132	368	137	418	055
219	151	269	089	319	114	369	079	419	036
220	086	270	147	320	184	370	068	420	051
221	136	271	154	321	118	371	058	421	070
222	148	272	087	322	105	372	081	422	080
223	107	273	177	323	186	373	045	423	072
224	132	274	154	324	141	374	072	424	073
225	180	275	140	325	173	375	060	425	076
226	118	276	093	326	124	376	050	426	083
227	106	277	148	327	140	377	075	427	080
228	086	278	088	328	103	378	044	428	082
229	143	279	157	329	165	379	076	429	081
230	158	280	136	330	172	380	039	430	057
231	122	281	094	331	185	381	058	431	078
232	096	282	155	332	094	382	071	432	052
233	143	283	163	333	094	383	029	433	063
234	151	284	123	334	091	384	072	434	065
235	163	285	110	335	164	385	063	435	052
236	132	286	125	336	172	386	080	436	081
237	168	287	147	337	174	387	083	437	056
238	125	288	092	338	136	388	050	438	081
239	164	289	091	339	164	389	070	439	058
240	162	290	169	340	101	390	082	440	083
241	106	291	180	341	131	391	078	441	072
242	085	292	149	342	129	392	058	442	016
243	159	293	115	343	144	393	080	443	069
244	136	294	155	344	178	394	069	444	076
245	152	295	142	345	088	395	040	445	063
246	144	296	157	346	183	396	046	446	028
247	122	297	104	347	146	397	067	447	082
248	185	298	086	348	099	398	047		
249	159	299	109	349	116	399	047		
250	136	300	132	350	108	400	065		

Glossary of Symbols

The letters X and Y (and Z when a third letter is needed) are here customarily used to denote random variables and observations on individuals. The other English letters, capital or small, are used as convenience may require to denote constants in an equation, or to name groups or categories within groups. Letters at the first of the alphabet are used most often for this purpose. Such casual uses to which one letter might be put as well as another, will not be included in this glossary. Small letters from the middle of the alphabet, especially i and j but also h, k, and l, are used as variable subscripts. (See pages 112 and 197.)

Parameters are customarily denoted by Greek letters and sample statistics by English. However, certain exceptions have been made, as in the use of χ^2 to denote a statistic and of F, P, and Q to denote the frequency and proportion in a population.

The use of multiple subscripts has been treated on page 196. The use of subscripts in multiple and partial correlation and regression is discussed in Chapter 13.

A bar over any letter indicates the sample mean of the variable denoted by the letter.

Greek letters and English letters are listed separately according to their respective alphabets. Symbols of operation are listed separately.

a	(1) Constant term in regression equation; (2) observed frequency in one class of double dichotomy.
a_i	(1) Frequency in ith row and first column of a sample in which horizontal trait is dichotomous, or similarly for reversal of rows and columns (see page 99); (2) constant term in the regression equation for the ith group.
A	(1) Constant term in regression equation; (2) Σa_i; (3) alternative to a stated hypothesis; (4) arbitrary origin.
b	Frequency observed in one class of a double dichotomy.
b_i	(1) Frequency in ith row and second column of a sample in which horizontal trait is dichotomous (see page 99); (2) regression coefficient for the ith group.
b_{yx}	Regression coefficient in the sample equation to estimate y from x, or Y from X (similarly b_{xy}, b_{12}, etc.).
b^*_{yx}	Analogous to b_{yx} except that each variable is expressed as a multiple of its standard deviation, or $b_{yx}s_x/s_y$.
$b_{12\cdot34}$	Coefficient for the term involving x_2 (or X_2) in the sample regression equation to estimate x_1 (or X_1) from x_2, x_3, and x_4 (or X_2, X_3, and X_4). (See Chapter 13 for use of other subscripts.)
$b^*_{12\cdot34}$	Analogous to $b_{12\cdot34}$ except that each variable is expressed as a multiple of its standard deviation, or $b_{12\cdot34}s_2/s_1$.
B	(1) Σb_i; (2) a term in Bartlett's test for homogeneity of variance.
B'	Approximation to B in Bartlett's test.

c (1) Observed frequency in one class of a double dichotomy; (2) the number of columns in a layout of rows and columns.

C (1) Coefficient of contingency; (2) a class or category, usually with subscripts to indicate which class; (3) the mean square among columns as in Chapter 13; (4) sum of squares or sum of products as used in Chapter 15; (5) elements of the inverse matrix in multiple regression.

C_{xxi} The sum of the squares of deviations from the mean, or $\Sigma(X - \overline{X}_i)^2$ for the ith group or category, and similarly for C_{yyi}. (See Chapter 15.)

C_{xxb} Sum of squares between groups, or $\sum_{i=1}^{k} N_i(\overline{X}_i - \overline{X})^2$, and similarly for C_{yyb}.

C_{xxw} Sum of squares within groups, or $\sum_{i=1}^{k} \sum_{\alpha=1}^{N_i} (X_{i\alpha} - \overline{X}_i)^2$; and similarly for C_{yyw}. (See Chapter 15.)

C_{xyi} The sum of products $\Sigma(X_{i\alpha} - \overline{X}_i)(Y_{i\alpha} - \overline{Y}_i)$ for the ith group or category. (See Chapter 15.)

C_{xyb} Sum of cross products for means, or $\sum_{i=1}^{k} N_i(\overline{X}_i - \overline{X})(\overline{Y}_i - \overline{Y})$. (See Chapter 15.)

C_{xyw} Sum of cross products within groups, or $\sum_{i=1}^{k} \sum_{\alpha=1}^{N_i} (X_{i\alpha} - \overline{X}_i)(Y_{i\alpha} - \overline{Y}_i)$. (See Chapter 15.)

C_{xxT} Sum of squares for total group, or $\sum_{i=1}^{k} \sum_{\alpha=1}^{N_i} (X_{i\alpha} - \overline{X})^2$ and similarly for C_{yyT}. (See Chapter 15.)

C_{xyT} Sum of cross products for total group, or $\sum_{i=1}^{k} \sum_{\alpha=1}^{N_i} (X_{i\alpha} - \overline{X})(Y_{i\alpha} - \overline{Y})$. (See Chapter 15.)

$C(A < \mu < B) = 1 - \alpha$ A statement made with confidence coefficient $1 - \alpha$ that μ lies between A and B, and similarly for statements about other parameters.

d (1) An error of measurement, as in Chapter 12; (2) $\mu_A - \mu_H$ as on page 163; (3) $\overline{X}_i - \overline{X}$ as on page 128; (4) observed frequency in one class of a double dichotomy. In some texts d indicates the deviation of a score from its mean but it is not so used here.

d.f. Degrees of freedom. See also n.

D (1) Weighted difference between means as on page 399; (2) difference between two scores of same individual as on page 152; (3) maximum vertical difference between two cumulative frequency polygons in K–S test.

e (1) A mathematical constant approximately equal to 2.718 occurring frequently in equations of probability distributions; (2) an error of measurement as used in Chapter 12.

E Mean square for error as used in Chapter 14.

E_{xy}, E_{yx} — Correlation ratio in a sample. (In some texts the symbols η_{xy} and η_{yx} are used, but here the latter denote population values of the correlation ratio.)

$E(\ )$ — The expectation of, or expected value of whatever variable is denoted within the parenthesis, as $E(X)$, $E(X - \mu)^2$, $E(p)$, etc. (see page 27).

f — Frequency in a sample.

F — (1) Frequency in a population; (2) variance ratio in a sample, ordinarily used with a subscript to denote the probability under some hypothesis of obtaining a smaller value by chance.

$F_{.95}$ — The 95th percentile of the variance ratio distribution, and similarly for other subscripts.

$F_{\max}$ — The ratio of the largest to the smallest variance (see page 192).

H — Test statistic for comparing samples by means of the sums of ranks.

$H : \mu = A$ — The hypothesis that the mean of a population is equal to A, and similarly for other hypotheses.

h — A variable subscript.

i — (1) A variable subscript (see pages 112 and 197); (2) the width of a class interval.

j — A variable subscript.

k — (1) The number of groups, classes, variables, strata, and the like; (2) a variable subscript.

l_i — Weight given ith variable, used on page 356.

m_i — Weight given ith variable, used on page 356.

m — (1) The number of terms accumulated in one tail of the binomial distribution as used in Table IV; (2) the number of items in a test; (3) the number of clusters in a cluster sample, as used on page 176.

M — (1) The number of cases in a finite population (see page 167); (2) the number of clusters in a finite population (see page 176).

n — (1) The number of degrees of freedom; (2) the number of cases in a subclass (occasional use).

n_1 — The number of degrees of freedom for the numerator mean square of a variance ratio.

n_2 — The number of degrees of freedom for the denominator mean square of a variance ratio.

N — The number of cases in a sample, sometimes used with a subscript to indicate a subsample.

$N!$ — Factorial N (see page 18).

$\binom{N}{r}$ — The number of combinations of N things taken r at a time.

p — The proportion of elements in one class of a dichotomous sample.

p_i — The proportion of elements in ith class of a sample.

P — The proportion of elements in one class of a dichotomous population.

P_i — The proportion of elements in ith class of a population.

$P(X \text{ is in } C_i)$ — Probability that X is in the ith class. (See page 13 for variants.)

$P(X_2 \text{ is in } C_j \mid X_1 \text{ is in } C_j)$ — Probability that X_2 will fall in the jth class if X_1 falls in the ith class. (See page 14 for variants of this.)

$P(A < x < B)$ — Probability that x will fall between the fixed values A and B.

q — $1 - p$

Q — $1 - P$

r — (1) Coefficient of correlation; (2) the number of rows in a layout of rows and columns.

r_{bis} — Biserial correlation.

r_{pb} — Point biserial correlation.

r_t — Tetrachoric correlation.

$r_{x.yz}$, $r_{1.23}$ — Coefficient of multiple correlation. (See Chapter 13 for use of subscripts. See $R_{x.yz}$ below).

$r_{xy.z}$, $r_{12.3}$ — Coefficient of partial correlation (see Chapter 13 for use of subscripts).

r_{xx} — Coefficient of reliability.

${}_pr_{xx}$ — Spearman-Brown coefficient of reliability when test length is increased p times.

${}_{pq}r_{xy}$ — Estimate of correlation between two tests when one is lengthened p times and the other q times.

R — (1) Rank order correlation; (2) row mean square in analysis of variance.

R_i — Sum of ranks for group i.

$R_{Hi} \cdot R_{Li}$ — The number of correct responses to the ith item among the upper and lower groups, when these groups have been selected on the basis of total test score.

$R_{x.yz}$, $R_{1.23}$ — Coefficient of multiple correlation. (See Chapter 13 for use of subscripts. Also written $r_{x.yz}$, $r_{1.23}$.)

s — (1) Standard deviation of a sample, used often with a subscript to name the variable; (2) standard error of a statistic as estimated from sample values, used with a subscript to name the statistic, as $s_{\overline{X}}$, s_p, etc. (see σ).

$s_{y.x}$ — The standard error of estimate for a sample (see $s^2_{y.x}$).

s^2 — Variance, or square of the standard deviation, with meanings analogous to those stated above for s.

$s^2_{y.x}$ — Variance of y-residuals from regression line to estimate y from x, and similarly for other subscripts. (See Chapter 10 for formula which differs slightly from formula in some other texts.)

S — Sum of squares used in analysis of variance and covariance. For meaning of S_w, S_b, S_t, S_1, S_2, S_3 and S_4, see Chapter 15.

t — (1) Ratio of a variable with unit normal distribution to the sample estimate of the standard error of that variable; (2) the number of observations in a tied set, as in Chapter 18.

T — $(t - 1)t(t + 1)$ where t is the number of observations in a tied set.

T_i — The total of all scores in group i or $\Sigma X_{i\alpha}$.

T_i' — The total sum of deviations of coded scores in group i from an arbitrary origin, or $T_i' = \Sigma N_i x'_{i\alpha}$.

u — (1) Ordinate of unit normal curve; (2) statistic into which the variance ratio F is transformed, as in Chapter 17.

v — The number of runs in a sample (see Chapter 18).

w, W — Width of a confidence interval.

W — Coefficient of concordance.

x — Deviation of a score from its sample mean, $x = X - \overline{X}$. (Similarly for other letters.)

x' Deviation of a score from an arbitrary origin, $x' = X - A$.

X A gross score. (Similarly for other letters.)

$\overline{X}$ Mean of a sample. (Similarly for other letters.)

$\tilde{x}, \tilde{X}$ Sample estimate computed from a regression equation.

$X_{.50}$ Median of a sample.

$X_{.25}$ 25th percentile of a sample.

$X_{H\alpha}, X_{L\alpha}$ Test score of an individual in the upper or lower group.

$y, y', Y, \tilde{}, \tilde{Y}$ Analogous to $x, x', X, \tilde{x}, \tilde{X}$.

y Ordinate of population distribution on a continuous variable.

z A variable with unit normal distribution, or an abscissa of the normal probability curve. (In other texts this letter is sometimes used for an ordinate of the normal probability curve but is not so used here.)

z_r Transformation used in testing significance of a correlation coefficient.

z^* Transformation used in testing significance of a biserial coefficient of correlation.

α (1) Level of significance; risk of Type I error; (2) subscript attached to a statistic (as z_α, t_α, $\chi^2_{1-\alpha}$) to indicate probability of obtaining a smaller value of the statistic by chance; (3) subscript attached to X, x, Y, or y to indicate that the observation is for the αth individual.

β (1) Probability of accepting a hypothesis when an alternative is true, risk of Type II error; (2) population regression coefficient. (For subscripts used with β see Chapters 10 and 13.)

β^* Population regression coefficient when variables are expressed as multiples of their standard deviations. (Subscripts same as for β.)

ζ_r Population value corresponding to the statistic z_r.

ζ^* Population value corresponding to z^*.

η_{yx}, η_{xy} Correlation ratio in the population.

μ Population mean. (Subscript may be used to indicate the variable or statistic of which it is the mean.)

$\xi_{.50}$ Median of a population (see Chapter 16).

$\xi_{.25}$ $\xi_{.10}$, etc. Percentile of a population, the percent of cases with lower scores being indicated by the subscript (see Chapter 16).

π 3.1416, or the ratio of the circumference of a circle to its diameter.

ρ Correlation coefficient in a population. (In some other sources it is used to denote a coefficient of rank order correlation but is not so used here.)

ρ_{xx}, ρ_{yy} Reliability coefficient in a population.

$\rho_{12.34}$ Coefficient of partial correlation in a population. (For other subscripts, see Chapter 13.)

$\rho_{1.234}$ Coefficient of multiple correlation in a population, correlation of x_1 with regression estimate of x_1 made from best linear combination of x_2, x_3 and x_4. (For other subscripts, see Chapter 13.)

σ (1) Standard deviation of a population, often used with a subscript to name the variable as σ_x, σ_y; (2) standard error of a statistic, used with a subscript to name the statistic, as $\sigma_{\overline{X}}$, σ_p, σ_s, etc.; (3) standard error of estimate for a population = standard deviation of residuals from a regression equation, used with subscripts as $\sigma_{1.234}$, in which

	the primary symbol before the period names the variable estimated from the regression equation and the secondary subscripts following the period name the independent variables employed in the equation.
σ^2	Variance of a population, with subscripts as for σ.
Σ	The sum of.
$\sum_{i=a}^{b} X_i$	$X_a + X_{a+1} + \cdots + X_b$ (see pages 111 and 197).
τ	(1) A measure of relation based on order, discussed in Chapter 11; (2) the "true score" of an individual on X, discussed in Chapter 12.
υ	The "true score" of an individual on Y, discussed in Chapter 12.
ϕ	(1) A measure of relationship between two dichotomous variables, discussed in Chapter 11; (2) a transformation of percents to angles, described in Chapter 16.
χ^2	Chi-square.
$\chi^2_{.05}$	The fifth percentile of the χ^2 distribution. (In other sources this symbol may mean the 95th percentile.)
χ_r^2	Chi-square computed from ranks.
χ_y^2	Chi-square after application of Yates' correction.
$X > Y$ or $Y < X$	X is greater than Y, or Y is less than X.
$X \geqq Y$ or $Y \leqq X$	X is greater than or equal to Y; X is not less than Y; Y is less than or equal to X; or Y is not greater than X.
$=$	Is equal to.
$\neq$	Is not equal to.
$\cong$	Is approximately equal to.
$\lvert a \rvert$	The absolute or numerical value of a, the sign being taken as positive.
$\sqrt{a}$	The positive square root of a.
$a^{\frac{1}{2}}$	The positive square root of a.

Answers to Problems

Exercise 2.1, page 17

1. b. $P(X = 1) = P(X = 2) = \cdots = P(X = 6)$
   c. $P(X = 1 \text{ or } X = 2) = P(X = 1) + P(X = 2) = \frac{1}{3}$
   d. $P(X = 1) + P(X = 3) + P(X = 5) = \frac{1}{6} + \frac{1}{6} + \frac{1}{6} = \frac{1}{2}$
   f. $P(X \neq 6) = 1 - P(X = 6) = 1 - \frac{1}{6} = \frac{5}{6}$
2. a. The probability that 3 will appear on both throws.
   b. The probability that the sum of the numbers appearing on the two throws will be 2.
   c. The probability that the sum of the numbers appearing on the two throws will be 3.
   d. The probability that the second number will be 5 if the first number is 6.
   e. The probability that the second number will be 6 when the first number is 6.
   f. The probability that both numbers will be odd.
   g. The probability that both numbers will be smaller than 6.
   h. The probability that the sum of the two numbers will be 11.

Exercise 2.2, page 19

2. a. 120 b. 210 c. $\frac{1}{20}$ d. 10 e. 6 f. 16 g. 35 h. $\frac{240}{11}$

Exercise 2.3, page 26

1. $(.7 + .3)^4 = .240 + .412 + .265 + .076 + .008 = 1.001$
2. a. $(.5 + .5)^3 = .125 + .375 + .375 + .125 = 1.000$
   b. $(.5 + .5)^6 = .016 + .094 + .234 + .312 + .234 + .094 + .016 = 1.000$
   c. $(.5 + .5)^{10} = .001 + .010 + .044 + .117 + .205 + .246 + .205 + .117 + .044 + .010 + .001 = 1.000$
4. a. $(.4 + .6)^3 = .064 + .288 + .432 + .216 = 1.000$
   b. $(.4 + .6)^6 = .004 + .037 + .138 + .276 + .311 + .187 + .047$
   c. $(.4 + .6)^{10} = .000 + .002 + .011 + .042 + .111 + .201 + .251 + .215 + .121 + .040 + .006$
5. a. $(.8 + .2)^3 = .512 + .384 + .096 + .008$
   b. $(.8 + .2)^6 = .262 + .393 + .246 + .082 + .015 + .002 + .000$
   c. $(.8 + .2)^{10} = .107 + .268 + .302 + .201 + .088 + .026 + .006 + .001 + .000 + .000$

Exercise 2.5, page 30

1. a. $E(Np) = NP = 10(.5) = 5$ b. No; No. c. Yes $E(Np) = 20(.5) = 10$
   d. $\sigma_p{}^2 = NPQ = 10(.5)^2 = 2.5$; 500 observations are actually a sample; 1000 observations provide better approximation than 500.
   e. Yes. $\sigma^2 = 20(.5)^2 = 5.0$
2. c. Different only because of sampling error.
   d. No; 500 observations are subject to sampling error.

Exercise 2.6, page 36

3. a. .12 b. .14 c. .99 d. .05 e. .99
f. .98 g. .05 h. .22 i. .03 j. .85
k. .10 l. .60 m. .005 n. .002 o. .06

4. a. 1.037 b. -1.751 c. .385 d. .6745 e. 1.645
f. 1.960 g. 2.576 h. -2.576 i. 1.96 j. .6745

Exercise 3.1, page 51

1. If $p = .4$, accept all stated hypotheses except $P = .9$.
If $p = .5$, accept all stated hypotheses except $P = .16$ and $P = .94$.
If $p = .2$, reject all stated hypotheses except $P = .04$ and $P = .49$.

2. If $p = .4$, range is $.12 < P < .75$.
If $p = .5$, range is $.18 < P < .82$.
If $p = .2$, range is $.02 < P < .55$.

Exercise 3.2, page 57

5. a. $.41 < P < .82$ b. $.56 < P < .74$ c. $.59 < P < .71$
d. $.11 < P < .45$ e. $.14 < P < .40$ f. $.22 < P < .28$

6. As N increases, width of interval decreases.

7. $.05 < P < .17$

8. $.65 < P < .83$

Exercise 3.3, page 59

2. a. $X \leqq 3$ and $X \geqq 11$ b. $X \leqq 4$ and $X \geqq 14$ c. $X \leqq 7$ and $X \geqq 18$

Exercise 3.4, page 63

3. a. HJ b. HK c. AB d. AC e. JM
f. KM g. BD h. CD i. BD j. CD

4. $\alpha = .02$; $\alpha = .11$

5. $P = .80$

6. $\alpha = .11$

7. α = ordinate at point H; $\beta = 1 -$ ordinate at alternative to H.

8. $\alpha = .172$. See A of Figure 3–5.

9. $\alpha = .172$. See B of Figure 3–5.

Exercise 3.5, page 66

3. .17; .11; .17

4. more satisfactory.

5. a. about .05 b. about .2 c. about .4
d. about .95 e. about .8 f. about .6

6. A; C

7. C; A

10.

Situation	*Decision*	*Risk of error* α	β
1	R	.071	O
2	A	0	X
3	R	.115	O
4	A	0	X
5	A	0	X

Exercise 3.6, page 76

1. $.36 < P < .48$
2. Yes; $p = .48$; $z = -3.46$; $z_{.02} = -2.05$; Reject $H: P \geqq .60$
3. $N = 72$ 4. $N = 63$ 5. $N = 813$

Review Exercise, page 79

3. *R*II; *A*I; *R*II; *A*I; *A*I

Exercise 4.1, page 92

1. a. The probability of obtaining a random sample which will yield a value of χ^2 less than 9.9 in a situation in which there are 21 degrees of freedom is .02.
   h. In χ^2 problems involving 25 degrees of freedom, 90% of random samples may be expected to yield values of χ^2 between 14.6 and 37.7.
   m. The probability that a random sample will show a value of χ^2 larger than 42 if the number of degrees of freedom is 22 cannot be read exactly from Table VIII but that probability is between .005 and .01; there is probability between .005 and .01 of obtaining $\chi^2 > 42$ if the degrees of freedom are 22; between .5% and 1% of all random samples may be expected to produce a value of χ^2 larger than 42 if the appropriate number of degrees of freedom is 22.

2. and 3.

	$\chi^2_{.95}$		$\chi^2_{.99}$	
b.	14.1	*A*	18.5	*A*
c.	14.1	*R*	18.5	*A*
d.	14.1	*R*	18.5	*R*
e.	25.0	*A*	30.6	*A*
f.	37.7	*R*	44.3	*R*
g.	43.8	*A*	50.9	*A*
h.	26.3	*R*	32.0	*A*
i.	19.7	*R*	24.7	*A*
j.	9.5	*R*	13.3	*A*

Exercise 4.2, page 94

1. a. $n = 3$, $N = 10$ b. $n = 3$, $N = 50$
2. Better fit in (*b*) because N is larger.
3.

Number of heads:	0	1	2	3	4
Expected frequency:	4	16	24	16	4
Observed frequency:	2	12	23	20	7

   $\chi^2 = 5.29$; $\chi^2_{.95} = 9.5$; No 4. $\chi^2 = 10.58$
5. $\chi^2 = 5.29r$. Multiplying observed and theoretic frequencies by r makes χ^2 r times as large.

Exercise 5.1, page 113

2. a. $\sum_{i=6}^{9} X_i$ b. $\sum_{i=5}^{8} 4x_i = 4 \sum_{i=5}^{8} x_i$ c. $\sum_{i=6}^{8} 3x_iy_i = 3 \sum_{i=6}^{8} x_iy_i$

   d. $\sum_{i=5}^{8} (Y_i - A) = \sum_{i=5}^{8} Y_i - 4A$ e. $\sum_{i=1}^{6} f_iX_i$

Exercise 5.1, page 113 cont.

3. a. 60 b. 5 c. 0 d. 26 e. 12
   f. 134 g. 625 h. 300 i. 125 j. + 26
4. a. 2 b. 6 c. 424 d. 129 e. 9
   f. 64 g. 64 h. 26 i. 26

Exercise 5.2, page 117

2. $\overline{X} = 81.3$, $s = 5.40$
3. a. $\overline{X} = 11$, $s^2 = 35.5$ b. $\overline{X} = 1.5$, $s^2 = 29.9$ c. $\overline{X} = 2.57$, $s^2 = 6.95$

Review Exercise, page 123

a. π, e b. μ, σ, $\mu_{\bar{x}}$ c. $\bar{x}$, s, χ^2, $\overline{X} - \mu$ d. Σ

σ_p does not fall into any of the classes named, for its value depends upon sample size as well as population P.

Exercise 7.1, page 144

1. a. 2.5 b. 1 c. .5 d. .05
   e. .4 f. .8 g. 2 h. 4
2. .044; .913; .0001; .9998

Exercise 7.2, page 146

4. a. $t_{.05} = -2.35$ and $t_{.95} = 2.35$ when $n = 3$
   b. $t_{.05} = -1.75$ and $t_{.95} = 1.75$ when $n = 16$
   c. $t_{.05} = -1.645$ and $t_{.95} = 1.645$ when $n = 500$
5. $t_{.10} = -3.08$ and $t_{.90} = 3.08$ when $n = 1$
   $t_{.10} = -1.37$ and $t_{.90} = 1.37$ when $n = 10$
   $t_{.10} = -1.282$ and $t_{.90} = 1.282$ when $n = 400$
6. a. $P > .20$ when $n = 1$ b. $.05 < P < .10$ when $n = 3$ c. $.001 < P < .01$ when $n = 500$

Exercise 7.3, page 151

3. 95%; all 4 or 100%
   90%; all 4 or 100%
   50%; 3 or 75%
   10%; 1 or 25%
4. $C(25.6 < \mu < 28.8) = .99$; $C(26.0 < \mu < 28.4) = .95$

Exercise 7.4, page 160

1. $t = 2.22$. If $\alpha = .05$, reject $H : \mu_1 = \mu_2$. If $\alpha = .01$, accept H.
2. $\overline{D} = 1.48$; $s_{\overline{D}} = .754$; $t = 1.96$; $t_{.975} = 2.02$
   If $\alpha = .05$, accept $H : \mu_1 = \mu_2$
3. For grip, $t = \dfrac{2.2}{\sqrt{3.35}} = 1.2$

   For balance, $t = \dfrac{1.95}{\sqrt{.5914}} = 2.53$

Exercise 7.5, page 169

1. a. .158 b. .475 c. .053
2. a. .224 b. .5 c. .167

Exercise 7.5, page 169 cont.

3. $N = 750$

4. a. $t = 4.4/3.92 = 1.12$; $t_{.995} = 3.25$; accept H
   b. $t = 4.4/4.1 = 1.07$; accept H
   c. $n = 9.54 - 2 = 7.5$ or 7; accept H

7. a. $t = 3.2/1.386 = 2.31$; $t_{.975} = 2.20$; reject H
   b. Accept H without computation as $\overline{X} < 35$
   c. $t = -2.308$; $t_{.05} = -1.80$; reject H
   d. $28.75 < \mu < 34.85$
   e. $27.49 < \mu < 36.11$

8. a. (7.10), normal
   b. (7.10), t, $n = 5$
   c. (7.21), normal
   d. (7.21), t, $n = 31$
   e. (7.24), normal
   f. (7.24), t, $n = 11.6$

9. a. (6) b. (1) c. (1) or (2) d. (6)

10. (1) $N = 292$ (2) $N_1 = N_2 = 420$ (3) $N_1 = 346, N_2 = 577$
    (4) $N_1 = N_2 = 47$ (5) $N_1 = 44, N_2 = 87$

Exercise 8.1, page 183

8. 90%; 3 or 75%
   80%; 3 or 75%
   60%; 1 or 25%
   40%; 1 or 25%

9. $\chi^2 = 4031.7/400 = 10.08 < \chi^2_{.50}$

10. $4.53 < \sigma^2 < 7.42$

Exercise 8.2, page 187

	F	$F_{.95}$	$F_{.99}$	*Probability*
2. a.	1.38	1.74	2.20	$P > .10$
b.	2.88	1.95	2.56	$P < .02$
c.	1.76	2.18	3.09	$P > .10$
d.	4.78	2.90	4.73	$.02 < P < .10$
e.	2.19	1.72	2.19	$P = .02$

Exercise 9.1, page 198

See Table 9.1, page 199

Exercise 10.1, page 242

Data required for 1 and 2:

$\overline{Y} = 50.83$; $(N-1)s_y^2 = 2869.8$; $s_y^2 = 70.00$; $s_y = 8.367$
$\overline{X} = 47.10$; $(N-1)s_x^2 = 5078.6$; $s_x^2 = 123.85$; $s_x = 11.13$
$s^2_{y.x} = 45.75$; $s_{y.x} = 6.764$; $b_{yx} = .453$ $r_{yx} = .602$

1. a. By (10.27), $t = \dfrac{(.453 - 0)(11.13)\sqrt{41}}{6.764} = 4.77$

   By (10.28), $t = \dfrac{.602\sqrt{40}}{\sqrt{1 - (.602)^2}} = 4.77$

   $t_{.995} = 2.70$ Reject $H: \beta_{yx} = 0$

Exercise 10. 1, page 242 cont.

b. By (10.27), $t = \dfrac{(.453 - .6)(11.13)\sqrt{41}}{6.764} = -1.55$

$t_{.975} = 2.02$ Accept $H : \beta_{yx} = .6$

c. By (10.25), $t = \dfrac{(50.83 - 52)\sqrt{42}}{6.764} = -1.11$

Accept $H : \mu_y = 52$

2. a. By (10.32), $.261 < \beta_{yx} < .644$
b. By (10.31), $48.72 < \mu_y < 52.94$
c. By (10.33), $30.9 < \sigma^2_{y.x} < 75.0$
d. By (10.34), $45.5 < \mu_{y.x} < 49.8$

3. $\overline{X} = 24.2$; $\overline{Y} = 69.0$; $b_{yx} = .217$
$\tilde{Y} = 63.8 + .217X$; $s^2_{y.x} = 54.1$
$-.125 < \beta_{yx} < .559$
$64.6 < \mu_y < 73.4$
$33.3 < \sigma^2_{y.x} < 103.2$
Accept $H : \beta_{yx} = 0$ and $H : \beta_{yx} \leqq 0$; Reject $H : \beta_{yx} = .6$

Exercise 10.2, page 252

$r = .06$	$N = 5$	$N = 26$	$N = 82$	$N = 102$	$N = 401$
$\dfrac{r\sqrt{N-2}}{\sqrt{1-r^2}}$	.104	.294	.538	.601	1.20
$r\sqrt{N-1}$	·120	.300	.540	.603	1.20
$r = .20$					
$\dfrac{r\sqrt{N-2}}{\sqrt{1-r^2}}$	.354	1.00	1.83	2.04	4.08
$r\sqrt{N-1}$	.400	1.00	1.80	2.01	4.00
$r = .60$					
$\dfrac{r\sqrt{N-2}}{\sqrt{1-r^2}}$	1.30	3.67	6.71	7.50	14.98
$r\sqrt{N-1}$	1.20	3.00	5.40	6.03	12.00

Highly satisfactory agreement for N large and r near zero.

Exercise 10.3, page 257

1. $t = 1.33$
2. $t = 2.03$

Exercise 10.4, page 258

1. a. $\overline{X} = 31.38$; $\overline{Y} = 49.15$; $b_{yx} = .652$, $s_x = 7.25$
$s_y = 9.42$ $r_{xy} = .502$; $s_{y.x} = 8.19$
b. $\tilde{Y} = .652X + 28.69$
c. 75%
d. $t = 5.7$

Exercise 10.4, page 258 cont.

e. If $X = 62$, $\tilde{Y} = 69.11$; if $X = 38$, $\tilde{Y} = 53.47$; if $X = 54$, $\tilde{Y} = 63.90$

f. (1) $53.17 < \mu_{y.x} < 58.97$ (2) $.425 < \beta_{yx} < .879$

(3) $.336 < \rho < .635$ (4) $49.7 < \sigma^2_{y.x} < 86.8$

2. a. $\tilde{Y} = 20.16 + .812X$ **b.** $\tilde{X} = 20.60 + .456Y$ **c.** $.439 < \rho < .737$

d. $r = .6085$; $z_r = .707$

$\rho = .6000$ $\zeta = .693$

$t = (.707 - .693)\sqrt{119} = 1.53$

Accept $H: \rho = .60$

e. $t = -14.6$

3. a. $b_{yx}b_{xy} = (.96)(1.42) > 1.00$

b. Because $\Sigma xy > \sqrt{\Sigma x^2 \Sigma y^2}$, $r > 1.00$

c. r, b_{yx}, and b_{xy} must all have same sign.

d. r^2 should be equal to $b_{yx}b_{xy}$, but $.36 \neq (.8)(.9)$.

e. $s_{y.x}$ cannot be larger than s_y.

f. Same difficulty as in **c.**

g. $b_{yx} = -.9$ and $b_{xy} = -.6$. Same difficulties as in **c** and **d.**

h. $b_{yx} = rs_y/s_x = (.5)(10)/4 = 1.25$, not .25.

i. b_{yx} should be $(.5)(3)/6 = .25$ instead of 1.00.

b_{xy} should be $(.5)(6)/3 = 1.00$ instead of .25.

4. $t = \dfrac{z_A - z_B}{\sqrt{.0117}} = -.68$

Exercise 13.1, page 326

1. $\tilde{Y} = 22.68 + .214X_1 + .477X_2$

2. $R_{y.12} = .642$

3. $F = \dfrac{R^2_{y.12}}{1 - R^2_{y.12}} \cdot \dfrac{95}{2} = 33.3$

4. a. $\tilde{Y} = A_{y.267} + b_{y2.67}X_2 + b_{y6.27}X_6 + b_{y7.26}X_7$

b. $b^*_{y2.67} + r_{26}b^*_{y6.27} + r_{27}b^*_{y7.26} = r_{y2}$

$r_{26}b^*_{y2.67} + b^*_{y6.27} + r_{67}b^*_{y7.26} = r_{y6}$

$r_{27}b^*_{y2.67} + r_{67}b^*_{y6.27} + b^*_{y7.26} = r_{y7}$

c. $R_{y.267} = \sqrt{r_{y2}b^*_{y2.67} + r_{y6}b^*_{y6.27} + r_{y7}b^*_{y7.26}}$

5. a. $b^*_{y4.6} = \dfrac{r_{y4} - r_{y6}r_{46}}{1 - r^2_{46}}$ **b.** $b^*_{y6.4} = \dfrac{r_{y6} - r_{y4}r_{46}}{1 - r^2_{46}}$

c. $b_{y4.6} = b^*_{y4.6}\dfrac{s_y}{s_4} = \dfrac{r_{y4} - r_{y6}r_{46}}{1 - r^2_{46}} \cdot \dfrac{s_y}{s_4}$ **d.** $b_{y6.4} = b^*_{y6.4}\dfrac{s_y}{s_6}$

e. $A = \overline{Y} - b_{y6.4}\overline{X}_6 - b_{y4.6}\overline{X}_4$ **f.** $R_{y.46} = \sqrt{r_{y4}b^*_{y4.6} + r_{y6}b^*_{y6.4}}$

g. $b^*_{y4.6} + r_{46}b^*_{y6.4} = r_{y4}$ $r_{46}b^*_{y4.6} + b^*_{y6.4} = r_{y6}$

6. a. $b^*_{13.7} = \dfrac{r_{13} - r_{17}r_{37}}{1 - r^2_{37}}$ **b.** $b^*_{17.3} = \dfrac{r_{17} - r_{13}r_{37}}{1 - r^2_{37}}$ **c.** $b_{13.7} = b^*_{13.7}\dfrac{s_1}{s_3}$ **d.** $b_{17.3} = b^*_{17.3}\dfrac{s_1}{s_7}$

e. $A = \overline{X}_1 - b_{13.7}\overline{X}_3 - b_{17.3}\overline{X}_7$ **f.** $R_{1.37} = \sqrt{r_{13}b^*_{13.7} + r_{17}b^*_{17.3}}$

g. $b^*_{13.7} + r_{37}b^*_{17.3} = r_{13}$ $r_{37}b^*_{13.7} + b^*_{17.3} = r_{17}$

Exercise 13.2, page 345

1. a. $r_{63.2} = \dfrac{r_{63} - r_{62}r_{23}}{\sqrt{1 - r^2_{62}}\sqrt{1 - r^2_{23}}}$

b. $r_{y3.7} = \dfrac{r_{y3} - r_{y7}r_{37}}{\sqrt{1 - r^2_{y7}}\sqrt{1 - r^2_{37}}}$

c. $r_{21.y} = \dfrac{r_{21} - r_{2y}r_{1y}}{\sqrt{1 - r^2_{2y}}\sqrt{1 - r^2_{1y}}}$

2. $r_{24.56} = \dfrac{r_{24.5} - r_{26.5}r_{46.5}}{\sqrt{1 - r^2_{26.5}}\sqrt{1 - r^2_{46.5}}}$

3. $r_{43.2567} = \dfrac{r_{43.256} - r_{47.256}r_{37.256}}{\sqrt{1 - r^2_{47.256}}\sqrt{1 - r^2_{37.256}}}$

4. $r_{43.2567} = b_{43.2567}b_{34.2567}$

5. $$\begin{aligned} 1 - R^2_{3.126} &= (1 - r^2_{31})(1 - r^2_{32.1})(1 - r^2_{36.12}) \\ &= (1 - r^2_{36})(1 - r^2_{31.6})(1 - r^2_{32.16}) \text{ etc.} \end{aligned}$$

Index to Subject Matter

Index of Authors